QA
371
G6

4/66

D0567425

Elements of Ordinary Differential Equations

**International Series in
Pure and Applied Mathematics**

William Ted Martin and E. H. Spanier

Consulting Editors

AHLFORS Complex Analysis
BELLMAN Stability Theory of Differential Equations
BUCK Advanced Calculus
CODDINGTON AND LEVINSON Theory of Ordinary
    Differential Equations
DETTMAN Mathematical Methods in Physics and Engineering
EPSTEIN Partial Differential Equations
GOLOMB AND SHANKS Elements of Ordinary Differential
    Equations
GRAVES The Theory of Functions of Real Variables
GREENSPAN Introduction to Partial Differential Equations
GRIFFIN Elementary Theory of Numbers
HAMMING Numerical Methods for Scientists and Engineers
HILDEBRAND Introduction to Numerical Analysis
HOUSEHOLDER Principles of Numerical Analysis
LASS Elements of Pure and Applied Mathematics
LASS Vector and Tensor Analysis
LEPAGE Complex Variables and the Laplace Transform
    for Engineers
NEHARI Conformal Mapping
NEWELL Vector Analysis
ROSSER Logic for Mathematicians
RUDIN Principles of Mathematical Analysis
SAATY AND BRAM Nonlinear Mathematics
SIMMONS Introduction to Topology and Modern Analysis
SNEDDON Elements of Partial Differential Equations
SNEDDON Fourier Transforms
STOLL Linear Algebra and Matrix Theory
STRUBLE Nonlinear Differential Equations
WEINSTOCK Calculus of Variations
WEISS Algebraic Number Theory

Elements
of Ordinary
Differential
Equations

Second Edition

Michael Golomb
Professor of Mathematics
Purdue University

Merrill Shanks
Professor of Mathematics
Purdue University

McGraw-Hill Book Company
New York   St. Louis   San Francisco   Toronto   London

Elements of Ordinary Differential Equations

Copyright © 1965 by McGraw-Hill, Inc.   All Rights Reserved.

Copyright, 1950, by McGraw-Hill, Inc.   All Rights Reserved.   Printed
in the United States of America.   This book, or parts thereof,
may not be reproduced in any form without permission of the
publishers.   *Library of Congress Catalog Card Number* 63-23387

23706

Preface

Students in American colleges and universities who major in mathematics, science, or engineering commonly take a course in differential equations as one of their first electives. As a consequence, the introductory course in differential equations takes on a unique importance in scientific education. The potential benefits of such a course can be realized only if through it the student is introduced to more advanced mathematical thought while he is learning technique and manipulative skill. Furthermore, in no other part of college mathematics is the interaction between mathematics and the physical sciences so conspicuous and of such obvious mutual benefit as in the field of differential equations. With this view in mind we have tried, in this book, to exploit and reinforce the reader's physical and geometrical intuition (while he is developing analytical technique) and at the same time to bridge the gulf between live mathematics and conventional formalism.

In addition, we believe that a book which a student uses as a first text in differential equations should be a reference book to which he can return for self-study and which will lead him naturally to the more advanced treatises. Accordingly, we have included much more material than can be taught in any one course, some of which is usually found only in more advanced texts.

This second edition represents an extensive revision of the first. The changes are in part due to our teaching experiences and those of our colleagues in using the first edition and are in part responses to changes that have taken place during the past decade in the mathematics curricula of colleges and universities. At present, the student

v

D. HIDEN RAMSEY LIBRARY
ASHEVILLE-BILTMORE COLLEGE
ASHEVILLE, NORTH CAROLINA

in a first course in differential equations is much more likely to have been exposed to some rigorous mathematical reasoning, to the use of precise definitions and notation, to more advanced algebraic and analytic concepts, and to the relevance of numerical methods. New features of this edition include (1) a greatly expanded treatment of numerical methods, (2) existence and uniqueness proofs based upon the convergence of numerical approximation procedures, (3) a more extensive and systematic treatment of applications, including more advanced topics such as the phase-plane method, which is best discussed in connection with applications, (4) the Laplace-transform method and its relation to integral operators, (5) use of better functional notation and more precise definitions of solution families and local and global solutions, and (6) a revised and greatly expanded list of problems for both the development of technique and the extension of the theory.

This edition, as was the first, is designed for a variety of courses. Among the many possibilities we choose to suggest the following three:

Course A (A first course, slighting the theory and based on calculus alone)
Chapter I, Sections 1 to 5, and 6 in part.
Chapter II.
Chapter IV, Selected topics including Sections 1 and 2 and at least three more sections, possibly 5, 9, and 12.
Chapter V, Sections 1 to 10.
Chapter VII, Sections 1 to 4.
Chapter VIII, Sections 1 to 3.

Course B (A course to follow some introductory differential equations in calculus, but still not too theoretical)
Chapter I, Sections 5 and 6.
Chapter II, for review only.
Chapter III, Sections 1 and 2.
Chapter IV, Sections 1, 2, 5, 9, and 12.
Chapter V, Sections 10 to 14, with a review of the first nine sections.
Chapter VI, Sections 1 to 10 and 12.
Chapter VII, Sections 1 to 5.
Chapter VIII, Sections 1 to 3.
Chapter X, Sections 1 to 4.

Course C (A course emphasizing theory and presuming some familiarity with first-order equations)
Chapter I, Sections 5 and 6.

Chapter III, Sections 1 to 3.
Chapter IV, Sections 1 to 3, 8, and 10.
Chapter V, Sections 12 to 14.
Chapter VI, Sections 1 to 5, 8, 12, and 14.
Chapter VIII, Sections 1, 2, and 4.
Chapter IX, Section 1.
Chapter X, Sections 1 to 5 and 7.

For the reader who wishes to use this book for untutored study of the subject, we have provided careful explanations and discussions, many illustrative examples, and problems ranging from routine computation to exercises that demand high skill and some originality (these are marked by stars). There is a complete list of answers to the problems, and hints are given for some of the more difficult ones.

Michael Golomb

Merrill Shanks

Contents

chapter i

Some Basic Facts and Techniques

The study of differential equations had its origin in the investigation of physical laws. Because the basic physical laws are generally stated in a form involving derivatives (i.e., as differential equations), the determination of the relations among the quantities concerned requires the solution of differential equations. With this practical stimulus the theory of differential equations has been developed by a multitude of investigators and is still growing at a rapid rate and still receiving impetus from physical problems. In spite of its intimate relation to applications the theory of differential equations has an independent existence of its own, consisting of a self-coherent body of knowledge. It is a fact, perhaps curious to one unacquainted with the details, that only by the independent study of the theory and methodology of differential equations can sufficient clarity of understanding be obtained to allow confident application to physical problems.

The present chapter deals with some fundamental concepts, methods, and results for first-order differential equations and aims at giving the reader sufficient insight into the problem to remove some of the mystery from the subject.

1. Differential Equations Defined

Suppose that $x, y, z, \ldots$ are real variables and that $u, v, w, \ldots$ are functions of $x, y, z, \ldots$. A differential equation (abbreviated

D.E.) asserts that there is some functional relationship among the variables x, y, z, . . . , the values of the functions u, v, w, . . . , and some of the derivatives of u, v, w, . . . at x, y, z, ... For example,

(1.1) $$\frac{d^2s}{dt^2} + t^2 \frac{ds}{dt} - 3ts = t + 1 \qquad s = s(t)$$

(1.2) $$\frac{d^2u}{dx^2}\frac{du}{dx} + 3u = 5 \qquad u = u(x)$$

(1.3) $$F\left(x, y, \frac{dy}{dx}\right) = 0 \qquad y = y(x)$$

(1.4) $$\frac{\partial^2 u}{\partial x^2} + \frac{\partial^2 u}{\partial y^2} = g(x, y) \qquad u = u(x, y)$$

(1.5) $$\frac{d^3u}{dt^3} + \left(\frac{dv}{dt}\right)^4 = 0 \qquad u = u(t) \qquad v = v(t)$$

If there is but one independent variable, as in Eqs. (1.1) to (1.3) and (1.5), the differential equation is called *ordinary*. If there are several independent variables, so that the derivatives involved are *partial derivatives*, the equation is a *partial* differential equation, as is (1.4). This book is concerned solely with ordinary differential equations, so that the term differential equation will always mean ordinary differential equation unless the contrary is explicitly stated.

Differential equations are also classified according to the order of the highest derivative involved. Thus (1.3) is of the first order, (1.1), (1.2), and (1.4) are of the second order, and (1.5) is of the third order.

PROBLEMS

1. Classify as to order:

(a) $x^3 \dfrac{d^3y}{dx^3} + e^y \left(\dfrac{d^2y}{dx^2}\right)^3 = 7$

(b) $\dfrac{d^4y}{dx^4} + 5\left(\dfrac{dy}{dx}\right)^2 + 8y = \sin x$

(c) $\dfrac{dz}{dt} = \tan z + t$

(d) $\dfrac{d^2u}{dt^2}\dfrac{du}{dt} + \left(\dfrac{du}{dt}\right)^3 + u = 0$

(e) $x \dfrac{dy}{dx} + y = e^x$

(f) $\sin \dfrac{dy}{dx} + \dfrac{dy}{dx} = y$

2. The following represents a class of differential equations, one for each real value of the parameter α. Classify as to order for each α.

$$(\alpha^4 - 1)\frac{d^2y}{dx^2} + y\frac{dy}{dx} - \alpha^2 y = 0$$

2. Solution or Integral of a Differential Equation

The general ordinary differential equation of the nth order in one unknown function is

$$(2.1) \qquad f\left(x, y, \frac{dy}{dx}, \cdots, \frac{d^n y}{dx^n}\right) = 0$$

where the function $f(x, y, y', \ldots, y^{(n)})$ is defined for certain values of $x, y, y', \ldots, y^{(n)}$. In particular cases the range of values for which the function is defined is usually evident from its form, but in any theoretical discussion of (2.1) we would have to be sure of the domain of definition of the function as well as its continuity and differentiability properties.

By a solution, or integral,† of (2.1) is meant a function $y(x)$ such that when y and its derivatives are substituted in (2.1) there results an identity in x.

Example 1. Show that the functions

$$y(x) = \pm \sqrt{x^2 - cx}$$

are integrals of

$$2xy \frac{dy}{dx} = x^2 + y^2$$

Differentiating the functions, we have

$$\frac{dy}{dx} = \frac{\pm (2x - c)}{2 \sqrt{x^2 - cx}}$$

Substituting in the differential equation yields

$$\frac{2x(\pm \sqrt{x^2 - cx})[\pm (2x - c)]}{2 \sqrt{x^2 - cx}} = x^2 + x^2 - cx$$

or

$$2x^2 - cx = 2x^2 - cx$$

which is an identity in x.

Sometimes it is inconvenient to express y explicitly in terms of x. In this case the solution may be given in the implicit form $g(x, y) = 0$. This equation defines y implicitly in terms of x. The derivatives are then expressed in terms of x and y; when these derivatives are sub-

---

† The terms "integral" and "solution" when applied to differential equations are synonymous. Integration in the sense of elementary calculus will often be referred to as *quadrature*.

stituted in the differential equation, there results either an identity in x and y or an equation which is valid by virtue of the equation $g(x, y) = 0$.

Example 2. The differential equation of Example 1 will serve to illustrate the implicit form for a solution. Squaring the previous solution yields

$$y^2 = x^2 - cx$$

Differentiating implicitly yields

$$2y\frac{dy}{dx} = 2x - c$$

or

$$\frac{dy}{dx} = \frac{2x - c}{2y}$$

Substituting in the differential equation gives

$$2xy\frac{2x - c}{2y} = x^2 + y^2$$

or

$$2x^2 - cx = x^2 + y^2$$

which is an identity by virtue of $y^2 = x^2 - cx$.

The implicit form of a solution, although often unavoidable, is not as satisfactory a form as the explicit one. In certain ways it is incomplete and often poses problems more difficult than those which must be solved to obtain it. In Example 1 the explicit form $y(x) = \pm \sqrt{x^2 - cx}$ shows at a glance that the solution is defined only for $x(x - c) \geq 0$ and is differentiable only for $x(x - c) > 0$. It also shows that none of these integral curves connects a point in the upper half of the xy plane with a point in the lower half, since the solutions are not differentiable at $y = 0$. The implicit form $y^2 = x^2 - cx$ of Example 2 does not so readily reveal these facts. In this case it would not take too much analysis to get the same facts from the implicit form, since it is a pure quadratic in y. However, in most cases the analysis of implicit solutions is a task of great difficulty and complexity.

To analyze each case would only obscure the issue at hand. For this reason we propose to ignore these problems, although their importance and relevance cannot be denied. We shall speak of a *formal solution* when we are not sure of whether we have one, none, or several solutions, or what their domain of definition is, if the ordinary processes of differentiation and substitution in the given differential equation lead to an identity. Many of the solutions in Chaps. I and II are formal in this sense.

Sometimes it is preferable to express the solution in *parametric form*, say $x = f(t)$, $y = g(t)$. This pair of functions may define a function $y(x)$. To verify that $x = f(t)$, $y = g(t)$ is a solution of a differential equation it is not necessary to eliminate t. One substitutes $f(t)$ for x, $g(t)$ for y, $(dg/dt)/(df/dt)$ for dy/dx, and corresponding expressions for d^2y/dx^2, ... The resulting equation must be an identity in t.

Example 3. The function $y(x)$, defined parametrically by

$$x = c(1 + \cosh t) \qquad y = c \sinh t$$

is, for each constant c, a solution of the D.E. of Example 1. Differentiation yields

$$\frac{dx}{dt} = c \sinh t \qquad \frac{dy}{dt} = c \cosh t$$

Thus

$$\frac{dy}{dx} = \coth t$$

Substitution in the D.E. gives

$$2c^2(1 + \cosh t) \sinh t \coth t = c^2(1 + \cosh t)^2 + c^2 \sinh^2 t$$

or

$$2(1 + \cosh t) \cosh t = 1 + 2 \cosh t + \cosh^2 t + \sinh^2 t$$

which is an identity.

PROBLEMS

1. Verify the following formal solutions of the corresponding differential equations. [Symbols a, b, c, c_1, c_2, A, B, C, D represent arbitrary constants in the solutions; r in (f) and m in (j) and (l) represent constant coefficients in the equations.]

(a) $y = a^2 + \dfrac{a}{x}$, $x^4 \left(\dfrac{dy}{dx}\right)^2 = y + x \dfrac{dy}{dx}$

(b) $y = x \sin (a - x)$, $y = x \dfrac{dy}{dx} + x \sqrt{x^2 - y^2}$; $x \cos (a - x) > 0$

(c) $y = \dfrac{x^2 + \log x^2 + 1}{(1 + x^2)^2}$, $x(1 + x^2) \dfrac{dy}{dx} + 4x^2y - 2 = 0$

(d) $x^2 = cy + c^2$, $xy'^2 = 2yy' + 4x$

(e) $\sin y + y = x$, $\dfrac{dy}{dx} (y \cos y - \sin y + x) = y$

(f) $(x - a)^2 + (y - b)^2 = r^2$, $y''^2 r^2 = (1 + y'^2)^3$

(g) $x = a \cos^3 t$, $y = a \sin^3 t$, $xy'^3 + y = 0$

(h) $\sin x^2 + \sin y^2 = c$, $x \cos x^2 + yy' \cos y^2 = 0$

(i) $y(x) = c_1 e^{2x} + c_2 e^{-3x} - \frac{1}{6}x - \frac{1}{36}$, $y'' + y' - 6y = x$

(j) $y(t) = A \cos (mt + B)$, $\dfrac{d^2y}{dt^2} + m^2 y = 0$

(k) $\sin u = (A + Br)e^r + e^{-r}$, $\dfrac{d^2u}{dr^2} \cos u - \left(\dfrac{du}{dr}\right)^2 \sin u - 2\left(\dfrac{du}{dr}\right) \cos u$

$+ \sin u = 4e^{-r}$

(l) $x(t) = e^{mt}(A \cos mt + B \sin mt) + e^{-mt}(C \cos mt + D \sin mt)$, $\dfrac{d^4x}{dt^4}$

$+ 4m^4 x = 0$

(m) $x(t) = \cos mt (A \cosh mt + B \sinh mt) + \sin mt (C \cosh mt +$

$D \sinh mt)$, $\dfrac{d^4x}{dt^4} + 4m^4 x = 0$

(n) $y(x) = cx + f(c)$, $y = xy' + f(y')$

(o) $y(x) = J_{\frac{1}{2}}(x) = \left(\dfrac{2}{\pi x}\right)^{\frac{1}{2}} \sin x$, $x^2 y'' + xy' + (x^2 - \frac{1}{4})y = 0$

Here $J_{\frac{1}{2}}$ is the Bessel function of order $\frac{1}{2}$, and the D.E. is the Bessel equation for $n = \frac{1}{2}$.

(p) $y(x) = J_0(x) = \displaystyle\sum_{k=0}^{\infty} \dfrac{(-1)^k}{k!} \left(\dfrac{x}{2}\right)^{2k}$, $xy'' + y' + xy = 0$

(HINT: The ratio test shows that the series converges for all x; therefore it may be differentiated termwise.) Here J_0 is the Bessel function of order 0, and the D.E. is the corresponding Bessel equation for $n = 0$.

(q) $y(x) = T_n(x) = \cos (n \arccos x)$, $(1 - x^2)y'' - xy' + n^2 y = 0$

Here $T_n(x)$ is the Tchebycheff (or Čebychev) polynomial of degree n, and the D.E. is a special case of the hypergeometric equation.

(r) $y(x) = H_n(x) = e^{x^2} \dfrac{d^n}{dx^n} (e^{-x^2})$, $y'' - 2xy' + 2ny = 0$

Here $H_n(x)$ is the Hermite polynomial of degree n, and the D.E. is Hermite's equation.

2. Verify that the functions $y(x)$ implicitly defined by $(x - a)^2 + (y - b)^2 = r^2$ (a, b, r arbitrary constants greater than zero) are integrals of the D.E.

$$\dfrac{d}{dx} [y''(1 + y'^2)^{-\frac{3}{2}}] = 0$$

Give geometric interpretations of the integrals and the differential equation.

3. Solution by Quadrature

Before we embark on a general discussion of the problems arising in connection with the solution of differential equations, we shall, in this section and the next, solve some special differential equations more or less by inspection, without guidance from a general theory.

The simplest type of differential equation is

$$(3.1) \qquad\qquad y' = f(x)$$

where $f(x)$ is a continuous function of x alone. Its solution is

$$(3.2) \qquad y(x) = \int f(x)\,dx + c = F(x) + c$$

where $F(x)$ is any indefinite integral of $f(x)$ [also called the *primitive* of $f(x)$]. The arbitrary constant c is a constant of integration, and different values of c give different solutions. It is shown in the calculus that each solution of the equation $y' = f(x)$ is obtained from $y(x) = F(x) + c$ by assigning some particular value to the constant c.

The determination of the function $F(x) = \int f(x)\,dx$ is performed by the various methods developed in the calculus, by the use of tables of integrals, and by numerical or graphical integration with or without the aid of computing machines. This aspect of the solution of differential equations (referred to as *quadrature*) is considered as elementary (i.e., belonging to a lower rank of operations), and its execution is ignored in the theory of differential equations. Thus, we may leave the solution of the D.E. $y' = e^{-x^2}$ in the form $y(x) = \int e^{-x^2}\,dx + c$ without bothering to decide whether $\int e^{-x^2}\,dx$ can be expressed in terms of more elementary function or not.

If the solution $y(x) = F(x) + c$ is graphed in the xy plane, a family of curves is obtained, one for each value of c (see Fig. 1). A *particular* (or specific) solution is singled out by assigning a specific value to c. This is most often done by stipulating that the solution assume a given value y_0 at a given x_0 [on the graph this means that the curve should pass through a point (x_0, y_0)]. This condition, which singles out a particular solution from the infinitely many solutions (3.2), is referred to

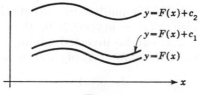

$$y = F(x) + c_2$$
$$y = F(x) + c_1$$
$$y = F(x)$$

Fig. 1

as an *initial condition*, abbreviated I.C. (because it assigns an initial value y_0 to the solution at an initial point x_0):

$$(3.3) \qquad y = y_0 \quad \text{when} \quad x = x_0 \quad \text{or} \quad y(x_0) = y_0$$

To satisfy this condition, one substitutes (3.3) in (3.2) and determines c:

$$(3.4) \qquad y_0 = F(x_0) + c \qquad c = y_0 - F(x_0)$$

Thus, the particular solution becomes

$$(3.5) \qquad y(x) = y_0 + F(x) - F(x_0)$$

If the value y_1 of the solution at $x = x_1$ is desired, one has, in terms of the definite integral,

$$(3.6) \qquad y_1 = y_0 + F(x_1) - F(x_0)$$
$$= y_0 + \int_{x_0}^{x_1} f(x) \, dx$$

Example 1. A particle moves along a straight line with acceleration which varies in time t according to the function te^{-2t}. (*a*) If the velocity at $t = 0$ is v_0, will the particle ever reverse its motion? (*b*) If the velocity at $t = 0$ is 0, what is it at $t = 1$?

We have $dv/dt = te^{-2t}$; hence

$$v = v_0 + \int_0^t te^{-2t} \, dt$$

or, upon quadrature,

$$v(t) = v_0 + \tfrac{1}{4} - \tfrac{1}{4}e^{-2t} - \tfrac{1}{2}te^{-2t}$$

This function has the value of v_0 at $t = 0$, tends to $v_0 + \tfrac{1}{4}$ as $t \to +\infty$ ("terminal velocity"), and is monotone nondecreasing since $dv/dt = te^{-2t} \geq 0$. Hence the answer to (*a*) is yes if $-\tfrac{1}{4} < v_0 < 0$, and no if $v_0 \leq -\tfrac{1}{4}$ or $v_0 \geq 0$. For (*b*) we have

$$v(1) = 0 + \int_0^1 te^{-2t} \, dt = \tfrac{1}{4} - \tfrac{3}{4}e^{-2} = 0.1485$$

The differential equation of the form

$$(3.7) \qquad y' = g(y)$$

where $g(y)$ is a continuous function of the dependent variable y alone, can also be readily solved by a quadrature. If $y(x)$ is a solution of (3.7) in a region in which $y'(x) = g(y(x)) > 0$, then $y(x)$ is monotone increasing, and $y = y(x)$ can be inverted, giving $x = x(y)$. But it is known from calculus that $dx/dy = 1/(dy/dx)$; hence

$$(3.8) \qquad \frac{dx}{dy} = \frac{1}{g(y)}$$

and therefore

(3.9) $$x(y) = \int \frac{dy}{g(y)} + c = G(y) + c$$

where $G(y)$ is any primitive of $1/g(y)$. Since $dG/dy = 1/g(y) > 0$ in the considered region, $x - c = G(y)$ can be inverted, giving the explicit $y(x)$. Thus, every solution $y(x)$ of (3.7) for which $g(y(x)) > 0$ can be obtained from (3.9) for some value of c. Conversely, if c is any constant and $y(x)$ is a solution of (3.9) for which $g(y(x)) > 0$, then $y(x)$ is an integral of (3.7), for, by (3.9), $dx/dy = G'(y) = 1/g(y)$; hence $dy/dx = g(y)$. The same conclusions hold in a region in which $g(y(x)) < 0$ throughout.

Example 2. Some substances (and populations) grow or decay in time at a rate proportional to some power of the existing amount. Thus if $x(t)$ is the amount at time t, then

$$\frac{dx}{dt} = kx^r$$

where k and r are constants. For the inverse function $t(x)$, we have

$$\frac{dt}{dx} = \frac{1}{k} x^{-r}$$

Hence

$$t(x) = \frac{1}{k} \int x^{-r} \, dx = \begin{cases} c + \dfrac{1}{k(1-r)} x^{1-r} & \text{if } r \neq 1 \\ c + \dfrac{1}{k} \log x & \text{if } r = 1 \end{cases}$$

The constant c can be determined if one knows the amount x_0 present at time $t = 0$. Then

$$t(x) = \begin{cases} \dfrac{1}{k(1-r)} (x^{1-r} - x_0^{1-r}) & \text{if } r \neq 1 \\ \dfrac{1}{k} \log \dfrac{x}{x_0} & \text{if } r = 1 \end{cases}$$

Inverting these relations, one gets the explicit solution

$$x(t) = \begin{cases} [x_0^{1-r} + (1-r)kt]^{1/(1-r)} & \text{if } r \neq 1 \\ x_0 e^{kt} & \text{if } r = 1 \end{cases}$$

PROBLEMS

1. Solve the following equations (implicit and formal solutions are permissible in some cases):

(a) $(1 + x)y' = x$

(b) $(1 + x^2)y' = x$

(c) $(1 + x^3)y' = x$

(d) $\dfrac{m}{2}\left(\dfrac{dx}{dt}\right)^2 + mgx = mgh$ (m, g, h constants)

(e) $\dfrac{m}{2}\left(\dfrac{dx}{dt}\right)^2 + kx^2 = E$ (m, k, E constants)

(f) $(1 + x^2)y' = \arctan x$

(g) $\dfrac{d}{dx}(xe^x y) = 2e^{2x}$

(h) $\sqrt{4z^3 - g_2 z - g_1}\,\dfrac{dw}{dz} = 1$ (g_2, g_1 constants)

(i) $\dfrac{d}{dx}\sqrt{x^2 + y^2} = \dfrac{x}{\sqrt{x^2 + a^2}}$ (a constant)

(j) $\dfrac{d}{dx}\sqrt{1 + u^2} = 1 + u^2$ (HINT: Put $y = \sqrt{1 + u^2}$.)

(k) $y' = 1 + 2|x|$

(l) $y' = \begin{cases} 0 & x \le 0 \\ \sin x & 0 < x < \pi \\ 0 & x \ge \pi \end{cases}$

(m) $y' = |\sin x|$

2. Determine the integrals of the following differential equations satisfying the given conditions:

(a) $(1 + x^2)y' = 1$, $y(1) = \dfrac{\pi}{2}$

(b) $(1 + 4x^2)y' = 2$, $\lim\limits_{x\to\infty} y(x) = 0$

(c) $\dfrac{d}{dx}e^y = -e^{-x}$, $y(0) = 0$

(d) $\dfrac{d}{dx}(e^{-x^2}y') = xe^{-x^2}$, $y(0) = 1$

(e) $\dfrac{dy}{dx} + \dfrac{d}{dx}\left(\dfrac{x^2}{y}\right) = 2$, $y(1) = 1$

(f) $e^y y' = x^4$, $y(1) = 1$

3. If $v\,dv/ds = 1/(1 + s^2)$ and $v = v_0$ when $s = 0$, find $\lim\limits_{s\to\infty} v(s)$. HINT: Observe that $v\,dv/ds = (d/ds)(\tfrac{1}{2}v^2)$.

4. If $y' = xe^{-x^4}$ and $y(0) = -1$, find $\lim\limits_{x\to\infty} y(x)$.

5. If $xy' - \sin x$ and $y(0) = 0$, find $\lim\limits_{x\to\infty} y(x)$.

6. If $xy' = x^r e^{-x}$ (r a positive constant) and $y(0) = 0$, find $\lim_{x \to \infty} y(x)$.

7. In the following a few terms of the power-series expansions will give sufficiently accurate answers:

    (a) $(1 + x^2)y' = \sin x$, $y(0) = 1$; find $y(0.2)$.
    (b) $(d\phi/dx)^2 - 0.75 \sin^2 \phi = \cos^2 \phi$, $x(0) = 0$; find $x(0.4)$.

8. Show that every solution of $y' = f$, f odd [that is, $f(x) = -f(-x)$] is even [that is, $y(x) = y(-x)$].

9. Show that exactly one solution of $y' = f$, f even, is odd. HINT: What must $y(0)$ be if y is odd?

10. Give a condition both necessary and sufficient for the function f, of period p, so that every integral of $y' = f$ is of period p. HINT: Experiment with $y' = \sin x$, $y' = 1 + \sin x$, $y' = |\sin x|$.

11. The relation $f'(x) = \pm \sqrt{1 - f^2(x)}$ holds for the function $f(x) = \sin x$. Find all differentiable functions $f(x)$ for which $f'(x) = \pm \sqrt{1 - f^2(x)}$.

4. Solution by Separation of Variables

A somewhat more general type of first-order differential equation can be solved almost as easily as those in the previous section. Consider the differential equation

$$(4.1) \qquad \frac{dy}{dx} = \frac{f(x)}{g(y)}$$

Of course, this equation has meaning only in parts of the xy plane in which $g(y) \neq 0$. Since only connected parts need be considered, we may assume that in each such part either $g(y) > 0$ throughout or $g(y) < 0$ throughout. Assume $y(x)$ is a solution of (4.1) which we wish to determine. When this hypothetical solution is substituted in (4.1) we obtain the identity (in x)

$$(4.2) \qquad g(y(x)) \frac{dy}{dx} = f(x)$$

Since the two functions of x to the left and right of the equality sign are equal, their indefinite integrals can differ only by a constant:

$$(4.3) \qquad \int g(y(x)) \frac{dy}{dx}\, dx = \int f(x)\, dx + c$$

The integral on the left of (4.3) is known from the *change-of-variable rule* in the integral calculus. If $G(y) = \int g(y)\, dy$ and $F(x) = \int f(x)\, dx$ (G is the primitive of g, and F is the primitive of f), then (4.3) is nothing but

$$(4.4) \qquad G(y(x)) = F(x) + c$$

This equation gives the sought solution $y(x)$ *implicitly*. It may be solved for $y(x)$ if an explicit form is desired. In this connection it should be noticed that, since $g(y) > 0$ throughout or $g(y) < 0$ throughout, $G(y) = \int g(y)\, dy$ is strictly monotone (increasing and decreasing, respectively); hence G has an inverse function; that is, (4.4) *can* be solved for $y(x)$. As our derivation shows, *every* solution of (4.1) is obtainable from (4.4). Also, differentiation of (4.4) shows that any differentiable function $y(x)$ satisfying (4.4) for some value of c is a solution of (4.1).

If a differential equation of first order can be cast in the form (4.1), it is said to have *separable variables*. The method of solution described above for this type of equation is called *separation of variables*. In telegraphic style, the steps from (4.1) to (4.2) to (4.3) to (4.4) are written as follows:

$$\frac{dy}{dx} = \frac{f(x)}{g(y)}$$

(4.5)
$$g(y)\, dy = f(x)\, dx$$
$$\int g(y)\, dy = \int f(x)\, dx + c$$
$$G(y) = F(x) + c$$

As for Eq. (3.1), we again find infinitely many solutions, one for each value of the arbitrary constant c. The remarks made concerning Eq. (3.1) about the use of initial condition (3.3) to single out a particular solution hold for (4.1) without change. The solution satisfying $y(x_0) = y_0$ is given by

(4.6)
$$G(y) - G(y_0) = F(x) - F(x_0)$$

If the value y_1 of the solution at $x = x_1$ is desired, it may be found in terms of definite integrals from the equation

(4.7)
$$\int_{y_0}^{y_1} g(y)\, dy = \int_{x_0}^{x_1} f(x)\, dx$$

Example 1.   Solve

$$xy\frac{dy}{dx} = (y - 1)(x + 1)$$

and determine the particular solution for which $y = -\frac{1}{2}$ when $x = -\frac{1}{2}$.

Here the variables may be separated by dividing both sides by $x(y - 1)$. Then

$$\frac{y}{y - 1}\, dy = \frac{x + 1}{x}\, dx$$

and integration gives

$$y + \ln |y - 1| = x + \log |x| + c$$

or

$$\log\left|\frac{y-1}{x}\right| = x - y + c$$

$$|y - 1| = |x|e^{x-y+c} = k|x|e^{x-y}$$

where the constant k is used for e^c. In this problem four regions must be considered: $y > 1, x > 0; y > 1, x < 0; y < 1, x > 0; y < 1, x < 0$. If, for example, $y < 1, x > 0$, then the above solution appears as

$$1 - y = kxe^{x-y}$$

with $k > 0$. But if we allow both positive and negative values for k, then the solution can be written as

$$y - 1 = kxe^{x-y}$$

in all four regions. To find the particular solution in question, we substitute $x = y = -\frac{1}{2}$ and find $k = 3$. Thus,

$$y - 1 = 3xe^{x-y}$$

It would be impossible in this case to find an explicit expression for $y(x)$ in terms of elementary functions.

PROBLEMS

1. Solve by separation of variables (implicit and formal solutions are permissible):

(a) $y' = \dfrac{y-1}{xy}$

(b) $y^3 + x^3y' = 0$

(c) $xyy' = (x + a)(y + b)$ (a, b constants)

(d) $(x + A)(y + B)y' = (x + a)(y + b)$ (a, b, A, B constants)

(e) $y' = \dfrac{1 - y^2}{1 - x^2}$

(f) $xy' = (1 - 2x^2)\tan y$

(g) $(y^2 + y - 1)xy' + y(y^2 - 1) = 0$

(h) $L\dfrac{di}{dt} + Ri = 0$ (L, R constants)

(i) $e^{2x}y' = 2(y^{\frac{1}{2}} + y^{\frac{3}{2}})$

(j) $(x^2 - 1)y' = \tan y$

(k) $(a^2 + x^2)y' + (a^2 + y^2) = 0$ (a constant)

(l) $y' = e^{x+y}$

(m) $y' = 1 - y^2$

(n) $y' = \dfrac{y^2 - 2y + 5}{x^2 - 2x + 2}$

2. Determine the integrals of the following differential equations satisfying the given conditions:

(a) $y^2(1 + x) - x^3y' = 0$, $y(1) = 2$
(b) $(\cos^2 x)y' = \sin x \cos^2 y$, $y(\pi) = 0$

(c) $\rho \dfrac{d\theta}{d\rho} = k$ (k constant), $\theta(1) = 0$

(d) $e^x \sin y + y'(1 + e^x) \cos y = 0$, $y(0) = \dfrac{\pi}{4}$

(e) $x^2yy' - 1 = x^2$, $y(2) = 2$
(f) $(1 + e^x)y' = e^{3x}y$, $y(\log 2) = 3$
(g) $y(xy' - y) = xy'$, $y(2) = 1$
(h) $(xy - 1)(y' + 1) = (y - x)(y' - 1)$, $y(2) = 1 + e$
(i) $y' = \cos y[\cos (x + y) + \cos (x - y)]$, $y\left(\dfrac{\pi}{6}\right) = \dfrac{\pi}{4}$

(j) $yy' = xe^{x^2+y^2}$, $y(\sqrt{\log 2}) = 0$
(k) $ye^{2x}y' + x(1 + y^2) = 0$, $y(0) = 0$

3. Show how a differential equation of the type

$$y' = \frac{f(x)}{g(x + y)} - 1$$

can be solved by a modified method of separation of variables.   HINT: Make the substitution u for $x + y$.

4. Show how a differential equation of the type

$$y' = \frac{f(x)}{g[y - h(x)]} + h'(x)$$

can be solved.   HINT: See Prob. 3.

★**5.** Find all differentiable functions f which satisfy the functional equation

$$f(x_1 + x_2) = f(x_1)f(x_2)$$

for all x_1, x_2.   HINT: Show that f satisfies the differential equation

$$\frac{d}{dx} f(x) = kf(x)$$

for some constant k.

5. Direction Fields

Information about the qualitative nature of solutions can often be obtained by a simple graphical procedure.   Suppose the differential equation is

(5.1) $\dfrac{dy}{dx} = f(x, y)$

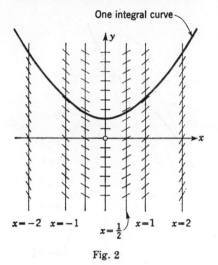

Fig. 2

where $f(x, y)$ is a continuous function of x and y in some rectangle R,†
$a < x < b, c < y < d$.

A solution, or integral, of (5.1) is a function $y(x)$ such that

$$\frac{dy}{dx} = f(x, y(x))$$

whenever the point $(x, y(x))$ lies within R.   Thus if the solution $y(x)$ is
represented graphically as a curve and (x, y) is a point on it, the slope
of the tangent is given by (5.1).   In other words, as soon as we know
that an integral curve passes through a point, we also know the direction of the curve at that point.   This situation is described by saying
that (5.1) defines a *direction field*.‡   A direction field, then, is given if
with each point (x, y) there is associated a number $p = f(x, y) = y'$
which is the slope of a line through that point.   The direction field
can be represented graphically by drawing at (x, y) a short line segment
with slope $p = f(x, y)$.   This line segment is called a *line element*.

Example 1.   The direction field $p = x$ is indicated in Fig. 2, where some
line elements are drawn for $x = -2, -1, -\frac{1}{2}, 0, \frac{1}{2}, 1, 2$.

† As mentioned before, in most applications the domain in which $f(x, y)$ is
defined is evident from the form of the function and in many cases will be the whole
plane.   The situation described here contains all cases of interest to us.   If we
agree that a, b, c, or d may be $\pm \infty$, we include the possibility that $f(x, y)$ is defined
over the whole plane, a half plane, a quadrant, or an infinite or semi-infinite strip.

‡ "Slope field" would be a more appropriate name, but direction field is a long-
established term.

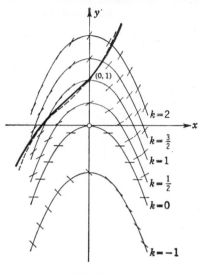

Fig. 3

Suppose now that we are given a curve $y = y(x)$, in the rectangle R, which has at each point a tangent whose slope is given by (5.1). The function $y(x)$ then is an integral of the differential equation, so we see that finding an integral is equivalent to finding a curve which has at each of its points the same direction as that of the direction field. Such a curve can be sketched roughly freehand after the direction field is drawn.

To draw the direction field for a given differential equation (5.1), a device may be used called the *method of isoclines*. An *isocline* is a curve through the direction field along which $p = f(x, y)$ is constant. It is itself *not* an integral curve. The family of isoclines then is the family of curves $f(x, y) = p$. Choosing a few values for p will indicate the family of isoclines. Now along each isocline draw several parallel line elements, i.e., line segments of slope $f(x, y) = p$. This gives us a sketch of the direction field. This is the procedure used in Fig. 2, where the light lines are the isoclines.

Example 2. Sketch the direction field of

$$\frac{dy}{dx} = x^2 + y \qquad R \text{ the whole plane}$$

by the method of isoclines, and draw the integral curve which passes through the point $(0, 1)$.

The solution is given in Fig. 3. The isoclines are the parabolas

$$x^2 + y = p$$

which appear in Fig. 3 for $p = 2, \frac{3}{2}, 1, \frac{1}{2}, 0, -1$. The heavy solid curve is approximately the integral curve through $(0, 1)$ and is drawn freehand to coincide as well as possible with the direction field. The dashed line is the exact solution through $(0, 1)$,

$$y = 3e^x - x^2 - 2x - 2$$

obtained by methods given in the next chapter.

How an analysis of the direction field can be used to obtain qualitative information about the behavior of the solutions is illustrated in the next example. It should be pointed out that for many purposes qualitative analyses of the kind appearing in this example and in the problems below are most useful and preferable to incompletely analyzed quantitative results.

Example 3.   Sketch the direction field of the differential equation

$$\frac{1 + y'}{1 - y'} = 2\sqrt{x + y}$$

Show that each integral, except one, attains its minimum on the line $x + y = \frac{1}{4}$.

The direction field in this example is restricted to $x + y \geq 0$, which is the half plane to the right of the line $x + y = 0$. The isoclines are the straight lines

$$x + y = \left(\frac{1}{2}\frac{1 + p}{1 - p}\right)^2 \qquad -1 \leq p < 1$$

all of slope -1. Several of them are drawn in Fig. 4, and some integrals are sketched.

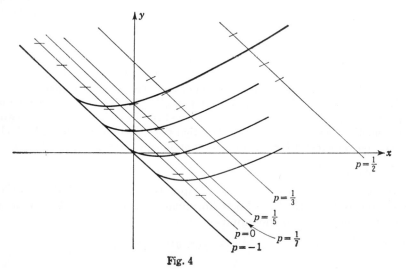

Fig. 4

The line $x + y = 0$ is an isocline ($p = -1$) and an integral of the given equation (see also Prob. 3 below). If $y(x)$ is any other integral, then its slope is between -1 and 0 if $x + y(x) < \frac{1}{4}$, and is between 0 and 1 if $x + y(x) > \frac{1}{4}$. Hence $y(x)$ attains its minimum where $x + y(x) = \frac{1}{4}$.

PROBLEMS

1. Draw the direction fields for the following differential equations, and sketch some of the integrals.

(a) $y' = -x^2$ (b) $y' = x - 2y$

(c) $y' = \dfrac{1}{y}$ (d) $y' = xy$

(e) $y' = \operatorname{sgn} y$ (The *signum function* is defined as follows: $\operatorname{sgn} y = 1$ if $y > 0$; $\operatorname{sgn} y = -1$ if $y < 0$; $\operatorname{sgn} 0 = 0$.)

(f) $y' = \frac{1}{4}[y]$ (The *bracket function* is defined as follows: if $n \leq y < n + 1$, where n is an integer, then $[y] = n$.)

2. The following are implicit differential equations which, when solved for y', may lead to more than one slope p at a given point (x, y). The corresponding direction field may then be considered as the superposition of several fields (as if they were drawn on several transparent sheets and laid on top of each other). Draw these fields and sketch some of the integrals.

(a) $y'^2 = x^2 + y^2$

(b) $xy' - y = \sqrt{y'^2 - 1}$

(c) $y^2 - (1 - x^2)y'^2 = 0$

3. Prove that if the slope of the direction field of $y' = f(x, y)$ has the constant value k along the line $y = kx + b$, then this line is an integral.

4. Prove that if $y(x)$ is a solution of the equation $y' = -y(x^2 - y^2)$ for which $|y(x_0)| < |x_0|$, then $|y(x)| < |x|$ for all x for which $|x| > |x_0|$. HINT: A rough picture of the direction field shows the trend of the integrals.

5. Suppose the continuous function $f(x, y)$ is positive for all x, y. Show that if $y(x)$ is any integral of the equation $y' = xyf(x, y)$, then, for all $x \neq 0$, $y(x) > y(0)$ if $y(0) > 0$, and $y(x) < y(0)$ if $y(0) < 0$. HINT: Examine the direction field in the four quadrants and on the lines separating them.

6. Given the implicit differential equation $y'^2 - axy' + ay = 0$, where a is a positive constant. Find the points in the plane through which exactly two, one, and no integral curves pass. Show that the locus of points through which exactly one integral curve passes is itself an integral curve.

6. Numerical Methods

In many cases it is impossible or impractical to solve the differential equation by analytical methods (formulas). This is especially true if the function $f(x, y)$ in the equation

(6.1) $$y' = f(x, y)$$

is not given analytically, but empirically (table of measured values, table of computed values, values stored on the memory tape of a computing machine, etc.). Even when there is a relatively simple analytic solution the applied mathematician may not be interested in it, since he needs precise numerical results for which the analytical solution may be of little use. For these and other reasons it is important to study methods by which (6.1) can be solved numerically. A large literature has grown up on this subject, with many early contributions from astronomers who needed precise numerical solutions for the differential equations which describe the motions of heavenly bodies. Many of the recent contributions were stimulated by the advent of large automatic computing machines which are capable of carrying out immensely long and intricate computing programs with precision and dispatch.

Only a few elementary numerical methods can be taken up here. Preference is given to those which give reasonably accurate results after a few calculations performed with the aid of logarithmic tables, slide rules, or desk calculators.

Numerical methods must not be viewed as substitutes which give approximately correct results in situations in which analytical methods are unavailable or too laborious. To calculate π accurately to 10 decimal places (a $10D$ approximation of π) is a mathematical problem in its own right, quite distinct from the problem of finding formulas such as $\pi = 4(1 - \frac{1}{3} + \frac{1}{5} \cdots)$ or $\pi = 6 \int_0^{\frac{1}{2}} (1 - x^2)^{-\frac{1}{2}} \, dx$. Similarly, if $y(x)$ is a solution of (6.1) uniquely defined by some initial condition such as $y(x_0) = y_0$, then for any x_1 in the domain of $y(x)$, the number $y(x_1)$ can be determined to any desired degree of accuracy by a numerical method if sufficient labor is spent on the effort; this is true regardless of whether one has a formula for the solution $y(x)$ or not.

When a numerical method is used, one does not find the solution $y(x)$ for all x of some interval, but rather for a discrete sequence† of points, usually equidistant, say

(6.2) $x_0 \qquad x_1 = x_0 + h \qquad x_2 = x + 2h \qquad \cdots \qquad x_n = x_0 + nh$

The positive number h is the *tabular difference*. Even when the solution is sought for only a few of the points (6.2), say only for the last one, it is calculated at the other points so as to obtain the desired degree of accuracy. We shall denote the values of the solution $y(x)$ at the points (6.2) by corresponding subscripts; hence

(6.3) $y_0 = y(x_0) \qquad y_1 = y(x_0 + h) \qquad y_2 = y(x_0 + 2h) \qquad \cdots$

$$y_n = y(x_0 + nh)$$

† For this reason these methods are also called *discrete* or *finite-difference* methods.

The values of the function $f(x, y)$ at the tabulated points are denoted by

(6.4) $f_0 = f(x_0, y_0)$ $f_1 = f(x_1, y_1)$ $f_2 = f(x_2, y_2)$ $\cdot$ $\cdot$ $\cdot$

$$f_n = f(x_n, y_n)$$

Euler-Cauchy Method I.   From (6.1), by substituting the solution $y(x)$, integrating, and using the initial condition $y(x_0) = y_0$, one finds

$$y(x) = y_0 + \int_{x_0}^{x} f(s, y(s)) \, ds$$

In particular, for $x = x_1$,

(6.5) $y_1 = y_0 + \int_{x_0}^{x_1} f(x, y(x)) \, dx$

The quadrature in (6.5) cannot be carried out explicitly, since $y(x)$ is not known. But if h is sufficiently small, then the variable of integration x in (6.5) varies only over the small interval $(x_0, x_0 + h)$, and one may assume that $f(x, y(x))$ does not change much over this interval. If then one considers $f(x, y(x))$ as constant, having everywhere in the interval $(x_0, x_0 + h)$ the value that it has at the left endpoint, $f(x_0, y_0)$, one gets†

(6.6) $y_1 = y_0 + hf_0$

Having calculated y_1 by (6.6), one then has an approximate value of $f_1 = f(x_1, y_1)$ and can calculate y_2 in a similar way:

$$y_2 = y_1 + hf_1$$

Then one calculates $y_3, y_4, \ldots$, or, generally,

(6.7) $y_k = y_{k-1} + hf_{k-1}$ $k = 1, 2, 3, \ldots$
E.C.M. I

This formula says that y_k is calculated from y_{k-1} in the same way as y_1 is calculated from y_0, y_2 from y_1, etc. All the other rules to be given below are also of this *recursive* type.

The simple process described by (6.7) is commonly known as the *Euler-Cauchy* method (also the *polygonal method;* Leonhard Euler, 1707–1783; Augustine Cauchy, 1789–1857). We shall refer to it as E.C.M. I. Although it will usually give sufficiently accurate results only if the tabular difference h is quite small, it is a useful method.

---

† Strictly speaking, this notation is objectionable because y_1 was to denote the value $y(x_1)$ of the true solution, whereas the value y_1 in (6.6) is an approximation. The same is true of the numbers $y_2, \ldots, y_k, f_k$, etc., below. However, the notation is suggestive and is commonly used. It will not lead to error if the distinction is kept in mind.

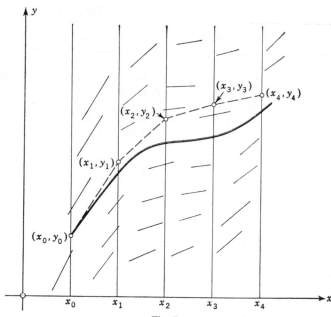

Fig. 5

Formula (6.7) has a simple geometric interpretation. In Fig. 5 a portion of the direction field for an equation $y' = f(x, y)$ is sketched, and the exact solution $y(x)$ for which $y(x_0) = y_0$ is indicated by the solid line. Since $y' = f(x, y)$, f_0 is the slope of the curve $y = y(x)$ at the point (x_0, y_0). Hence y_1 is obtained by following the tangent line to the curve $y = y(x)$ at (x_0, y_0) until the point with abscissa $x_1 = x_0 + h$ is reached. The exact value $y(x_1)$, which is the ordinate of the curve for $x = x_1$, is replaced by y_1, which is the ordinate of the tangent line for $x = x_1$. The number y_2 is obtained by drawing through the previously found point (x_1, y_1) the line of slope f_1 and following it to the point with abscissa $x_2 = x_1 + h$, and so forth. The integral curve $y = y(x)$ is approximated by the polygonal line with vertices (x_0, y_0), (x_1, y_1), $(x_2, y_2, \ldots)$.

It is seen in this discussion that although y_1 does not differ too much from the correct $y(x_1)$, y_2 differs considerably from the correct $y(x_2)$. This is due to the fact that the curve $y = y(x)$ changes its slope along the interval (x_1, x_2) rather rapidly soth at the assumption, implicit in (6.7), that the slope of $y(x)$ does not change much along an interval of length h is not valid for the chosen value of h.

Example 1. Find $y(2)$ if $y(x)$ is the solution of $dy/dx = (x + y)/2$ for which $y(0) = 2$.

TABLE 1. $h = 0.5$

x_k	f_{k-1}	$y_k = y_{k-1} + hf_{k-1}$
0.0	.....	2.000
0.5	1.000	2.500
1.0	1.500	3.250
1.5	2.125	4.313
2.0	2.907	5.767

TABLE 2. $h = 0.2$

x_k	f_{k-1}	$y_k = y_{k-1} + hf_{k-1}$
0.0	.....	2.000
0.2	1.000	2.200
0.4	1.200	2.440
0.6	1.420	2.724
0.8	1.662	3.056
1.0	1.982	3.442
1.2	2.221	3.886
1.4	2.543	4.395
1.6	2.898	4.975
1.8	3.288	5.632
2.0	3.716	6.375

TABLE 3. $y(x) = 4e^{\frac{1}{2}x} - x - 2$

x_k	y_k	x_k	y_k	x_k	y_k	x_k	y_k
0.1	2.194	0.6	2.800	1.1	3.832	1.6	5.304
0.2	2.220	0.7	2.976	1.2	4.088	1.7	5.660
0.3	2.348	0.8	3.168	1.3	4.364	1.8	6.040
0.4	2.480	0.9	3.372	1.4	4.656	1.9	6.444
0.5	2.636	1.0	3.595	1.5	4.968	2.0	6.873

Tables 1 and 2 show the calculations carried out according to formula (6.7) with $h = 0.5$ and $h = 0.2$, respectively. Table 3 gives the exact values calculated from the formula $y(x) = 4e^{\frac{1}{2}x} - x - 2$, determined by the methods of Chap. II (in all cases the results are rounded off to four decimal digits).

The error in E.C.M. I may be seen as follows. Expand the solution in a first-degree Taylor polynomial near x_0. Then

$$y(x) = y(x_0) + (x - x_0)y'(x_0) + R_2(x)$$

where R_2 is the remainder term. Then, since $y'(x_0) = f_0$,

(6.8) $$y_1 = y(x_0 + h) = y_0 + hf_0 + R_2(x_1)$$

Equation (6.8) agrees with the E.C. formula (6.6) if $R_2(x_1)$, which is the error, is neglected. Lagrange's form for the remainder gives

(6.9) $$R_2(x_1) = \tfrac{1}{2}h^2 y''(\xi_2)$$

where $x_0 < \xi_2 < x_1$. Then, if M_2 is an upper bound for $|y''(x)|$ in the interval (x_0, x_1), we have

$$|\text{Error}| = |R_2(x_1)| \le \tfrac{1}{2}h^2 M_2$$

From this last inequality we say that the error, also called the *discretization error*, is of the *order of h^2*, ignoring the bound M_2, which is usually not known.

Euler-Cauchy Method II.   Our error estimate for E.C.M. I suggests a way to improve the method by using a Taylor polynomial of degree 2:

$$y(x) = y(x_0) + (x - x_0)y'(x_0) + \tfrac{1}{2}(x - x_0)^2 y''(x_0) + R_3(x)$$

Then

(6.10) $y_1 = y(x_0 + h) = y_0 + hf_0 + \tfrac{1}{2}h^2 y''(x_0) + R_3(x_1)$

To calculate $y''(x_0)$, we differentiate $y'(x) = f(x, y(x))$.   By the chain rule,

$$\begin{aligned} y''(x_0) &= f_x(x_0, y_0) + f_y(x_0, y_0)y'(x_0) \\ &= f_x(x_0, y_0) + f_y(x_0, y_0)f_0 \end{aligned}$$

Then, neglecting the remainder in (6.10), we obtain the Euler-Cauchy method of order 2:

(6.11) $y_1 = y_0 + hf_0 + \tfrac{1}{2}h^2(f_{x0} + f_{y0}f_0)$
E.C.M. II $f_{x0} = f_x(x_0, y_0) \qquad f_{y0} = f_y(x_0, y_0)$

The (discretization) error is

$$R_3(x_1) = \tfrac{1}{6}h^3 y'''(\xi_3)$$

where $x_0 < \xi_3 < x_1$.   If M_3 is an upper bound for $|y'''(x)|$ on (x_0, x_1), then the magnitude of the error is at most $\tfrac{1}{6}h^3 M_3$.   We say that the error is *of order h^3*.

One can then calculate y_2 from y_1 in the same way, y_3 from y_2, etc. However, formula (6.11) is not convenient for computations, since the values of the partial derivatives of $f(x, y)$ are needed, nor is it sufficiently accurate away from the initial point.   It is used as a "starter formula" to obtain y_1 and possibly a few of $y_2, y_3, \ldots$; then one of the refinements discussed below is used to obtain the remaining y_k.   (For another formula of this kind, see Prob. 9.)

Example 2.   For the equation of Example 1, the partial derivatives of the function $f(x, y) = \tfrac{1}{2}(x + y)$ are easily calculated, and one has

$$y_1 = y_0 + \frac{h}{2}(x_0 + y_0) + \frac{h^2}{2}\left[\tfrac{1}{2} + \tfrac{1}{4}(x_0 + y_0)\right]$$

This and corresponding formulas for $y_2, y_3, \ldots$ are used to recalculate the solution of Example 1 for the tabular difference $h = 0.5$.   The results are given

TABLE 4

x_k	hf_{k-1}	$hf_{k-1} + \frac{1}{2}h^2(f_{x,k-1} + f_{k-1}f_{y,k-1})$	y_k
0	. . . . .	. . . . .	2.000
0.5	0.500	0.125	2.625
1.0	0.750	0.156	3.531
1.5	1.063	0.196	4.790
2.0	1.454	0.245	6.489

in Table 4. Comparison with Tables 1 to 3 shows that the new values are more accurate than those obtained by the E.C.M. I formula (6.7), even when the latter is used with the smaller step $h = 0.2$.

Adams-Bashforth Rules. The Euler-Cauchy formula (6.7) gives poor results because the variable integrand $f(x, y(x))$ in (6.5) is replaced with the constant value $f(x_0, y_0)$. In E.C.M. II the function $f(x, y(x))$ is replaced with its Taylor polynomial of degree 2. Another way of achieving a similar improvement is to replace $f(x, y(x))$ with a linear interpolation polynomial, i.e., a linear polynomial which coincides with function $f(x, y(x))$ at $x = x_0$ and $x = x_1$, namely,

$$(6.12) \qquad\qquad f_0 + \frac{x - x_0}{h}(f_1 - f_0)$$

When (6.12) is substituted for $f(x, y(x))$ in (6.5), one obtains

$$(6.13) \qquad\qquad y_1 = y_0 + h\frac{f_0 + f_1}{2}$$

One can show that the discretization error in this formula is of order h^3. These formulas form the beginning of a chain of more complex formulas based on interpolation polynomials similar to (6.12), but of higher degree. The most commonly used of these goes under the name of the *Adams-Bashforth formula* (John C. Adams, 1819–1892; F. Bashforth), and we shall therefore refer to (6.13) as an A.B. formula. (For further formulas of this kind, see Probs. 4, 5, 7, 8.)

Equation (6.13) is not an explicit formula for y_1, since the unknown also appears in the term $f_1 = f(x_1, y_1)$. In most cases it is impractical to solve (6.13) for y_1. Since the term $f(x_1, y_1)$ appears multiplied by $\frac{1}{2}h$ in (6.13), one may replace y_1 in it with a preliminary approximant y_1^* whose error is of order h^2, say the one calculated by E.C.M. I, Eq. (6.6). With this replacement, (6.13) becomes an explicit formula for y_1, and the error in this new formula is still of order h^3. Thus the

TABLE 5

x_k	hf_{k-1}	$y_k^* = y_{k-1} + hf_{k-1}$	$f_k^* = f(x_k, y_k^*)$	$\frac{1}{2}h(f_{k-1} + f_k^*)$	$y_k = y_{k-1} + \frac{1}{2}h(f_{k-1} + f_k^*)$
0.0	.....	.....	.....	.....	2.000
0.5	0.500	2.500	1.500	0.625	2.625
1.0	0.781	3.406	2.203	0.948	3.573
1.5	1.143	4.716	3.108	1.348	4.921
2.0	1.605	6.526	4.263	1.868	6.789

sequence of operations of this, the A.B. method I, is

(6.14a)
A.B.M. I
$$y_1^* = y_0 + hf_0 \qquad f_1^* = f(x_1, y_1^*)$$

(6.14b)
$$y_1 = y_0 + h\frac{f_0 + f_1^*}{2}$$

Similarly y_k is calculated from y_{k-1}. In this connection (6.14a) is called a *predictor formula*, and (6.14b) a *corrector formula*. The scheme of calculations contained in Eqs. (6.14) is the *method of Heun*. Since we obtain it as a modification of (6.13), we also refer to (6.14) as an A.B. formula (with predictor).

Example 3. Reverting again to the problem of Example 1, we now apply A.B.M. I with tabular difference $h = 0.5$. The results are tabulated in Table 5. Comparison with Tables 3 and 4 shows that the results obtained by this method are even better than those obtained with E.C.M. II.

Runge-Kutta Rules. The next methods to be taken up have the common feature that they make use of the values of $f(x, y(x))$ not only at $x = x_0, x_0 + h, x_0 + 2h, \ldots$, but also at intermediate points such as $x_0 + \frac{1}{2}h, x_0 + \frac{3}{2}h, \ldots$. Since, to start with, we do not know the value $y(x_0 + \frac{1}{2}h)$, we use for it the approximation obtained from E.C.M. I:

$$y(x_0 + \tfrac{1}{2}h) = y_0 + \tfrac{1}{2}hf_0$$

We now determine coefficients p, q so that, approximately,

$$(6.15) \quad y(x_0 + h) = y_0 + h[pf(x_0, y_0) + qf(x_0 + \tfrac{1}{2}h, y_0 + \tfrac{1}{2}k_1)]$$
$$k_1 = hf_0$$

For $h = 0$ the two sides of (6.15) are equal. To get a good approximation, we also demand that the first and second derivatives at $h = 0$ be equal. This leads to the equations

$$f_0 = (p + q)f_0$$
$$f_{x0} + f_0 f_{y0} = qf_{x0} + qf_0 f_{y0}$$

which obviously are satisfied if $p = 0$, $q = 1$. Thus, the sequence of operations to calculate y_1 of this, the R.K. method I (or improved polygonal method), is

(6.16)
R.K.M. I

$$k_1 = hf_0$$
$$k_2 = hf(x_0 + \tfrac{1}{2}h, y_0 + \tfrac{1}{2}k_1)$$
$$y_1 = y_0 + k_2$$

In a similar way y_2 is calculated after y_1 is found, and so on.

More rules of this kind, derived in a similar way, are found in Probs. 11 to 13. They are called *Runge-Kutta rules* (C. D. T. Runge, 1856–1927; M. W. Kutta, 1867–1944). The one expressed in (6.16) leads to a discretization error of order h^3 since it was derived by equating the zeroth-, first-, and second-order derivatives of the two sides of (6.15). The following, with an error of order h^5, is the most commonly used of the R.K. rules. We state it without proof and denote it as the R.K. method II. (See Ref. 1.)

(6.17)
R.K.M. II

$$k_1 = hf_0$$
$$k_2 = hf(x_0 + \tfrac{1}{2}h, y_0 + \tfrac{1}{2}k_1)$$
$$k_3 = hf(x_0 + \tfrac{1}{2}h, y_0 + \tfrac{1}{2}k_2)$$
$$k_4 = hf(x_0 + h, y_0 + k_3)$$
$$y_1 = y_0 + \tfrac{1}{6}(k_1 + 2k_2 + 2k_3 + k_4)$$

Example 4. Returning once more to the problem of Example 1, we apply the R.K. method (6.16) with tabular difference $h = 0.5$. The results are tabulated in Table 6. They are not quite as good as those obtained by A.B.M.

TABLE 6

x_k	hf_{k-1}	$hf(x_{k-1} + \tfrac{1}{2}h, y_{k-1} + \tfrac{1}{2}hf_{k-1})$	y_k
0.0	. . . . .	. . . . .	2.000
0.5	0.500	0.625	2.625
1.0	0.781	1.883	3.508
1.5	1.127	1.331	4.839
2.0	1.585	1.845	6.684

TABLE 7

x	k_1	$2k_2$	$2k_3$	k_4	$\tfrac{1}{6}(k_1 + 2k_2 + 2k_3 + k_4)$	y
0.0	. . . . .	. . . . .	. . . . .	. . . . .	. . . . .	2.000
0.5	0.500	1.250	1.282	0.785	0.636	2.636
1.0	0.784	1.889	1.929	1.150	0.959	3.595
1.5	1.149	2.710	2.761	1.619	1.373	4.968
2.0	1.617	3.763	3.830	2.221	1.905	6.873

I (see Table 5), but better than those obtained by E.C.M. II (see Table 4). In Table 7 the results obtained by the more accurate R.K. method (6.17) are summarized. Comparison with Table 3 shows that the y values obtained in this way are accurate to four decimal digits.

It should be observed that if we say the discretization error of a certain finite-difference method is of order h^r, we mean that y_1 as calculated by the method differs from the true $y(x_1) = y(x_0 + h)$ by at most Mh^r, where M is some constant independent of h. However, we are usually interested in the difference between the computed and true values at some *fixed* x, say $x = x_0 + L$, not at x_1. In other words, we are interested in the error which results because of the *recursive* application of the method, by which first $y(x_0 + h)$ is computed, then $y(x_0 + 2h)$, and so on, until one arrives at $y(x_0 + L)$. The number of steps in this recursion increases as h decreases; it is L/h (we may ignore the fact that this is not always an integer). Since the discretization error at each step is possibly as large as Mh^r, the discretization error in the computation of $y(x_0 + L)$ is bounded by

$$C \frac{L}{h} Mh^r = M_1 h^{r-1}$$

where C, M_1 are constants independent of h.† Thus, the *order of the discretization error in the computation of $y(x)$ at some fixed x is lower by 1 than the discretization error in the computation of $y_1 = y(x_0 + h)$.*

Milne's Method. In the following we shall use not only x_0, y_0, f_0; x_1, y_1, f_1; . . . [see (6.2) to (6.4)], but also

(6.18)
$$\begin{array}{lll} x_{-1} = x_0 - h & x_{-2} = x_0 - 2h & \cdots \\ y_{-1} = y(x_{-1}) & y_{-2} = y(x_{-2}) & \cdots \\ f_{-1} = f(x_{-1}, y_{-1}) & f_{-2} = f(x_{-2}, y_{-2}) & \cdots \end{array}$$

We approximate the function $y'(x) = f(x, y(x))$ with the quadratic interpolation polynomial

(6.19) $$f_0 + \frac{x - x_0}{h} (f_1 - f_0) + \frac{(x - x_0)(x - x_1)}{2h^2} (f_1 - 2f_0 + f_{-1})$$

which agrees with $f(x, y(x))$ at x_{-1}, x_0, and x_1. Now we integrate this approximation of $y'(x)$ between x_{-1} and x_1 and obtain an A.B. formula:

(6.20) $$y_1 = y_{-1} + \frac{h}{3} (f_1 + 4f_0 + f_{-1})$$

† In computing y_k from y_{k-1} the discretization error is not simply increased by Mh^r. A verification of the error bound Mh^{r-1} at $x_0 + L$ can be based on the inequality of Prob. 2, Sec. 1, Chap. III.

The discretization error in this A.B. formula is not only of order h^4 as one might expect from the derivation, but even of order h^5, since adding to (6.19) a correction term of degree 3 in $(x - x_0)$ would not change (6.20).

Equation (6.20) is not an explicit formula for y_1, since the term $f_1 = f(x_1, y_1)$ on the right of (6.20) contains y_1. As with the A.B. formula (6.13), we replace y_1 on the right of (6.20) with a preliminary value y_1^*, which in this case should approximate y_1 with an error of order at least h^4. To this purpose we replace the unknown function $y'(x) = f(x, y(x))$ with the quadratic extrapolation polynomial†

$$(6.21) \quad f_{-1} + \frac{x - x_{-1}}{h} (f_0 - f_{-1}) + \frac{(x - x_{-1})(x - x_0)}{2h^2} (f_0 - 2f_{-1} + f_{-2})$$

Then integration of this polynomial between x_{-3} and x_1 yields an A.B. formula:

$$(6.22) \qquad y_1 = y_{-3} + \frac{4h}{3} (2f_0 - f_{-1} + 2f_{-2})$$

This is an explicit formula for y_1 provided the values $y_{-3}, y_{-2}, y_{-1}, y_0$ are already known. The discretization error is again of order h^5, since adding a correction term of degree 3 in $(x - x_{-1})$ to (6.21) would not change (6.22).

If (6.22) is used as a predictor formula for (6.20), one has the Milne method:

$$(6.23a) \qquad y_1^* = y_{-3} + \frac{4h}{3} (2f_0 - f_{-1} + 2f_{-2})$$

$$(6.23b) \qquad f_1^* = f(x_1, y_1^*)$$

$$(6.23c) \qquad y_1 = y_{-1} + \frac{h}{3} (f_1^* + 4f_0 + f_{-1})$$

The *Milne method* (W. E. Milne, 1890–   ) is one of the most commonly used numerical methods. It is of recursive type; y_2 is found from y_1, y_0, y_{-1}, y_{-2} in the same way as y_1 is found from $y_0, y_{-1}, y_{-2}, y_{-3}$, and so forth. The initial values $y_0, y_{-1}, y_{-2}, y_{-3}$ must be given (y_0 is always given) or found by one of the other numerical methods (which in this connection is called a *starter formula*), frequently the R.K. or E.C. method. Since (6.23a) and (6.23c) are approximations of about the same accuracy (the discretization error in either case is of order h^5), (6.23a) may be used as a check on (6.23c). It can be shown that if the difference $E = |y_1^* - y_1|$ is small, then the difference between y_1 and the true value $y(x_1)$ is small (approximately $\frac{1}{30}E$). Therefore, if $y(x_1)$

† We call (6.21) an extrapolation polynomial of $f(x, y(x))$ because it is used on the interval $-3h \leq x \leq h$, while it coincides with $f(x, y(x))$ only at $x = -2h, -h, 0$.

is calculated according to both (6.23a) and (6.23c) and the difference $E = |y_1^* - y_1|$ turns out to be negligible (for the desired accuracy), then one may assume that y_1 is a sufficiently accurate approximation to $y(x_1)$.

Example 5. We use the Milne method to find the solution $y(x)$ of Example 1 for $x = 2.0$, assuming that we know $y(0)$, $y(0.5)$, $y(1.0)$, $y(1.5)$ as given in Table 3. Here $h = 0.5$.

$$
\begin{array}{llll}
x_{-3} = 0 & x_{-2} = 0.5 & x_{-1} = 1.0 & x_0 = 1.5 \\
y_{-3} = 2 & y_{-2} = 2.636 & y_{-1} = 3.595 & y_0 = 4.968 \\
f_{-3} = 1 & f_{-2} = 1.568 & f_{-1} = 2.298 & f_0 = 3.234
\end{array}
$$

TABLE OF NUMERICAL METHODS

For easy reference we collect the numerical methods developed in the text (others are to be found among the problems). It should be observed that the notation is somewhat changed. The terms $0(h^2)$, $0(h^3)$, etc., refer to discretization errors of order h^2, h^3, etc., for a single step from x_{k-1} to x_k.

E.C.M. I (polygonal method):

$$f_{k-1} = f(x_{k-1}, y_{k-1})$$
$$y_k = y_{k-1} + hf_{k-1} + 0(h^2)$$

E.C.M. II:

$$f_{k-1} = f(x_{k-1}, y_{k-1}) \quad p_{k-1} = f_x(x_{k-1}, y_{k-1}) \quad q_{k-1} = f_y(x_{k-1}, y_{k-1})$$
$$y_k = y_{k-1} + hf_{k-1} + \tfrac{1}{2}h^2(p_{k-1} + f_{k-1}q_{k-1}) + 0(h^3)$$

A.B.M. I (Heun's method):

$$f_{k-1} = f(x_{k-1}, y_{k-1}) \quad y_k^* = y_{k-1} + hf_{k-1} \quad f_k^* = f(x_k, y_k^*)$$
$$y_k = y_{k-1} + \tfrac{1}{2}h(f_{k-1} + f_k^*) + 0(h^3)$$

R.K.M. I (improved polygonal method):

$$f_{k-1} = f(x_{k-1}, y_{k-1}) \quad f_{k-\frac{1}{2}} = f(x_{k-1} + \tfrac{1}{2}h, y_{k-1} + \tfrac{1}{2}hf_{k-1})$$
$$y_k = y_{k-1} + hf_{k-\frac{1}{2}} + 0(h^3)$$

R.K.M. II (Runge-Kutta method):

$$f_{k-1} = f(x_{k-1}, y_{k-1}) \quad f_{k-\frac{1}{2}} = f(x_{k-1} + \tfrac{1}{2}h, y_{k-1} + \tfrac{1}{2}hf_{k-1})$$
$$f_{k-\frac{1}{2}}^* = f(x_{k-1} + \tfrac{1}{2}h, y_{k-1} + \tfrac{1}{2}hf_{k-\frac{1}{2}})$$
$$f_k^* = f(x_k, y_{k-1} + hf_{k-\frac{1}{2}}^*)$$
$$y_k = y_{k-1} + \tfrac{1}{6}h(f_{k-1} + 2f_{k-\frac{1}{2}} + 2f_{k-\frac{1}{2}}^* + f_k^*) + 0(h^5)$$

Milne's method:

$$f_r = f(x_r, y_r) \quad r = k - 3, k - 2, k - 1$$
$$y_k^* = y_{k-4} + \frac{4h}{3}(2f_{k-3} - f_{k-2} + 2f_{k-1}) + 0(h^5)$$
$$f_k^* = f(x_k, y_k^*)$$
$$y_k = y_{k-2} + \frac{h}{3}(f_{k-2} + 4f_{k-1} + f_k^*) + 0(h^5)$$

Formulas (6.23) give

$$y_1^* = 6.871 \qquad f_1^* = 4.435 \qquad y_1 = 6.873$$

The difference $E = |y_1^* - y_1|$ equals 0.002, and $\frac{1}{30}E$ is much smaller than 10^{-3}. Thus we infer that $y_1 = 6.873$ is accurate to four decimals, and the conclusion is confirmed by comparison with the exact value given in Table 3.

PROBLEMS

1. In the following problems the numerical method to be used is indicated by the letters E.C., A.B., or R.K., respectively, with a number referring to a formula in this section. The tabular difference h to be used is also specified. The calculations are to be carried out with at least four decimal digits accuracy. Most of them can be done using pencil, slide rule, and numerical tables only; for a few of them the use of a desk calculator may be appropriate.

(a) $y' = x - 5y$, $y(-0.5) = 1$; find $y(0)$ by E.C.M. I; $h = 0.1$.

(b) $y' = \frac{1}{2}(x + y)$, $y(2) = 6.873$; find $y(2.5)$ by E.C.M. I; $h = 0.05$.

(c) $y' = \log_{10}(4x + y)$, $y(0) = 1$; find $y(2)$ by E.C.M. I; $h = 0.2$.

(d) $y' = (x^2 - y^2)/(1 + x^2 + y^2)$, $y(0) = 0$; find $y(1)$ and $y(-1)$ by E.C.M. I; $h = 0.1$.

(e) $(1 + x^2y^2)y' = 1$, $y(0) = 0$; find $y(1.5)$ and $y(-1.5)$ by E.C.M. II; $h = 0.5$.

(f) $y' = x^2y - xy^2$, $y(0) = -1$; find $y(1)$ and $y(-2)$ by E.C.M. II; $h = 0.25$.

(g) $y' = y$, $y(0) = 1$; find $y(1)$ by E.C.M. I, $h = 0.01$.

(h) $y' = y$, $y(0) = 1$; find $y(1)$ by E.C.M. II; $h = 0.1$.

(i) $y' = \sin(x^2 - 2xy + y^2)$, $y(1) = 1$; find $y(-1)$ by E.C.M. I; $h = 0.2$.

(j) $y' = \log_y x$, $y(1) = 2.718$; find $y(5)$ by E.C.M. I; $h = 0.5$.

(k) $y' = x - 5y$, $y(-0.5) = 1$; find $y(0)$ by A.B.M. I; $h = 0.1$.

(l) $(1 + x^2y^2)y' = 1$, $y(0) = 0$; find $y(1.5)$ and $y(-1.5)$ by A.B.M. I; $h = 0.5$.

(m) $y' = y$, $y(0) = 1$; find $y(1)$ by A.B.M. I; $h = 0.1$.

(n) $y' = \sqrt{x + y}$, $y(100) = -96$; find $y(110)$ by A.B.M. I; $h = 1$.

(o) $y' = x - 5y$, $y(-0.5) = 1$; find $y(0)$ by R.K.M. I; $h = 0.1$.

(p) $y' = y$, $y(0) = 1$; find $y(1)$ by R.K.M. I; $h = 0.1$.

(q) $y' = x^2 + 3y$, $y(0) = 5$; find $y(-1)$ by R.K.M. I; $h = 0.2$.

(r) $y' = -2xy$, $y(0) = 1$; find $y(2)$ by R.K.M. II; $h = 0.5$.

(s) $y' = (x^2 - y^2)/(1 + x^2 + y^2)$, $y(0) = 0$; find $y(2)$ and $y(-2)$ by R.K.M. II; $h = 0.5$.

2. Apply Milne's method with suitable tabular difference to the equation $dy/dx = y$ so as to obtain $e^{1.2}$, $e^{1.4}$, $e^{1.6}$, $e^{1.8}$, $e^{2.0}$ accurate to six decimals. The values of y_0, y_{-1}, y_{-2}, y_{-3} are to be found by the E.C. method of sufficiently high order.

3. Show that the indefinitely extended E.C. method, applied to the problem $dy/dx = y$, $y(0) = 1$, leads to the expansion

$$y(h) = 1 + \frac{h}{1!} + \frac{h^2}{2!} + \cdots + \frac{h^n}{n!} + \cdots$$

of the exponential function.

4. In the A.B. formula (6.14) consider y_1 not as the final approximation to $y(x_1)$, but as another preliminary value y_1^{**} from which the final approximation y_1 is calculated. Rule (6.14) is then replaced by

$$y_1^* = y_0 + hf_0 \qquad f_1^* = f(x_1, y_1^*)$$

$$y_1^{**} = y_0 + \frac{h}{2}(f_0 + f_1^*) \qquad f_1^{**} = f(x_1, y_1^{**})$$

$$y_1 = y_0 + \frac{h}{2}(f_0 + f_1^{**})$$

Use this method to recompute Table 5.

5. Using the first-degree extrapolation polynomial

$$f_0 + \frac{x - x_0}{h}(f_0 - f_{-1})$$

as an approximation to $y'(x) = f(x, y(x))$, derive an A.B. formula (of order h^3)

$$y_1 = y_0 + \frac{h}{2}(3f_0 - f_{-1})$$

6. Use the A.B. formula of Prob. 5 recursively to recompute Table 5; to start the process, use $y_{-1} = y_0 - hf_0$.

7. Using the second-degree interpolation polynomial

$$f_0 + \frac{x - x_0}{h}(f_0 - f_{-1}) + \frac{(x - x_0)(x - x_{-1})}{2h^2}(f_1 - 2f_0 + f_{-1})$$

as an approximation to $y'(x) = f(x, y(x))$, derive an A.B. formula (of order h^4)

$$y_1 = y_0 + \frac{h}{12}(5f_1 + 8f_0 - f_{-1})$$

8. Using the second-degree extrapolation polynomial

$$f_{-1} + \frac{x - x_{-1}}{h}(f_{-1} - f_{-2}) + \frac{(x - x_{-1})(x - x_{-2})}{2h^2}(f_0 - 2f_{-1} + f_{-2})$$

as an approximation to $y'(x) = f(x, y(x))$, derive an A.B. formula (of order h^4)

$$y_1 = y_0 + \frac{h}{12}(23f_0 - 16f_{-1} + 5f_{-2})$$

9. Approximate the value $y_1 = y(x + h)$ of the solution $y(x)$ of $y' = f(x, y)$, $y(x_0) = y_0$, with a Taylor polynomial of degree 3, and derive the E.C. formula

$$y_1 = y_0 + hf_0 + \frac{h^2}{2}(f_{x0} + f_0 f_{y0}) + \frac{h^3}{6}(f_{x0} f_{y0} + f_0 f_{y0}^2 + f_{xx0} + 2f_0 f_{xy0}$$
$$+ f_0^2 f_{yy0})$$

which differs from the correct value of y_1 by less than $\frac{1}{24}h^4 M_4$. NOTATION: f_{xx0} is the second partial derivative of $f(x, y)$ taken at x_0, y_0. M_4 is an upper bound for $|y^{(4)}(x)|$ on (x_0, x_1).

10. For the solution of Example 1, find $y(0.5)$ by the A.B. formula of Prob. 7 $(h = 0.5)$.

11. With the notation $k_1 = hf_0$ determine coefficients p, q such that, approximately (making the first and second derivatives agree at x_0),

$$y(x_0 + h) = y_0 + h[pf(x_0, y_0) + qf(x_0 + \tfrac{2}{3}h, y_0 + \tfrac{2}{3}k_1)]$$

and obtain the R.K. formula (of order h^3)

$$k_1 = hf_0$$
$$k_2 = hf(x_0 + \tfrac{2}{3}h, y_0 + \tfrac{2}{3}k_1)$$
$$y_1 = y_0 + \tfrac{1}{4}k_1 + \tfrac{3}{4}k_2$$

★12. Let k_1, k_2 be defined as in (6.17). Determine the coefficients p, q, r so that, approximately,

$$y(x_0 + h) = y_0 + h[pf(x_0, y_0) + qf(x_0 + \tfrac{1}{2}h, y_0 + \tfrac{1}{2}k)$$
$$+ rf(x_0 + h, y_0 - k_1 + 2k_2)]$$

and obtain the R.K. formula (of order h^4)

$$k_1 = hf_0$$
$$k_2 = hf(x_0 + \tfrac{1}{2}h, y_0 + \tfrac{1}{2}k_1)$$
$$k_3 = hf(x_0 + h, y_0 - k_1 + 2k_2)$$
$$y_1 = y_0 + \tfrac{1}{6}(k_1 + 4k_2 + k_3)$$

★13. Let k_1, k_2 be defined as in (6.17), and let $k_2' = hf(x_0 + \tfrac{1}{2}h, y_0 + \tfrac{1}{4}k_1 + \tfrac{1}{4}k_2)$. Determine the coefficients p, q, r so that, approximately,

$$y(x_0 + h) = y_0 + h[pf(x_0, y_0) + qf(x_0 + \tfrac{1}{2}h, y_0 + \tfrac{1}{4}k_1 + \tfrac{1}{4}k_2)$$
$$+ rf(x_0 + h, y_0 - k_2 + 2k_2')]$$

and obtain the R.K. formula (of order h^5)

$$k_1 = hf_0$$
$$k_2 = hf(x_0 + \tfrac{1}{2}h, y_0 + \tfrac{1}{2}k_1)$$
$$k_2' = hf(x_0 + \tfrac{1}{2}h, y_0 + \tfrac{1}{4}k_1 + \tfrac{1}{4}k_2)$$
$$k_3 = hf(x_0 + h, y_0 - k_2 + 2k_2')$$
$$y_1 = y_0 + \tfrac{1}{6}(k_1 + 4k_2' + k_3)$$

14. Show that if $f(x, y)$ is independent of y, then A.B.M. I becomes the trapezoidal rule for quadratures:

$$\int_{x_0}^{x_n} f(x) \, dx = \frac{h}{2} \, (f_0 + 2f_1 + 2f_1 + 2f_2 + \cdots + 2f_{n-1} + f_n)$$

15. Show that if $f(x, y)$ is independent of y, then both R.K.M. II and the R.K. formula of Prob. 12 become Simpson's rule for quadratures:

$$\int_{x_0}^{x_n} f(x) \, dx = \frac{h}{6} \, (f_0 + 4f_{\frac{1}{2}} + 2f_1 + 4f_{\frac{3}{2}} + 2f_2 + \cdots + f_n)$$

16. Apply E.C.M. I with $h = 1/n$ to approximate $y(1)$ if $y' = y$, $y(0) = 1$. Show that the exact value of $y(1)$ is approached as $n \to \infty$.

17. Apply A.B.M. I with $h = 1/n$ to approximate $y(1)$ if $y' = y$, $y(0) = 1$. How close is this to the accurate value if $n = 10$?

18. Apply R.K.M. I with $h = 1/n$ to approximate $y(1)$ if $y' = y$, $y(0) = 1$. How close is this to the accurate value if $n = 10$?

★19. Apply R.K.M. II with $h = 1/n$ to approximate $y(1)$ if $y' = y$, $y(0) = 1$. How close is this to the accurate value if $n = 5$?

20. The problem $dy/dx = -\alpha y$ $(\alpha > 0)$, $y(0) = y_0 \neq 0$, has the solution $y(x) = y_0 e^{-\alpha x}$; therefore, $\lim_{n \to \infty} y_n = \lim_{n \to \infty} y_0 e^{-\alpha n h} = 0$. Show (a) that $\lim y_n = 0$ if y_n is computed according to E.C.M. I and (b) that $\lim y_n = \infty$ if $\alpha h > 2$ and y_n is computed according to A.B.M. I. (This is an example of computational instability. One says A.B.M. I is *computationally unstable* for the given equation if $\alpha h > 2$.) Also show that this instability does not occur if the implicit A.B. formula (6.13) is used in place of the explicit (6.14).

7. Round-off Errors

All numerical computations are subject to round-off errors since they use finite expansions (decimal, binary, or others), usually of fixed length for all the numbers involved. If N digits after the decimal point are carried, then the round-off error† in representing an arbitrary number may be as much as $\pm \frac{1}{2} 10^{-N}$. If k numbers are added, the computed sum may be off by $\pm \frac{1}{2} k 10^{-N}$. Where one deals with a fixed number of arithmetical operations, the round-off error can be controlled relatively easily. However, where improved accuracy can be obtained only by increasing the number of arithmetical operations, as when we decrease the tabular difference h and hence increase the number of steps leading from $y(x_0)$ to $y(x_0 + L)$ in order to diminish the discretization error, the round-off errors must be carefully examined, since their accumulation may destroy the validity of the result.

† A more significant measure of accuracy is the *relative round-off error*, which is the quotient of the round-off error and the number represented. The relative error is more difficult to handle. If, however, all numbers involved in a calculation are of the same order of magnitude, then the absolute round-off error represents the relative round-off error fairly well.

Let us consider E.C.M. I:

(7.1) $y_k = y_{k-1} + hf_{k-1}$

According to it, the solution $y(x)$ of $y' = f(x, y)$, $y(x_0) = y_0$, can be calculated at any fixed x, say $x = x_0 + L = x_0 + nh$, with a discretization error E_d of order h; hence

(7.2) $|E_d| \le M_d h$

where M_d is independent of h. Each step of these n computations involves many operations and a round-off error which partially adds to the round-off error in the preceding calculation. Without going into the details of the calculations, one may assume that the round-off error in one such step is realistically appraised as some small integral multiple of $\frac{1}{2}10^{-N}$ (if N digits after the decimal point are carried) and that it is essentially independent of h. Since the errors in the $n = L/h$ steps may add,[†] the round-off error E_r in computing $y(x_0 + L)$ by formula (7.1) is estimated by the inequality

(7.3) $|E_r| \le M_r h^{-1}$

where M_r is a constant independent of h, usually quite small since it is a moderate multiple of $10^{-N}L$.

The round-off error is as likely as not of the same sign as the discretization error, so the total error E (discretization plus round-off error) in computing $y(x_0 + L)$ by formula (7.1) satisfies the inequality

(7.4) $|E| \le M_d h + M_r h^{-1}$

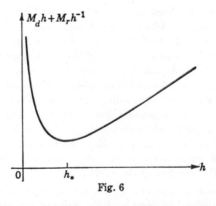

Fig. 6

---

† Here one assumes that an error in y_{k-1} results in an error of the same order in y_k. This is true if f and $\partial f/\partial y$ are continuous (see the inequality of Prob. 2, Sec. 1, Chap. III).

Therefore E need not tend to 0 as $h \to 0$. Decreasing the tabular difference h indefinitely need not lead to indefinitely improved accuracy. The upper bound in (7.4) as a function of h is graphed in Fig. 6. It has a minimum for $h = h_*$,

$$(7.5) \qquad\qquad h_* = \sqrt{\frac{M_r}{M_d}}$$

and this minimum is

$$(7.6) \qquad\qquad E_* = 2\sqrt{M_d M_r}$$

If for illustration we make the reasonable assumption that $M_r = 10^{-N} M_d$, then the smallest upper bound in (8.4) is obtained for $h = 10^{-\frac{1}{2}N}$, and it is $E = 2M_d 10^{-\frac{1}{2}N}$. Therefore, in this case, one cannot hope to have errors much smaller than $10^{-\frac{1}{2}N}$ if N digits after the decimal point are carried; this accuracy is attained with the tabular difference $10^{-\frac{1}{2}N}$. Also in this case one sees that the round-off error is negligible as compared with the discretization error as long as $M_r h^{-1}/M_d h = 10^{-N} h^{-2}$ is small compared with unity, that is, h is large compared with $10^{-\frac{1}{2}N}$.

In the more sophisticated numerical methods the discretization error is of order higher than 1, say $|E_d| \leq M_d h^k$, but the round-off error in most cases satisfies inequality (7.3), since the computation of $y(x_0 + L)$ requires $n = L/h$ steps and a fixed number (independent of h) of arithmetical operations per step. For these methods the minimum E of the total error is attained at some h larger than that given by (7.5) and is smaller than (7.6), and the round-off becomes prominent at larger h.

The bounds for the round-off errors given in this section are very pessimistic, since they assume that each computation contributes a round-off error of the same sign and of the largest possible value. Although such a situation is possible, it is extremely unlikely. In the vast majority of cases where many round-off errors arise, they tend to cancel each other at least partially. A more realistic treatment of the likely effect of round-off errors should be based on a statistical analysis, but the problems connected with such treatment are formidable, and the results achieved so far are not fully convincing.

PROBLEM

To see an example of how round-off errors accumulate, approximate e^{-1} by computing $y(1)$ according to E.C.M. I, given $y' = -y$ and $y(0) = 1$, where all numbers are to be rounded off to one place after the decimal point. Show that the total error is about twice as large for $h = 0.1$ as for $h = 0.2$.

8. The Method of Successive Approximations

The method of this section (known as *Picard's method;* E. Picard, 1856–1941) is of both practical and theoretical importance. It provides a numerical method that is often used and is the basis of Picard's proof of the existence of solutions to first-order differential equations.

We wish to solve the initial-value problem

$$(8.1) \qquad\qquad y' = f(x, y) \qquad y(x_0) = y_0$$

In this section we shall simply formulate the *method*, assuming that f has suitable properties to permit the operations involved. For a proof of the validity see Ref. 1.

The first step is the observation that a solution of Prob. (8.1) is also a solution of the *integral equation*

$$(8.2) \qquad\qquad y(x) = y_0 + \int_{x_0}^{x} f(s, y(s))\, ds$$

Conversely, a solution of (8.2) is a solution of (8.1). One starts with a zeroth-order approximation, say $y_0(x)$ (which in most cases is taken to be the constant y_0), and one substitutes this in the integral of (8.2), thus obtaining a first-order approximation, say $y_1(x)$:

$$(8.3) \qquad\qquad y_1(x) = y_0 + \int_{x_0}^{x} f(s, y_0(s))\, ds$$

The calculation of $y_1(x)$ requires a more or less complicated quadrature. A second-order approximation, say $y_2(x)$, is obtained from $y_1(x)$,

$$y_2(x) = y_0 + \int_{x_0}^{x} f(s, y_1(s))\, ds$$

and, generally, an $(n + 1)$st-order approximation $y_{n+1}(x)$ is obtained from the nth-order approximation:

$$(8.4) \qquad\qquad y_{n+1}(x) = y_0 + \int_{x_0}^{x} f(s, y_n(s))\, ds$$

Each step requires an additional quadrature.

Under suitable hypotheses on f, the sequence of approximations $y_n(x)$ will converge on some interval $|x - x_0| \le a$ to a function $y(x)$ which solves (8.2) and hence (8.1).

The method is practical when one has a computer to carry out the necessary quadratures quickly. It will be applied here only to a few simple problems which do not require a computer for the quadratures.

Example 1.   Solve the initial-value problem

$$y' = y \qquad y(0) = 1$$

by the method of successive approximations.

The problem is equivalent to

$$y(x) = 1 + \int_{0}^{x} y(s)\, ds$$

We start with the zeroth-order approximation $y_0(x) = 1$.   Then

$$y_1(x) = 1 + \int_0^x ds = 1 + x$$

$$y_2(x) = 1 + \int_0^x (1 + s) \, ds = 1 + x + \frac{x^2}{2}$$

$$y_{n+1}(x) = 1 + \int_0^x \left(1 + s + \frac{s^2}{2} + \cdots + \frac{s^n}{n!} \right) ds$$

$$= 1 + x + \frac{x^2}{2} + \cdots + \frac{x^{n+1}}{(n+1)!}$$

It is seen in this case that

$$y(x) = \lim_{n \to \infty} y_n(x) = e^x$$

Example 2.   Starting with the zeroth-order approximation $y_0(x) = 0$, find the third-order approximation $y_3(x)$ to the solution of the problem

$$y' = x^2 - y^2 \qquad y(0) = 0$$

The problem is equivalent to

$$y(x) = \int_0^x [s^2 - y^2(s)] \, ds$$

Hence,

$$y_1(x) = \int_0^x (s^2 - 0) \, ds = \frac{x^3}{3}$$

$$y_2(x) = \int_0^x \left(s^2 - \frac{s^6}{9} \right) ds = \frac{x^3}{3} - \frac{x^7}{63}$$

$$y_3(x) = \int_0^x \left(s^2 - \frac{s^6}{9} + \frac{2s^{10}}{189} - \frac{s^{14}}{3,969} \right) ds$$

$$= \frac{x^3}{3} - \frac{x^7}{63} + \frac{2x^{11}}{2,079} - \frac{x^{15}}{59,535}$$

PROBLEMS

In these problems $y_0(x)$, $y_1(x)$, $\ldots$, $y_n(x)$ denote successive approximations of order 0, 1, $\ldots$, n; $y(x)$ denotes $\lim_{n \to \infty} y_n(x)$.

1. For the problem $y' = x + y$, $y(0) = 0$, choose $y_0(x) \equiv 0$ and find $y_n(x)$, $y(x)$.

2. For the problem $y' = 2xy$, $y(0) = 1$, choose $y_0(x) \equiv 1$ and find $y_n(x)$, $y(x)$.

3. For the problem $y' = x^2 y + 1$, $y(0) = 0$, choose $y_0(x) \equiv 0$ and find $y_n(x)$.

4. For the problem $y' = e^x + y^2$, $y(0) = 1$, choose $y_0(x) \equiv 1$ and find $y_3(x)$.

5. For the problem $y' = (x + y + 1)/(x + 1)$, $y(0) = 0$, choose $y_0(x) \equiv 0$ and find $y_4(x)$.

6. For the problem $y' = (x + 2y)/(2x + y)$, $y(1) = 1$, choose $y_0(x) \equiv x$ and find $y(x)$.

7. Show that if in the problem $y' = f(x, y)$, $y(x_0) = y_0$, we have $y_2(x) = y_3(x)$, then $y(x) = y_2(x)$.

8. The problem $y' = y$, $y(0) = 1$, has the solution $y(x) = e^x$. Show that the successive approximations $y_n(x)$ converge to e^x even if one starts with the remote approximation $y_0(x) = e^{10x}$.

9. For the problem $y' + p(x)y = 0$, $y(x_0) = y_0$, choose $y_0(x) \equiv y_0$ and prove $y(x) = y_0 e^{-P(x)}$, where $P(x) = \int_{x_0}^{x} p(s)\, ds$.

chapter ii

Techniques for Solving First-order Equations

The preceding chapter provided a general introduction to the problems posed by first-order differential equations. That D.E.'s do have solutions and that one can, at least approximately, find them should be clear from the discussion of direction fields and numerical methods. But so far only one type of first-order equation has been solved in closed form, namely, that for which the variables can be separated.

In this chapter, several other types of first-order equations are taken up which can be solved by various formulas or formal procedures. The situation is similar to that encountered in the integral calculus. After it is established that for every continuous function $f(x)$ there is a differentiable function $F(x) = \int f(x)\,dx$ whose derivative is $f(x)$, there remains the task of developing formulas and techniques by which the integral $F(x)$ can be found. It is well known that even for many elementary functions $f(x)$ the integral $\int f(x)\,dx$ cannot be obtained in terms of the elementary functions. It would be surprising if anything less involved were to occur in differential equations. In fact, it is not true that every first-order differential equation whose formulation involves only elementary functions can be solved by the elementary operations of calculus, even if the operation of quadrature is included. The situation we are confronted with is as follows: to consider those types of first-order equations which are simple enough to be solved by the elementary operations and which occur often enough to justify their consideration.

The most important types of first-order equations, next to that with separable variables, are *linear equations* and *exact equations*. The most important techniques of solution, next to separation of variables, are those of *variation of parameter, integrating factors*, and various kinds of *substitutions*. These and related topics are taken up in this chapter.

1. Linear Equations

The general form of a first-order linear differential equation in $y(x)$ is

$$(1.1) \qquad A(x)\frac{dy}{dx} + B(x)y + C(x) = 0$$

where the coefficients $A(x)$, $B(x)$, $C(x)$ are functions of the independent variable x alone (or constants). We usually assume that (1.1) is divided through by $A(x)$ [in intervals of x in which $A(x) \neq 0$] and that the term $C(x)/A(x)$ is transposed to the right side of the equation. Then we have the linear equation in *normal form:*

$$(1.2) \qquad \frac{dy}{dx} + P(x)y = Q(x)$$

If $Q = 0$, (1.2) is said to be *linear homogeneous*, for then each nonzero term of the equation is of the first degree in y and y'. The homogeneous equation has the distinguishing property that $y = 0$ is a particular solution, the so-called *trivial solution*. We first solve the *corresponding homogeneous equation*

$$(1.3) \qquad \frac{dy}{dx} + P(x)y = 0$$

Here the variables are separable, and one finds directly

$$\log |y| = -\int P(x)\,dx + \text{constant}$$

or

$$(1.4) \qquad y(x) = Ce^{-\int P\,dx}$$

where C is a constant of integration. It is seen that *all the solutions of the homogeneous linear equation are obtained from any one particular non-trivial solution by taking all possible constant multiples.* Therefore, (1.4) is called the *general solution* of (1.3).

Proceeding to the nonhomogeneous equation (1.2), we first observe a relation between the solutions of (1.2) and (1.3). In this connection, (1.3) is referred to as the *reduced equation*. If y_1 and y_2 are solutions of (1.2), that is,

$$(1.5) \qquad \begin{aligned} y_1' + Py_1 &= Q \\ y_2' + Py_2 &= Q \end{aligned}$$

then if $z(x) = y_1(x) - y_2(x)$,

$$(1.6) \qquad z' + Pz = 0$$

Thus, the difference of any two solutions of the nonhomogeneous equation (1.2) is a solution of the reduced equation. Conversely, if y_p is a *particular* solution of the *complete equation* (1.2), and if y_c is a solution of the corresponding homogeneous equation (1.3), then

$$(1.7) \qquad y = y_c + y_p$$

is another solution of (1.2). In other words: *Every solution of the complete equation is obtained from one particular solution by adding to it the general solution of the reduced equation.*

We shall use y_c to denote the general solution of (1.3) and refer to it as the *complementary function*. As will be seen in Chaps. V and VI, formula (1.7) applies to linear D.E. of any order.

Since the general solution of the reduced equation (1.3) can be obtained by a quadrature alone [see (1.4)], it remains to find some particular solution of (1.2). Sometimes this can be done by inspection. For example, to solve

$$y' + x^3y = 2x^3$$

one guesses readily that $y = 2$ is a solution. Then, using (1.4) for the general solution of the reduced equation, one finds the general solution

$$y(x) = 2x^3 + ce^{-x^4/4}$$

A systematic way of finding a particular solution of (1.2) is the following. First find the general solution (1.4) of the homogeneous equation (1.3). Then replace the constant C with an as yet undetermined function $u(x)$, and consider the function

$$(1.8) \qquad y(x) = u(x)e^{-\int P\,dx}$$

We shall determine u so that y as given by (1.8) is a particular integral of (1.2). Because of the replacement of the constant C by the variable $u(x)$, the technique is known as *variation of parameters*. It is due to J. L. Lagrange (1736–1813) and finds even more useful application in the solution of linear differential equations of higher order (see Chaps. V, VI, and IX).

Differentiation of (1.8) gives

$$y' = (u' - Pu)e^{-\int P\, dx}$$

If y is to be a solution of (1.2), then

$$(u' - Pu)e^{-\int P\, dx} + Pue^{-\int P\, dx} = Q$$
$$u' = Qe^{-\int P\, dx}$$
(1.9)
$$u = \int Qe^{-\int P\, dx}\, dx$$

It is not necessary to add a constant of integration, since we wish to find only some particular solution of (1.2). Substitution of (1.9) in (1.8) gives us the desired particular solution:

(1.10) $$y_p(x) = e^{-\int P\, dx} \int Qe^{\int P\, dx}\, dx$$

Thus the general solution of nonhomogeneous equation (1.2) is

$$y(x) = y_p(x) + y_c(x) \qquad \text{(particular solution}$$
$$\text{+ complementary function)}$$
(1.11) $$= e^{-\int P\, dx} \int Qe^{\int P\, dx}\, dx + Ce^{-\int P\, dx}$$

Some students may wish to memorize formula (1.11); others may prefer to recall its genesis: solution of the homogeneous part to get y_c, followed by parameter variation to get y_p. When formula (1.11) is applied, it must be remembered that P, Q *refer to the coefficients of the normal form* (1.2).

Example 1. Solve

$$x\frac{dy}{dx} - 4y - x^5 = 0$$

Separation of variables in the reduced equation $xy' - 4y = 0$ gives

$$y_c = ce^{\int (4/x)\, dx} = cx^4$$

One puts

$$y_p = x^4 u$$

Then

$$y_p' = x^4 u' + 4x^3 u$$

and substitution in the given D.E. leads to

$$x^5 u' + 4x^4 u - 4x^4 u - x^5 = 0$$

That is,

$$u' = 1$$

Therefore

$$u(x) = x \quad \text{and} \quad y_p(x) = x^5$$

The general solution of the given D.E. is therefore

$$y(x) = x^5 + cx^4$$

PROBLEMS

1. Solve the following:

(a) $y' + \dfrac{1}{x} y = 2$

(b) $y' - \dfrac{1}{x} y = x$

(c) $xy' + y = \cot x$

(d) $(1 + x^2)y' - xy + 1 = 0$

(e) $\dfrac{d\rho}{d\theta} - \rho \sin \theta = \sin 2\theta$

(f) $(x^2 + x + 1)y' + 2(2x + 1)y = x$

(g) $(x + x^3)y' + 4yx^2 = 2$

(h) $y' + 2y \sec 2x = 2 \tan^2 x \cos 2x$

(i) $y' - y \sec x = 1 + \sin x$

(j) $\sin u \dfrac{dv}{du} - (u - v) \cos u = 0$

(k) $\cos \theta \dfrac{d\rho}{d\theta} - 2\rho \sin \theta = -\sin 2\theta$

(l) $y' + ay = e^{-ax}$ (a constant)

(m) $y' + ay = xe^{-ax}$ (a constant)

(n) $y' + ay = x^m e^{-ax}$ (a, m constants; $m \neq -1$)

(o) $5x^3 + (4x^2 - 2)y + x(x^2 - 1)\dfrac{dy}{dx} = 0$

2. Find integral curves of the following equations which pass through the points indicated:

(a) $x^2 y' - (x + 1)y = x$, $(1, -2)$

(b) $y' + y \cos x = \sin 2x$, $(\pi, 0)$

(c) $y' - y = (x - 1)e^x - x^3 + 3x^2$, $(0, -4)$

(d) $(1 + x^2)(\arctan x)y' + y = x$, $(-1, -1)$

(e) $\dfrac{d\rho}{d\theta} - \rho \tan \theta = \cos 2\theta$, $\left(\dfrac{\pi}{6}, \dfrac{1}{2\sqrt{3}}\right)$

(f) $2(1 - x^2)y' - 2xy = a(x^3 - x)$, $\left(0, \dfrac{a}{3}\right)$

(g) $(1 + y^2) + 2xy \dfrac{dy}{dx} = \tan y \dfrac{dy}{dx}$, $(0, 0)$

(h) $L \dfrac{di}{dt} + Ri = E \sin \omega t$; $i = 0$ when $t = 0$

(i) $m \dfrac{dv}{dt} + \gamma v = F \cos \omega t$; $v = 0$ when $t = 0$

2. Exact Equations

These equations are of considerable importance because, at least theoretically, every first-order equation can be reduced to one of this type.

Let $u(x, y)$ be a smooth† function of the two variables x, y. Then for each value of the constant c (from some domain) the equation

$$(2.1) \qquad\qquad u(x, y) = c$$

may represent implicitly some smooth function $y = y(x)$; that is,

$$u(x, y(x)) = c$$

for all x in some interval. If the last equation is differentiated one obtains

$$(2.2) \qquad\qquad M + N \frac{dy}{dx} = 0$$

where

$$M(x, y) = \frac{\partial}{\partial x} u(x, y) \qquad N(x, y) = \frac{\partial}{\partial y} u(x, y)$$

This equation is independent of the value of the constant c in (2.1). Thus, the infinitely many functions implicitly defined by (2.1) are solutions of the D.E. (2.2). Conversely, if $y = y(x)$ in any smooth solution of (2.2), then

$$0 = M(x, y(x)) + N(x, y(x)) \frac{dy}{dx} = \frac{\partial u}{\partial x} + \frac{\partial u}{\partial y} \frac{dy}{dx} = \frac{d}{dx} u(x, y(x))$$

Hence $u(x, y(x)) = $ constant, and $y(x)$ is one of the functions defined by (2.1).

Equation (2.1) also implicitly represents functions $x = x(y)$, and these functions satisfy the equation

$$(2.3) \qquad M \frac{dx}{dy} + N = 0 \qquad M = \frac{\partial u}{\partial x} \qquad N = \frac{\partial u}{\partial y}$$

† A function (of one or several variables) is said to be *smooth* if it has first-order derivatives which are continuous.

Still another possibility is that (2.1) implicitly represents function pairs $x = x(t)$, $y = y(t)$ (curves in *parametric* form) and these pairs satisfy the equation

$$(2.4) \qquad M \frac{dx}{dt} + N \frac{dy}{dt} = 0 \qquad M = \frac{\partial u}{\partial x} \qquad N = \frac{\partial u}{\partial y}$$

The three differential equations (2.2) to (2.4) are essentially the same equation; we consider them as three versions of the D.E.

$$(2.5) \qquad\qquad M \, dx + N \, dy = 0$$

This is a D.E. of first order in *differential form*. We use this form frequently when the solution is expected to be given in implicit form as in (2.1), with neither x nor y preferred as independent variable.

We have been led to a definition and a theorem.

Definition. The D.E.

$$M(x, y) \, dx + N(x, y) \, dy = 0 \qquad \text{differential form}$$

$$(2.6) \qquad \left. \begin{array}{l} M(x, y) + N(x, y) \dfrac{dy}{dx} = 0 \\[2mm] M(x, y) \dfrac{dx}{dy} + N(x, y) = 0 \end{array} \right\} \qquad \text{derivative form}$$

is called *exact* if there is a smooth function $u(x, y)$ such that

$$(2.7) \qquad\qquad \frac{\partial u}{\partial x} = M \qquad \text{and} \qquad \frac{\partial u}{\partial y} = N$$

Theorem 1. *The solution of the exact D.E. (2.6) is given implicitly by*

$$u(x, y) = c$$

Equation (2.6) simply states that the differential of the function $u(x, y)$ is zero along each solution curve.

Example 1. The D.E.

$$2x + y + (x + 2y) \frac{dy}{dx} = 0$$

states that

$$\frac{d}{dx} (x^2 + xy + y^2) = 0$$

Hence it is exact, and $x^2 + xy + y^2 = c$ is its solution.

Example 2. The D.E.

$$\frac{y^2 - xy}{xy^2} \, dx + \frac{x}{y^2} \, dy = 0$$

can be rearranged to read

$$\frac{dx}{x} - \frac{y\,dx - x\,dy}{y^2} = 0$$

and states that

$$d\left(\log|x| - \frac{x}{y}\right) = 0$$

Hence it is exact, and $\log|x| - x/y = c$ is its solution.

From Examples 1 and 2 and from the definition it is clear that exact equations are easy to solve if one can recognize they are exact and if one can find the desired function u. What is needed is a test for exactness.

Theorem 2. *If M, N are smooth functions of x and y, then the D.E.*

(2.6) $$M(x, y)\,dx + N(x, y)\,dy = 0$$

is exact if and only if

(2.8) $$\frac{\partial M}{\partial y} = \frac{\partial N}{\partial x}$$

Proof. The only if part is easy, for if (2.6) is exact, then

$$\frac{\partial M}{\partial y} = \frac{\partial}{\partial y}\left(\frac{\partial u}{\partial x}\right) = \frac{\partial}{\partial x}\left(\frac{\partial u}{\partial y}\right) = \frac{\partial N}{\partial x}$$

where we have used the theorem from calculus which asserts that $\partial^2 u/\partial x\,\partial y = \partial^2 u/\partial y\,\partial x$ if the derivatives are continuous.

Now suppose that (2.8) is satisfied. We explicitly construct a function u satisfying (2.7). Let us put

(2.9) $$u(x, y) = \int^x M(x, y)\,dx + C(y)$$

where $C(y)$, the constant of integration, is a function of y which will be determined shortly, and $\int^x$ signifies that we are integrating with respect to x holding y constant. Clearly, $\partial u/\partial x = M(x, y)$.

Now from (2.7) we want $\partial u/\partial y$ to equal $N(x, y)$, so we set

(2.10) $$\frac{\partial u}{\partial y} = \frac{\partial}{\partial y}\int^x M(x, y)\,dx + \frac{dC}{dy} = N(x, y)$$

and investigate whether $C(y)$ may be determined to fit our requirements. Solving for dC/dy, we get

(2.11) $$\frac{dC}{dy} = N(x, y) - \frac{\partial}{\partial y}\int^x M(x, y)\,dx$$

and C may be found by a quadrature.

Now this "constant" of integration $C(y)$ must be a function of y alone; consequently the right member in (2.11) *must* be independent of x. This will be the case if and only if

$$(2.12) \qquad \frac{\partial}{\partial x}\left[N(x, y) - \frac{\partial}{\partial y}\int^x M(x, y)\, dx\right] = 0$$

Carrying out the differentiation in (2.12), we have

$$\frac{\partial N}{\partial x} - \frac{\partial}{\partial x}\frac{\partial}{\partial y}\int^x M\, dx = \frac{\partial N}{\partial x} - \frac{\partial}{\partial y}\frac{\partial}{\partial x}\int^x M\, dx = \frac{\partial N}{\partial x} - \frac{\partial M}{\partial y} = 0$$

by virtue of (2.8). This completes the proof of the theorem and supplies a method for the determination of u by quadratures. In Examples 1 and 2 we found u by inspection, but the method of the proof, formulas (2.9) to (2.11), will always work.

Example 3. Show that $(x + y^2)\, dy + (y - x^2)\, dx = 0$ is exact, and integrate.

We have $N(x, y) = x + y^2$ and $M(x, y) = y - x^2$, so that $\partial M/\partial y = 1 = \partial N/\partial x$ and (2.8) is satisfied.

To integrate the equation it is desirable to carry out the operations of (2.9) and (2.10). Thus,

$$u(x, y) = \int^x (y - x^2)\, dx + C(y) = xy - \frac{x^3}{3} + C(y)$$

whence

$$\frac{\partial u}{\partial y} = x + \frac{dC}{dy} = N = x + y^2$$

Therefore,

$$\frac{dC}{dy} = y^2$$

and

$$C(y) = \frac{y^3}{3}$$

It is unnecessary at this point to add the constant of integration, for $C(y)$ is *any* function satisfying (2.10). Hence,

$$u(x, y) = xy - \frac{x^3}{3} + \frac{y^3}{3}$$

and the integral of the differential equation is

$$xy - \frac{x^3}{3} + \frac{y^3}{3} = k = \text{constant}$$

The solution of an exact equation can also be obtained by the use of *line integrals*. Just as the solution of the problem

$$\frac{du}{dx} = M(x) \qquad u(x_0) = u_0$$

is given by

$$u(x) = u_0 + \int_{x_0}^{x} M(\xi)\, d\xi$$

so the solution of the problem

(2.13) $\dfrac{\partial u}{\partial x} = M(x, y) \qquad \dfrac{\partial u}{\partial y} = N(x, y) \qquad u(x_0, y_0) = u_0$

is given by

(2.14) $u(x, y) = u_0 + \displaystyle\int_{(x_0,\, y_0)}^{(x,\, y)} [M(\xi, \eta)\, d\xi + N(\xi, \eta)\, d\eta]$

The integral in (2.14) is a line integral (see, for example, Ref. 3) and is meaningful only after a path joining the initial point (x_0, y_0) to the end point (x, y) is specified (see Fig. 1). Any path lying in a region in which the exactness conditions (2.8) are satisfied may be used. Certain paths are preferable because they facilitate the calculation of the integral (2.14). In answer to the question concerning whether different solutions of problem (2.13) are obtained by the choice of different paths in (2.14), we state an important theorem from calculus: *The line integral (2.14) has the same value along two paths joining the initial point (x_0, y_0) to the end point (x, y) if the exactness conditions (2.8) are satisfied throughout the region enclosed by the two paths* (see Ref. 3).

To verify that u as given by (2.14) actually satisfies (2.8), we compute $\partial u/\partial x$. Now

(2.15) $u(x + \Delta x, y) - u(x, y) = \displaystyle\int_{(x,\, y)}^{(x+\Delta x,\, y)} [M(\xi, \eta)\, d\xi + N(\xi, \eta)\, d\eta]$

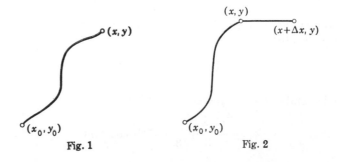

Fig. 1   Fig. 2

because the integral for $u(x + \Delta x, y)$ can be split into an integral from (x_0, y_0) to (x, y) and the above integral from (x, y) to $(x + \Delta x, y)$. If we integrate along the straight line between (x, y) and $(x + \Delta x, y)$, then $\eta = y$ and $d\eta = 0$ in (2.15), whence

$$\Delta u = u(x + \Delta x, y) - u(x, y) = \int_x^{x+\Delta x} M(\xi, y)\, d\xi = M(x_1, y)\, \Delta x$$

(where x_1 is between x and $x + \Delta x$), by the mean-value theorem for integrals. Therefore,

$$\frac{\partial u}{\partial x} = \lim_{\Delta x \to 0} \frac{\Delta u}{\Delta x} = \lim_{\Delta x \to 0} M(x_1, y) = M(x, y)$$

That $\partial u / \partial y = N$ can be proved similarly.

Example 4. In Example 1 it was seen that $(x + y^2)\, dy + (y - x^2)\, dx = 0$ is exact. Therefore, its solution may be written as

$$(2.16) \qquad u(x,y) = u_0 + \int_{(x_0,\, y_0)}^{(x,\, y)} [(\eta - \xi^2)\, d\xi + (\xi + \eta^2)\, d\eta] = c$$

To evaluate this line integral, let us choose a path joining $(0, 0)$ to (x, y) which consists of the line segment from $(0, 0)$ to $(x, 0)$ and the line segment from $(x, 0)$ to (x, y). On the first segment η has the fixed value zero $(d\eta = 0)$, and ξ varies from 0 to x; on the second segment ξ has the fixed value x $(d\xi = 0)$, and η varies from 0 to y. Thus (2.16) becomes, neglecting u_0,

$$\int_0^x (-\xi^2)\, d\xi + \int_0^y (x + \eta^2)\, d\eta = c$$

or

$$-\frac{x^3}{3} + xy + \frac{y^3}{3} = c$$

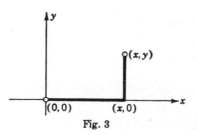

Fig. 3

PROBLEMS

1. Determine which of the following equations are exact:

(a) $x(1 - x)\dfrac{dy}{dx} + (1 - 2x)y = e^x$

(b) $x(1 - x)\dfrac{dy}{dx} + (1 - 2x)y = e^y$

(c) $y(1 - y)\dfrac{dx}{dy} + (1 - 2y)x = e^y$

(d) $y(1 - y)\dfrac{dy}{dx} + (1 - 2y)x = e^x$

(e) $x^2(1 - x^2)\dfrac{dy}{dx} + 2(1 - 2x^2)xy = f(x)$

(f) $(ax^2 + 2bxy + cy^2)\,dx + (bx^2 + 2cxy + ky^2)\,dy = 0$ $(a, \ b, \ c, \ k$ constants)

(g) $\dfrac{x\,dy}{(x^2 + y^2)^2} - \dfrac{y\,dx}{(x^2 + y^2)^2} = 0$

(h) $\dfrac{F(x)}{M(x, y)}\,dx + \dfrac{G(y)}{M(x, y)}\,dy = 0$

(i) $xy(x\,dy + y\,dx) = 0$

(j) $f(xy)(x\,dy + y\,dx) = 0$

(k) $f(x^2 + y^2)(x\,dx + y\,dy) = 0$

(l) $f\left(\dfrac{y}{x}\right)(x\,dy - y\,dx) = 0$

(m) $\dfrac{f(y/x)}{x^2 + y^2}(x\,dy - y\,dx) = 0$

2. Integrate the following exact equations by inspection:

(a) $x^2\,dy + 2xy\,dx = 0$

(b) $y\,dy + \dfrac{y\,dx - x\,dy}{x^2} = 0$

(c) $(1 + e^y)e^x\,dx + (1 + e^x)e^y\,dy = 0$

(d) $\dfrac{y/x}{x^2 + y^2}(x\,dy - y\,dx) = 0$

(e) $\dfrac{f(y/x)}{x^2 + y^2}(x\,dy - y\,dx) = 0$

3. Test the following equations for exactness and, if exact, solve:

(a) $(x^2 - y^2)\,dx = 2xy\,dy$

(b) $(3y - 2x)\,dx + (4y + 3x)\,dy = 0$

(c) $\dfrac{dx}{x^2 + x} = \dfrac{dy}{y^2 - y}$

(d) $\dfrac{x^2 y + 1}{y}\, dx + \dfrac{y - x}{y^2}\, dy = 0$

(e) $\dfrac{2x + y}{y - 1}\, dx - \left(\dfrac{x + \frac{1}{2}}{y - 1}\right)^2 dy = 0$

(f) $(ax + by)\, dx - (bx + cy)\, dy = 0$

(g) $(\cos x + x \cos y)\, dy - (y \sin x - \sin y)\, dx = dx$

(h) $\dfrac{y}{1 - x^2 y^2}\, dx + \dfrac{x}{1 - x^2 y^2}\, dy + x\, dx = 0$

(i) $\left[y \log (x^2 + y^2) + \dfrac{2x^2 y}{x^2 + y^2} + y \right] dx + \left[x \log (x^2 + y^2) + \dfrac{2xy^2}{x^2 + y^2} + x \right] dy = 0$

(j) $\sin x \sin^2 y\, dx - (\cos x \cos 2y \tan y + \cos x \tan y)\, dy = 0$

(k) $2 \cos^2 x \cos 2y\, dy - \sin 2x \sin 2y\, dx = 0$

(l) $y^{\frac{1}{2}}[(xy)^{\frac{1}{2}} + (xy)^{\frac{3}{2}}]\, dx + x^{\frac{1}{2}}[(xy)^{-\frac{1}{2}} + (xy)^{-\frac{3}{2}}]\, dy = 0$

(m) $\dfrac{1 - 3y}{(2x - 3y + 1)^2}\, dx + \dfrac{3x}{(2x - 3y + 1)^2}\, dy = 0$

(n) $\dfrac{(x + y)^2}{1 + (x + y)^2}\, dx - \left[\dfrac{1}{1 + (x + y)^2} - 1 \right] dy = 0$

4. Using line integrals, find the integral curves of the following **exact** equations which pass through the given points.

(a) $(y^2 - 2xy)\, dx - (x^2 - 2xy)\, dy = 0$, $(1, -1)$

(b) $(2x + e^x \sin y)\, dx + e^x \cos y\, dy = 0$, $\left(0, \dfrac{\pi}{2}\right)$

(c) $\cos x \cos y\, dx - \sin x \sin y\, dy = 0$, $\left(\dfrac{\pi}{2}, \dfrac{\pi}{3}\right)$

(d) $\dfrac{x + y}{x^2 + y^2}\, dx - \dfrac{x - y}{x^2 + y^2}\, dy = 0$, $(1, 1)$

5. Show that if the equation $M(x, y)\, dx + N(x, y)\, dy = 0$ is exact, then the equation $[M(x, y) + f(x)]\, dx + [N(x, y) + g(y)]\, dy = 0$ is exact for every pair of smooth functions f, g.

6. Show that if the equation $M(x, y) + N(x, y)\, dy/dx = 0$ is exact, then the equation $M(x, y) + N(x, y)\, dy/dx = f(x)$ is not exact unless f is the constant function.

★7. Show that if the equation $M(x, y)\, dx + N(x, y)\, dy = 0$ is exact, then the equation $u(x, y)[M(x, y)\, dx + N(x, y)\, dy] = 0$ is not exact for every smooth function u but is exact if $u(x, y) = $ constant is the solution of the first equation.

3. Integrating Factors

It may happen that the equation

$$(3.1) \qquad M(x, y)\, dx + N(x, y)\, dy = 0$$

is not exact as it stands but that multiplying both sides of (3.1) by a function $\mu(x, y)$ will render it exact. Such a function is called an *integrating factor*. The situation is exemplified by the following:

Example 1. Solve $x\, dy - y\, dx = (x^2 + y^2)\, dx$.
Dividing through by $x^2 + y^2$ [the integrating factor is $1/(x^2 + y^2)$], we have

$$\frac{x\, dy - y\, dx}{x^2 + y^2} = dx$$

and dividing numerator and denominator of the left side by x^2 yields

$$\frac{(x\, dy - y\, dx)/x^2}{1 + y^2/x^2} = dx$$

The left member is now recognizable as the differential of arctan (y/x), so the general solution may be written down by inspection and is

$$\arctan \frac{x}{y} = x + c$$

From the above example it is clear that the discovery of an integrating factor may require considerable ingenuity and familiarity with the formulas of calculus. Consequently, the technique is severely limited by the skill of the user. Although it is not a simple matter to write down an integrating factor, it can easily be shown that the general equation of the first order (3.1) always possesses an integrating factor. This may be seen as follows:

Equation (3.1) is equivalent to

$$(3.2) \qquad \frac{dy}{dx} = -\frac{M(x, y)}{N(x, y)}$$

From the existence theorem of Chap. III it follows that the integral curves of (3.2) can be parameterized in any region in which $\partial(-M/N)/\partial y$ exists. If these integral curves are written in the form $y = f(x, c)$, we may suppose that one can solve for the parameter c, obtaining

$$u(x, y) = c$$

which is merely an implicit form for the family of integral curves. Therefore,

$$(3.3) \qquad du = \frac{\partial u}{\partial x}\,dx + \frac{\partial u}{\partial y}\,dy = 0$$

and

$$M\,dx + N\,dy = 0$$

both hold along an integral curve. Consequently,

$$\frac{dy}{dx} = \frac{-M}{N} = \frac{-\partial u/\partial x}{\partial u/\partial y}$$

or

$$(3.4) \qquad \frac{\partial u/\partial x}{M} = \frac{\partial u/\partial y}{N}$$

If we denote the common ratio in (3.4) by $\mu(x,\,y)$, we have

$$\frac{\partial u}{\partial x} = \mu M \qquad \frac{\partial u}{\partial y} = \mu N$$

and (3.3) becomes

$$du = \frac{\partial u}{\partial x}\,dx + \frac{\partial u}{\partial y}\,dy = \mu(M\,dx + N\,dy) = 0$$

In other words, μ is an integrating factor.

It is easy to establish an equation for the integrating factors of (3.1). By the theorem of the preceding section, the equation $\mu(M\,dx + N\,dy) = 0$ is exact if and only if

$$\frac{\partial}{\partial y}\,(\mu M) = \frac{\partial}{\partial x}\,(\mu N)$$

This gives for μ the linear partial differential equation

$$(3.5) \qquad N\frac{\partial \mu}{\partial x} - M\frac{\partial \mu}{\partial y} + \mu\left(\frac{\partial N}{\partial x} - \frac{\partial M}{\partial y}\right) = 0$$

Of course, if (3.1) is exact to start with, that is, $\partial N/\partial x = \partial M/\partial y$, then $\mu = 1$ satisfies (3.5), and no integrating factor is needed.

As has been mentioned, to find an integrating factor is, in general, as difficult as solving the differential equation. However, certain simple differential forms frequently occur, and it may help to be able to recognize integrating factors for these forms. The functions suggested below are possible integrating factors of the differential equation when the differential equation contains the given differential form. That the suggested factors do render the differential form exact will be obvious after proper rearrangement or from the test for exactness.

If the differential equation contains the form	Try as an integrating factor
$x\,dy + y\,dx$	xy or a function of xy
$x\,dx + y\,dy$	$x^2 + y^2$ or a function of $x^2 + y^2$
$x\,dy - y\,dx$	$\dfrac{1}{x^2}$ or $\dfrac{1}{y^2}$ or $\dfrac{1}{x^2 + y^2}$ or $\dfrac{1}{x^2}$ times a function of $\dfrac{y}{x}$

If no simple integrating factor is recognized, one may systematically search for one of a special type—for example, for an integrating factor that is a function of x alone or y alone. If such integrating factors exist (which can be decided from the form of the given equation), then it is relatively easy to find them with the aid of (3.5) (see Probs. 2 and 4 below). The general linear equation of the first order,

$$(3.6) \qquad dy + P(x)y\,dx = Q(x)\,dx$$

which was treated in Sec. 1, can also be solved by the method of integrating factors. The function $e^{\int P(x)\,dx}$ is recognized as an integrating factor. Indeed,

$$e^{\int P(x)\,dx}[dy + P(x)y\,dx] = d(ye^{\int P(x)\,dx}) = e^{\int P(x)\,dx}Q(x)\,dx$$

which yields

$$ye^{\int P\,dx} = \int e^{\int P\,dx}Q\,dx + c$$

and the general solution is

$$y(x) = e^{-\int P\,dx}\int e^{\int P\,dx}Q\,dx + ce^{-\int P\,dx}$$

This is the solution (1.11) of Sec. 1. Remembering that $e^{\int P\,dx}$ is an integrating factor of (3.6) probably provides the easiest solution of the linear D.E.

PROBLEMS

1. Solve the following equations by finding an integrating factor:

(a) $x \, dy - y \, dx = (y^2 + 1) \, dy$
(b) $x \, dy + y \, dx + x^2 y^4 \, dy = 0$
(c) $x \, dy - y \, dx = (9x^2 + y^2) \, dx$

(d) $dy + \dfrac{y}{x} \, dx = \cos x \, dx$

(e) $y^2 \, dx + x(x \, dy - y \, dx) = 0$
(f) $x \, dy - y \, dx = x^2 y^4 (x \, dy + y \, dx)$
(g) $x \, dy - y \, dx = 2(x \, dx + y \, dy)$
(h) $(2x^2 + xy + 1)y \, dx + (x + 2y)(x^2 + 1) \, dy = 0$
(i) $(\sin x + \cos x \tan y)(dx + dy) + 2 \sin y \, dy = 0$
(j) $(1 + \sin x \sin y) \, dx = \csc x \cot x \, dx - \cos y \, dy$
(k) $x^3 y \, dx + (x^4 - y^4) \, dy = 0$
(l) $(y + \sqrt{x^2 - y^2}) \, dx - x \, dy = 0$

2. Using (3.5), show that if

$$\frac{1}{N} \left(\frac{\partial M}{\partial y} - \frac{\partial N}{\partial x} \right)$$

is independent of y, then $M \, dx + N \, dy = 0$ has an integrating factor μ which is a function of x alone. Show that μ then satisfies

$$\frac{1}{M} \frac{d\mu}{dx} = \frac{1}{N} \left(\frac{\partial M}{\partial y} - \frac{\partial N}{\partial x} \right)$$

Apply this result to find an integrating factor for $(x^2 y^4 + x^6) \, dx - x^3 y^3 \, dy = 0$.

3. Use the result of Prob. 2 to find an integrating factor of $(x^3 + xy^3) \, dx + 3y^2 \, dy = 0$. Then solve the equation.

4. Find a relation satisfied by an integrating factor μ which is a function of y alone.

★5. Find a relation satisfied by an integrating factor μ which is a function of $(ax + by)$ alone (a, b given constants).

★6. Find a relation satisfied by an integrating factor μ which is a function of the ratio x/y alone.

★7. The *Bernoulli equation* (see Sec. 4)

$$\frac{dy}{dx} + P(x)y = Q(x)y^m$$

has the integrating factor $y^{-m} e^{(1-m) \int P(x) \, dx}$. Verify this and solve

$$\frac{dy}{dx} + y = xy^3$$

★8. Show that if both $\mu(x, y)$ and $\nu(x, y)$ are integrating factors of the D.E. $M\,dx + N\,dy = 0$, then

$$M\frac{\partial}{\partial x}\left(\frac{\mu}{\nu}\right) - N\frac{\partial}{\partial y}\left(\frac{\mu}{\nu}\right) = 0$$

where $\nu(x, y) \neq 0$.

★9. Use the result of Prob. 8 to show that

$$\frac{\partial}{\partial x}\left(\frac{\mu}{\nu}\right)dx + \frac{\partial}{\partial y}\left(\frac{\mu}{\nu}\right)dy = 0$$

along an integral curve of $M\,dx + N\,dy = 0$ and hence that $\mu/\nu = $ constant (if solvable for y or x) is a general integral of $M\,dx + N\,dy = 0$.

10. Show that $\mu = e^{\frac{1}{2}x^2}$ and $\nu = y^3 + x^2 - 2$ are integrating factors of the D.E. in Prob. 3, and find its solution by the result of Prob. 9.

11. Suppose that μ is an integrating factor of $M\,dx + N\,dy = 0$, and u is a function such that $\partial u/\partial x = \mu M$ and $\partial u/\partial y = \mu N$. Show that if φ is an arbitrary function, then $\mu\varphi(u)$ is also an integrating factor of $M\,dx + N\,dy = 0$.

4. Change of Variables

In formal integration the method of change of variables (or substitution) is a major one. The same is true in differential equations. In general, only experimentation supported by experience and ingenuity will disclose the right substitution for a given equation. However, for a few common types of equations, substitutions suggest themselves.

A. We first consider equations of the type

$$(A) \qquad\qquad \frac{dy}{dx} = f(ax + by) \qquad a, b \text{ constants}$$

in which the right-hand term is not a general function of the two variables x and y, but a function of the single variable $(ax + by)$. We may assume $a, b \neq 0$, for otherwise the variables are separable. We introduce the new dependent variable

$$(4.1) \qquad\qquad Y = ax + by$$

leaving the independent variable x unchanged. Then

$$(4.2) \qquad\qquad y = \frac{1}{b}(Y - ax) \qquad \frac{dy}{dx} = \frac{1}{b}\left(\frac{dY}{dx} - a\right)$$

and (A) becomes

$$\frac{1}{b}\left(\frac{dY}{dx} - a\right) = f(Y)$$

or

(4.3)
$$\frac{dY}{dx} = a + bf(Y)$$

and the variables are separable.

B. Next we consider equations of the type†

(B)
$$\frac{dy}{dx} = f\left(\frac{y}{x}\right)$$

in which the right-hand term depends only on the ratio y/x. One sees readily that equations of the form

(B')
$$\frac{dy}{dx} = g\left(\frac{ax + by}{cx + dy}\right) \qquad a, b, c, d \text{ constant}$$

are of the same type, since one may write (B') as

$$\frac{dy}{dx} = g\left(\frac{a + by/x}{c + dy/x}\right) = f\left(\frac{y}{x}\right)$$

In the case of (B), one introduces the new dependent variable

(4.4)
$$u = \frac{y}{x}$$

leaving the independent variable x unchanged. Then

(4.5)
$$y = xu \qquad \frac{dy}{dx} = u + x\frac{du}{dx}$$

and (B) becomes

(4.6)
$$u + x\frac{du}{dx} = f(u)$$
$$\frac{du}{dx} = \frac{f(u) - u}{x}$$

and the variables are separable.

C. The equation

(C)
$$\frac{dy}{dx} = f\left(\frac{ax + by + p}{cx + dy + q}\right) \qquad a, b, c, d, p, q \text{ constant}$$

---

† In the first edition of this book and in many other texts such equations are called *homogeneous*. This name may be misleading since it is more commonly applied to linear equations of the form $y' + Py = 0$.

in which the right-hand term depends only on the ratio of the linear expressions $ax + by + p$ and $cx + dy + q$, is related to the preceding type. If f is the identity function, so that (C) reads

$$(C') \qquad \frac{dy}{dx} = \frac{ax + by + p}{cx + dy + q}$$

then (C) is called the *linear fractional equation*.

The object now is to change the variables in (C) so that it is transformed into an equation of type (B). The simple substitution

$$(4.7) \qquad X = x - h \qquad Y = y - k$$

with properly chosen constants h, k will do this. Then

$$(4.8) \qquad \begin{aligned} ax + by + p &= aX + bY + (ah + bk + p) \\ cx + dy + q &= cX + dY + (ch + dk + q) \\ \frac{dy}{dx} &= \frac{dY}{dX} \end{aligned}$$

If now h and k are chosen as solutions of the linear equations

$$(4.9) \qquad ah + bk + p = 0 \qquad ch + dk + q = 0$$

then (C) becomes

$$(4.10) \qquad \frac{dY}{dX} = f\left(\frac{aX + bY}{cX + dY}\right)$$

which is of type (B).

Equations (4.9) can always be solved for h, k, except in the special case in which

$$(4.11) \qquad \Delta = ad - bc = 0$$

If then $b \neq 0$, we have $cx + dy = m(ax + by)$, where m is the constant d/b, and (C) becomes

$$(4.12) \qquad \frac{dy}{dx} = f\left[\frac{ax + by + p}{m(ax + by) + q}\right]$$

which is of type (A). If, however, b and Δ are both zero, then $a = 0$ and (C) is of type (A), or $d = 0$ and the variables are separable.

The substitution (4.7) has a simple geometric interpretation. It means translating the origin of the xy plane to the point with coordinates $x = h$, $y = k$ at which the two lines

$$ax + by + p = 0 \qquad cx + dy + q = 0$$

intersect. The exceptional case $\Delta = 0$ arises when these lines do not intersect but are parallel (or even coincident).

The point $x = h$, $y = k$ at which both numerator and denominator of (C) vanish [or, equivalently, the point $X = 0$, $Y = 0$ at which numerator and denominator of (4.10) vanish] is called a *singular point* of the differential equation. At this point the existence and uniqueness theorem of Sec. 3, Chap. III, does not apply. Examination of special cases shows that there may be zero, one, two, or infinitely many integral curves passing through the singular point of the linear fractional equation (C').

Example 1. Solve

$$\frac{dy}{dx} = \frac{x + y - 1}{x + 4y + 2}$$

Solving $h + k - 1 = 0$, $h + 4k + 2 = 0$ simultaneously, we find $h = 2$, $k = -1$, whence $x = X + 2$, $y = Y - 1$, and

$$\frac{dY}{dx} = \frac{X + Y}{X + 4Y}$$

Now the equation is in form (B), and its solution can be effected by the substitution $Y = Xu$, whereby it becomes

$$u + X \frac{du}{dX} = \frac{X + uX}{X + 4uX} = \frac{1 + u}{1 + 4u}$$

or

$$X \frac{du}{dX} = \frac{1 - 4u^2}{1 + 4u}$$

Separation of variables gives

$$\frac{1 + 4u}{1 - 4u^2} du = \frac{dX}{X}$$

Quadrature yields

$$(1 + 2u)(1 - 2u)^3 X^4 = C$$

Hence

$$(X + 2Y)(X - 2Y)^3 = C$$

and finally

$$(x + 2y)(x - 2y - 4)^3 = c$$

for the solution of the given equation.

Example 2. Solve

$$\frac{dy}{dx} = \left(\frac{x + y - 1}{x + y + 1} \right)^2$$

Here $\Delta = 0$, and the equation is of type (A).   Letting $Y = x + y$, we have

$$\frac{dY}{dx} - 1 = \left(\frac{Y-1}{Y+1}\right)^2$$

and

$$\frac{dY}{dx} = 2\,\frac{Y^2+1}{(Y+1)^2}$$

whence we easily obtain

$$Y + \log (Y^2 + 1) = 2x + \text{constant}$$

and

$$(x + y)^2 = ce^{x-y} - 1$$

For the more general equation

$$\frac{dy}{dx} = \frac{a_1x + b_1y + c_1x^2 + d_1xy + e_1y^2 + \cdots}{a_2x + b_2y + c_2x^2 + d_2xy + e_2y^2 + \cdots}$$

an extensive study has been made of the behavior of the integral curves near the *singular point* $x = 0$, $y = 0$.   The results of these investigations are of considerable current interest for nonlinear problems, but cannot be taken up in an elementary book.

D. The equation

$$(D) \qquad\qquad \frac{dy}{dx} + P(x)y = Q(x)y^m$$

in which the exponent m is not necessarily an integer, is called *Bernoulli's equation*.   For $m = 0$ this is the linear equation of Sec. 1, and for $m = 1$ one has an equation with separable variables.   We assume $m \neq 1$, and introduce the new dependent variable

$$(4.13) \qquad\qquad Y = y^{1-m}$$

leaving the independent variable x unchanged.   Then

$$y = Y^{1/(1-m)} \qquad \frac{dy}{dx} = \frac{1}{1-m}\,Y^{m/(1-m)}\,\frac{dY}{dx}$$

and (D) becomes

$$\frac{1}{1-m}\,Y^{m/(1-m)}\,\frac{dY}{dx} + P(x)\,Y^{1/(1-m)} = Q(x)\,Y^{m/(1-m)}$$

or

$$\frac{dY}{dx} + (1-m)P(x)Y = (1-m)Q(x)$$

This is a linear equation which can be solved by the method of Sec. 1 or by finding an integrating factor.

PROBLEMS

1. Solve the following equations with the aid of a suitable substitution:

(a) $\dfrac{dy}{dx} = a^2(x+y)^2$ (a constant)

(b) $2\dfrac{dy}{dx} = 3(1-x+2y) + (x-2y)^2$

(c) $2\dfrac{dy}{dx} = 3(1+2x+3y)^2$

(d) $\dfrac{dy}{dx} = 4(3+x-y)^2$

(e) $(2x-5y)\,dx + (4x-y)\,dy = 0$
(f) $2xy\,dx + (y^2-x^2)\,dy = 0$
(g) $(x+y)\,dx - (x-y)\,dy = 0$
(h) $(2x^2+3y^2)y' + 3x^2 + 4xy = 0$

(i) $xy' = y - x\sin\dfrac{y}{x}$

(j) $x^4y' = 6x^2y(xy' - y)$
(k) $x^2y' = y(x + \sqrt{x^2 + 4y^2})$
(l) $xy' = y - x$
(m) $(5x-y+9)\,dx + (x-5y-3)\,dy = 0$
(n) $(x-2y)\,dx - (x-2y-2)\,dy = 0$
(o) $(6x-y)y' = 6x - y + 4$
(p) $(2x-6y+1)y' = x - 3y + 3$
(q) $x^2y' = (1+2x-y)^2$
(r) $(x+y+a)^2y' = 2(y+a)^2$ (a constant)
(s) $(3x-2y-4)^2y' = (2x-3y+1)^2$
(t) $(x-6y)^2y' = 6y^2 - 2xy + 3$

2. Solve the following Bernoulli equations:

(a) $xy' + y = 2xy^2$
(b) $y' + y = y^2\cos 2x$
(c) $y' + ay = Ay^2\sin\omega x$ (a, A, ω constant)
(d) $4y' + 2y = xy^3$
(e) $y' + y = xy^{\frac{3}{2}}$
(f) $y' + y\tan x = y^3\sec x$
(g) $3y' + y\sec x = y^4(1-\sin x)^2$
(h) $y' + ay = Ax^my^le^{(l-1)ax}$ (A, a, m, l constant; $m \neq -1, l \neq 1$)
(i) $xy' + (a+bx^my)y = 0$ (a, b, m constant)
(j) $2yy' + ay^2 = A\sin x$ (a, A constant)
(k) $2xy^3y' + x^4 - y^4 = 0$
(l) $xy^{m-1}y' + ay^m = Ax^n$ (a, A, m, n constant)

*3. Determine an integrating factor for the Bernoulli equation $y' + P(x)y = Q(x)y^m$. HINT: Use the fact that the substitution $Y = y^{1-m}$ renders the equation linear.

4. In the following problems make the suggested substitutions and solve:

(a) $xy' - 2y + a^2y^2 = b^2x^4$ (a, b constant); $Y = x^{-2}y$

(b) $y' - x(\sin 2y - x^2 \cos^2 y) = 0$; $Y = \tan y$

(c) $xy' + (1 - \log xy)y = 0$; $Y = xy$

(d) $yy' + x(1 + \sqrt{x^2 + y^2}) = 0$; $Y = x^2 + y^2$

(e) $x \, dx + y \, dy + y \, dx - x \, dy = 0$; $X = x^2 + y^2$, $Y = y/x$

(f) $[x(1 - x^2 - y^2) + y]y' + x - (1 - x^2 - y^2)y = 0$; $x = \rho \cos \theta$, $y = \rho \sin \theta$

5. A suitable substitution will render each of the following equations linear. Using this hint, solve them.

(a) $(\sin y)y' - x \cos y = Ax$ (A constant)

(b) $y' - y \log y \tan x = y$

(c) $y' + 25e^{-y} \cos x = 2$

(d) $\sqrt{1 + x^2} \, (\sec^2 x)y' = 2x - \tan y$

*6. Equations of the form

$$\frac{dy}{dx} + ay^2 = Ax^m \qquad a, A, m \text{ constant}$$

are called *Riccati equations*. Only for the exponents $m = 0, -\frac{4}{1}, -\frac{4}{3}, -\frac{8}{3}, -\frac{8}{5}, -\frac{12}{5}, -\frac{12}{7}, \ldots$ can they be solved in an elementary manner. One way of doing this is by repeated substitutions. For example, the case $m = -\frac{8}{3}$ is first reduced to that of $m = -\frac{4}{3}$, then to $m = -\frac{4}{1}$, finally to $m = 0$. Use the suggested substitutions to solve the following equations:

(a) $y' + ay^2 = Ax^{-4}$; $X = 1/x$, $Y = \frac{1}{2}x - x^2y$

(b) $y' + ay^2 = Ax^{-\frac{4}{3}}$; $X = x^{-\frac{1}{3}}$, $Y = -3A/ay$. Solve; then obtain an equation similar to (a).

chapter iii

Existence, Uniqueness, and Geometry of Solutions

In this chapter the solution of differential equations of the first order is considered from a theoretical point of view. Although individual differential equations can be solved analytically or numerically without much theory—differential equations had been solved and used for close to two centuries before any general theory was developed—a bit of theory helps to develop insight and power. The topics dealt with in this chapter are convergence of approximations, existence and uniqueness of particular solutions, and the totality or family of solutions.

In order not to lengthen the exposition unduly, we shall assume that the reader has had either a rather rigorous first calculus course or some introduction to what is called advanced calculus.

1. A Basic Inequality

We first observe that the linear D.E.

$$(1.1) \qquad y'(x) = Ay(x) + B \qquad A \neq 0$$

with constant coefficients A, B and initial condition $y(x_0) = 0$ has the solution

$$(1.2) \qquad\qquad y(x) = \frac{B}{A}\left(e^{A(x-x_0)} - 1\right)$$

If we replace the equality sign in (1.2) with the sign $\leq$, then we obtain a *differential inequality* in the place of the differential equation. The solution is then also an inequality, as is stated in the following theorem.

Theorem 1. *If $y(x_0) = 0$ and*

$$(1.3) \qquad |y'(x)| \leq A|y(x)| + B \qquad \text{for} \qquad |x - x_0| \leq a$$

where $A > 0$, $B \geq 0$ are constants, then

$$(1.4) \qquad |y(x)| \leq \frac{B}{A}\left(e^{A|x-x_0|} - 1\right) \qquad \text{for} \qquad |x - x_0| \leq a$$

Proof. It suffices to prove (1.4) for $x_0 < x \leq x_0 + a$. If $y(x) = 0$, then (1.4) is trivially true. If $y(x) > 0$, let x_1 be the closest point to the left of x for which $y(x_1) = 0$; that is, $x_0 \leq x_1 < x$ and $y(x_1) = 0$, but $y(s) > 0$ for $x_1 < s \leq x$. Then, by (1.3),

$$y'(s) \leq Ay(s) + B \qquad \text{for} \qquad x_1 \leq s \leq x$$

Hence

$$e^{-As}[y'(s) - Ay(s)] \leq Be^{-As}$$

$$\frac{d}{ds}\left(e^{-As}y\right) \leq Be^{-As}$$

$$\int_{x_1}^{x} \frac{d}{ds}\left(e^{-As}y\right) ds \leq \int_{x_1}^{x} Be^{-As} ds$$

or, since $y(x_1) = 0$,

$$e^{-Ax}y(x) \leq \frac{B}{A}\left(e^{-Ax_1} - e^{-Ax}\right)$$

$$y(x) \leq \frac{B}{A}\left(e^{A(x-x_1)} - 1\right)$$

$$(1.5) \qquad\qquad \leq \frac{B}{A}\left(e^{A(x-x_0)} - 1\right)$$

which proves (1.4) for the case $y(x) > 0$. If $y(x) < 0$, let

$$u(x) = -y(x)$$

From (1.3) we get the same inequality for u, and the case $u(x) > 0$ applies. Then (1.5) for u is valid:

$$0 < -y(x) = u(x) \le \frac{B}{A}\left(e^{A(x-x_0)} - 1\right)$$

Therefore, for $y(x) < 0$,

(1.6) $$y(x) \ge -\frac{B}{A}\left(e^{A(x-x_0)} - 1\right)$$

Hence, combining (1.5) and (1.6),

$$|y(x)| \le \frac{B}{A}\left(e^{A(x-x_0)} - 1\right)$$

which proves (1.4).

PROBLEMS

1. Suppose the forcing function $f(t)$ in the equation

$$\frac{dx}{dt} + \frac{4}{1+t^2}x = f(t)$$

is known to within an error less than δ. Show that if $x(t_0)$ is known precisely for some initial t_0, then the indeterminacy in $x(t)$ for any t is at most $\frac{1}{4}\delta(e^{4|t-t_0|} - 1)$.

2. Prove that if $|y'(x)| \le A|y(x)| + B$ for $|x - x_0| \le a$, where $A > 0, B \ge 0$ are constants, then $|y(x)| \le [|y(x_0)| + B/A](e^{A|x-x_0|} - 1)$ for $|x - x_0| \le a$.

3. Prove that if $y(x_0) = 0$ and

$$|y'(x)| \le P(x)|y(x)| + Q(x) \qquad \text{for} \qquad |x - x_0| \le a$$

where $P(x) > 0, Q(x) \ge 0$ are continuous functions, then

$$|y(x)| \le e^{\int_{x_0}^{x} P(t)\, dt} \int_{x_0}^{x} Q(s) e^{-\int_{x_0}^{s} P(t)\, dt}\, ds$$

for $|x - x_0| \le a$.

2. Convergence of Approximate Solutions; Uniqueness

In solving the problem

(2.1) $$\frac{dy}{dx} = f(x, y) \qquad y(x_0) = y_0$$

by an approximate method, numerical or otherwise, we may find a function $\bar{y}(x)$, satisfying the same I.C., which is not a solution of (2.1) but rather of

$$(2.2) \qquad \frac{d\bar{y}}{dx} = f(x, \bar{y}) + h(x, \bar{y}) \qquad \bar{y}(x_0) = y_0$$

where we know nothing about the error term $h(x, \bar{y})$ except that $|h(x, \bar{y}(x)| \leq \epsilon$ for some constant ϵ. How far off is $\bar{y}(x)$ from the true solution $y(x)$? To answer this question satisfactorily we need some knowledge of the smoothness of the function $f(x, y)$. We state the result in the following:

Theorem 1. *Suppose*

(a) $\qquad \dfrac{dy}{dx} = f(x, y) \qquad \dfrac{d\bar{y}}{dx} = f(x, \bar{y}) + h(x, \bar{y})$

$\qquad\qquad y(x_0) = \bar{y}(x_0) = y_0$

(b) *$f(x, y)$, $h(x, y)$ are defined and continuous in the rectangle R_0: $|x - x_0| \leq a$, $|y - y_0| \leq b$, and the curves $(x, y(x))$, $(x, \bar{y}(x))$ lie in R_0 for $|x - x_0| \leq a$.*
(c) *$f(x, y)$ has a continuous partial derivative with respect to y, and $|(\partial f/\partial y)(x, y)| \leq A$ in R_0, where $A > 0$.*

(d) $\qquad\qquad\qquad |h(x, y)| \leq \epsilon \qquad$ *in R_0*

Then

$$|\bar{y}(x) - y(x)| \leq \frac{\epsilon}{A} (e^{A|x - x_0|} - 1) \qquad \text{for} \qquad |x - x_0| \leq a$$

Proof. Put $u(x) = \bar{y}(x) - y(x)$. Then, because of assumption a, $u(x_0) = 0$ and

$$(2.3) \qquad \frac{du}{dx} = f(x, y + u) - f(x, y) + h(x, y + u)$$

By the mean-value theorem of the differential calculus,

$$f(x, y + u) - f(x, y) = u \frac{\partial f}{\partial y} (x, \eta)$$

where η is between y and $y + u$. Therefore, by assumptions b and c,

$$(2.4) \qquad |f(x, y + u) - f(x, y)| \leq A|u|$$

This, together with assumption d, used in (2.3), gives the differential inequality

$$(2.5) \qquad \left| \frac{du}{dx} \right| \leq A |u| + \epsilon$$

The conclusion of Theorem 1 then follows from Theorem 1, Sec. 1. This completes the proof.

Observe that assumption c of Theorem 1 is used only to establish inequality (2.4). Therefore, assumption c may be replaced by the weaker condition

$$(2.6) \quad |f(x, y_1) - f(x, y_2)| \leq A |y_1 - y_2| \qquad \text{for } (x, y_1) \text{ and } (x, y_2) \text{ in } R_0$$

which is another form of (2.4). Equation (2.6) is known as a *Lipschitz condition* (R. Lipschitz, 1832–1903).

An immediate though somewhat unexpected side result of the preceding theorem is the conclusion that through a given point (x_0, y_0) in R_0 there passes no more than one integral curve of $y' = f(x, y)$. Indeed if $y(x)$, $\bar{y}(x)$ are any two solutions, i.e.,

$$\frac{dy}{dx} = f(x, y) \qquad \frac{d\bar{y}}{dx} = f(x, \bar{y})$$
$$y(x_0) = \bar{y}(x_0) = y_0$$

then Theorem 1 applies with $h(x, y) \equiv 0$; hence $\epsilon = 0$, and the conclusion is $y(x) - \bar{y}(x) \equiv 0$ for $|x - x_0| \leq a$. Thus we have proved the following:

Theorem 2 (Uniqueness). *Suppose $f(x, y)$ is defined and continuous in the rectangle R_0 and has a continuous partial derivative or satisfies a Lipschitz condition there. Then there can be no more than one integral curve of $y' = f(x, y)$ in R_0 passing through a given point.*

Example 1. The equation

$$(2.7) \qquad y' = 2\sqrt{y} \qquad y \geq 0$$

is to be examined for the uniqueness of its solution.

The restriction $y \geq 0$ is clearly necessary, since $\sqrt{y}$ is not defined (as a real-valued function) for $y < 0$. For $y > 0$ we may divide (2.7) by $\sqrt{y}$ and obtain, after integration,

$$(2.8) \qquad y(x) = (x - c)^2 \qquad x > c$$

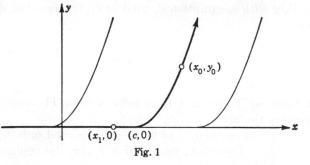

Fig. 1

as the only solutions of (2.7) for $y > 0$. Thus if (x_0, y_0) is an arbitrary point
in the upper half plane $(y_0 > 0)$, then there is exactly one integral curve of
(2.7) passing through it:

$$y(x) = (x - x_0 + \sqrt{y_0})^2 \qquad x > x_0 - \sqrt{y_0}$$

This is in accordance with Theorem 2. The function $f(x, y)$ in this example is
$2\sqrt{y}$, which is continuous and has a continuous derivative with respect to
y in any rectangle R_0 that is contained in the upper half plane.

Now consider a point $(x_1, 0)$ on the x axis. Among the solutions of (2.7) is
clearly the function $y(x) \equiv 0$. Thus, the x axis is one integral curve through
$(x_1, 0)$. Are there others? If so, they must reach the region $y > 0$ some-
where, and the only solutions contained in this region are given by (2.8). The
curve (2.8) is the right half of a parabola in the upper half plane which is
tangent to the x axis at $x = c$. Thus we have infinitely many integral curves
through $(x_1, 0)$, composites of two pieces: a straight segment along $y = 0$
from $x = -\infty$ to $x = c \geq x_1$ and the right half of a parabola given by (2.8)
(these solutions are graphed in Fig. 1). Since $\partial f/\partial y$ does not exist at $y = 0$
(nor does f satisfy a Lipschitz condition at $y = 0$), the existence of infinitely
many integral curves through $(x_1, 0)$ does not contradict Theorem 2.

We return to the problem (2.1) and assume now that we do not know
how to solve it or even whether it has a solution at all. We only
grant that we can produce a sequence of approximate solutions $y_1(x)$,
$y_2(x), \ldots$ which satisfy not (2.1), but

$$(2.9) \quad \frac{dy_k}{dx} = f(x, y_k) + h_k(x, y_k) \qquad y_k(x_0) = y_0 \qquad k = 1, 2, \ldots$$

where the error terms $h_k(x, y_k(x))$ tend to zero as k increases indefinitely.
We wish to show that the sequence $y_1(x)$, $y_2(x), \ldots$ converges to a
function $y(x)$ which is a true solution of (2.1).

Theorem 3. *Suppose $y_1, y_2, \ldots, y_m, \ldots$ are functions such that*

$$(a) \quad \frac{dy_n}{dx} = f(x, y_n) + h_n(x, y_n) \qquad y_n(x_0) = y_0 \qquad n = 1, 2, \ldots$$

(b) $f(x, y)$, $h_n(x, y)$ are defined and continuous in the rectangle R_0: $|x - x_0| \leq a$, $|y - y_0| \leq b$, and the curves $(x, y_n(x))$ lie in R_0 for $|x - x_0| \leq a$.

(c) $f(x, y)$ has a continuous partial derivative with respect to y, and $|(\partial f/\partial y)(x, y)| \leq A$, $(A > 0)$ in R_0 [or (2.6) is satisfied].

(d) $|h_n(x, y)| \leq \epsilon_n$ for all (x, y) in R_0, and $\lim_{n \to \infty} \epsilon_n = 0$.†

Then the sequence $y_1(x), y_2(x), \ldots$ converges uniformly in $|x - x_0| \leq a$ to a function $y_*(x)$; the curve $(x, y_*(x))$ lies in R_0, and

$$\frac{dy_*}{dx} = f(x, y_*) \qquad y_*(x_0) = y_0$$

Also,

$$|y_n(x) - y_*(x)| \leq \frac{\epsilon_n}{A} (e^{A|x - x_0|} - 1)$$

Proof. Let m, n be any two positive integers. Then, proceeding as in the proof of Theorem 1, we have

$$\frac{d}{dx} (y_m - y_n) = f(x, y_m) - f(x, y_n) + h_m(x, y_m) - h_n(x, y_n)$$

$$\left| \frac{d}{dx} (y_m - y_n) \right| \leq A|y_m - y_n| + \epsilon_m + \epsilon_n$$

(2.10) $$|y_m(x) - y_n(x)| \leq \frac{\epsilon_m + \epsilon_n}{A} (e^{A|x - x_0|} - 1)$$

$$\text{for} \qquad |x - x_0| \leq a$$

Thus, for all x in the interval $|x - x_0| \leq a$,

$$|y_m(x) - y_n(x)| \leq \frac{\epsilon_m + \epsilon_n}{A} e^{aA}$$

and since $\epsilon_n \to 0$, this implies, by the Cauchy convergence criterion, that the sequence $y_1(x), y_2(x), \ldots$ converges uniformly in $|x - x_0| \leq a$ to a continuous function $y_*(x)$. Since $y_n(x_0) = y_0$ for every n, we also have $y_*(x_0) = y_0$; since all curves $(x, y_n(x))$ lie in R_0, so does the limit curve $(x, y_*(x))$. From (2.10) it follows, if we let m increase, that

(2.11) $$|y_*(x) - y_n(x)| \leq \frac{\epsilon_n}{A} (e^{A|x - x_0|} - 1)$$

It remains to prove that $y_*' = f(x, y_*)$. Assumption (a) may be written in integrated form:

(2.12) $$y_n(x) = y_0 + \int_{x_0}^{x} [f(s, y_n(s)) + h_n(s, y_n(s))]\, ds$$

† A statement equivalent to (d) is: The sequence $h_1(x, y), h_2(x, y), \ldots$ converges to zero uniformly in R_0.

Since $f(x, y)$ is continuous, and the sequence $y_1(x)$, $y_2(x)$, . . . converges uniformly to $y_*(x)$, the sequence $f(x, y_1(x))$, $f(x, y_2(x))$, . . . converges uniformly to $f(x, y_*(x))$. By assumption (d) the sequence $h_1(x, y_1(x))$, $h_2(x, y_2(x))$, . . . converges uniformly to zero. Thus (2.12) gives, in the limit as $n \to \infty$,

$$(2.13) \qquad y_*(x) = y_0 + \int_{x_0}^{x} f(s, y_*(s)) \, ds$$

By the fundamental theorem of the calculus, $y_*(x)$ has a derivative, and $y_*' = f(x, y_*)$. Theorem 3 is completely proved.

Observe that Theorem 3 does not yet permit us to assert that $y' = f(x, y)$, $y(x_0) = y_0$ has a solution, because Theorem 3 requires the existence of the approximating functions y_n which satisfy (a).

PROBLEMS

1. Assume $|Q(x)| \leq q < 1$ for $|x| \leq 1$. Find $\lim_{n \to \infty} y_n(1)$ if $y_n' + 2y_n = 4x^2 + [Q(x)]^n$ and $y_n(0) = 1$. Use the results of this section to justify the answer.

★2. Assume $P(x)$ is continuous on $|x| \leq r$, and $f(x)$ is a function whose Maclaurin expansion converges to $f(x)$ uniformly in $|x| \leq r$. Let $y_k(x)$ be the known solution of $y' + Py = x^k$, $y(0) = 0$ ($k = 0, 1, 2, . . .$). Find a series expansion of $y(x)$ if $y' + Py = f$, $y(0) = y_0$.

3. Convergence of Numerical Methods; Existence

While all examples in preceding sections lead us to believe that the differential equation of the first order

$$(3.1) \qquad \frac{dy}{dx} = f(x, y)$$

always has a solution, and moreover (at least) one for each prescribed initial point

$$(3.2) \qquad y(x_0) = y_0$$

we cannot as yet be assured of this fact. This assurance is provided by an *existence theorem*. Such a theorem asserts that a given problem has, under certain circumstances, a solution and, possibly with certain further restrictions, that the solution is unique (a *uniqueness* theorem). It is an important part of every mathematical theory to provide theorems which assure us that solutions for certain problems exist.

We have already dealt with uniqueness (see Theorem 2 of Sec. 2). For an existence proof we have a good start in Theorem 3 of Sec. 2, which asserts the existence of a solution of (3.1), (3.2) provided that we can construct solutions of a sequence of equations which approximate (3.1) with error terms that tend to zero. This is indeed accomplished by any of the numerical methods described in Sec. 7, Chap. I. In the theorem to follow we use for this purpose the simplest of all these methods, the E.C.M. I.

Theorem 1. *Suppose*

(a) $y_n(x)$ *is the approximate solution of (3.1), (3.2) constructed by E.C.M. I [Eq. (7.7) of Chap. I] with tabular difference $h = a/n$.*
(b) $f(x, y)$ *is defined and continuous in the rectangle R_0: $|x - x_0| \leq a$, $|y - y_0| \leq b$; $|f(x, y)| \leq B$ in R_0, and $aB \leq b$.*
(c) $f(x, y)$ *has a continuous partial derivative with respect to y, and $|(\partial f/\partial y)(x, y)| \leq A$ in R_0 [or (2.6) is satisfied].*

Then the sequence $y_1(x), y_2(x), \ldots$ converges uniformly in $|x - x_0| \leq a$ to a solution $y_*(x)$ of (3.1), (3.2) and

$$(3.3) \quad |y_*(x) - y_n(x)| \leq \frac{\epsilon_n}{A} \left(e^{A|x-x_0|} - 1 \right) \qquad for \qquad |x - x_0| \leq a$$

where ϵ_n is an upper bound for the oscillation of the function $f(x, y)$ in R_0 when x is given an increment less than or equal to a/n and y is given an increment less than or equal to b/n.

Before proving the theorem, we make three remarks.
Remark 1. This theorem allows us to estimate how small the tabular difference h should be chosen so as to attain with the E.C.M. I process a solution of desired accuracy over the whole interval $|x - x_0| \leq a$.
Remark 2. Since $f(x, y)$ is assumed to be continuous in the closed rectangle R_0, there is always a number B such that $|f(x, y)| \leq B$ in R_0. The role of the assumption

$$(3.4) \qquad\qquad aB \leq b$$

in *(b)* is to make sure that each of the approximations $(x, y_n(x))$ lies in R_0. Indeed, since $y_n(x_0) = y_0$ and the slope of $y_n(x)$ is nowhere greater than B or smaller than $-B$, we have, for all x with $|x - x_0| \leq a$,

$$(3.5) \quad |y_n(x) - y_0| = \left| \int_{x_0}^{x} y_n'(s)\, ds \right| \leq B|x - x_0| \leq aB \leq b$$

Remark 3. Let

$$\epsilon_n^* = \text{supremum } |f(x_1, y_1) - f(x_2, y_2)|$$

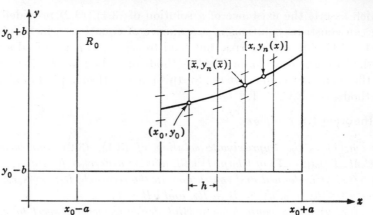

Fig. 2

for (x_1, y_1) and (x_2, y_2) in R_0 and $|x_1 - x_2| \leqq a/n$, $|y_1 - y_2| \leqq b/n$.
Because f is continuous in the closed rectangle R_0, ϵ_n^* exists, and
$\lim\limits_{n \to \infty} \epsilon_n^* = 0$. When ϵ_n^* is used for ϵ_n in (3.3), the estimate is as sharp
as possible.

Proof of Theorem 1. Let the integer n be chosen, and let x be an
arbitrary abscissa, $x_0 < x < x_0 + a$. The interval from x_0 to $x_0 + a$
is divided into n subintervals of length h each, and x lies in one of them.
Let $\bar{x}$ denote the left end point of the subinterval in which x lies (we
admit that x may coincide with $\bar{x}$). Then $y_n(x)$ (whose graph is a
polygonal line; see Fig. 2) has at x the slope that the direction field of
(3.1) has at $(\bar{x}, y_n(\bar{x}))$; that is, we have

$$(3.6) \qquad y_n'(x) = f(\bar{x}, y_n(\bar{x}))$$

Now (3.6) may be written as

$$(3.7) \qquad y_n'(x) = f(x, y_n(x)) + h_n(x)$$

where

$$h_n(x) = f(\bar{x}, y_n(\bar{x})) - f(x, y_n(x))$$

Thus $h_n(x)$ is no greater than the oscillation of $f(x, y)$ as we change
from $\bar{x}$ to x and from $y_n(\bar{x})$ to $y_n(x)$. But $|\bar{x} - x| \leqq h = a/n$, and

$|y_n(\bar{x}) - y_n(x)| \leq Bh \leq b/n.$ Therefore, by (2.5),

$$|h_n(x)| \leq \epsilon_n$$

We now find all the hypotheses of Theorem 3 of the preceding section satisfied.† Therefore the conclusions also hold, and Theorem 1 is proved.

Example 1. Estimate how small the tabular difference h should be taken so that the error between the true solution of

$$y' = x^2 + y^2 \qquad y(0) = 0$$

and the one obtained by the recursive application of the E.C.M. I. method is less than 10^{-1} at $x = \frac{1}{2}$.

Here $f(x, y) = x^2 + y^2$, and in R_0: $x \leq \frac{1}{2}$, $y \leq b$ we have $|f(x, y)| \leq \frac{1}{4} + b^2 = B$. Thus, $\frac{1}{2}B < b$ if we choose, for example, $b = \frac{1}{4}$. Since $\partial f/\partial y = 2y$, we have $|\partial f/\partial y| \leq 0.5$ in R_0; hence we may take A as 0.5. Then (3.3) gives

$$|y_*(x) - y_n(x)| \leq 2\epsilon_n(e^{\frac{1}{2}|x|} - 1) \leq 2\epsilon_n(e^{\frac{1}{4}} - 1) \leq 0.6\epsilon_n \qquad \text{for} \qquad |x| \leq \frac{1}{2}$$

Hence, if we choose $h = \frac{1}{2}n$ so that

$$0.6|(x_1{}^2 + y_1{}^2) - (x_2{}^2 + y_2{}^2)| = 0.6|(x_1 - x_2)(x_1 + x_2) + (y_1 - y_2)(y_1 + y_2)|$$
$$\leq 0.6(h \cdot 1 + \frac{1}{2}h \cdot \frac{1}{2}) < 10^{-1}$$

then $|y_*(\frac{1}{2}) - y_n(\frac{1}{2})| < 10^{-1}$. This will be true if $h \leq 0.13$.

Theorem 1 assures us that E.C.M. I is an efficient numerical method in that it gives an approximate solution which differs from the true solution over the whole interval $|x - x_0| \leq a$ by less than any prescribed error if h is small enough. Other numerical methods, described in Sec. 7, Chap. I, will usually give better approximations. If $y_n(x)$ is the solution of (3.1), (3.2) constructed by one of the numerical methods of Sec. 7, Chap. I, with tabular difference $h = a/n$, then one sees exactly as above that $y_n'(x) = f(x, y_n(x)) + h_n(x)$, where $h_n(x)$ is an error term typical for the method. It is easy to show that $|h_n(x)| \leq \epsilon_n$ for $|x - x_0| \leq a$, where the ϵ_n are numbers that tend to zero as $n \to \infty$. This suffices, by Theorem 2, Sec. 2, to prove that the $y_n(x)$ converge to the true solution $y_*(x)$ uniformly on $|x - x_0| \leq a$. However, to

---

† There is one difference: The function $h_n(x)$, representing the difference between the piecewise-constant function $f(\bar{x}, y_n(\bar{x}))$ and the continuous function $f(x, y_n(x))$, is not continuous, but *piecewise continuous*. This is not essential, since nothing is changed in the conclusions of Theorems 1 and 2 of Sec. 2 if the continuity of the functions h, h_n in x is replaced by piecewise continuity.

show that one method converges faster than another, it is necessary to have good estimates for the ϵ_n; these are not easy to derive for the more sophisticated methods.

Observe that our discussion above does not consider round-off errors. All computation is presumed exact.

Estimations similar to those in the preceding example, which determine the size of the tabular difference for a desired degree of accuracy before the computation is started, are only rarely carried out. Given the lightning speed with which electronic computers perform elementary operations, it is much more economical to start with a tentative value of h and to repeat the computations with gradually diminishing h until no significant change appears in the results.

As remarked above, Theorem 1 contains an existence theorem. We isolate the pertinent part and combine it with the uniqueness theorem of Sec. 2 to obtain the following:

Theorem 2 (Existence and Uniqueness). *If f and $\partial f/\partial y$ are continuous in some rectangle $R: a_1 \leq x \leq a_2, b_1 \leq y \leq b_2$, then through each point (x_0, y_0) interior to R there passes a unique integral curve of the equation $dy/dx = f(x, y)$.*

As remarked before, the hypothesis that $f(x, y)$ has a continuous derivative $\partial f/\partial y$ in R may be replaced by the weaker one that $f(x, y)$ satisfies a Lipschitz condition (2.6) in R. Without some such condition uniqueness cannot be proved, as Example 1 of Sec. 2 shows. Existence of solutions can, however, be proved under much weaker conditions; in particular, the continuity of $f(x, y)$ alone suffices to guarantee the existence of solutions (this is the so-called *theorem of Peano;* G. Peano 1858–1932).

Theorem 2 assures us that through any point (x_0, y_0) interior to R there exists a unique integral curve over *some* interval $|x - x_0| \leq a_0$.

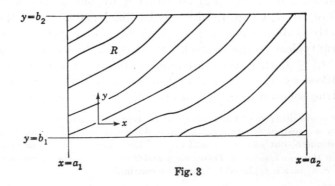

Fig. 3

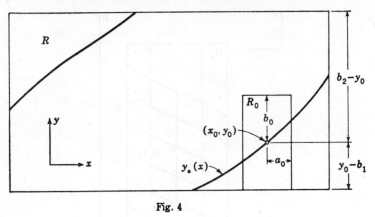

Fig. 4

As indicated in Fig. 3, there is no necessity for any integral curve to extend from one end of the rectangle to the other; i.e., not every solution need exist over the whole interval $a_1 \leq x \leq a_2$. To apply Theorem 1, a rectangle R_0 with center at (x_0, y_0) should be found in which the condition $aB \leq b$ of hypothesis b is satisfied. To achieve this, one first chooses b_0 such that the rectangle R_0 with center at (x_0, y_0) and vertical side $2b_0$ fits into the rectangle R (see Fig. 4). Then a_0 is so chosen that $a_0 B \leq b_0$, where B is the maximum of $|f(x, y)|$ in R_0. The size $2a_0$ of the interval over which the existence of the solution through (x_0, y_0) is asserted will, in general, depend on the point (x_0, y_0), and it is therefore not possible to give a positive lower bound for these sizes. As Fig. 3 shows, some integrals may exist over the whole length of R, others only over small intervals. However, a common minimum interval always exists if we restrict ourselves to integral curves with initial points sufficiently close to each other.

Indeed, as remarked above, the integral curve $y = y_*(x)$ passing through (x_0, y_0) exists at least over the interval $|x - x_0| \leq a_0 = b_0/B$, where b_0 is the smaller of the numbers $b_2 - y_0$, $y_0 - b_1$ (see Fig. 4). Therefore, all the integral curves with initial point on the segment

$$I_y: x = x_0, \ |y - y_0| \leq \frac{b_0}{2}$$

exist at least over the interval

$$I_x: |x - x_0| \leq \frac{b_0}{2B}$$

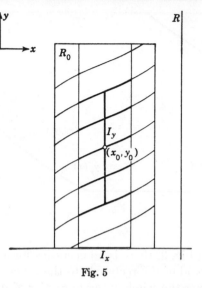

Fig. 5

(see Fig. 5). We find a band of integral arcs with initial points on the
segment I_y, all of them having their left end points at the abscissa
$x_0 - b_0/2B$ and their right end points at the abscissa $x_0 + b_0/2B$. This
band of integral arcs, very similar to a family of parallel lines, gives a
good idea of what the totality of solutions is like in the neighborhood
of the point (x_0, y_0). Since the point (x_0, y_0) is an arbitrary point in
the interior of R, one can find for each such point as center a segment
I_y and an interval I_x such that the integral curves through the points
of I_y form a band over the interval I_x.

We shall call each such band a *local solution family* of the equation
$y' = f(x, y)$. A local solution family contains every integral curve that
crosses the segment I_y, at least that part of it with abscissas in I_x. Such
local solution families do not go only with the interior points of the
rectangle R. Any point (x_0, y_0) in the neighborhood of which f and
$\partial f/\partial y$ are continuous can be considered as an interior point of some
rectangle R for which Theorem 2 holds. Therefore, to each such point
there corresponds a local solution family.

The arcs in a local solution family can be labeled with one real
parameter: one simply labels each arc with the ordinate of the point
on I_y lying on it. For this reason one says that the arcs of a local
solution family form a *one-parameter family*.

Suppose that P_* is a point such that f and $\partial f/\partial y$ are continuous
in some neighborhood of P_*, but not at P_* itself. Then every point

P_0 near P_* is the midpoint of a local solution family, but P_* itself need not be.

Example 2. The function

$$g(x, y) = \begin{cases} \dfrac{2xy}{x^2 + y^2} & (x, y) \neq (0, 0) \\ 0 & (x, y) = (0, 0) \end{cases}$$

is continuous and is differentiable everywhere except at $(0, 0)$. We are to investigate the solutions of $y' = g(x, y)$ in the neighborhood of $(0, 0)$.

The solution is readily found by the method of Sec. 3, Chap. II. It is $(y - c)^2 - x^2 = c^2$. Some of the integral curves are sketched in Fig. 6. One observes that, whereas in the neighborhood of every point $(x_0, y_0) \neq (0, 0)$ there is a one-parameter family of integral curves, this is not so near $(0, 0)$. There are integral curves passing through $(0, 0)$ in spite of the discontinuity of $f(x, y)$ at $(0, 0)$; indeed, infinitely many integral curves pass through $(0, 0)$! We have seen above that near a point at which f and $\partial f/\partial y$ are continuous, a local solution family consists of a one-parameter family. This example shows that this need not be true near a point at which f is discontinuous.

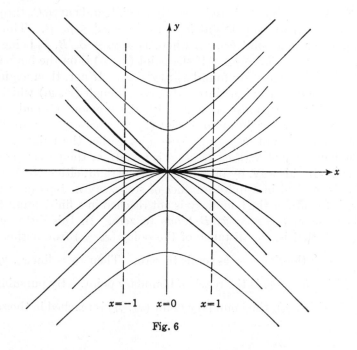

Fig. 6

All of the above results deal with the "local behavior" of integral curves in an unspecified but sufficiently small neighborhood of the initial point. We add an important result on the "global behavior" of integral curves which sheds much light on the whole picture of the solutions of (3.1).

From Fig. 3 it seems plausible that any integral curve C_0 that passes through an interior point (x_0, y_0) of the rectangle R in which f and $\partial f/\partial y$ are continuous must reach the boundaries of R. Theorem 2 assures us only of the existence of a solution curve over a sufficiently small interval about x_0. However, if (x_1, y_1), with $x_1 > x_0$, is another interior point of R reached by the curve C_0, then Theorem 2 can be applied again with (x_1, y_1) playing the role of the initial (x_0, y_0), and another extension of C_0 to some point (x_2, y_2), with $x_2 > x_1$, can be obtained. We prove that if C_0 is extended in this way, the solution curve does reach the boundary of R_0.

Theorem 3. *If f and $\partial f/\partial y$ are continuous in a rectangle R: $a_1 \leq x \leq a_2$, $b_1 \leq y \leq b_2$, then every integral curve of $y' = f(x, y)$ that passes through an interior point (x_0, y_0) of R has two points (x_L, y_L) and (x_R, y_R) on the boundary of R, with $x_L < x_0 < x_R$.*

Proof. By Theorem 2 there is exactly one integral curve C_0 through the point (x_0, y_0) which exists at least for $|x - x_0| \leq \beta_0/B$. Thus C_0 can be pursued to a point (x_1, y_1) where $x_1 = x_0 + \beta_0/B$, β_0 being the smaller of $|b_2 - y_0|$, $|b_1 - y_0|$. If the point (x_1, y_1) is on the boundary of R, then we have already found x_R: $x_R = x_1$. If not, then again by Theorem 2 there is a unique integral curve through (x_1, y_1) which, to the left of this point, must coincide with the previous C_0 and which can be pursued to the right up to a point (x_2, y_2) where $x_2 = x_1 + \beta_1/B$, β_1 being the smaller of $|b_2 - y_1|$, $|b_1 - y_1|$. Either the point (x_2, y_2) is on the boundary of R (then $x_R = x_2$ is found), or the process can be continued. In this way, by pursuing C_0 to the right, either the boundary of R is reached in a finite number of steps, say n steps (and thus $x_R = x_n$ is found), or the boundary is not reached in a finite number of steps because $x_{n+1} - x_n = \beta_n/B$ tends to zero. In this latter case, $\lim_{n \to \infty} \beta_n = 0$, that is, the distance of the point (x_n, y_n) from either the line $y = b_1$ or the line $y = b_2$ tends to zero. Then $x_R = \lim_{n \to \infty} x_n$, $y_R = \lim_{n \to \infty} y_n$ (either b_1 or b_2) is the reached boundary point. By pursuing C_0 to the left of (x_0, y_0), the boundary point (x_L, y_L) is reached in the same way.

PROBLEMS

1. Determine, by the use of Theorem 2, regions of existence and uniqueness of solutions for each of the following equations:

(a) $y' = \tan y$

(b) $y' = \dfrac{x^2 y^2}{x^2 + y^2}$

(c) $y' = \dfrac{1}{x^2 - y^2}$

(d) $y' = \log(1 + x^2 + y^2)$

(e) $y' = \log(1 - y^2)$

(f) $y' = \log|1 - y^2|$

★(g) $y' = |y|$ (Make use of the remark about the Lipschitz condition.)

(h) $y' = y|y|$

(i) $y' = \sqrt{36 - 4x^2 - 9y^2}$

(j) $y' = \begin{cases} x + y \sin y & y \geq 0 \\ x + y^2 & y < 0 \end{cases}$

2. Discuss the existence and uniqueness of solutions of the equation $y' = 100 + y^2$. Show that no integral of this equation exists over an interval larger than $\pi/10$.

3. Discuss the existence and uniqueness of solutions of the equation $y' = 3\sqrt{xy}$ in all parts of the xy plane. Sketch a typical solution.

4. Discuss the existence and uniqueness of solutions of the equation $y' = \sqrt{|y|}$. Show that the solution curves passing through $(a, 0)$ form a two-parameter family.

5. Discuss the existence and uniqueness of solutions of the equation

$$y' = \begin{cases} \sqrt{y} & y \geq 0 \\ -\sqrt{-y} & y < 0 \end{cases}$$

Show that each integral exists for all x.

6. Discuss the existence and uniqueness of solutions of the equation

$$y' = \begin{cases} \dfrac{2y}{x} & x \neq 0 \\ 0 & x = 0 \end{cases}$$

Show that there is no integral curve passing through $(0, b)$ if $b \neq 0$, whereas a two-parameter family of integral curves passes through $(0, 0)$.

7. The integral $y_0(x)$ of the differential equation $y' = (x^2 - y^2) \sin y + y^2 \cos y$ vanishes for $x = x_0$. Show that $y_0(x) \equiv 0$.

8. Can one conclude from Theorem 2 that the only solution $y(x)$ of the equation $y' = y|y|$ for which $y(x_0) = 0$ is $y(x) \equiv 0$?

9. For the differential equation $y' = 2x^2 + 3y^2$ in the square R: $-5 \leq x \leq 5$, $-5 \leq y \leq 5$ find a segment I_y and an interval I_x, centered about the point $(0, 3)$, such that every solution crossing I_y exists over the interval I_x.

10. Let the $y_n(x)$ of Theorem 1 be the approximate solutions of (3.1), (3.2) constructed by the A.B. method, Eqs. (7.16), Chap. I, with tabular difference $h = a/n$. Show that in this case, too,

$$y_n'(x) = f(x, y_n(x)) + h_n(x) \qquad |h_n(x)| \leq \epsilon_n \qquad \text{for} \qquad |x - x_0| \leq a$$

where the ϵ_n are numbers which tend to 0 as $n \to \infty$.

chapter **iv**

Applications of First-order Equations

In this chapter differential equations are studied as the mathematical formulation of problems arising in various fields of science and engineering. In most cases the differential equation which is the mathematical model of a physical situation is not given but is part of the problem and must be set up by the use of general laws and formulas which themselves are mathematical models of more rudimentary situations. Usually, the differential equation alone is not a sufficiently complete formulation of the problem but must be accompanied by accessory conditions specifying initial values of the variables involved. The questions that are asked in many of these problems are not adequately answered by finding the solution of the differential equation as a function; this function must be evaluated for certain arguments or analyzed for certain qualitative features. Thus, the solution of a typical applied problem requires three steps: formulation of the problem as a differential equation with initial conditions, solution of the problem by analytical or numerical methods, and quantitative or qualitative interpretation of the solution function to give explicit answers to the questions asked.

It is a widely held belief that students of mathematics proper need not concern themselves with extramathematical applications. We think that ignoring or, worse, cultivating disdain for applications is harmful to the development of mathematics, as it tends to isolate mathematics from the rest of human culture.   But more specifically the development of the theory of differential equations, from its beginnings to the present day, is intimately tied up with the development of scientific theories and practice.   Even in this elementary treatise there is no better way of dealing with certain parts of the theory, such as *singular points* and the *phase-plane method*, than in connection with physical problems.   The student who believes he can ignore the applications loses out on essential parts of the theory as well.

The applications given here are not meant for specialists in the various branches of science and engineering but deal with general situations that find parallels in many fields.   The nonmathematical scientific substance in these applications is very light, and to deal with it the knowledge of some elementary laws is sufficient.   The choice of applications in this chapter is also limited by the fact that the only problems considered are those whose solution can be reduced to solving a single differential equation of the first order.

The chapter is divided into five parts as follows: Part A, Curves; Part B, Growth, Decay, Change; Part C, Flows; Part D, Motions; and Part E, Circuits.

A. CURVES

1. Differential Equations of Curves

Many geometric problems give rise to differential equations.   In most of these cases it is not functions that are to be found as solutions, but *curves*.   A curve in the xy plane can be represented as the graph of a function $y = y(x)$ or $x = x(y)$ only in special cases.

When a differential equation whose solutions are to represent curves rather than functions is to be set up, one may proceed in one of several ways.

Method a.   One may divide the xy plane into regions such that within each region are only those arcs of the solution curves which are graphs of differentiable functions of the variable chosen as independent.

Example 1.   The circle with center at the origin and radius a cannot be the graph of a function $y(x)$ or a function $x(y)$, although portions of it can be, as is shown in Fig. 1.   The functions thus defined are differentiable except at the end points of their domains.   It is seen that the various parts of the curve which are represented as graphs of functions $y(x)$ and $x(y)$ overlap and together cover the whole curve.

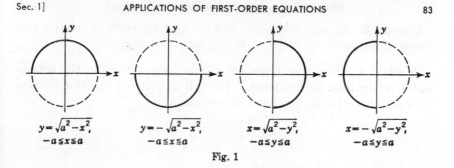

$y = \sqrt{a^2 - x^2}$, $y = -\sqrt{a^2 - x^2}$, $x = \sqrt{a^2 - y^2}$, $x = -\sqrt{a^2 - y^2}$,
$-a \leq x \leq a$ $-a \leq x \leq a$ $-a \leq y \leq a$ $-a \leq y \leq a$

Fig. 1

Method b. One may choose coordinates other than rectangular ones—for example, polar coordinates—in terms of which the solution curves can perhaps be represented as graphs of differentiable functions.

For later use we remind the reader of a calculus formula. If a curve is given in polar coordinates, and ψ is the angle (see Fig. 2) between the radius vector and the tangent line (directed toward increasing θ), then

(1.1) $$\rho \frac{d\theta}{d\rho} = \tan \psi \quad \text{or} \quad \frac{1}{\rho} \frac{d\rho}{d\theta} = \cot \psi$$

depending on whether the curve is given by functions $\rho = \rho(\theta)$ or $\theta = \theta(\rho)$.

Observe that in Fig. 2 we have

(1.2) $$\tau = \theta + \psi$$

In other quadrants, however, a different relation obtains, because the usual definition of the inclination τ restricts it to $0 \leq \tau < \pi$. If, however, we think of the tangent line as continually rotating, then τ can increase beyond π, and (1.2) can remain valid. We shall adopt this convention.

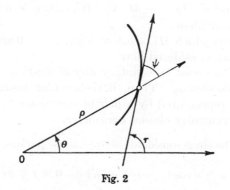

Fig. 2

Example 2. If polar coordinates ρ, θ are used, the circle of radius a with center at the pole is the graph of the constant function $\rho = a$.

Method c. One may represent curves by *equations* in the coordinates rather than by functions. Then, if $u(x, y)$ is a function defined over some portion of the plane, the equation

$$u(x, y) = 0$$

may represent an entire curve.

Example 3. The circle with center at the origin and radius a has the equation

$$x^2 + y^2 - a^2 = 0$$

The four arcs of the circle given by the functions of Fig. 1 will have slopes dy/dx or dx/dy given by

$$x + y \frac{dy}{dx} = 0 \qquad \text{or} \qquad x \frac{dx}{dy} + y = 0$$

The differential form

$$x \, dx + y \, dy = 0$$

comprises both cases.

In general, in geometric problems, we write differential equations in the differential form

$$(1.3) \qquad M(x, y) \, dx + N(x, y) \, dy = 0$$

Then, *near* a point at which $M \neq 0$, the curve is the graph of a function $y(x)$, where $dy/dx = -N/M$. Where $N \neq 0$, the curve is the graph of $x(y)$, and $dx/dy = -M/N$. If neither M nor N is zero, the two forms are equivalent.

Points (x_0, y_0) at which $M(x_0, y_0) = N(x_0, y_0) = 0$ are called *singular points* and are not considered here.

Method d. The most satisfactory way of dealing with curves is by *parametric representation*. Then, if rectangular coordinates x, y are used, a curve is represented by a pair of equations $x = x(t)$, $y = y(t)$, where t is a conveniently chosen parameter.

Example 4. The circle considered above has the parametric representation

$$x = a \cos t \qquad y = a \sin t \qquad 0 \leq t \leq 2\pi$$

It also has many other representations, one of them being

$$x = \frac{a(1 - t^2)}{1 + t^2} \qquad y = \frac{2at}{1 + t^2} \qquad -\infty < t < \infty$$

For this representation the point $(-a, 0)$ is omitted.

We now turn to problems in which curves are determined by differential equations.

Example 5.   Find the curve passing through the point $(3, 4)$ and such that its normal at any point coincides in direction with the radius vector to that point from the origin.

If the curve is represented by $y = y(x)$, then, since y/x is the slope of the radius vector,

$$\frac{dy}{dx} = -\frac{x}{y}$$

This is equivalent (for $y \neq 0$) to

$$x + y\frac{dy}{dx} = 0 \qquad \text{or} \qquad x\,dx + y\,dy = 0$$

If $y = 0$, then $x \neq 0$, and we obtain $x\,dx + y\,dy = 0$ by a similar argument. Hence the curve is represented by $x^2 + y^2 = \text{constant}$.   Since it passes through $(3, 4)$, its equation is $x^2 + y^2 = 25$.

Example 6.   A curve has the property that the angle of inclination of its tangent line at any point is three times the inclination of the radius vector to that point from the origin.   Find all curves with this property.

We use polar coordinates and the notation of Fig. 2.   The problem asserts that $\tau = 3\theta$, and since $\tau = \theta + \psi$ it follows that

$$\psi = 2\theta$$

Therefore, because of (1.1), we have the D.E.

$$\cot \psi = \cot 2\theta = \frac{1}{\rho}\frac{d\rho}{d\theta}$$

The variables are separated, and we easily find that

(1.4) $$\rho^2 = a^2|\sin 2\theta|$$

where a^2 is a constant of integration.

What we have shown is that *if* the geometric condition of the problem is satisfied, then ρ and θ must satisfy Eq. (1.4).   But the converse is not necessarily true.   The graph of (1.4) is shown in Fig. 3.   It consists of two lemniscates.   The "leaf" in the first quadrant certainly solves the geometric problem.

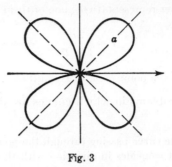

Fig. 3

We must also look for curves which cannot be represented by $\rho = \rho(\theta)$. These are the rays $\theta = $ constant, and for them the conditions of the problem imply that $\theta = 0$.

PROBLEMS

1. Determine those curves for which the normal at (x, y) has an intercept on the x axis equal to $2x$.

2. Find the family of curves which intersect the family of straight lines $y = \lambda x$ at a constant angle α.

3. Determine the curves which intersect each of the parabolas $y = x^2 + \lambda$ at an angle of $45°$.

4. Determine the curves which intersect each of the curves $y = \tan(x + \lambda)$ at an angle of $45°$.

5. Three vertices of a rectangle R lie on the y axis, at the origin, and on the x axis, while the fourth vertex moves along a curve $y = y(x)$ so that the rate of change of the area of R with respect to x is proportional to the area. Find the curve.

6. A boy standing on the (straight) edge of a pond has a boat on the end of a string of length l directly offshore from where he is standing. He walks along the bank pulling the boat. Find the path of the boat. Show that the path approaches the shoreline asymptotically. (This is a plane problem, and the height of the boy above the water is taken as zero.)

★7. Solve Prob. 6 for the case of a round pond of radius $a > l$. Show that the path of the boat spirals toward the circle of radius $\sqrt{a^2 - l^2}$.

★8. Show that if a mirror focuses a parallel beam on a point, its shape is that of a paraboloid of revolution. HINT: By symmetry we may confine ourselves to two dimensions. Use polar coordinates with the beam in the direction of the polar axis.

9. Determine those curves for which the tangent line at (x, y) has intercepts on the x and y axes whose sum is $2(x + y)$.

10. Determine the curves for which the radius vector from the origin makes the constant angle arccot a with the tangent line.

11. Find the curve whose arc length from the abscissa 0 to the abscissa x is sinh x.

12. Find the curve whose arc length from the ordinate 0 to the ordinate y is $\frac{3}{2}y^{\frac{2}{3}}$.

13. O and P_0 are two points in a plane. Find the curve passing through P_0 for which the arc length from P_0 to any point P on the curve is twice the difference between $\overline{OP}$ and $\overline{OP_0}$. The arc length for a curve $\rho = \rho(\theta)$ in polar coordinates is

$$\int \sqrt{\rho^2 + \left(\frac{d\rho}{d\theta}\right)^2}\, d\theta$$

⋆14. An airplane is searching for an enemy motorboat in a dense fog. For one instant the fog lifts, and the boat is seen 5 miles away; then the fog descends again. If the speed of the plane is 240 miles per hour, and the speed of the boat is 60 miles per hour, what path could the plane follow to be certain to intercept the boat, assuming that, at the instant it is seen by the plane, the boat immediately starts out in a straight course in an arbitrary direction? HINT: Use polar coordinates with the pole at the position of the boat when sighted.

2. Orthogonal Trajectories

An orthogonal trajectory to a family of curves is a curve which meets each member of the family at a right angle. Such curves are important in the study of many plane vector fields, such as electric, magnetic, fluid-flow, and heat-flow fields.

For a precise definition of orthogonal trajectories we need the concept of a *one-parameter family of curves*. We give a rather restrictive definition which is general enough for the purpose at hand. We consider only curves that have continuously turning tangent lines (so-called *smooth* curves). In the neighborhood of any point on such a curve, the curve can be represented as either $y = y(x)$ or $x = x(y)$, where $y(x)$ and $x(y)$ are functions with continuous derivatives. We consider only portions of the curves lying in some rectangle $R : a_1 \leq x \leq a_2, b_1 \leq y \leq b_2$. Several such rectangles may be fitted together to encompass larger portions of the curves.

Definitions

1. A collection $\mathfrak{F}$ of smooth curves lying in a rectangle R is a *one-parameter* family if there is, through each interior point of R, one and only one curve of $\mathfrak{F}$.

2. Consider a smooth curve C which intersects some of the curves of $\mathfrak{F}$. The curve C is an *orthogonal trajectory* of $\mathfrak{F}$ if C makes a right angle with each of the curves of $\mathfrak{F}$ that C intersects.

We are interested in collections of orthogonal trajectories of $\mathfrak{F}$, in particular those which themselves form a one-parameter family.

3. Two one-parameter families $\mathfrak{F}_I$, $\mathfrak{F}_{II}$ of smooth curves in R are *orthogonal families* if each curve of $\mathfrak{F}_{II}$ is an orthogonal trajectory of $\mathfrak{F}_I$ (or, equivalently, if each curve of $\mathfrak{F}_I$ is an orthogonal trajectory of $\mathfrak{F}_{II}$).

If $\mathfrak{F}_I$, $\mathfrak{F}_{II}$ are orthogonal families in R, then through each interior point P of R there pass exactly two curves, one belonging to $\mathfrak{F}_I$, the other to $\mathfrak{F}_{II}$, and the curves intersect at right angles at P. The problem we wish to solve is to find $\mathfrak{F}_{II}$ when $\mathfrak{F}_I$ is given. There is an obvious graphical solution. With $\mathfrak{F}_I$ there goes a direction field; call it $\mathfrak{D}_I$. It is obtained by associating with each interior point P of R a line segment that is tangent to the curve that passes through P. Then another direction field $\mathfrak{D}_{II}$ is constructed by associating with each point P of R a line segment that is orthogonal (perpendicular) to the line element of $\mathfrak{D}_I$ at P. With the aid of the direction field $\mathfrak{D}_{II}$ we draw curves, as in Sec. 6, Chap. I, and obtain any number of members of the family $\mathfrak{F}_{II}$ (see Fig. 4).

The graphical procedure can be translated into an analytic procedure. If we use an *equation* to describe a single curve of $\mathfrak{F}_I$ [rather than $y = y(x)$ or $x = x(y)$], then $\mathfrak{F}_I$ is given by an equation

$$(2.1) \qquad\qquad f_I(x, y, \lambda) = 0$$

where the parameter λ labels the different curves of $\mathfrak{F}_I$. Since through each interior point (x, y) of R there passes exactly one curve of $\mathfrak{F}_I$, the parameter λ in (2.1) is a function of the point (x, y); hence (2.1) may be solved for λ to obtain

$$(2.2) \qquad\qquad \lambda = \lambda(x, y)$$

The slope of the curve with label $\lambda = \lambda(x, y)$ at the point (x, y) is obtained by differentiating (2.1) implicitly:

$$(2.3) \qquad \frac{\partial f_I}{\partial x}(x, y, \lambda)\, dx + \frac{\partial f_I}{\partial y}(x, y, \lambda)\, dy = 0$$

If we now use (2.2) for λ in (2.3), we obtain an equation:

$$(2.4) \qquad\qquad M(x, y)\, dx + N(x, y)\, dy = 0$$

This is the equation for the direction field $\mathfrak{D}_I$.

Since the slope of the orthogonal direction field $\mathfrak{D}_{II}$ at (x, y) must be the negative reciprocal of the slope of direction field $\mathfrak{D}_I$ at (x, y), we obtain immediately the equation for the direction field $\mathfrak{D}_{II}$:

$$(2.5) \qquad\qquad N(x, y)\, dx - M(x, y)\, dy = 0$$

It remains to solve the D.E. (2.5). The solution may be written in the form

$$(2.6) \qquad\qquad f_{II}(x, y, \mu) = 0$$

where the parameter μ (the constant of integration) labels the members of family $\mathfrak{F}_{II}$.

In summary, the steps in the procedure are as follows: (1) Start with the equation $f_I(x, y, \lambda) = 0$ for the given family $\mathfrak{F}_I$. (2) Derive by differentiation and elimination of λ the D.E.

$$M(x, y)\, dx + N(x, y)\, dy = 0$$

of the direction field $\mathfrak{D}_I$. (3) Write the D.E.

$$N(x, y)\, dx - M(x, y)\, dy = 0$$

of the direction field $\mathfrak{D}_{II}$. (4) Solve the last equation, obtaining the equation $f_{II}(x, y, \mu) = 0$ for the orthogonal family $\mathfrak{F}_{II}$.

Example 1. Find the family orthogonal to the family of curves $y^2 - \lambda x^3$.

This is a family $\mathfrak{F}_I$ of semicubical parabolas (with the line $y = 0$ thrown in for good measure) (see Fig. 4). They form a one-parameter family as defined above in any rectangle R that encloses no point of the y axis. Differentiation gives $2y\, dy = 3\lambda x^2\, dx$, and substitution of $\lambda = x^{-3}y^2$ results in

$$3x^{-1}y^2\, dx - 2y\, dy = 0$$

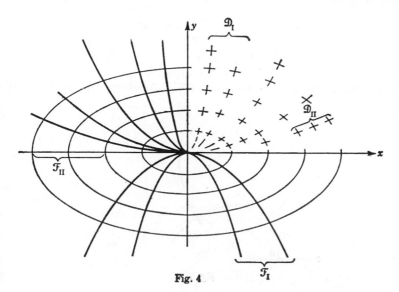

Fig. 4

This is the D.E. of direction field $\mathfrak{D}_\mathrm{I}$. Therefore, the D.E. of direction field $\mathfrak{D}_\mathrm{II}$ is

$$2y\,dx + 3x^{-1}y^2\,dy = 0$$

Separation of variables and integration give the equation of the family $\mathfrak{F}_\mathrm{II}$ orthogonal to $\mathfrak{F}_\mathrm{I}$:

$$2x^2 + 3y^2 = \mu$$

This is a family of similar ellipses with common center at the origin (see Fig. 4).

The following remark is of interest. In a rectangle R that encloses part of the y axis, family $\mathfrak{F}_\mathrm{I}$ is not a one-parameter family as defined above because none of its members passes through a point on the y axis [except through $(0, 0)$]. This can be remedied. If $\mathfrak{F}_\mathrm{I}$ is written as $x^3 = ky^2$, where $k = \lambda^{-1}$, then the line $x = 0$ appears as a member of $\mathfrak{F}_\mathrm{I}$ for the parameter value $k = 0$. This line does not appear as a member of the original family because $k = 0$ corresponds to the fictitious value $\lambda = \infty$. With the line $x = 0$ included as a member of family $\mathfrak{F}_\mathrm{I}$, we have a one-parameter family in any rectangle R that does not enclose the origin. The orthogonal family $\mathfrak{F}_\mathrm{II}$ is not altered by the inclusion of $x = 0$ in $\mathfrak{F}_\mathrm{I}$.

For some problems polar coordinates are convenient.

Example 2. Find the family orthogonal to the family $\mathfrak{F}_\mathrm{I}$ of cardioids $\rho = \lambda(1 + \cos\theta)$.

Differentiating, we get

$$d\rho + \lambda \sin\theta\,d\theta = 0$$

Eliminating the parameter λ gives

$$(2.7) \qquad d\rho + \frac{\rho \sin\theta}{1 + \cos\theta}\,d\theta = 0$$

This is the D.E. of the direction field $\mathfrak{D}_\mathrm{I}$ for the given family $\mathfrak{F}_\mathrm{I}$.

To find the D.E. of the direction field orthogonal to $\mathfrak{D}_\mathrm{I}$, we need to extend formula (1.1). We use the notation of Fig. 5, where ψ_II and τ_II are the

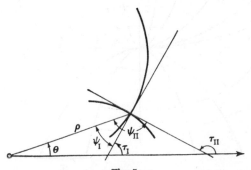

Fig. 5

angles for the orthogonal trajectory corresponding to the angles ψ_I and τ_I for the given family.   Clearly

$$\psi_{II} = \psi_I \pm \frac{\pi}{2}$$

whence

(2.8) $$\tan \psi_{II} = \tan\left(\psi_I \pm \frac{\pi}{2}\right) = -\cot \psi_I$$

Therefore, by (1.1),

(2.9) $$\left(\rho \frac{d\theta}{d\rho}\right)_{II} = -\left(\frac{1}{\rho}\frac{d\rho}{d\theta}\right)_I$$

whence the D.E. for the orthogonal trajectories is

$$\rho \frac{d\theta}{d\rho} = \frac{\sin \theta}{1 + \cos \theta}$$

The variables are separable, and integration gives

$$\rho = c(1 - \cos \theta)$$

This is the equation of the orthogonal family $\mathfrak{F}_{II}$ (see Fig. 6).   Since $\rho = c(1 - \cos \theta)$ represents the same curve as $\rho = -c(1 + \cos \theta)$, we see that the member of $\mathfrak{F}_{II}$ with label c is the same as the member of $\mathfrak{F}_I$ with label $\lambda = -c$.   Thus the given family is self-orthogonal.

Family $\mathfrak{F}_I$ of this example is not a one-parameter family in any rectangle. However, if we restrict the parameter λ to only *positive* values, then $\mathfrak{F}_I$ is a

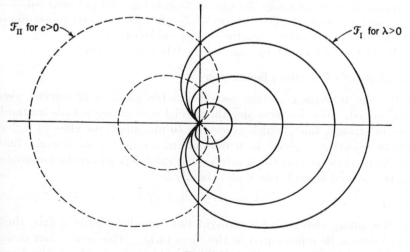

$\mathfrak{F}_{II}$ for $c>0$ $\mathfrak{F}_I$ for $\lambda>0$

Fig. 6

one-parameter family in any rectangle R not enclosing points with $\theta = \pi$. The parameter values c in $\mathfrak{F}_{II}$ are then also restricted to *positive* values, and $\mathfrak{F}_{II}$ is a one-parameter family in any rectangle R not enclosing points with $\theta = 0$.

PROBLEMS

1. Find the families orthogonal to the following families in rectangular coordinates (λ is the parameter; a is a fixed constant):

(a) $(x - \lambda)^2 + y^2 = \lambda^2$ (b) $xy = \lambda$

(c) $x^2 + ay^2 = \lambda$ (d) $x^a + y^a = \lambda \ (a \neq 2)$

(e) $y = \lambda e^{-x^2}$ (f) $y(x^2 + \lambda) = 2a$

(g) $\dfrac{x^2}{a^2} + \dfrac{y^2}{\lambda^2} = 1$ (h) $y = \lambda e^{x^a}$

2. Find the families orthogonal to the following families in polar coordinates (λ is the parameter; a, b are fixed constants).

(a) $\rho = \lambda \cos \theta$ (b) $\rho^2 = \lambda \cos 2\theta$

(c) $\rho^a = \lambda \cos b\theta$ (d) $\rho^2(1 - \cos \theta) \sin \theta = \lambda$

(e) $\rho(1 + a \cos \theta) = \lambda$ (f) $\rho\theta = \lambda$

(g) $\rho e^{\cos \theta} = \lambda$ (h) $\rho = \lambda(a \cos \theta + b \sin \theta)$

3. Let $f_1(x, y, \lambda) = 0$ be a one-parameter family $\mathfrak{F}_I$ of curves, and

$$M(x, y) \, dx + N(x, y) \, dy = 0$$

the D.E. of the corresponding direction field $\mathfrak{D}_I$. What is the D.E. of the direction field for the family $\mathfrak{F}_{II}$ whose members intersect the curves of $\mathfrak{F}_I$ at the constant angle α? (The curves of $\mathfrak{F}_{II}$ are called *isogonal trajectories* of the family $\mathfrak{F}_I$; orthogonal trajectories are a special case.)

4. Do Prob. 3 for a family $f_1(\rho, \theta, \lambda) = 0$ in polar coordinates.

3. Clairaut's Equation; Envelopes

In the preceding section one-parameter families of curves were considered. We now consider the special case of one-parameter families of straight lines, which gives rise to an important class of differential equations. Since in a one-parameter family of straight lines both the slope m and the y intercept b may depend on the parameter λ, the general equation of such a family is

(3.1) $$y = m(\lambda)x + b(\lambda)$$

If the family also contains straight lines parallel to the y axis, these lines cannot be represented in the form (3.1). This is a minor defect which could easily be rectified; it is ignored here to avoid complications.

If family (3.1) consists of *parallel* straight lines, then $m(\lambda)$ is independent of λ. We are not interested in this trivial case, and assume this is not so. Then we may use the slope $m(\lambda)$ itself as a label (at least for some interval of λ values) and call the new label λ again; (3.1) then takes the form

$$(3.2) \qquad y = \lambda x + \varphi(\lambda)$$

where $\varphi(\lambda)$ is the y intercept of the line whose slope equals λ. The collection of tangent lines to a smooth curve can be written in this form, as may be seen in the following example.

Example 1. Find the family of tangent lines to the parabola $y = x^2$.

We find the equation of the tangent at an arbitrary point $P_1(x_1, y_1)$ on the parabola. The slope at P_1 is $2x_1$; hence the tangent is given by

$$y - y_1 = 2x_1(x - x_1) = 2x_1 x - 2x_1{}^2$$

Because P_1 is on the parabola, $y_1 = x_1{}^2$, and we obtain for the tangent line

$$y = 2x_1 x - x_1{}^2$$

Since the slope is $m = 2x_1$, this last equation may be written as

$$(3.3) \qquad y = mx - \frac{m^2}{4}$$

Regarding m as a parameter, we see from (3.3) that the tangents to $y = x^2$ form a one-parameter family.

Clearly (3.3) is an equation with one parameter. Also, by examining **Fig. 7**, one sees that, through each point of the plane "outside" the parabola, there

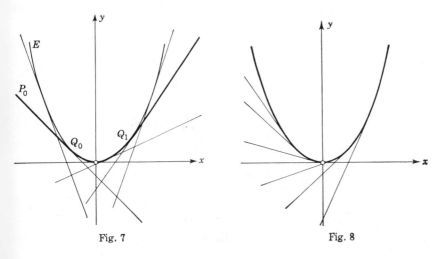

Fig. 7   Fig. 8

are two lines of (3.3) [because (3.3) is a quadratic in m]. How then can (3.3) be a one-parameter family in the sense of the definition of Sec. 2? All that need be done is to consider a point lying outside the parabola, choose one of the lines through the point, and consider, for the family, only those lines with slopes near the chosen line (i.e., lines tangent to a small arc of the parabola). Then in some rectangle R enclosing the chosen point, we shall have a one-parameter family in R. (See Fig. 8.)

In essentially the same way as in Example 1, it is possible to show that, for every smooth curve, the set of tangent lines along a sufficiently small arc forms a one-parameter family. We shall now prove the converse, that every one-parameter family of the form of (3.2) is the set of tangent lines to some curve. The only exceptions are bundles of lines passing through one point. If (3.2) represents a family of lines passing through (x_0, y_0), then for all λ

$$(3.4) \qquad y_0 = \lambda x_0 + \varphi(\lambda) \qquad \varphi(\lambda) = y_0 - \lambda x_0$$

that is, $\varphi(\lambda)$ is a linear function. Conversely, if $\varphi(\lambda)$ is a linear function, that is, $d^2\varphi/d\lambda^2 \equiv 0$, then (3.2) represents lines all passing through one point.

Theorem 1. *If φ has a continuous second derivative $d^2\varphi/d\lambda^2$ which nowhere vanishes, then the family of straight lines $y = \lambda x + \varphi(\lambda)$ is the set of tangent lines to a smooth curve E.*

Proof. We determine the equation of the curve E, which is called the *envelope* of the family. Let us assume for the moment that the existence of E is already proved. Then we may speak of the point at which the member of the given family carrying the label λ is tangent

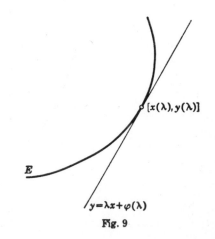

$[x(\lambda), y(\lambda)]$

E

$y = \lambda x + \varphi(\lambda)$

Fig. 9

to E; let its coordinates be denoted as $x(\lambda)$, $y(\lambda)$ (see Fig. 9).   Then

(3.4) $$y(\lambda) = \lambda x(\lambda) + \varphi(\lambda)$$

and, since this is an identity in λ, we may differentiate with respect to λ and get

(3.5) $$y'(\lambda) = x(\lambda) + \lambda x'(\lambda) + \varphi'(\lambda)$$

But the slope of E at $(x(\lambda), y(\lambda))$ is $dy/dx = y'(\lambda)/x'(\lambda)$ and is equal to the slope of the straight line which is tangent to E at $(x(\lambda), y(\lambda))$, namely, λ, so that $y'(\lambda) = \lambda x'(\lambda)$.   Therefore (3.5) gives

(3.6) $$x(\lambda) + \varphi'(\lambda) = 0$$

In Eqs. (3.4) and (3.6) we have two equations for the coordinates $x(\lambda)$, $y(\lambda)$ of the points of E.   These equations therefore are a parametric representation of E.

So far we have assumed that E exists.   Now we reverse the above argument and prove that there is a curve whose set of tangent lines is the given family $\mathfrak{F} \colon y = \lambda x + \varphi(\lambda)$.   Let E be the curve given by the parametric equations†

(3.7) $$x = -\varphi'(\lambda) \qquad y = -\lambda \varphi'(\lambda) + \varphi(\lambda)$$

The slope of E is

$$\frac{y'(\lambda)}{x'(\lambda)} = \frac{-\lambda \varphi'' - \varphi' + \varphi'}{-\varphi''} = \lambda$$

Therefore, E has the slope λ at the point $(x(\lambda), y(\lambda))$, the same as has the straight line of the given family that passes through this point. Therefore E is the envelope of the family.

Example 2.   Determine the envelope of the one-parameter family of lines

(3.8) $$y = \lambda x \pm \sqrt{\lambda^2 - 1}$$

In this case $\varphi(\lambda) = \pm \sqrt{\lambda^2 - 1}$, and (3.6) becomes

(3.9) $$x \pm \frac{\lambda}{\sqrt{\lambda^2 - 1}} = 0$$

If (3.9) is used in (3.8), we get

(3.10) $$y = \pm \frac{1}{\sqrt{\lambda^2 - 1}}$$

† Because $\varphi''(\lambda) \neq 0$, the first of Eqs. (3.7) maps an interval of λ values one-to-one on an interval of x values.   Thus (3.7) actually represents a curve.   Since one may solve $x = -\varphi'(\lambda)$ for λ in terms of x, the second equation in (3.7) will give y in terms of x.   The curve E is therefore the graph of a function $y(x)$.

Equations (3.9) and (3.10) give a parametric representation of the envelope. Elimination of λ gives

$$x^2 - y^2 = 1$$

Thus the envelope is recognized as a hyperbola.

Now consider the direction field defined by the one-parameter family (3.2). This is obtained by differentiating with respect to x and eliminating λ. We have $y = \lambda x + \varphi(\lambda)$, and $dy/dx = \lambda$, so

$$(3.11) \qquad y = x\frac{dy}{dx} + \varphi\left(\frac{dy}{dx}\right)$$

This is the D.E. of the direction field associated with (3.2). Conversely, (3.2) is a one-parameter family of solutions of (3.11), that is, a local solution family. Differential equations of the form of (3.11) are called *Clairaut equations* (A.C. Clairaut, 1713–1765). A one-parameter family of solutions of such an equation can be written down at sight: $y = \lambda x + \varphi(\lambda)$. This is often called the *general solution* of the Clairaut equation, and it is indeed a local solution family near any point not on the envelope E of the family $y = \lambda x + \varphi(\lambda)$. The envelope E is also a solution of (3.11), since at each of its points it has the slope of the direction field at that point. Thus we have two kinds of solutions for a Clairaut equation such as (3.11): the straight lines $y = \lambda x + \varphi(\lambda)$, one of which passes through every point of the plane, and their envelope E found as above. The envelope is often called a *singular integral* of the Clairaut equation because it cannot be obtained in the usual way from the general solution $y = \lambda x + \varphi(\lambda)$ by assigning a particular value to the constant of integration λ. The singular solution is absent in the case in which $\varphi(\lambda)$ is a linear function, since in this case the envelope E reduces to a point.

Example 3. Find the general and singular solutions of the D.E.

$$y = xy' \pm \sqrt{y'^2} - 1$$

This is a Clairaut equation. Its general solution is $y = cx \pm \sqrt{c^2 - 1}$ (c is a constant of integration). The envelope of this family of lines was found in Example 2. Thus the singular solution is $y = \pm \sqrt{x^2 - 1}$.

It is interesting to note that both the general and singular solutions of a Clairaut equation

$$(3.12) \qquad y = px + \varphi(p) \qquad p = \frac{dy}{dx}$$

can be found by differentiation.   Indeed, differentiation of (3.12) gives

$$p = p + x \frac{dp}{dx} + \varphi'(p) \frac{dp}{dx}$$

or

$$\frac{dp}{dx} [x + \varphi'(p)] = 0$$

This last equation is satisfied if $dp/dx = 0$, that is, $p = \lambda = $ constant, which leads to the general solution $y = \lambda x + \varphi(\lambda)$.   The other factor, $x + \varphi'(p) = 0$, if solved for p and substituted in (3.12), leads to the singular solution.

As we have seen above, there are two solutions through each point on the envelope E of the general solution of Clairaut's equation: a straight-line solution and the envelope, provided the latter is not reduced to a point.   Indeed there are infinitely many solutions through each point P_0 of the plane: one follows the line from P_0 to the point Q_0 of tangency with E, moves along the envelope through an arbitrary arc $Q_0 Q_1$, and then moves off on the line tangent to E at Q_1 (see Fig. 7). The resulting curve is smooth (although "pieced together") and is an integral curve of the Clairaut equation.

The reader may ask here why the uniqueness theorem of Chap. III does not apply.   The answer is that the Clairaut equation (3.11) is not of the form $dy/dx = f(x, y)$ for which the uniqueness theorem is formulated.   One may try to cast it in this form by solving (3.11) first for dy/dx.   If this is done for the equation of Example 3, one finds

$$y' = \frac{xy \pm \sqrt{1 - x^2 + y^2}}{1 - x^2}$$

This is now in the form $y' = f(x, y)$.   However, any rectangle R in which f and $\partial f/\partial y$ are continuous would have to exclude the points at which $x^2 - y^2 = 1$, which are exactly the points of the singular solution E.   This is no accident.   In general, the singular solution E of the Clairaut equation $y - xp - \varphi(p) = 0$ is found by putting the derivative of this equation with respect to p equal to zero: $x + \varphi'(p) = 0$. Therefore one cannot hope to solve this equation for p to get the normal form $p = f(x, y)$ with f and $\partial f/\partial y$ continuous near a point on E.

PROBLEMS

1. Determine an equation of the form $y = \lambda x + \varphi(\lambda)$ for the family of lines tangent to each of the following curves (a and p are constants):

(a) $x^2 + y^2 = a^2$

(b) $x^p + y^p = a^p$ ($x > 0, y > 0, a > 0, p \neq 0, 1$)

(c) $y^3 = x - a$

(d) $y = \sin^2 x$

(e) $x = a(\varphi - \sin \varphi), y = a(1 - \cos \varphi)$

2. Find the envelope for each of the following families of straight lines:

(a) $y = \lambda x + \dfrac{2}{3 \sqrt{3\lambda}}$

(b) $y = \lambda x + \frac{1}{16} \lambda^4$

(c) $y = \lambda x + a(1 - \lambda^{\frac{2}{3}})^{\frac{1}{2}}$

(d) $y = \lambda x + (1 - \sqrt[3]{\lambda})^3$ ($x > 0, \lambda < 0$)

3. (a) Determine an equation of the form $y = \lambda x + \varphi(\lambda)$ for the family of normals to the ellipse $x^2/a^2 + y^2/b^2 = 1$.

(b) Find the envelope of this family. (The envelope of the family of normals of a curve is the *evolute* of the curve.)

4. (a) Determine the equation of the family of lines obtained by having the end points of a segment of length a move along two fixed perpendicular lines.

(b) Find the envelope of this family.

5. Find general and singular solutions of the following Clairaut equations:

(a) $(y - y'x)^2 = 4(1 + y'^2)$

(b) $y = y'x + y'^3$

(c) $y = y'x + y'^p$ ($p \neq 0, 1$)

(d) $(y - y'x)^4 = (1 - y'^{\frac{2}{3}})^3$

6. Find a solution curve of the Clairaut equation $y = y'x + y'^2$ which passes through the two points $(-5, -4)$ and $(5, -4)$.

4. The General First-order Equation

The Clairaut equation is a special case of an equation of the form

$$(4.1) \qquad\qquad g(x, y, y') = 0$$

which we call a *general D.E. of the first order*.† If $g(x, y, p) = 0$ can be solved for p in some region of xyp space, resulting in an equation of the form $p = f(x, y)$, then we are back to the situation discussed in preceding sections. Quite often the equation $g(x, y, p) = 0$ has several solutions $p = f_1(x, y), \ldots, p = f_m(x, y)$, all valid in the same rectangle R of the xy plane.

† If the terminology customary in the theory of partial differential equations were followed, $y' = f(x, y)$ would be called *quasilinear*, and $g(x, y, y') = 0$ would be called *nonlinear*.

Example 1. The equation

(4.2) $$2xy - (2x + y)p + p^2 = 0$$

has the two solutions $p = 2x$ and $p = y$. Therefore, the general D.E.

(4.3) $$2xy - (2x + y)y' + y'^2 = 0$$

leads to the two differential equations

(4.4) $$y' = 2x \quad \text{and} \quad y' = y$$

both valid in the whole xy plane. Each integral of either equation must be considered an integral of (4.3). Thus we have at least two one-parameter families of solutions of (4.3):

(4.5) $$y = x^2 + c \quad \text{and} \quad y = ke^x$$

Actually, there are more solutions. Along the line $y = 2x$ the direction fields of (4.4) coincide, and therefore a solution $y = x^2 + c$ may be pieced together with a solution $y = ke^x$ at the line $y = 2x$ to give a new smooth solution of (4.3). This gives rise to a new solution at each point of the line $y = 2x$. These "composite" functions are solutions of (4.3) but are not solutions (near $y = 2x$, at any rate) of Eqs. (4.4) into which (4.3) factors.

The phenomenon observed in Example 1—that D.E. (4.3) has solutions which are not solutions of either of the two equations into which (4.3) factors—occurs for many general differential equations

$$g(x, y, y') = 0$$

If the equation $g(x, y, p) = 0$ has more than one solution valid in the same region of xyp space, say $p = f_1(x, y)$, $p = f_2(x, y)$, . . . , then there may be points at which several of these solutions coincide, say

(4.6) $$p_0 = f_1(x_0, y_0) = f_2(x_0, y_0) = \cdots$$

In this case an integral curve of the equation $y' = f_1(x, y)$ passing through (x_0, y_0) has the same slope there as an integral curve of the equation $y' = f_2(x, y)$ has at (x_0, y_0). Therefore an arc of the one curve may be pieced together with an arc of the other curve at the point (x_0, y_0), resulting in a smooth function y which is a solution of $g(x, y, y') = 0$ without necessarily being a solution of either $y' = f_1(x, y)$ or $y' = f_2(x, y)$.

The set of values $x = x_0$, $y = y_0$, $p = p_0$ at which the coalescence expressed in (4.6) happens are among those for which

$$\frac{\partial g(x, y, p)}{\partial p} = 0$$

The triples $x = x_0$, $y = y_0$, $p = p_0$ for which the two equations

$$(4.7) \qquad g(x, y, p) = 0 \qquad \frac{\partial}{\partial p} g(x, y, p) = 0$$

hold simultaneously are called *singular elements* of the D.E.

$$g(x, y, y') = 0$$

(or of the direction field associated with it), and the points (x_0, y_0) which "carry" the singular elements are called *singular points*. In Example 1 all the points along the line $y = 2x$ are singular. In the case of a Clairaut equation $y - xy' - \varphi(y') = 0$, all the points of the singular solution (the envelope of the family of straight-line solutions) are singular, since they satisfy the two equations

$$g(x, y, p) = y - xp - \varphi(p) = 0$$
$$\frac{\partial g}{\partial p}(x, y, p) = -x - \varphi'(p) = 0$$

PROBLEMS

1. Show that, by the definition of this section, the common zeros of the functions A and B are the singular points of the D.E. $A(x, y)y' + B(x, y) = 0$.

2. Determine the singular elements of the following differential equations:

(a) $y'^2 = x - y$
(b) $(y' - x)^2 + y^2 - 4y' = 0$
(c) $y'^2 + xy' - y = 0$
(d) $y'^2 - xy' + y^2 = 0$
(e) $y'^4 - (x^2 - y^2 + 2xy)y'^2 + 2xy(x^2 - y^2) = 0$

3. Find the singular points of the D.E. $y'^4 - 16y^2 = 0$, and show that there is a smooth integral curve through any two points (x_1, y_1), (x_2, y_2), with $x_1 \neq x_2$.

4. Show that $y = x^2$ $(-\infty < x < \infty)$ is a solution of the D.E. $(y' - 2\sqrt{|y|})(y' + 2\sqrt{|y|}) = 0$ but is not a solution of either $y' - 2\sqrt{|y|} = 0$ or $y' + 2\sqrt{|y|} = 0$. Find all solutions of this kind.

5. Show that the solutions of the D.E. $y'^2 + [f(x, y) - 1/f(x, y)]y' - 1 = 0$ form a self-orthogonal family.

B. GROWTH, DECAY, CHANGE

5. Rate Problems

In the simplest cases the dependent variable x is given explicitly as a function of the time t, $x = f(t)$. In this case the rate of change is

$dx/dt = f'(t)$, and finding x when the derivative is known reduces to a quadrature. In an important class of problems the rate of change of x is proportional to x, which yields a simple differential equation with the variables separable.

Interest on money, at the rate r per period, is *compounded* when the interest at the end of some fixed period is added to the principal at the end of that period. That is, if A is the amount of the money and t the period, we have

$$(5.1) \qquad \Delta A = rA \, \Delta t$$

Interest is said to be *compounded continuously* if we have instead of (5.1) the following:

$$(5.2) \qquad \frac{dA}{dt} = rA$$

Example 1. Find the time required for \$1 to double when invested at the rate of 5 per cent per annum compounded continuously.

Let $A(t)$ denote the amount at the end of t years; then

$$\frac{dA}{dt} = 0.05A$$

whence

$$\log A = 0.05t + c$$

and

$$A(t) = Ce^{0.05t}$$

When $t = 0$, $A = 1$, and therefore $C = 1$. If $A(t) = 2$ then

$$2 = e^{0.05t}$$

or

$$t = \frac{\log 2}{0.05} = 20 \log 2 = 13.86$$

In other words, to double your money at 5 per cent compounded continuously would take 13.86 years.

Example 2. Radioactive elements decompose at a fixed rate.† That is, if $A(t)$ is the mass of a radioactive substance present at time t, then the rate of change per unit mass $(1/A) \, dA/dt$ is a constant, say r. In this case r is of course negative. We are dealing once more with Eq. (5.2). The time required for A to decrease to one-half its original value is called the *half-life* of the radioactive element. Since the general solution of (5.2) is

$$(5.3) \qquad A(t) = A_0 e^{rt}$$

† This law has a statistical basis. It is true for large numbers of atoms but does not apply to individual atoms.

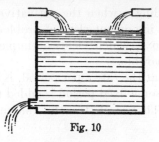

Fig. 10

the half-life is easily found by setting $A = \frac{1}{2}A_0$ in (5.3) and solving for t. We obtain

$$\text{Half-life} = -\frac{\log 2}{r}$$

As an example, the half-life of strontium 90 is 25 years, whence

$$r = -\log \tfrac{2}{25} = -0.0277$$

Example 3. A tank of 100 gallons capacity is initially full of water. Pure water is allowed to run into the tank at the rate of 1 gallon per minute, and at the same time brine containing $\frac{1}{4}$ pound of salt per gallon flows into the tank at the rate of 1 gallon per minute. The mixture flows out at the rate of 2 gallons per minute. (It is assumed that there is perfect mixing.) Find the amount of salt in the tank after t minutes (See Fig. 10).

Let $S(t)$ be the amount of salt in pounds in the tank at time t. The concentration in pounds per gallon will be $S/100$. Hence salt leaves the tank at the rate of $2S/100$ pounds per minute. Since $\frac{1}{4}$ pound enters per minute,

$$\frac{dS}{dt} = \tfrac{1}{4} - 2\,\frac{S}{100}$$

whence

$$\frac{dS}{25 - 2S} = \frac{dt}{100}$$

and we find easily that

$$S(t) = \tfrac{25}{2} - S_0 e^{-t/50}$$

where S_0 is the constant of integration. Since $S = 0$ when $t = 0$, we find that $S_0 = \frac{25}{2}$, and so

$$S(t) = \tfrac{25}{2}(1 - e^{-t/50})$$

Significant rate problems also occur in the analysis of chemical reactions, as the next example illustrates.

Example 4. Two substances X and Y react to form a third substance Z at a rate which is proportional to the product of the masses of X and Y as yet untransformed. (The conditions under which this situation prevails are discussed in chemistry textbooks, the law being referred to as the *law of mass action*.)   Find the amount z (grams) of the substance Z as a function of the time t (seconds) reckoned from the start of the reaction.

Suppose that initially we have x grams of the substance X and y grams of the substance Y and that α grams of X combines with β grams of Y to form $\alpha + \beta$ grams of Z. If $z(t)$ represents the number of grams of Z present at time t, then it contains $\alpha z/(\alpha + \beta)$ grams of X and $\beta z/(\alpha + \beta)$ grams of Y. Thus the amounts of X and Y remaining are $x - \alpha z/(\alpha + \beta)$ and $y - \beta z/(\alpha + \beta)$, respectively, so that

$$(5.4) \qquad \frac{dz}{dt} = k\left(x - \frac{\alpha z}{\alpha + \beta}\right)\left(y - \frac{\beta z}{\alpha + \beta}\right)$$

where k is the constant of proportionality.   Equation (5.4) may be written as

$$\frac{dz}{dt} = \frac{k\alpha\beta}{(\alpha + \beta)^2}\left(\frac{\alpha + \beta}{\alpha}x - z\right)\left(\frac{\alpha + \beta}{\beta}y - z\right)$$

or

$$(5.5) \qquad \frac{dz}{dt} = K(A - z)(B - z)$$

where

$$K = \frac{k\alpha\beta}{(\alpha + \beta)^2} \qquad A = \frac{\alpha + \beta}{\alpha}x \qquad B = \frac{\alpha + \beta}{\beta}y$$

In (5.5) the variables are separable, and (5.5) may be rewritten as

$$\frac{dz}{(A - z)(B - z)} = K\, dt$$

There are two essentially different cases to be considered.   If $A = B$, then the left member of the above equation integrates by the "power formula," whereas if $A \neq B$ exponential functions arise.   Here we suppose $A \neq B$ and without loss of generality may suppose the substances labeled so that $A > B$.   Then, expanding in partial fractions,

$$\frac{dz}{(A - z)(B - z)} = -\frac{1}{A - B}\frac{dz}{A - z} + \frac{1}{A - B}\frac{dz}{B - z}$$

whence

$$\frac{1}{A - B}\log\frac{A - z}{B - z} = Kt + C_1$$

$$\frac{A - z}{B - z} = Ce^{K(A-B)t}$$

and

$$z(t) = \frac{A - BCe^{K(A-B)t}}{1 - Ce^{K(A-B)t}}$$

Since, further, $z = 0$ when $t = 0$, we find easily that $C = A/B$, so that

$$z(t) = \frac{AB(1 - e^{-K(A-B)t})}{A - Be^{-K(A-B)t}}$$

We see from this last equation that as $t \to \infty$, $z(t) \to B$.

PROBLEMS

1. If the half-life of radium is 1,600 years, how long will it take a mass of radium to disintegrate until but 10 per cent remains?

2. Find the value of $100 compounded continuously for a period of 10 years at the rate of 4 per cent per year.

3. A man is fortunate enough to have a certain sum of money invested so as to compound continuously at 5 per cent per year. He withdraws money continuously at a constant rate (this could be approximately realized by a daily withdrawal) so as to draw $1,000 per year. At the end of 10 years his fund is exhausted. How much did he start with?

4. Bacteria, when grown in a nutrient solution, increase at a rate proportional to the number present. If in a particular culture the number doubles in 2 hours and there were 10^6 at the end of 10 hours, how many were there initially?

5. A tank contains 100 gallons of brine containing 50 pounds of dissolved salt. Pure water runs into the tank at the rate of 1 gallon per minute, and brine flows out (assume continuous perfect mixing) at the rate of 1 gallon per minute. How long will it take to reduce the salt concentration to one-half its initial value?

6. A large tank contains 100 gallons of pure water. A salt solution containing 1 pound of salt per gallon flows into the tank at the rate of 2 gallons per minute, while from another pipe a salt solution containing 2 pounds of salt per gallon flows in at the rate of 2 gallons per minute. The mixture flows out of the tank at the rate of 3 gallons per minute. Find the amount of salt and the concentration at the end of 100 minutes.

7. A room contains 5,000 cubic feet and a concentration of 0.5 per cent CO_2 by volume. The CO_2 content is being increased at the constant rate of 0.1 cubic foot per minute by the occupants of the room. Blowers are turned on, pumping air with 0.04 per cent CO_2 by volume. How much air must be pumped in order eventually to bring the CO_2 concentration down to 0.05 per cent? How long will it be before the CO_2 concentration is down to 0.1 per cent?

8. Newton's law of cooling asserts that the rate at which a body cools is proportional to the difference in temperature between the body and its surroundings. Write a differential equation which expresses this relation. If a body cools from 40 to 30°F in 10 minutes when the ambient air is at 10°F, how long will it take to cool from 80 to 50°F when the ambient air is at 30°F?

9. Show that if the atmosphere is at rest

$$\frac{dp}{dh} = -\rho(h)g$$

where $p(h)$ is the pressure (pounds per square foot) and $\rho(h)$ the density (slugs per cubic foot) at altitude h (feet). Using this equation, determine the pressure $p(h)$ if (a) the atmosphere is isothermal: $p = k\rho$ and (b) the atmosphere is adiabatic: $p = k\rho^{1.4}$.

10. A material containing S pounds of salt is stirred with G gallons of pure water. The salt dissolves at a rate proportional to the product of the amount of undissolved salt and the difference between the concentration of the liquid and that of a saturated solution (3 pounds of salt per gallon). Find an expression giving the amount of undissolved salt as a function of time.

11. An insect colony has constant birth and death rates, that is, births (or deaths) per 1,000 of population per day. (In a human population such data would be given per year.) Assuming that the population can vary continuously, describe the growth or decay of the population.

12. An insect colony has a constant birth rate, but in addition to a constant death rate there are losses, due to struggle between individuals for the limited food supply, which are proportional to the square of the live population. Describe the growth and decay of the colony, and show that eventually it either dies out or reaches a stationary level.

13. In the preceding problem assume that, due to a growing food supply, the coefficient of the quadratic term is an exponentially decreasing function of time. Describe the growth and decay of the colony.

14. An insect colony X is invaded by parasites Y whose eggs hatch in the attacked insects, thereby killing them. If $x(t)$, $y(t)$ are the numbers of individuals of X, Y, respectively, at the time t, then under certain conditions the equations

$$\frac{dx}{dt} = \alpha_1 x - \gamma_1 xy \qquad \frac{dy}{dt} = \gamma_2 xy - \alpha_2 y$$

hold, where α_1, α_2, γ_1, γ_2 are positive constants. Find a functional relation between x and y that does not contain t. Show that the parasite species Y cannot exterminate the host species X completely.

15. Derive a formula for the amount u of a substance U formed from substances X, Y, and Z if α, β, γ grams of X, Y, Z, respectively, unite to form $\alpha + \beta + \gamma$ grams of U. Assume that at time $t = 0$ one has x, y, z grams of X, Y, Z, respectively, and none of U is present.

C. FLOWS

6. Problems of Fluid Flow

Consider the tank of Fig. 11 which is filled with liquid whose depth at time t is $x(t)$. The depth varies because the liquid flows through

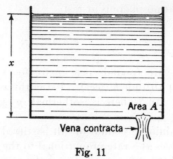

Fig. 11

a small orifice located at the bottom of the tank. By balancing the kinetic against the potential energy along streamlines, it is shown in physics that the velocity of efflux of the liquid from the orifice is

$$(6.1) \qquad\qquad v_e = \sqrt{2gx}$$

(this is the same as the velocity in free fall through the vertical distance x), where g is the acceleration of gravity. It is assumed that there is no difference in atmospheric pressure between the upper level of the liquid and the level at the orifice. Another assumption made in deriving the above formula is that the flow is steady (i.e., the velocity field does not change in time). Although the flow cannot be steady if the level of the liquid falls, we may apply formula (6.1) to our problems and derive results that are not too inaccurate.

If A is the cross-sectional area of the orifice, one would suppose that the volume rate of flow for depth x is $A\sqrt{2gx}$. This is not the case, however, as the stream contracts slightly on emerging from the orifice and forms a somewhat narrower cross section called the *vena contracta*. The amount of contraction depends on the orifice shape. Thus the volume rate of flow is

$$kA\sqrt{2gx}$$

where k is a constant depending on the orifice and usually is about 0.6, which is the figure we shall use in our problems.

Example 1. A tank with a base 2 feet square contains 4 feet of water. A 2-inch-diameter circular orifice is located at the bottom. How long will it take for the tank to empty itself?

The volume at any instant is $V(t) = 4x(t)$, and

$$\frac{dV}{dt} = -0.6A\sqrt{2gx}$$

where $A = \pi/144$ square feet.   Then

$$4 \frac{dx}{dt} = \frac{-0.6\pi}{144} \sqrt{64x} = \frac{-\pi \sqrt{x}}{30}$$

and

$$2x^{\frac{1}{2}} = \frac{-\pi t}{120} + C$$

Since $x = 4$ when $t = 0$, we have $C = 4$, and we find that

$$x(t) = \left(2 - \frac{\pi t}{240} \right)^2$$

Therefore $x = 0$ when $t = 480/\pi$ seconds $= 8/\pi$ minutes.

Example 2.   Consider the preceding problem with the difference that the tank is closed with 4 feet of air at twice atmospheric pressure above the water. As the water level falls, the volume $v(t)$ of the air increases and its pressure $p(t)$ decreases according to the relation

(6.2) $vp = \text{constant}$

At time t there exists a pressure differential $\Delta p(t) = p(t) - p_0$ (p_0 is atmospheric pressure) between the upper level of the water and the orifice level; for this case the velocity of efflux is no longer given by formula (6.1), but by

(6.3) $v_e = \sqrt{2g \left(x + \frac{\Delta p}{\gamma} \right)}$

where γ is the specific weight of the liquid (γ/g is the density).

The volume of the air above the water at time t is $16 + 4(4 - x) = 32 - 4x$; hence by (6.2) the pressure is $p = 32p_0/(32 - 4x) = 8p_0/(8 - x)$.   The resulting pressure differential is

$$\Delta p = \frac{8p_0}{8 - x} - p_0 = \frac{x}{8 - x} p_0$$

and (6.3) gives

$$v_e = \sqrt{2g \left(x + \frac{x}{8 - x} \frac{p_0}{\gamma} \right)}$$

Clearly, p_0/γ is the height of a water column (in feet) supported by the standard atmosphere, which we take to be 34 feet.   Then

$$v_e = 8 \sqrt{\frac{42x - x^2}{8 - x}}$$

and, proceeding as in Example 1, we have

$$4 \frac{dx}{dt} = - \frac{\pi}{30} \sqrt{\frac{42x - x^2}{8 - x}}$$

or

$$\sqrt{\frac{8-x}{42x-x^2}}\, dx = -\frac{\pi}{120}\, dt$$

Since x varies from 4 to 0 in the time T in which the tank empties itself, we have

$$T = \frac{120}{\pi} \int_0^4 \sqrt{\frac{8-x}{42x-x^2}}\, dx$$

The integral is not elementary and is best evaluated by numerical methods.

7. Problems of Heat Flow

If one or more hot bodies are placed in a colder medium, the heat from the bodies is disseminated by conduction† to the surrounding medium. If the bodies are kept at constant temperature, a steady state will be reached after a long period of time. In general the temperature at any point of the medium will be a function of the coordinates of the point, and a description of the temperature variation will involve partial derivatives. In certain simple cases, however, the temperature will depend only on a single space coordinate x, and only ordinary derivatives will arise. It is then found that

(7.1) $$Q = -kA \frac{dT}{dx}$$

where Q is the quantity of heat flowing per unit time across a surface of area A perpendicular to the x direction, T is the temperature, and k is a constant of the medium, called the *thermal conductivity*. The minus sign signifies that the heat flows in the direction of decreasing temperature.

Since we are dealing with the steady-state condition, the heat flow across one surface must be the same as that across any other surface, so that the quantity Q in (7.1) is constant.

The constant k in (7.1) will of course depend on the units used. In the problems that follow we suppose T to be in degrees Fahrenheit, Q in British thermal units (Btu), x in feet, and t in seconds.

The coefficient of thermal conductivity k may depend on x if the medium is not homogeneous, and it may depend on T if the conduction properties of the medium change with temperature. The constant Q is not known to start with, and to compensate for this lack of data some information on T is necessary in addition to the usual initial condition. This may be supplied by specifying the temperature at the *two* end

† Heat is of course also transferred by radiation, but we neglect this, as it is small at low temperatures.

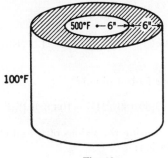

Fig. 12

faces of the body or by specifying a relation concerning the heat loss (or gain) through the end faces of the body. Such a relation is given by *Newton's law of cooling*, which says that the rate of heat loss to the surrounding medium at the face of the cooling body is proportional to the difference in temperatures; that is,

$$Q = cA(T_e - T_a)$$

where T_e is the temperature of the exposed face of area A, T_a the temperature of the surrounding medium, and c a coefficient of (interface) conductivity.

Example 1. A steam pipe (infinitely long) of diameter 1 foot has a cylindrical jacket 6 inches thick made of an insulating material ($k = 0.00033$). If the pipe is kept at 500°F, and the outside of the jacket at 100°F, find the temperature distribution in the jacket. What is the heat loss per day per foot of pipe?

Here T is a function only of the distance r from the center of the pipe, and the area A per unit length is $2\pi r$. Hence,

$$Q = \text{constant} = -2\pi rk\frac{dT}{dr}$$

and

$$Q\frac{dr}{r} = -2\pi k\,dT$$

The general solution of this D.E. is

(7.2) $$Q \log r = -2\pi kT + C$$

Since $T = 500$ at $r = \frac{1}{2}$, and $T = 100$ at $r = 1$, we have

$$Q \log \tfrac{1}{2} = -2\pi k(500) + C$$
$$Q \log 1 = -2\pi k(100) + C$$

which, when solved for Q and C, yield

$$C = 200\,\pi k \qquad Q = \frac{800\pi k}{\log 2} = 1.2 \text{ (Btu/sec)/ft}$$

The heat loss per day per foot of pipe is

$$Q(60)(60)(24) = 103{,}680 \text{ Btu}$$

Solving for T in (7.2) and using the values of Q and C gives the temperature distribution in the insulation:

$$T(r) = 100 - 400\,\frac{\log r}{\log 2}$$

8. Some Thermodynamic Relations

The ideas of line integrals, exact differentials, and integrating factors find important applications in thermodynamics. We consider here only the heat-work exchange in a *perfect gas*. The amount of heat Q that flows into the gas while it changes its pressure p and volume v from the values p_0, v_0 to p_1, v_1 is given by

$$(8.1) \qquad Q = \int_{(p_0,\,v_0)}^{(p_1,\,v_1)} (c_v\,dp + c_p p\,dv)$$

where c_v, c_p are constants (the specific heats of the gas at constant volume and constant pressure, respectively). The integral (8.1) is a *line integral* and can be evaluated only if a path (the graph of the physical transformation) is specified. Different paths will in general lead to different values for Q.

The factor $1/pv$ makes the integrand of (8.1) an exact differential, since

$$\frac{\partial}{\partial v}\left(\frac{c_v v}{pv}\right) = \frac{\partial}{\partial p}\left(\frac{c_p p}{pv}\right)$$

This integrating factor may be used to define absolute temperature T (or a constant multiple of it, depending on the temperature scale used):

$$(8.2) \qquad\qquad T = pv$$

The path-independent integral

$$(8.3) \qquad S = \int_{(p_0,\,v_0)}^{(p_1,\,v_1)} \frac{c_v v\,dp + c_p p\,dv}{T}$$

is called the *entropy* of the gas in the state $(p_1,\,v_1)$ [with respect to the state $(p_0,\,v_0)$]. For fixed $(p_0,\,v_0)$, S is only a function of p_1, v_1, which is easily calculated using (8.2):

$$(8.4) \quad S(p_1, v_1) = \int_{(p_0, v_0)}^{(p_1, v_1)} \left(c_v \frac{dp}{p} + c_p \frac{dv}{v} \right) = \log \left(\frac{p_1}{p_0} \right)^{vc} \left(\frac{v_1}{v_0} \right)^{c_p}$$

Example 1. Find the relation between p and v when a perfect gas undergoes a reversible adiabatic change (i.e., a process with no heat transfer).

An adiabatic process is described by the D.E.

$$(8.5) \qquad\qquad\qquad c_v v \, dp + c_p p \, dv = 0$$

If we set $\gamma = c_p/c_v$, then solution of (8.5) yields

$$pv^\gamma = \text{constant} = p_0 v_0^\gamma$$

PROBLEMS

1. Find the time required to empty a cylindrical tank 4 feet in diameter, containing 6 feet of water, through a 3-inch-diameter circular orifice in the bottom.

2. A conical reservoir is 8 feet across the top and 10 feet deep and contains 8 feet of water. There is a 2-inch-diameter hole in the apex. How long will it take to empty the reservoir?

3. Find the final water level for the tank of Prob. 1 if, in addition, water is being piped into the tank at the rate of 0.1 cubic foot per second.

★4. A tank with a square base 5 feet on a side has 4 feet of water in it when a seam in its side fails, forming a slit $\frac{1}{4}$ inch wide from top to bottom. Derive a formula giving the depth of water in terms of the time. (Assume that the coefficient of contraction is 0.8. The coefficient of contraction here is greater than that given previously because of the different character of the orifice.)

5. How long does it take to empty a full spherical tank of radius 2 feet through a 2-inch-diameter hole in the bottom? (Assume that there is a hole at the top so that no vacuum develops above the water; assume further that the entire orifice is at the bottom.)

6. In Prob. 2 assume that a constant pressure equal to $1\frac{1}{2}$ times atmospheric pressure (which is taken to be the equivalent of 34 feet of water) is mantained in the reservoir. How long will it then take to empty the reservoir?

7. A closed cylindrical tank 4 feet in diameter and 7 feet high is half full of water and otherwise contains air at $1\frac{1}{2}$ times the pressure of the atmosphere (which is taken to be the equivalent of 34 feet of water). The tank is emptied through a circular hole in the bottom 2 inches in diameter. No air is allowed to escape, but once outside and inside pressures are equalized, air streams into the tank to maintain equal pressures from then on. Set up an integral for the time it takes to empty the tank.

8. The side wall of an open reservoir is a surface of revolution; the bottom is flat. In a polar coordinate system with polar axis in the bottom of the reservoir and pole at the center of the bottom, the equation of the generating curve is $r = f(\theta)$. Establish a formula for the time it takes to empty the reservoir of liquid, which fills it to a height h, through a hole of area A in the bottom.

9. A hollow spherical shell of inner radius 1 foot and outer radius 2 feet has a source of heat inside it which keeps the interior at 400°F. If the conductivity k equals 0.0025, find the heat lost per hour when the exterior is kept at 100°F. Also find the temperature distribution as a function of the distance from the center of the shell.

10. A masonry wall is 2 feet thick $[k = 0.00075(2 + x)$, where x is the distance from the inner surface]. If the inner surface is at 72°F, and the outer surface at 32°F, find the heat loss per day per square foot of area.

11. A pipe 4 inches in diameter, containing a refrigerant at the constant temperature -30°F, is covered by a 3-inch jacket of insulating material of thermal conductivity 0.0002. If the temperature of the outside of the jacket is always 50°F, what are the temperature distribution in the insulating jacket and the heat gained by the refrigerant per day per foot of pipe?

12. A wall w feet thick ($k = 0.0005$) has its inner face at temperature T_1. The outer face is exposed to air at temperature T_2. The rate of heat loss to the air is proportional to the difference between the temperatures of the exposed face and the air. Find the heat lost per second per square foot in terms of T_1 and T_2. HINT: Rate of heat loss to air $= c(T_3 - T_2)$, where T_3 is the temperature of the outer face, and c is a constant of proportionality. Equate this loss to that through the wall.

13. The wall of a building has its inner face exposed to air of constant temperature T_i, and its outer face to air of constant temperature T_0. The thickness of the wall is w, its internal conductivity is variable, such that $k = k_0 + \alpha T$ (k_0, α constants), and the two interface conductivities are the same constant c. Find the rate of heat loss through the wall.

14. Evaluate the integrals (8.1) and (8.3) to find the heat input and entropy change of a perfect gas as its pressure and volume are changed from p_0, v_0 to p_1, v_1 by each of the following two-step processes:

(a) $p = $ constant, $v = $ constant.   (g) $p = $ constant, $S = $ constant.
(b) $v = $ constant, $p = $ constant.   (h) $S = $ constant, $p = $ constant.
(c) $p = $ constant, $T = $ constant.   (i) $v = $ constant, $S = $ constant.
(d) $T = $ constant, $p = $ constant.   (j) $S = $ constant, $v = $ constant.
(e) $v = $ constant, $T = $ constant.   (k) $T = $ constant, $S = $ constant.
(f) $T = $ constant, $v = $ constant.   (l) $S = $ constant, $T = $ constant.

15. To a perfect gas which initially has pressure p_0 and volume v_0, an increasing amount of heat Q is applied in a process in which the pressure increases according to the relation $p = p_0 + k \sqrt{Q}$. Find the volume v_1 when the pressur ise p_1.

16. $\mu = 1/pv$ is an integrating factor of the D.E. $c_v v \, dp + c_p p \, dv = 0$ whose general solution is $u = pv^\gamma = $ constant (see Example 1). By the remark of Prob. 11, Sec. 3, Chap. II, $\mu\varphi(u)$, for arbitrary φ, is also an integrating factor.

For $\varphi_1(u) = u$, one finds $\mu_1 = v^{\gamma-1}$, and for $\varphi_2(u) = u^{1/\gamma}$, one finds $\mu_2 = p^{1/\gamma-1}$. Verify directly that μ_1 and μ_2 are integrating factors. What are the functions S_1, S_2 corresponding to entropy S [Eq. (8.3)] that are obtained if the integrating factors μ_1, μ_2 are used in place of μ?

★**17.** Show that if $\mu(p, q)$ is *any* integrating factor of the equation $c_v v\, dp + c_p p\, dv = 0$, then $\mu(p, q)$ is a function of the entropy $S(p, q) = \log p^{c_v} v^{c_p}$ alone. HINT: Use the result of Prob. 9, Sec. 3, Chap. II.

18. By the first law of thermodynamics the differential $T\, dS - p\, dv$ must be exact: $T\, dS - p\, dv = dU$, where U is the internal energy of the system. Show that this is true for a perfect gas if and only if $c_p = 1 + c_v$ and find

$$U(p_1, v_1) = \int_{(p_0,\, v_0)}^{(p_1,\, v_1)} (T\, dS - p\, dv).$$

D. MOTIONS

9. Newton's Second Law

That force is proportional to mass times acceleration is Newton's second law of motion. Since force and acceleration are vector quantities, it is necessary to consider both direction and magnitude. However, if the motion is in a straight line, both force and acceleration are given by their components in the fixed direction. Newton's law then states that

$$\text{Force} = \text{constant} \times \text{mass} \times \text{acceleration}$$
$$F = kma$$

where the value of the constant of proportionality k depends on the units used to measure force, mass, distance, and time.

It is customary to choose a system of units such that the constant k has the value 1. There are three such systems in common use. These

Distance	Time	Mass	Force
Foot	Second	Slug	Pound
Foot	Second	Pound	Poundal
Centimeter	Second	Gram	Dyne

are given in the accompanying table. In the examples and problems below, the first of these systems of units (the foot-slug-second system) will be used exclusively. Note that at sea level a mass of 1 slug would weigh 32 pounds if we take the rough value of 32 feet per second per second for the acceleration of gravity.

In any of these systems of units, if a mass m moves in a straight line under the action of a force F, we have

$$\text{Force} = F = ma = \text{mass} \times \text{acceleration}$$

$$= m \frac{d^2s}{dt^2}$$

$$= m \frac{dv}{dt}$$

where s measures the distance of the particle from a fixed reference point, and $v = ds/dt$ is the velocity. Observe that the signs of s, v, and a are vital.

In many problems the force F is a known function of t, s, and possibly v: $F = F(t, s, v)$. Then Newton's law becomes a second-order differential equation

$$(9.1) \qquad m \frac{d^2s}{dt^2} = F\left(t, s, \frac{ds}{dt}\right)$$

for the unknown s as a function of t. However, in the following two cases (9.1) may be solved by means of *first*-order equations.

1. The force function F does not depend on the distance s. Then, with v written for ds/dt, (9.1) becomes

$$(9.2) \qquad m \frac{dv}{dt} = F(t, v)$$

and we have a first-order equation. Once v is found as a function of t, s is found by quadrature:

$$s = \int v(t)\, dt$$

Problems involving frictional forces, which often depend only on v, are handled this way.

2. The force function F does not depend on the time t (in this case the mechanical system is called *autonomous*). Then we write v for ds/dt and seek to determine velocity as a function of s,† $v(s)$. The acceleration is written as

$$(9.3) \qquad \frac{dv}{dt} = \frac{dv}{ds}\frac{ds}{dt} = v \frac{dv}{ds}$$

† Here the same symbol v is used for the physical quantity velocity, regardless of whether velocity is considered as a function of time or of distance. Thus, $v(t)$ and $v(s)$ signify different functions even though this use of the symbol v is objectionable from a mathematical point of view. However, this is the generally accepted practice in the physical sciences, and we are following this custom for the remaining part of this chapter. Since $v(1)$ is ambiguous, as it may mean the velocity at $t = 1$ or the velocity at $s = 1$, we write "$v(t)$ when $t = 1$" for the former, and "$v(s)$ when $s = 1$" for the latter.

and yields the first-order equation

$$(9.4) \qquad\qquad mv\frac{dv}{ds} = F(s, v)$$

After the solution $v(s)$ is determined, the equation of motion is found by integrating $1/v = dt/ds$:

$$(9.5) \qquad\qquad t = \int \frac{1}{v(s)}\, ds$$

The relation $v = v(s)$ is often used to represent the motion. When graphed in the sv plane, which is called the *phase plane*, the curve is called the *phase curve* of the motion.

Example 1. Consider a body of mass m falling with velocity v under the action of gravity and a frictional force proportional to v^α. Find v as a function of the time. From Newton's law

$$m\frac{dv}{dt} = mg - kv^\alpha$$

where k is a positive constant. Then

$$\frac{dv}{g - (k/m)v^\alpha} = dt$$

and the variables are separated. For "slow" motions α may often be taken equal to 1, rendering the integration easy. We get, in this case,

$$-\frac{m}{k}\log\left(g - \frac{k}{m}v\right) = t + \text{constant}$$

$$g - \frac{k}{m}v = Ae^{-kt/m}$$

and

$$v(t) = \frac{mg}{k} - Be^{-kt/m}$$

If $v = 0$ when $t = 0$, we find easily that $B = mg/k$, whence

$$v(t) = \frac{mg}{k}\left(1 - e^{-kt/m}\right)$$

As $t \to \infty$, v approaches the *terminal velocity* mg/k. For the distance s as a function of time, one finds by integration

$$s(t) = \frac{mg}{k}\left(t + \frac{m}{k}e^{-kt/m}\right) + \text{constant}$$

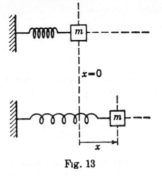

Fig. 13

As $t \to \infty$, uniform linear motion is asymptotically approached. The analysis here for the case $\alpha = 1$ represents rather well the situation for small droplets of water or oil falling in air.

Example 2. Consider a horizontal weightless spring (Fig. 13) with one end fixed while the other is attached to a mass of m slugs. The spring force is proportional to the displacement (*Hooke's law*). If the mass is moving with velocity v_0 when the spring is unstretched, find v as a function of the stretch.

Choose coordinates such that the mass is at $x = 0$ when the spring is unstretched. Then the spring force is $-kx$, where k is the "spring constant." The minus sign occurs because the force always acts toward $x = 0$. Then

$$-kx = m\,\frac{dv}{dt} = m\,\frac{dv}{dx}\frac{dx}{dt} = mv\,\frac{dv}{dx}$$

The variables are separable. The solution is

$$mv^2 = -kx^2 + c$$

Since $v = v_0$ when $x = 0$, we find that $mv_0{}^2 = c$, and hence

$$mv^2 + kx^2 = mv_0{}^2$$

Observe that this equation asserts that the kinetic energy of the mass plus the potential energy stored in the spring is constant.

The phase curves in this case are similar ellipses (see Fig. 14) with common center at the origin and principal axes along the x and v axes. It follows that all motions of the system (no matter what the initial conditions) are of the same kind, differing only by scale factors.

To find the stretch x as a function of the time t, we write the equation corresponding to (9.5):

$$t = \int \frac{dx}{\sqrt{v_0{}^2 - (k/m)x^2}}$$

$$= \sqrt{\frac{m}{k}}\,\arcsin\sqrt{\frac{k}{m}}\,\frac{x}{v_0} + c$$

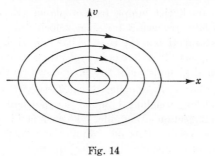

Fig. 14

If $x = 0$ when $t = t_0$, we find $c = t_0$; hence

$$(9.6) \qquad x(t) = v_0 \sqrt{\frac{m}{k}} \sin \sqrt{\frac{k}{m}} (t - t_0)$$

This is a simple harmonic motion with amplitude $v_0 \sqrt{m/k}$ and period $2\pi \sqrt{m/k}$.

PROBLEMS

1. A boy and his sled weigh 64 pounds ($g = 32$ feet per second per second). They are being pulled on level ground by the boy's father at a constant speed of 8 feet per second. At a command from his son the father exerts a constant force of 20 pounds on the towrope. If the resistance of the sled in pounds is equal to the speed in feet per second, find the speed after 5 seconds and the terminal speed.

2. At what angle must a hill be sloped so the boy and his sled of Prob. 1 will slide downhill at a terminal speed of 8 feet per second? Determine the speed down such a hill if the sled starts from rest.

3. The spring of Example 2 now hangs vertically. Find the velocity of the mass if $v = v_0$ when $x = 0$.

4. A hole is drilled through the earth (assumed to be a sphere of radius 4,000 miles) from the north to the south pole. Using the fact that, inside the earth, the gravitational attraction is proportional to the distance from the center of the earth, with what velocity will a mass dropped from the north pole reach the center of the earth?

5. The earth exerts a gravitational pull on a mass m a distance r from its center which is proportional to m and inversely proportional to r^2; that is, force $= km/r^2$. This force is mg ($g = 32$) when $r = 4,000$ miles. With what velocity must a projectile be fired vertically to escape the gravitational pull? (Centrifugal effects are neglected, as well as friction.)

6. A mass of 2 slugs slides on a table and is subjected to the periodic force $10 \sin 2t$. The friction is equal to twice the velocity. If the motion starts from rest, find v as a function of t.

7. An air-force parachutist jumps from a plane. Before pulling the rip cord he has essentially reached a terminal velocity of 180 feet per second. Find his velocity as a function of the time he has fallen if his wind resistance is proportional to his velocity. What is his velocity 5 seconds after he jumps?

8. The drag of an airplane is equal to kv^2. Show that the terminal velocity in level flight, under constant propeller thrust T, is $\sqrt{T/k}$.

9. A chain 50 feet long weighing 1 pound per foot hangs over a small frictionless pulley with 25 feet on either side. To each end is attached a 5-pound weight. One of the weights falls off. Find the velocity of the remaining weight as a function of its distance from the pulley.

10. A chain 50 feet long is on a smooth table with 5 feet hanging over the edge. The chain weighs 1 pound per foot and is initially at rest. Find the velocity of the end of the chain as a function of the length hanging over the edge.

11. Show that if a mass particle slides down a curved frictionless wire through a vertical distance h, the speed of the particle is $\sqrt{2gh}$.

12. Assume that the mass in Example 2 is 1 slug, the spring constant is 13 slugs per second per second, and a frictional force equal to six times the velocity in feet per second is present. Establish the phase curves, and deduce from them a qualitative description of the motion. (The only singular point $x = 0$, $v = 0$ in this example is a *focus.*)

13. A weightless spring of unstretched length l and spring constant k is suspended in a vertical position (upper end fastened) and holds a mass m. The mass holds an identical spring whose lower end is fastened. (a) Determine the phase curve of the motion that results when the mass is displaced horizontally a distance x_0 and released. (b) Set up an integral for the period of the motion.

14. In a horizontal table there is a straight groove along which a bead of mass m can slide freely (without friction). Attached to the bead is a thread which runs through a hole in the table at a distance a from the groove and carries a weight w at its other end. (a) Determine the phase curve of the motion of the bead if it is released at a distance x_0 from its equilibrium position. (b) Set up an integral for the period of the motion.

10. The Pendulum

Consider a common pendulum consisting of a mass m attached to one end of a weightless rod of length l which can rotate freely in a vertical plane. This is a case of circular motion, and its differential equation is obtained by equating the product of the mass and the tangential component of the acceleration to the tangential component of the gravitational force. The latter is (see Fig. 15) $-mg \sin \varphi$ and the D.E. of the motion is

$$ml\frac{d^2\varphi}{dt^2} = -mg \sin \varphi$$

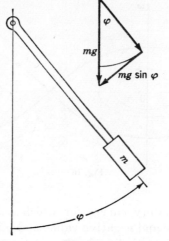

Fig. 15

or

(10.1)
$$\frac{d^2\varphi}{dt^2} = -\frac{g}{l}\sin\varphi$$

To discuss the motion in the phase plane, we put $d\varphi/dt = \omega$ and determine ω as a function of φ. Then (10.1) becomes

(10.2)
$$\omega\frac{d\omega}{d\varphi} = -\frac{g}{l}\sin\varphi$$

and integration gives

$$\omega^2 = \frac{2g}{l}\cos\varphi + c$$

If $\omega = \omega_0$ when $\varphi = 0$, then $c = \omega_0^2 - 2g/l$; hence

$$\omega^2 - \omega_0^2 = \frac{2g}{l}(\cos\varphi - 1)$$

or

(10.3) $\omega^2 + \omega_c^2\sin^2\dfrac{\varphi}{2} = \omega_0^2$ where $\omega_c = 2\sqrt{\dfrac{g}{l}}$

Several of the phase curves, for various values of ω_0, are shown in Fig. 16. It is seen that there are three different kinds of curves, corresponding to three different kinds of motion, which will now be discussed.

1. The closed oval curves for which $|\omega_0| < \omega_c$. On them, $|\varphi| \le \varphi_{max}$, where $\varphi_{max} = 2\arcsin|\omega_0/\omega_c| < \pi$, and ω becomes zero when $\varphi = \pm\varphi_{max}$; hence the pendulum swings periodically between the limits $\pm\varphi_{max}$.

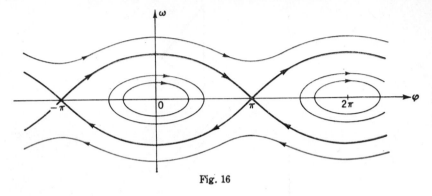

Fig. 16

2. The open undulatory curves for which $|\omega_0| > \omega_c$. On them φ reaches every positive and negative value, and ω is never zero; i.e., the pendulum executes a periodic circular motion, never changing its direction.

3. The two limit curves (both undulatory and halves of ovals) for which $\omega_0 = \pm\omega_c$ (i.e., the initial velocity has the "critical" value ω_c). They correspond to the case in which the pendulum moves toward its highest point $\varphi = \pm\pi$ in infinite time.

A qualitatively correct picture of the phase curves can be obtained, without the use of (10.3), directly from the D.E. (10.1) if its singular points (see Sec. 4, Chap. II) are analyzed. If Eq. (10.1) is written in the form

$$(10.4) \qquad \frac{d\omega}{d\varphi} = -\frac{g}{l}\frac{\sin\varphi}{\omega}$$

it is seen that the points $(0, 0)$, $(\pm\pi, 0)$, $(\pm 2\pi, 0)$, . . . of the plane are singular points. Since a shift in the φ direction by 2π leaves the direction field unchanged, we need consider only the two points $(0, 0)$ and $(\pi, 0)$. In the neighborhood of $(0, 0)$ we replace $\sin\varphi$ with φ, so that (10.4) becomes $d\omega/d\varphi = -g\varphi/l\omega$, with the solution

$$(10.5) \qquad \omega^2 + \frac{g}{l}\varphi^2 = c$$

For small values of c these curves (concentric ellipses) lie entirely in a small neighborhood of the singular point $(0, 0)$ and approximate the correct integral curves closely (see Fig. 16a). No integral curve passes through the singular point itself. Such a singular point is called a *vortex* (or *center*).

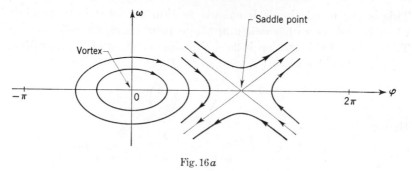

Fig. 16 a

In the neighborhood of the singular point $(\pi, 0)$ we replace $\sin \varphi$ with $\pi - \varphi$, so that (10.4) becomes $d\omega/d\varphi = -g(\pi - \varphi)/l\omega$, with the solution

$$(10.6) \qquad \omega^2 - \frac{g}{l}(\pi - \varphi)^2 = c$$

For $c = 0$ this is the pair of straight lines $\omega = \pm \sqrt{g/l}\,(\pi - \varphi)$ passing through the singular point $(\pi, 0)$ with slopes $\pm \sqrt{g/l}$; for other values of c these are concentric hyperbolas with the above lines as asymptotes (see Fig. 16a). The parts of these lines and curves that lie in a small neighborhood of $(\pi, 0)$ are good approximations to the correct integral curves. Thus, there are exactly two integral curves, of slopes $\pm \sqrt{g/l}$, passing through $(\pi, 0)$. Such a singular point is called a *saddle point*.

The points of the $\varphi\omega$ plane different from $(0, 0)$, $(\pm\pi, 0)$, $(\pm 2\pi, 0)$, . . . are regular (not singular) points, and exactly one integral curve passes through each of them by the existence and uniqueness theorem (see Sec. 3, Chap. III). We now have a complete qualitative picture of the phase curves, totally in agreement with Fig. 16.

We turn now to the motion as a function of time. For motions of the pendulum close to $\varphi = 0$, $\omega = 0$, D.E. (10.1) is usually "linearized," i.e., the nonlinear function $\sin \varphi$ is replaced with its linear approximation φ. Thus the equation becomes

$$\ddot{\varphi} = -\frac{g}{l}\varphi$$

and is of the same form as that for the linear spring of Example 2, Sec. 9. Using the results derived there, one obtains

$$\varphi(t) = \omega_0 \sqrt{\frac{l}{g}} \sin \sqrt{\frac{g}{l}}\,(t - t_0)$$

This is the usual simple harmonic motion executed by a pendulum when it swings with small amplitude near its equilibrium position. The period of this motion is $2\pi \sqrt{l/g}$ (independent of the amplitude).

In the nonlinear case we have from (10.3)

$$\omega = \frac{d\varphi}{dt} = \omega_0 \sqrt{1 - \left(\frac{\omega_c}{\omega_0}\right)^2 \sin^2 \frac{\varphi}{2}}$$

Hence

$$t - t_0 = \frac{1}{\omega_0} \int_{\varphi_0}^{\varphi} \frac{1}{\sqrt{1 - (\omega_c/\omega_0)^2 \sin^2 u/2}} \, du$$

This is an elliptic integral (if $\omega_0 \neq \omega_c$), and the inverse function is an elliptic function (see Ref. 3).

The pendulum, as well as the mass-spring system of the last section, illustrates the important class of *conservative systems* in which the force is independent of time and velocity: $F = F(s)$. In this case (9.4) integrates at once:

(10.7) $\frac{1}{2}mv^2 + V(s) = \text{constant}$ $V(s) = -\int F(s) \, ds$

This equation has a simple physical interpretation:

Kinetic energy + potential energy = constant = total energy

Observe that $V(s) = -\int F(s) \, ds$ is the work done by the system against the force F and hence is its potential energy. Thus, (10.7) expresses the law of conservation of energy.

PROBLEMS

1. For the pendulum of this section, assume $g/l = 4 \sec^{-2}$ and $\varphi_0 = \pi/2$. Find the period of the resulting motion, and compare it with that obtained from the linearized equation.

2. For the pendulum assume that the initial velocity is the critical one ($\omega_0 = \omega_c$). Obtain the equation of motion.

3. A mass m at a distance x from O is attracted to the point O by the force $F(x) = -ax^{-2} + bx^{-3}$, where a, b are positive constants. (a) Determine the phase curve of the motion if m is initially at rest at $x_0 > b/2a$. (b) Show that if $x_0 \neq b/a$ then the motion is periodic, and find its period. (c) What happens if $x_0 = b/a$? Why is the assumption $x_0 > b/2a$ made?

★4. Show that if $V(a) = V(b) = h$ and $V(s) < h$ for $a < s < b$, then the phase curve $\frac{1}{2}mv^2 + V(s) = h$ of a conservative mechanical system represents a periodic motion [that is, $s(t + T) = s(t)$] and the period of this motion is given by

$$T = \sqrt{2m} \int_a^b \frac{ds}{\sqrt{h - V(s)}}$$

*5. Assume that in Example 2, Sec. 9, there is added to the spring force a frictional force which equals q (a positive constant) if $v > 0$, and $-q$ if $v < 0$ (such a force is called *dry* or *Coulomb friction*). (a) Show that the phase curves are composed of semielliptical arcs joined at the x axis. (b) Show that if $(2n - 1)q/k < x_0 \leq (2n + 1)q/k$, then the mass comes to rest at the point $x_0 - 2nq/k$ after n swings.

11. Planetary and Satellite Motion

We study the motion of a planet in the gravitational field of the sun, which is assumed to be stationary (also the motion of a satellite around the earth and that of a charged particle in a Coulomb field of force).

In this case the force is directed toward a fixed point and is inversely proportional to the square of the distance from this point. We use polar coordinates r, θ with pole at the center of force and polar axis directed to the closest point on the orbit (the *perihelion*). In these coordinates Newton's equations are

(11.1)
$$m\left[\frac{d^2r}{dt^2} - r\left(\frac{d\theta}{dt}\right)^2\right] = F_r$$
$$m\left[r\frac{d^2\theta}{dt^2} + 2\frac{dr}{dt}\frac{d\theta}{dt}\right] = F_\theta$$

where F_r, F_θ are the radial and tangential components, respectively, of the total acting force. In our case $F_r = -mk/r^2$ (k a positive constant; in the case of satellite motion, $k = gR^2$, where R is the radius of the earth) and $F_\theta = 0$. Hence,

(11.2)
$$\frac{d^2r}{dt^2} - r\left(\frac{d\theta}{dt}\right)^2 = -\frac{k}{r^2}$$
$$r\frac{d^2\theta}{dt^2} + 2\frac{dr}{dt}\frac{d\theta}{dt} = 0$$

If the second of these equations is multiplied by r, it can be written as

$$\frac{d}{dt}\left(r^2\frac{d\theta}{dt}\right) = 0$$

Therefore, $\dot\theta = d\theta/dt$ satisfies the equation

(11.3)
$$r^2\dot\theta = \text{constant} = r_0^2\dot\theta_0$$

if $\dot\theta = \dot\theta_0$ when $r = r_0$. Equation (11.3) expresses the conservation of the angular momentum $r^2\dot\theta$ during the motion ("Equal areas are swept out in equal times"). Observe that this statement is Kepler's second law (J. Kepler, 1571–1630), and its validity depends only on the presence of a central force field.

If (11.3) is substituted in the first of (11.2), one obtains a single equation of motion:

$$(11.4) \qquad \frac{d^2r}{dt^2} = -\frac{k}{r^2} + \frac{r_0^4\dot{\theta}_0^2}{r^3}$$

To solve (11.4) we shall resort to a trick substitution which saves much labor. We put $r = 1/\rho$ and seek ρ as a function of θ. Then

$$\frac{dr}{dt} = -\frac{1}{\rho^2}\frac{d\rho}{dt} = -\frac{1}{\rho^2}\frac{d\rho}{d\theta}\frac{d\theta}{dt} = -r^2\dot{\theta}\frac{d\rho}{d\theta} = -r_0^2\dot{\theta}_0\frac{d\rho}{d\theta}$$

Then, using (11.4),

$$\frac{d^2r}{dt^2} = -r_0^2\dot{\theta}_0\frac{d^2\rho}{d\theta^2}\,\dot{\theta} = -k\rho^2 + r_0^4\dot{\theta}_0^2\rho^3$$

which again, by (11.3), reduces to

$$(11.5) \qquad \frac{d^2\rho}{d\theta^2} + \rho = \frac{k}{r_0^2v_0^2}$$

if we put $v_0 = r_0\dot{\theta}_0$.

Equation (11.5) is a second-order equation which may be solved by setting $\rho' = d\rho/d\theta$ and $d^2\rho/d\theta^2 = \rho'\,d\rho'/d\rho$. However, it is most easily solved by the methods of Chap. V (it is a linear equation with constant coefficients), and the reader is advised to verify that its solution is

$$\rho(\theta) = \frac{k}{r_0^2v_0^2} + A\cos(\theta - \alpha)$$

where A and α are constants. The constants are evaluated from the initial conditions. Let r_0 be the minimum value of r; then $r = r_0$ and $\dot{r} = 0$ (thus $\dot{\rho} = 0$ and $d\rho/d\theta = 0$) when $\theta = 0$. At $\theta = 0$ the velocity vector is tangential; hence $v_0 = r_0\dot{\theta}_0$ represents the speed. One gets $\alpha = 0$ and $A = (r_0v_0^2 - k)/r_0^2v_0^2$. Therefore,

$$r(\theta) = \left(\frac{k}{r_0^2v_0^2} + \frac{r_0v_0^2 - k}{r_0^2v_0^2}\cos\theta\right)^{-1} = \frac{r_0^2v_0^2/k}{1 + (r_0v_0^2/k - 1)\cos\theta}$$

$$(11.6) \qquad r(\theta) = \frac{p}{1 + e\cos\theta} \qquad p = \frac{r_0^2v_0^2}{k} \qquad e = \frac{r_0v_0^2}{k} - 1$$

Equation (11.6) is the equation of the orbit in polar coordinates and represents a conic section with eccentricity e: an ellipse if $e < 1$, a parabola if $e = 1$, and a hyperbola if $e > 1$ (see Fig. 17). The initial speed v_0 which gives the parabolic orbit [i.e., separates capture (elliptic) from escape (hyperbolic)] is denoted by v_c. Hence

$$(11.7) \qquad \frac{r_0v_c^2}{k} - 1 = 1 \qquad \text{or} \qquad v_c^2 = \frac{2k}{r_0}$$

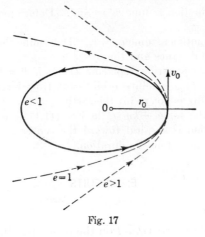

Fig. 17

The easiest way of finding the time dependence of r and θ is to utilize (11.3) and remember that the area swept out by the radius vector in time t is

$$(11.8) \qquad \tfrac{1}{2}\int_0^\theta r^2\, d\theta = \tfrac{1}{2}\int_0^t r^2\dot\theta\, dt = (\tfrac{1}{2}r_0^2\dot\theta_0)t$$

The first integral in (11.8) is easily calculated using (11.6). For the special case of an elliptic orbit in which a and b are the semiaxes of the ellipse and T is the period, we get

$$\pi ab = \tfrac{1}{2}r_0^2\dot\theta_0 T$$

If one uses $b = a\sqrt{1-e^2}$ and (11.6), one obtains *Kepler's third law,*

$$T = \frac{2\pi}{\sqrt{k}}\, a^{\frac{3}{2}}$$

which is usually stated as, "The square of the period is proportional to the cube of the major axis."

PROBLEMS

1. A satellite is one-fifteenth the earth radius R away from the earth at its point of closest approach to the earth (at the *perigee*).   (a) What speed must it have at this point if it is to escape the earth's gravitational field?   (b) What is its maximal distance from the earth if its perigee speed is three-fourths its escape speed?

2. With v_0 and v_c defined as in (11.5) and (11.7), show that necessarily $v_0^2 \geq \tfrac{1}{2}v_c^2$.

3. For a satellite motion assume $v_0^2 = \frac{1}{2}v_c^2$. Determine the motion and its period.

4. For a satellite motion assume $v_0 = v_c$. Determine the orbit equation and the relation between distance and time.

5. (a) What is the equation replacing (11.6) if $\theta = 0$ at the maximum distance r_1 (*apogee*) of a satellite orbit? (b) How large must the apogee speed be if the satellite is not to hit the earth?

6. Assume that the force $-km/r^2$ in Eq. (11.1) is replaced by $-km/r^3$. Show that the motion is a spiral toward the center of attraction which is traversed in finite time. Find its duration.

E. CIRCUITS

12. Simple Circuits

Let $q(t)$ be the charge at time t on the condenser in a circuit (see Fig. 18) containing a resistance R, inductance L, and capacitance C in series. A known e.m.f. (electromotive force) $E(t)$ is impressed across the circuit. The magnitudes q, E, L, R, C are in some physically consistent set of units which we shall take as coulombs, volts, henrys, ohms, and farads, respectively. From elementary physics we have the fundamental relation

$$(12.1) \qquad E(t) = L\frac{d^2q}{dt^2} + R\frac{dq}{dt} + \frac{1}{C}q$$

which asserts that the e.m.f. is equal to the sum of the voltage drops across the components. Differentiating this equation yields, if we put dq/dt equal to the current i in amperes,

$$(12.2) \qquad \frac{dE}{dt} = L\frac{d^2i}{dt^2} + R\frac{di}{dt} + \frac{1}{C}i$$

Equations (12.1) and (12.2) are both linear second-order equations. However, in special cases either (12.1) or (12.2) will be a first-order equation in either q or i. For example, if $L = 0$, D.E. (12.2) reduces

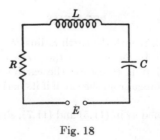

Fig. 18

to the equation

(12.3)
$$\frac{dE}{dt} = R\frac{di}{dt} + \frac{1}{C}i$$

and if no condenser is present in the circuit, $C = \infty$, and (12.1) reduces to

(12.4)
$$L\frac{di}{dt} + Ri = E$$

Both (12.3) and (12.4) are first-order linear equations and therefore solvable by our methods.

Example 1. Find the current in the simple circuit of Fig. 18 with $C = \infty$ (condenser absent) and $Et = E_0 \sin \omega t$.

From (12.4) we have the linear equation

$$\frac{di}{dt} + \frac{Ri}{L} = \frac{E_0}{L}\sin \omega t$$

Using the methods of Chap. II, we find that

$$i(t) = E_0\frac{R\sin \omega t - \omega L\cos \omega t}{R^2 + \omega^2 L^2} + ke^{-Rt/L}$$

If $i = i_0$ when $t = 0$, we have

$$i_0 = -\frac{E_0\omega L}{R^2 + \omega^2 L^2} + k$$

and

(12.5) $$i(t) = E_0\frac{R\sin \omega t - \omega L\cos \omega t}{R^2 + \omega^2 L^2} + \left(i_0 + \frac{E_0\omega L}{R^2 + \omega^2 L^2}\right)e^{-Rt/L}$$

Equation (12.5) can be put in a more useful form as follows: Let φ be that acute angle for which

$$\tan \varphi = \frac{\omega L}{R}$$

Then

$$\cos \varphi = \frac{R}{\sqrt{R^2 + \omega^2 L^2}} \qquad \sin \varphi = \frac{\omega L}{\sqrt{R^2 + \omega^2 L^2}}$$

and (12.5) may be written in the form

(12.6) $$i(t) = \frac{E_0}{\sqrt{R^2 + \omega^2 L^2}}\sin(\omega t - \varphi) + \left(i_0 + \frac{E_0\omega L}{R^2 + \omega^2 L^2}\right)e^{-Rt/L}$$

We see that the current is a sum of two terms:

(12.7)
$$i_S(t) = \frac{E_0}{\sqrt{R^2 + \omega^2 L^2}} \sin (\omega t - \varphi)$$

$$i_T(t) = \left(i_0 + \frac{E_0 \omega L}{R^2 + \omega^2 L^2} \right) e^{-Rt/L}$$

It is clear that after a sufficiently long span of time the second term is very small and negligible in comparison with the first term. One calls i_S the *steady-state* and i_T the *transient* current. If

$$i_0 = -\frac{E_0 \omega L}{R^2 + \omega^2 L^2} = \frac{E_0}{\sqrt{R^2 + \omega^2 L^2}} \sin (-\varphi) = i_S(0)$$

then there is no transient current. Thus the transient is due to the fact that the initial value i_0 that we have assumed for the total current does not agree with its steady-state value. One sees from (12.7) that there is no transient current if $L = 0$, which corresponds to the idealized condition in which the circuit is inertialess and can jump from the arbitrary initial value i_0 to its steady-state value $i_S(0)$. This reflects the fact that if $L = 0$ then (12.4) is not a differential equation and assigning an initial value to $i(t)$ is meaningless.

The steady-state current is a pure harmonic oscillation of the same *circular frequency* ω (number of oscillations per 2π seconds) as the e.m.f. Its amplitude is $E_0 / \sqrt{R^2 + \omega^2 L^2}$, whereas it would be E_0/R if no inductance were present. Thus the inductance L adds an effective resistance to the (Ohm) resistance R, and this resistance depends on the frequency ω. The total resistance $\sqrt{R^2 + \omega^2 L^2}$ is called the *impedance*. The steady-state current and voltage are out of phase by the "phase angle" φ. The e.m.f. has its maximum amplitude at time $t = \pi/2\omega, 3\pi/2\omega, 5\pi/2\omega, \ldots$, whereas the current has maxima at $\omega t - \varphi = \pi/2, 3\pi/2, 5\pi/2, \ldots$, that is, when $t = (\pi/2 + \varphi)/\omega, (3\pi/2 + \varphi)/\omega, \ldots$. In other words the current *lags* behind the voltage by a time φ/ω.

The current in a simple circuit with $L = 0$, capacitance C, and e.m.f. $E(t) = E_0 \sin \omega t$ may be found similarly from D.E. (12.3). The results are much the same qualitatively, except that the current is now found to *lead* the voltage. We omit the details.

While the simplest and most important e.m.f. is a simple sine wave, in many circuit problems it is necessary to consider more general e.m.f.'s and even discontinuous ones. One of the latter type, for example, could be generated by connecting a battery in the circuit and opening or closing the switch. If the battery has a constant e.m.f. of E_0 and the switch is closed at time $t = t_0$ after the initial time $t = 0$, then the graph of E appears as in Fig. 19.

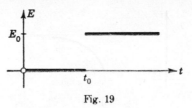

Fig. 19

Example 2. No current flows in a simple circuit without condenser. At time $t = t_0 > 0$, a switch supplying a constant e.m.f. of E_0 is closed. Find the current $i(t)$.

Equation (12.4) applies to the times when $E(t)$ is continuous, that is, away from $t = t_0$. Because $E(t)$ has a jump discontinuity at $t = t_0$, our earlier discussion does not explicitly cover this case. The function $E(t)$ considered here is a simple example of a type of function occurring often in electric circuits, namely, a *piecewise-continuous* function.†

Although $E(t)$ is but piecewise continuous, there is a *continuous* function $i(t)$ such that $i(t)$ has a continuous derivative wherever $E(t)$ is continuous and which satisfies (12.4) at those points. Observe that in this statement nothing is said about the derivative of $i(t)$ at points of discontinuity of $E(t)$, and in fact the derivative cannot exist at such points.

Our procedure is exactly the same as when $E(t)$ is continuous. We have the differential equation

$$\frac{di}{dt} + \frac{R}{L}\,i = \frac{1}{L}\,E$$

and the integrating factor $e^{Rt/L}$. Note that di/dt has discontinuities at the same points as $E(t)$. Then

$$e^{Rt/L}\left(\frac{di}{dt} + \frac{R}{L}\,i\right) = \frac{d}{dt}\,(ie^{Rt/L}) = \frac{1}{L}\,Ee^{Rt/L}$$

Integrating between the limits 0 and t, we obtain

$$\int_0^t \frac{d}{du}\,[i(u)e^{Ru/L}]\,du = i(t)e^{Rt/L} - i(0) = \frac{1}{L}\int_0^t E(u)e^{Ru/L}\,du$$

Since $i(0) = 0$, we have

(12.8)
$$i(t) = \frac{e^{-Rt/L}}{L}\int_0^t E(u)e^{Ru/L}\,du$$

In the integrand of (12.8), $E(u)$ is identically zero for $t < t_0$; for $t > t_0$, $E(t) = E_0$. Hence

$$i(t) = e^{-Rt/L}\,\frac{E_0}{L}\int_{t_0}^t e^{Ru/L}\,du = e^{-Rt/L}\,\frac{E_0}{R}\,(e^{Rt/L} - e^{Rt_0/L}) \qquad t \geq t_0$$

† See Sec. 14, Chap. VI, for a discussion of piecewise continuity.

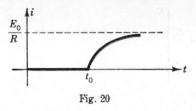

Fig. 20

or

$$(12.9) \qquad i(t) = \begin{cases} 0 & \text{for } t < t_0 \\ \dfrac{E_0}{R}\,(1 - e^{-R(t-t_0)/L}) & \text{for } t \geqq t_0 \end{cases}$$

The graph of (12.9) is drawn in Fig. 20. Observe that for large t, $i(t)$ is practically a constant: E_0/R. That is, E_0/R is the steady-state current, and $(-E_0/R)e^{-R(t-t_0)/L}$ is the transient. It should also be noted that i is continuous at $t = t_0$, but di/dt does not exist at $t = t_0$.

If more complicated piecewise-continuous e.m.f.'s are used, the procedure remains exactly the same in principle. A more complete discussion will be found in Chap. VI.

PROBLEMS

1. Find the current in a simple series circuit with no inductance ($L = 0$), a resistance R, and a capacitance C if the e.m.f. is $E(t) = E_0 \sin \omega t$, and $i = 0$ when $t = 0$. Show that the current leads the voltage.

2. In a simple series circuit without condenser, the inductance is 0.2 henry, the resistance is 10 ohms, and $E(t)$ is the 60-cycle sine wave of amplitude 160 volts; that is, $E(t) = 160 \sin 120\pi t$. Find $i(t)$ if $i = 0$ when $t = 0$. How long does it take for the transient to be reduced to one-millionth of the peak steady-state current?

3. A simple series circuit contains no inductance, a resistance R, and a capacitance C. A constant e.m.f. E_0 is applied at time $t = t_0$ when the charge q is zero. Find q as a function of t.

4. A series circuit contains a capacitance C and a resistance R, no inductance, and no e.m.f. The switch is closed at $t = 0$, when the charge q on the condenser is q_0. Find $q(t)$.

5. Show that in a simple series circuit with inductance L, no resistance, no condenser, and e.m.f. $E(t) = E_0 \sin \omega t$, the steady-state current lags the voltage by a phase angle of 90°.

6. Show that in a simple series circuit with zero inductance and resistance, capacitance C, and e.m.f. $E(t) = E_0 \sin \omega t$, the steady-state current leads the voltage by a phase angle of 90°.

7. A simple series circuit has inductance L, resistance R, and unlimited capacitance. It is connected to a battery of constant e.m.f. E, and the current has attained its steady-state value E/R when the battery is disconnected. Determine the decay of the current.

8. A simple series circuit has no inductance, resistance R_0, and a condenser of variable capacitance $C(t) = C_0 \sec^2 \omega t$. At time $t = 0$, when there is no charge on the condenser, a variable e.m.f. $E(t) = E_0 \cos^2 \omega t$ is switched on. Find the charge q as a function of time, and show that, in spite of the alternating e.m.f., it remains constant after a sufficiently long time.

9. A series battery circuit contains an inductance L, a resistance R, and a capacitance C for which the relation $4L = R^2C$ holds. The battery goes dead at an instant when the charge is $q_0 > 0$ and the current is $i_0 > 0$. Find the subsequent peak charge.

13. Nonlinear Circuits

The method of phase curves used for mechanical problems is useful here and permits us to deal with electrical systems described by second-order differential equations, as long as they are autonomous. Corresponding to distance and velocity, which are the phase variables in mechanical problems, we have here charge and current. Thus if E is constant in (12.1) (otherwise the system would not be autonomous), then, writing i for dq/dt, (12.1) becomes

$$(13.1) \qquad L\frac{di}{dt} + Ri + \frac{1}{C}q = E$$

and since we seek i as a function of q, we have $di/dt = i\, di/dq$; hence

$$Li\frac{di}{dq} + Ri + \frac{1}{C}q = E$$

or

$$L\frac{di}{dq} + \frac{Ri + (1/C)q - E}{i} = 0$$

This equation is of a type treated in Sec. 4, Chap. II, and can be solved by a simple substitution. Once i is determined as a function of q, say $i = f(q)$, it is easy to obtain i as a function of t as well. Since $dq/dt = i$, one has, if $q(t_0) = q_0$,

$$(13.2) \qquad t - t_0 = \int_{q_0}^{q} \frac{1}{f(u)}\, du$$

By inverting this equation, one finds q as a function of t; differentiation of this function gives i as a function of t.

The phase-plane method is much less practical for simple systems such as those described by (13.1) than the very elementary methods to be developed in the next chapter. However, for autonomous electrical systems involving *nonlinear elements*, the phase-plane method is indispensable.

Example 1. Study the oscillations of the charge q in a circuit consisting of a condenser in series with a coil containing an iron core (see Fig. 21).

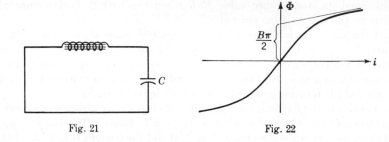

Fig. 21   Fig. 22

From elementary physics the voltage drop along the coil is $n \, d\Phi/dt$, where n is the number of turns of the coil, and Φ is the magnetic flux through a cross section. Φ is a complicated function of the current i flowing in the coil, but with some idealization (in particular, disregard of residual magnetism which leads to the phenomenon of hysteresis) the characteristic graph of Φ versus i appears as in Fig. 22 and may be approximated by

$$n\Phi(i) = Ai + B \arctan \frac{i}{K}$$

where A, B, K are positive constants. We then have

$$n \frac{d\Phi}{dt} = \left(A + \frac{BK}{i^2 + K^2} \right) \frac{di}{dt}$$

$$= \left(A + \frac{BK}{i^2 + K^2} \right) i \frac{di}{dq}$$

Thus, the equation in the phase variables q, i for the circuit of Fig. 21 becomes

$$\left(A + \frac{BK}{i^2 + K^2} \right) i \frac{di}{dq} + \frac{1}{C} q = 0$$

This can immediately be integrated by separation of variables:

(13.3) $$Ai^2 + BK \log \left[1 + \left(\frac{i}{K} \right)^2 \right] + \frac{1}{C} q^2 = c$$

When these equations are graphed (for some fixed values of A, B, K, C and various values of the constant of integration c), one obtains a set of ovals with common center at $q = 0$, $i = 0$. Each corresponds to a periodic oscillation. Half an oscillation takes place between successive times at which $i = 0$, that is, as q changes from $\pm \sqrt{cC}$ to $\mp \sqrt{cC}$. Therefore, the period T of oscillation could be found by first solving (13.3) for i, say $i = f(q)$, and then using (13.2):

$$T = 2 \int_{-\sqrt{cC}}^{+\sqrt{cC}} \frac{dq}{f(q)}$$

PROBLEMS

1. A simple series circuit with no resistance has inductance L, capacitance C, and a constant e.m.f. E. Find the current i as a function of the charge q and as a function of the time t. [The only singular point in the phase plane has coordinates $(CE, 0)$ and is a center.]

2. A capacitance C is connected in series with a diode. The diode acts as a nonlinear resistance, the relation between the current i and the voltage V of the diode being $i = (1/R)V + (1/S)V^2$, where R, S are positive constants. Find the voltage across the condenser at time t if it is V_0 at $t = 0$. How does this discharge compare with that through a linear resistance? HINT: The equation for the voltage is

$$C\frac{dV}{dt} + \frac{1}{R}V + \frac{1}{S}V^2 = 0$$

3. In a space-charge diode with parallel-plane plates the potential $V(x)$ at a distance x from the cathode satisfies Poisson's equation $d^2V/dx^2 = \rho(x)/\epsilon_0$, where $\rho(x)$ is the electronic charge density at distance x, and ϵ_0 is a constant called the *permissivity of vacuum*. Let $v(x)$ be the drift velocity of the electrons at distance x. Then the principle of conservation of charge gives $\rho(x)v(x) = $ constant $= j$, and conservation of energy gives $\frac{1}{2}mv^2 = eV$ (m and e are the mass and charge of the electron). Determine V as a function of x if $V = V_0$ and $dV/dx = 0$ at $x = 0$. HINT: Use the phase-plane method first to find the gradient $u = dV/dx$ as a function of V.

4. A series circuit contains a coil of inductance L_0 and a condenser. The capacitance of the condenser depends on the charge q according to $C(q) = C_0/(1 + Aq + Bq^2)$, where C_0, A, B are positive constants. (A condenser of this type is approximately realized if Rochelle salt is the dielectric substance). (a) Determine the current i as a function of q. (b) Set up an integral for the period of the oscillation.

★5. An electric charge q_0 on a condenser of capacitance C is discharged through a coil of inductance L in series with a nonlinear resistance element whose characteristic (see Fig. 23) is $V = Si^2$ if $i > 0$ and $V = -Si^2$ if $i < 0$ (replacing the Ohm characteristic $V = Ri$ of a linear resistance element). Sketch the phase curves (pieced together at the q axis from infinitely many smooth pieces) for this problem. Show that the discharge occurs through infinitely many oscillations.

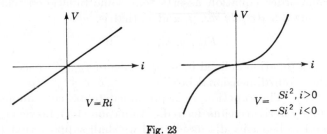

Fig. 23

chapter *V*

Second-order
Differential Equations

Second-order differential equations occur throughout the physical
sciences. It is no overstatement to say that without an understanding of at least linear second-order equations with constant coefficients
one cannot obtain a thorough grasp of the basic physical laws. One
of the reasons for the frequency of second-order equations is the fact
that Newton's law relates force to acceleration, and acceleration is the
second derivative of distance with respect to time. Fortunately, the
differential equations which arise in first approximations to physical
problems are often linear, and it is just this class of equations which we
mainly wish to discuss.

1. Some Simple Classes of Second-order Equations

A second-order equation asserts that some functional relationship
exists among d^2y/dx^2, dy/dx, y, and x; that is,

$$(1.1) \qquad F(x, y, y', y'') = 0$$

where F is a function defined in some region of $xyy'y''$ space, for example, in the "four-dimensional box" $a < x < b$, $c < y < d$, $e < y' < f$,
$g < y'' < h$. The function F is presumed to be continuous and to
have as many derivatives as desired. Equation (1.1), however, is much
too general to be easily discussed, and we shall suppose that (1.1) has

been solved for y'' in terms of x, y, y':

(1.2)
$$\frac{d^2y}{dx^2} = f\left(x, y, \frac{dy}{dx}\right)$$

where f is a function defined over some region of xyy' space, is continuous (or piecewise continuous), and perhaps has continuous partial derivatives $\partial f/\partial x$, $\partial f/\partial y$, $\partial f/\partial y'$.

To get oriented about what constitutes the manifold of solutions of an equation such as (1.2), we consider some special types of second-order equations whose solution can be reduced to that of first-order equations. The first type to be taken up is distinguished by the fact that the function $f(x, y, y')$ in (1.2) *does not depend on* y:

(1.3)
$$\frac{d^2y}{dx^2} = f\left(x, \frac{dy}{dx}\right)$$

If we consider the function $dy/dx = p$ as the unknown, then (1.3) becomes

(1.4)
$$\frac{dp}{dx} = f(x, p)$$

which is a first-order equation in p. This equation is solved by any of the methods at our disposal for such equations. A single solution of (1.4) is obtained if the value of p at some initial abscissa x_0 is given, say $p(x_0) = p_0$. Once this solution, $y' = p$, is found, y itself is found by a subsequent quadrature: $y(x) = \int p(x)\, dx$. A single function $y(x)$ is obtained in this last step if we are given the value of $y(x)$ at an initial abscissa, which usually is the same x_0 at which $y'(x)$ is given, say $y(x_0) = y_0$. In summary we may state: *The solution of D.E. (1.3) may be reduced to the solution of a first-order equation and a subsequent quadrature; a single solution is determined by specifying the initial conditions (I.C.)*

$$y(x_0) = y_0 \qquad y'(x_0) = y_0'$$

Example 1. Find all solutions of the equation

(1.5)
$$xy'' - 4y' = x^5$$

and find the particular solution for which $y(1) = -1$, $y'(1) = -4$.

This is a linear differential equation in $p = y'$; its solution is

(1.6)
$$y'(x) = x^5 + cx^4$$

where c is an arbitrary constant. A quadrature gives

$$y(x) = \tfrac{1}{6}x^6 + c_1 x^5 + c_2$$

where we have written c_1 for $c/5$, and where c_2 is another arbitrary constant. Every solution of (1.5) has now been found.

The desired particular solution is obtained from the I.C. $y'(1) = -4$ and $y(1) = -1$. Then

$$1 + 5c_1 = -4 \quad \text{and} \quad \tfrac{1}{6} + c_1 + c_2 = -1$$

so $c_1 = -1$ and $c_2 = -\tfrac{1}{6}$. The desired particular solution is

$$y(x) = \tfrac{1}{6}x^6 - x^5 - \tfrac{1}{6}$$

A second special case of (1.2) is that in which the *independent variable* x *is absent*:

$$(1.7) \qquad\qquad \frac{d^2y}{dx^2} = f\left(y, \frac{dy}{dx}\right)$$

Equations of this type have already been solved in Sec. 3 of Chap. IV. One introduces y as the independent variable† and $p = y'$ as the dependent variable. Then

$$\frac{d^2y}{dx^2} = \frac{dp}{dy}\frac{dy}{dx} = p\frac{dp}{dy}$$

and (1.7) becomes the first-order equation

$$p\frac{dp}{dy} = f(y, p)$$

Once the solution $p(y)$ is found, then, since $p = dy/dx$, the solution of (1.7) is found by quadrature:

$$(1.8) \qquad\qquad x(y) = \int \frac{dy}{p(y)}$$

To obtain y as a function of x, one solves (1.8) for y.

Example 2. Find the solution of

$$y'' = y'e^y$$

for which $y = 0$ and $y' = 2$ at $x = 0$.

Note that $y(x) =$ constant is a solution of the D.E. but does not satisfy the I.C. We therefore put $y' = p$, consider y as the independent variable, and obtain

$$p\frac{dp}{dy} = pe^y \quad \text{or} \quad \frac{dp}{dy} = e^y$$

---

† This can be done in the neighborhood of any point x_0 for which the solution $y(x)$ is such that $y'(x_0) \neq 0$. If the D.E. (1.7) has the solution $y(x) = c =$ constant, then the above method fails. Therefore, one should always look separately for a possible solution $y(x) = c$.

Therefore $p(y) = e^y + c_1$, and since $p = 2$ when $y = 0$, we get $c_1 = 1$, so

$$p(y) = \frac{dy}{dx} = e^y + 1$$

and

$$1 + e^{-y} = c_2 e^{-x}$$

From the I.C. $c_2 = 2$, and the desired solution is

$$y(x) = -\log (2e^{-x} - 1)$$

Example 3. Particularly simple is the case in which the right member of (1.7) does not involve y' either:

$$\frac{d^2 y}{dx^2} = f(y)$$

We obtain

$$p \frac{dp}{dy} = f(y)$$

$$\tfrac{1}{2} p^2 = \int f(y) \, dy = F(y)$$

Solving for p and remembering that $p = y'$, we obtain

$$\frac{dy}{dx} = \sqrt{2F(y)}$$

an equation with separable variables. The solution (in implicit form) is

$$x(y) = \int \frac{dy}{\sqrt{2F(y)}}$$

which contains another arbitrary constant and which, of course, must be considered for such y that $F(y) > 0$.

To illustrate, we find the solution of

$$\frac{d^2 x}{dt^2} + \frac{1}{\sqrt{2 - x}} = 0$$

for which $x = 1$ and $dx/dt = 2$ when $t = t_0$. Putting $dx/dt = p$, we have

$$p \frac{dp}{dx} = - \frac{1}{\sqrt{2 - x}}$$

$$\tfrac{1}{2} p^2 = 2 \sqrt{2 - x} + c_1$$

and since $p = 2$ for $x = 1$, $c_1 = 0$. Thus,

$$\frac{dx}{dt} = 2 \sqrt[4]{2 - x}$$

$$-\tfrac{2}{3}(2 - x)^{\frac{3}{4}} = t + c_2$$

Because $t = t_0$ when $x = 1$, $c_2 = -\frac{2}{3} - t_0$. The desired solution is

$$x(t) = 2 - [1 - \tfrac{3}{2}(t - t_0)]^{\frac{4}{3}}$$

An important lesson to be drawn from the above examples is that *the totality of solutions of a differential equation of the second order depends on two parameters* (due to two integrations being involved), and *one can single out a particular solution $y(x)$ by specifying the values of $y(x)$ and $y'(x)$ for an initial value of x.* Geometrically speaking, one specifies, in addition to a point (x_0, y_0) through which the integral curve is to pass, the slope y_0' which the curve is to have at (x_0, y_0).

PROBLEMS

1. (a) Verify that $y(x) = c_1 e^{-x} \sin 2(x + c_2)$ is, for every pair of constants c_1, c_2, a solution of $y'' + 2y' + 5y = 0$.

(b) Find the particular solution for which $y = 0$, $y' = \frac{1}{2}$ at $x = 0$.

2. (a) Verify that $y(x) = 1 + c_1 x + c_2 x^2$ is, for every pair of constants c_1, c_2, a solution of $x^2 y'' - 2xy' + 2y = 2$.

(b) Find the integral curve passing through $(-1, 0)$ with slope zero.

(c) Find the integral curve passing through $(1, 1)$ and $(-1, 3)$.

3. Find all solutions of $y'' = xe^{2x}$.

4. Solve $y'' = 1 + y'^2$, $y(0) = y'(0) = 0$.

5. Solve $(x + y')y'' + y' = 0$, $y(0) = 2$, $y'(0) = 1$.

6. Find all solutions of $(x^2 - x)y'' - y'(1 + y') = 0$.

7. Solve $y'' = x^2 y' + x^3 y''$, $y(0) = 0$, $y'(0) = 1$.

8. Solve $y'' = e^{-2y}$, $y = y' = 0$ at $x = -\pi/2$.

9. Solve $y'' = \sec^2 y \tan y$, $y(-1) = 0$, $y'(-1) = 1$.

10. Find $y(-1)$ if $y'' = y'e^y$, $y(0) = -1$, $y'(0) = 0$.

11. An integral curve of $yy'' + y'^2 - yy' = 0$ passes through the point $(\log 2, 2)$ with slope $\frac{1}{2}$. Find its equation.

12. Compute $y(0.5)$ if $y'' = x^2(1 + y'^2)^{\frac{3}{2}}$, $y(0) = y'(0) = 0$. First find $y'(0.1)$, $y'(0.2)$, ..., $y'(0.5)$ by the R.K. method (7.20), Chap. I, then $y(0.5)$ by Simpson's rule.

13. A dog is running due west at a speed of 30 feet per second when he sees, 200 feet straight ahead of him, a rabbit running due north at a speed of 20 feet per second. If the rabbit continues in the same direction at the same speed and if the dog runs so as to point always at the rabbit, how far is the dog from the rabbit after $6\frac{5}{16}$ seconds?

2. Linear Equations with Constant Coefficients

By far the most important type of second-order equations is *linear*, i.e., of the form

$$(2.1) \qquad A(x)\frac{d^2y}{dx^2} + B(x)\frac{dy}{dx} + C(x)y + D(x) = 0$$

where the "coefficients" $A(x)$, $B(x)$, $C(x)$, $D(x)$ are functions of the independent variable alone (or constants). We usually assume that (2.1) is divided through by $A(x)$ [in intervals of x in which $A(x) \neq 0$] and that the term $D(x)/A(x)$ is transposed to the right of the equation. Then we have the linear equation in *normal form*:

$$(2.2) \qquad \frac{d^2y}{dx^2} + P(x)\frac{dy}{dx} + Q(x)y = f(x)$$

If $f(x) = 0$, (2.2) is said to be *linear homogeneous*, for then each non-zero term of the equation is of the first degree in y, y', and y''. The homogeneous equation

$$(2.3) \qquad \frac{d^2y}{dx^2} + P(x)\frac{dy}{dx} + Q(x)y = 0$$

has several important properties:

1. $y(x) = 0$ is a particular solution of (2.3), the so-called *trivial solution*.

2. If $y_1(x)$ is a solution of (2.3), so is $c_1 y_1(x)$, where c_1 is an arbitrary constant.

3. If $y_1(x)$ and $y_2(x)$ are solutions of (2.3), so is $y_1(x) + y_2(x)$.

4. If $y_1(x)$ and $y_2(x)$ are linearly independent† solutions of (2.3), then *every* solution of (2.3) is given by

$$(2.4) \qquad c_1 y_1(x) + c_2 y_2(x)$$

where c_1 and c_2 are arbitrary constants. Hence in this case we are justified in speaking of (2.4) as *the* general solution.

The assertions 1 to 3 can be verified by direct substitution; this is left as an exercise for the reader (see also the discussion in Chap. VI). Assertion 4 is a special case of a general theorem given in Chap. VI. It is also true that solutions of (2.3) are defined for all values of x for which the coefficients $P(x)$ and $Q(x)$ are continuous and, in particular, for all x if these functions are constants. In this case we have the *linear homogeneous equation with constant coefficients*

$$(2.5) \qquad y'' + ay' + by = 0$$

whose solution will now be discussed.

---

† Two functions f and g are said to be linearly independent if $\alpha f + \beta g = 0$ implies that $\alpha = \beta = 0$ (see Sec. 4, Chap. VI). This means that one of the functions is not a constant times the other.

With property 4 to go by, it is clear that all we need find is a pair of linearly independent solutions. We observe that, because

$$\frac{d}{dx} e^{rx} = re^{rx}$$

it is likely that (2.5) has a solution of the form e^{rx}. We therefore try $y(x) = e^{rx}$ and obtain

$$r^2 e^{rx} + are^{rx} + be^{rx} = 0$$

Since $e^{rx} \neq 0$, we obtain a quadratic equation for r:

(2.6) $r^2 + ar + b = 0$

This is called the *auxiliary equation*.

Solving the quadratic equation (2.6) for r gives

(2.7) $r = \dfrac{-a \pm \sqrt{a^2 - 4b}}{2}$

If we denote the two roots of (2.6) by r_1 and r_2, then $e^{r_1 x}$ and $e^{r_2 x}$ are linearly independent solutions if $r_1 \neq r_2$. The general solution in this case is then

(2.8) $y(x) = c_1 e^{r_1 x} + c_2 e^{r_2 x}$

If the two roots of (2.6) are equal ($r_1 = r_2 = r$), direct substitution shows that xe^{rx} is also a solution, for

$$y = xe^{rx}$$
$$y' = xre^{rx} + e^{rx}$$
$$y'' = xr^2 e^{rx} + 2re^{rx}$$

and substituting y, y', y'' in the differential equation gives

$$y'' + ay' + by = xr^2 e^{rx} + 2re^{rx} + axre^{rx} + ae^{rx} + bxe^{rx}$$
$$= e^{rx}[x(r^2 + ar + b) + 2r + a] = 0$$

Here $r^2 + ar + b = 0$ because r is a root of the auxiliary equation (2.6), while $2r + a = 0$ because the roots are equal. Hence, if $r_1 = r_2 = r$, the general solution of (2.5) is

(2.9) $y(x) = c_1 e^{rx} + c_2 xe^{rx}$

since e^{rx} and xe^{rx} are linearly independent, as neither is a constant times the other.

Example 1.   Find the general solution of

$$y'' - 2y' - 3y = 0$$

The auxiliary equation is

$$r^2 - 2r - 3 = 0$$

with roots $r_1 = 3$ and $r_2 = -1$. The general solution is

$$y(x) = c_1 e^{3x} + c_2 e^{-x}$$

Example 2. Find the general solution of

$$y'' + 4y' + 4y = 0$$

The auxiliary equation is

$$r^2 + 4r + 4 = 0$$

with equal roots $-2, -2$. The general solution is

$$y(x) = c_1 e^{-2x} + c_2 x e^{-2x}$$

In Chap. VI when operational methods for solving linear equations with constant coefficients are discussed, it will be convenient to use the symbolic operator D to denote differentiation with respect to the independent variable; for example,

$$Dy = \frac{dy}{dx}$$

We further define

$$D^2 y = D(Dy) = \frac{d^2 y}{dx^2}$$

$$D^n y = D(D^{n-1} y) = \frac{d^n y}{dx^n}$$

and

$$(aD^n + bD^m)y = aD^n y + bD^m y$$

Our second-order equation (2.5) then may be written as

$$(D^2 + aD + b)y = 0$$

PROBLEMS

1. Find the general solutions of the following constant-coefficient equations:

(a) $y'' - y' - 2y = 0$
(b) $(D^2 + 3D + 2)y = 0$
(c) $(D^2 + 4D + 2)y = 0$
(d) $(D^2 + 2D)y = 0$
(e) $D^2 y + 6Dy + 9y = 0$
(f) $y'' = 9y$
(g) $y'' - 2\sqrt{5} y' + 5y = 0$
(h) $y'' - ky' - 3y = 0$

(i) $2y'' - y' - 3y = 0$

(j) $kly'' + (k - l)my' - m^2y = 0$

(k) $y'' - 2my' + m^2y = 0$

(l) $y'' = 15y - 2y'$

(m) $4y = 12y' - 9y''$

(n) $L\dfrac{d^2q}{dt^2} + R\dfrac{dq}{dt} + \dfrac{1}{C}q = 0,\ R^2 > 4\dfrac{L}{C}$

(o) $L\dfrac{d^2q}{dt^2} + R\dfrac{dq}{dt} + \dfrac{1}{C}q = 0,\ R^2 = 4\dfrac{L}{C}$

2. Find the particular integrals of the following equations, which have the initial values indicated:

(a) $y'' - y' - 2y = 0;\ y = 3,\ y' = 0,\ x = 0$

(b) $(D^2 - 4)y = 0;\ y = 1,\ y' = \frac{1}{2},\ x = 0$

(c) $y'' - 4y' + 4y = 0;\ y = 3,\ y' = 4,\ x = 0$

(d) $2y'' + y' - y = 0;\ y = 17,\ y' = 10,\ x = \log 4$

(e) $y'' - 5y' + 6y = 0;\ y = e^2,\ y' = 3e^2,\ x = 1$

(f) $y'' - 2y' - 3y = 0;\ y = 21.5,\ y' = 140,\ x = 1$

(g) $y'' + 2y' + y = 0;\ y = 2.00,\ y' = -0.97,\ x = 1.2$

(h) $y'' + 4y' + 2y = 0;\ y = -1,\ y' = 2 + 3\sqrt{2},\ x = 0$

(i) $y'' = y;\ y = 2.272,\ y' = 0.706,\ x = 0.5$

(j) $y'' - 2y' - 15y = 0;\ y' = 10,\ y'' = 2,\ x = 0$

(k) $L\dfrac{d^2q}{dt^2} + R\dfrac{dq}{dt} + \dfrac{1}{C}q = 0;\quad R = 3{,}000,\quad L = 100 \times 10^{-6},\quad C = 100 \times$

$10^{-12};\ q = 1 \times 10^{-8},\ \dfrac{dq}{dt} = 0,\ t = 0$

★(l) $y'' - y' - 2y = 0;\ y = 5,\ x = 0;$ minimum value of y is 4.09

★**3.** Show that if $a^2 - 4b > 0$ then no integral curve of (2.5) can cross the x axis at two distinct points.

★**4.** Show that if $a^2 - 4b > 0$ then no integral curve of (2.5) (except $y = 0$) can be tangent to the x axis.

★**5.** Let $r_1(\epsilon)$, $r_2(\epsilon)$ be roots of the auxiliary equation of $y'' + ay' + \frac{1}{4}(a^2 - \epsilon^2)y = 0$; then both $r_1(\epsilon)$ and $r_2(\epsilon)$ tend to $r = -\frac{1}{2}a$ as $\epsilon \to 0$. Show that the solution $y(x) = (1/\epsilon)(e^{r_1(\epsilon)x} - e^{r_2(\epsilon)x})$ tends to xe^{rx} as $\epsilon \to 0$.

6. The differential equation

$$x^2y'' + axy' + by = 0$$

where a, b are constants, is said to be an *Euler-type* equation. It has solutions of the form x^r. Show that r must satisfy the auxiliary equation

$$r(r - 1) + ar + b = 0$$

and that if this equation has two distinct real roots r_1, r_2, then the general solution of the Euler-type equation is $y(x) = c_1x^{r_1} + c_2x^{r_2}$.

7. Using the result of Prob. 6, find the general solutions of the following equations:

(a) $x^2 y'' + 2xy' - 6y = 0$
(b) $x^2 y'' + xy' - 16y = 0$
(c) $4x^2 y'' - 3y = 0$
(d) $x^2 y'' + xy' - 2y = 0$
(e) $x^2 y'' - 3xy' + y = 0$
(f) $(x + 1)^2 y'' - 6y = 0$

3. Complex Roots

In the previous discussion we tacitly assumed that the roots r_1 and r_2 of Eq. (2.6) were real numbers (the coefficients a and b are, of course, presumed real). We now inquire as to what meaning can be attached to our results if r_1 and r_2 are complex. Since a and b are real, complex roots of (2.6) are necessarily conjugate complex numbers which we denote by

$$r_1 = \alpha + \beta i \qquad r_2 = \alpha - \beta i$$

with α and β real.

It will be necessary now to use the following relation,† called *Euler's formula*, a derivation of which is given in many calculus texts:

$$(3.1) \qquad e^{ix} = \cos x + i \sin x$$

The general solution of (2.6) then is

$$\begin{aligned} y(x) &= c_1 e^{r_1 x} + c_2 e^{r_2 x} = c_1 e^{(\alpha+\beta i)x} + c_2 e^{(\alpha-\beta i)x} \\ &= e^{\alpha x}(c_1 e^{\beta i x} + c_2 e^{-\beta i x}) \\ &= e^{\alpha x}[c_1(\cos \beta x + i \sin \beta x) + c_2(\cos \beta x - i \sin \beta x)] \end{aligned}$$

If now we take c_1 and c_2 to be conjugate complex numbers,

$$c_1 = A + iB \qquad c_2 = A - iB$$

we get

$$\begin{aligned} y(x) &= e^{\alpha x}[(A + iB)(\cos \beta x + i \sin \beta x) + (A - iB)(\cos \beta x - i \sin \beta x)] \\ &= e^{\alpha x}(2A \cos \beta x - 2B \sin \beta x) \end{aligned}$$

For $A = \frac{1}{2}$, $B = 0$, we have

$$(3.2) \qquad y(x) = e^{\alpha x} \cos \beta x$$

and for $A = 0$, $B = -\frac{1}{2}$, we have

$$(3.3) \qquad y(x) = e^{\alpha x} \sin \beta x$$

---

† One can also regard Euler's formula as defining e^{ix}. Then define $e^{\alpha+i\beta} = e^\alpha e^{i\beta}$. Now one must show that the laws of exponents are valid and that

$$De^{(\alpha+i\beta)x} = (\alpha + i\beta)e^{(\alpha+i\beta)x}$$

Since the functions (3.2) and (3.3) are linearly independent solutions (for proof see Sec. 4, Chap. VI), the general solution of (2.5) is

$$(3.4) \qquad y(x) = e^{\alpha x}(c_1 \cos \beta x + c_2 \sin \beta x)$$

because of property 4, Sec. 2.

The reader unfamiliar with, or repelled by, complex exponents may want to verify independently that (3.2) and (3.3) are solutions. Direct substitution of these functions in the D.E. (3.4) will verify that both are solutions. To carry this out, it is necessary to recall the formulas for the sum and product of the roots of a quadratic equation:

$$r_1 + r_2 = 2\alpha = -a$$

and

$$r_1 r_2 = \alpha^2 + \beta^2 = b$$

The details of the verification are left as an exercise for the reader.

Equation (3.4) may be given a somewhat different form as follows. Multiplying and dividing the right member by $\sqrt{c_1{}^2 + c_2{}^2}$, we obtain

$$y(x) = \sqrt{c_1{}^2 + c_2{}^2}\, e^{\alpha x} \left(\frac{c_1}{\sqrt{c_1{}^2 + c_2{}^2}} \cos \beta x + \frac{c_2}{\sqrt{c_1{}^2 + c_2{}^2}} \sin \beta x \right)$$

Let δ_1 be a real number such that

$$\sin \delta_1 = \frac{c_1}{\sqrt{c_1{}^2 + c_2{}^2}} \qquad \cos \delta_1 = \frac{c_2}{\sqrt{c_1{}^2 + c_2{}^2}}$$

and let $A = \sqrt{c_1{}^2 + c_2{}^2}$. Then the above solution becomes

$$y(x) = Ae^{\alpha x}(\sin \delta_1 \cos \beta x + \cos \delta_1 \sin \beta x)$$
$$= Ae^{\alpha x} \sin (\beta x + \delta_1)$$

or

$$(3.5) \qquad y(x) = Ae^{\alpha x} \sin \beta(x + \delta)$$

where $\delta_1 = \beta \delta$.

Example 1. Find the general solution of

$$(D^2 + 2D + 4)y = 0$$

The auxiliary equation is

$$r^2 + 2r + 4 = 0$$

which has the complex roots $r = -1 \pm i \sqrt{3}$. Therefore the general solution is

$$y(x) = e^{-x}(c_1 \cos \sqrt{3}\, x + c_2 \sin \sqrt{3}\, x)$$

or

$$y(x) = Ae^{-x} \sin \sqrt{3}\, (x + \delta)$$

To recapitulate, we now have three possible forms for the general solution of the homogeneous equation (2.5) with constant coefficients, depending on the character of the roots of the auxiliary equation:

$$(3.6) \quad \begin{aligned} y(x) &= c_1 e^{r_1 x} + c_2 e^{r_2 x} & \text{roots real and unequal} \\ y(x) &= c_1 e^{r x} + c_2 x e^{r x} & \text{roots real and equal} \\ y(x) &= e^{\alpha x}(c_1 \cos \beta x + c_2 \sin \beta x) \\ &= A e^{\alpha x} \sin \beta(x + \delta) & \text{conjugate complex roots } \alpha \pm i\beta \end{aligned}$$

PROBLEMS

1. Find the general solutions of the following constant-coefficient equations:

(a) $(D^2 + 3D + 3)y = 0$

(b) $(D^2 - 2D + 2)y = 0$

(c) $y'' - 3y' + 2y = 0$

(d) $y'' - y' + 3y = 0$

(e) $2y'' - 5y' + 3y = 0$

(f) $\dfrac{d^2 s}{dt^2} - 3\dfrac{ds}{dt} - 4s = 0$

(g) $y'' - 2ky' + (k^2 + 1)y - 0$

(h)* $(2D^2 - 3D + 2)y = 0$

(i) $y'' - 4y' + (4 + k^2)y = 0$

(j) $(4D^2 - 24D + 37)y = 0$

(k) $(D^2 + 6D + 13)y = 0$

(l) $(k^2 D^2 - 4k^2 D + 4k^2 + 1)y = 0$

(m) $(k^2 D^2 + 2kD + k^2 + 1)y = 0$

(n) $L\dfrac{d^2 q}{dt^2} + R\dfrac{dq}{dt} + \dfrac{1}{C} q = 0, \ R^2 < 4\dfrac{L}{C}$

(o) $ay'' + 2y' + by = 0, \ ab > 1$

(p) $ay'' + 2y' + by = 0, \ ab = 1$

(q) $\dfrac{w}{g}\dfrac{d^2 x}{dt^2} + b\dfrac{dx}{dt} + kx = 0, \ b^2 - 4\dfrac{kw}{g} < 0$

(r) $\dfrac{w}{g}\dfrac{d^2 x}{dt^2} + b\dfrac{dx}{dt} + kx = 0, \ b^2 - 4\dfrac{kw}{g} = 0$

(s) $3\dfrac{d^2 w}{dz^2} + k\dfrac{dw}{dz} + 5w = 0, \ k^2 < 60$

2. Find the integrals of the following equations satisfying the initial values indicated ($y' = dy/dx, \ \dot{x} = dx/dt$):

(a) $y'' - y' + y = 0; \ y = 1, \ y' = \frac{7}{2}, \ x = 0$

(b) $y'' + 4y' + 13y = 0; \ y = 4, \ y' = 1, \ x = 0$

(c) $y'' + 2y' + 4y = 0; \ y = 3, \ y' = 0, \ x = 0$

(d) $\ddot{x} + 4\dot{x} + 4x = 0$; $x = 0.300$, $\dot{x} = 0.103$, $t = 1.5$

(e) $L\ddot{q} + R\dot{q} + (1/C)q = 0$; $C = 100 \times 10^{-12}$, $L = 100 \times 10^{-6}$, $R = 1,500$; $q = 0$, $\dot{q} = 0.01$, $t = 0$

(f) $(w/g)\ddot{x} + b\dot{x} + kx = 0$; $w = 20$, $g = 32$, $k = 10$, $b = 0.1$; $x = 2$, $\dot{x} = 0$, $t = 0$

(g) $4y'' + 4y' + 5y = 0$; $y = 0$, $y'' = -e^{-\pi/12}$, $x = \pi/6$

(h) $y'' + 2y' + 10y = 0$; $y = 0.59$, $y' = -0.59$, $x = \pi/6$

(i) $\ddot{x} - 2\dot{x} + 2x = 0$; $x = 1.732$, $\dot{x} = 0.732$, $t = 0$

(j) $y'' + 3y' + 2y = 0$; $y = 2e^{-2}$, $y' = -3e^{-2}$, $x = 1$

(k) $y'' + 2y' + 2y = 0$; $y = e^{-2}$, $y + y' = 0$, $x = 0$

3. Show that if two consecutive zeros of the solution $y(x) \neq 0$ of Eq. (2.5) are π apart, then $b = 1 + \frac{1}{4}a^2$.

4. Find the general solution of $y''' + 4y'' + 13y' = 0$.

5. Find the general solution of $y^{(4)} - 4y''' + 29y'' = 0$.

★6. Find the general solution of $y''' - 2y'' + y' - 2y = 0$.

4. The Nonhomogeneous Equation

We have obtained the general solution of the homogeneous equation (2.5) in the case of constant coefficients. We turn now to the nonhomogeneous equation

$$(4.1) \qquad \frac{d^2y}{dx^2} + P(x)\frac{dy}{dx} + Q(x)y = f(x)$$

The homogeneous equation with the same coefficients,

$$(4.2) \qquad \frac{d^2y}{dx^2} + P(x)\frac{dy}{dx} + Q(x)y = 0$$

will be referred to as the *reduced equation* in contrast to (4.1), which will be referred to as the *complete equation*.

Most methods of solution of the complete equation depend on knowing the general solution of the reduced equation. In addition, if we know a particular solution of the complete equation, then the general solution may be written down at once according to the following theorem:

Theorem. *If y_1 and y_2 are linearly independent solutions of the reduced equation, and w is any solution of the complete equation, then*

$$(4.3) \qquad y = c_1y_1 + c_2y_2 + w$$

is the general solution of the complete equation.

Proof that (4.3) satisfies (4.1) may be obtained by direct substitution:

$$y'' + Py' + Qy$$

reduces to

$$c_1(y_1'' + Py' + Qy_1) + c_2(y_2'' + Py_2' + Qy_2) + (w'' + Pw' + Qw)$$

The expressions in the first two sets of parentheses are zero since y_1, y_2 are solutions of the reduced equation. The last expression in parentheses is equal to f since w is a solution of (4.1). Hence

$$y'' + Py' + Qy = f$$

That (4.3) contains every solution of Eq. (4.2) is proved in Sec. 8, Chap. VI.

The expression (4.3) may be written in a somewhat different form as follows. Let $y_c = c_1y_1 + c_2y_2$ denote the general solution of the reduced equation, called the *complementary function*, and let y_p denote the solution w, called a *particular integral* of the complete equation. Then

(4.4) $$y = y_c + y_p$$

Expression (4.3) or (4.4) contains all solutions of the complete equation, so that once again we are justified in using the term *the* general solution. In addition, the solutions exist for all values of the independent variable x for which $P(x)$, $Q(x)$, and $f(x)$ are continuous.†

Since *any* solution of the complete equation suffices for purposes of writing the general solution, provided that we can solve the reduced equation, we now bend our energies to the development of techniques for finding such a particular solution. Two elementary methods for finding particular integrals are given in the next sections.

PROBLEMS

1. Prove that if $y = w$ is a solution of $y'' + Py' + Qy = f$, then $y = Aw$ is a solution of $y'' + Py' + Qy = Af$, A constant.

2. Prove that if $y = w_1$ is a solution of $y'' + Py' + Qy = f_1$ and $y = w_2$ is a solution of $y'' + Py' + Qy = f_2$, then $y = w_1 + w_2$ is a solution of $y'' + Py' + Qy = f_1 + f_2$.

3. Show that $y(x) = x^2 + 2x$ and $y(x) = \sin x$ are particular integrals for $y'' - y' = -2x$ and $y'' - y' = -\sin x - \cos x$, respectively. Hence find the general solution of $y'' - y' = x + \sin x + \cos x$.

4. What is the complementary function for the equation $(D^2 + D)y = \sin x$?

5. Suppose the initial conditions for the nonhomogeneous linear differential equation $y'' + Py' + Qy = f$ are $y(x_0) = y_0$, $y'(x_0) = y_1$. In the present context let us refer to $y(x_0) = 0$, $y'(x_0) = 0$ as the reduced I.C., in contrast to

† These facts are consequences of the general existence theorems for linear equations given in Chap. VI.

the former, which are the complete I.C. Show that the solution of the complete D.E. with the complete I.C. can be written as $y = y_1 + y_2$, where y_1 is the solution of the reduced D.E. with the complete I.C., and y_2 is the solution of the complete D.E. with the reduced I.C.

5. The Method of Undetermined Coefficients

This method is applicable only to equations with constant coefficients when the right member f is such that the form of a particular integral may be guessed. We illustrate with a few examples.

Example 1. Find a particular integral of

$$(D^2 + 5D + 6)y = x^2 + 2x$$

In this problem, since the right member is a polynomial, it is natural to seek a polynomial solution. Clearly the degree of polynomial should be at least 2. We try

$$y_p(x) = Ax^2 + Bx + C$$

Substituting in the differential equation yields

$$2A + 5(2Ax + B) + 6(Ax^2 + Bx + C) = x^2 + 2x$$

Now this equation will be an identity in x if the coefficients of like powers are equal. We have

$$6Ax^2 + (10A + 6B)x + (2A + 5B + 6C) = x^2 + 2x$$

and

$$6A = 1$$
$$10A + 6B = 2$$
$$2A + 5B + 6C = 0$$

Solving these equations yields

$$A = \tfrac{1}{6} \qquad B = \tfrac{1}{18} \qquad C = -\tfrac{11}{108}$$

whence the desired particular integral is

$$y_p(x) = \frac{18x^2 + 6x - 11}{108}$$

Example 2. Find the general solution of

$$(D^2 - 3D + 2)y = 2 \sin x$$

Here the auxiliary equation is $r^2 - 3r + 2 = 0$, and the complementary function is

$$y_c(x) = c_1 e^{2x} + c_2 e^x$$

To find a particular integral of the complete equation, we try

$$y_p(x) = A \sin x + B \cos x$$

Then

$$(D^2 - 3D + 2)y_p = -A \sin x - B \cos x - 3A \cos x + 3B \sin x$$
$$+ 2A \sin x + 2B \cos x$$
$$= (A + 3B) \sin x + (B - 3A) \cos x$$
$$= 2 \sin x$$

Hence, y_p will be a solution if

$$A + 3B = 2 \qquad B - 3A = 0$$

Solving, we find $A = \frac{1}{5}$, $B = \frac{3}{5}$, whence

$$y_p(x) = \tfrac{1}{5} \sin x + \tfrac{3}{5} \cos x$$

The general solution is

$$y(x) = c_1 e^{2x} + c_2 e^x + \tfrac{1}{5} \sin x + \tfrac{3}{5} \cos x$$

Example 3.   Find the general solution of

$$(D^2 + 1)y = \sin x$$

The auxiliary equation is $r^2 + 1 = 0$, which has the roots i, $-i$.   The complementary function therefore is

$$y_c(x) = c_1 \sin x + c_2 \cos x$$

Since the right member of the complete equation is $\sin x$, we are tempted to find a particular integral of the form $y_p(x) = A \sin x + B \cos x$.   But, as we have seen, this function solves the reduced equation.   We must therefore look elsewhere for a particular integral.

We have seen that if the roots of the auxiliary equation are repeated the second linearly independent solution of the reduced equation is obtained by multiplying by the factor x.   This suggests a possible solution to the problem. We try

$$y_p(x) = Ax \sin x + Bx \cos x$$

Then

$$y_p'(x) = A \sin x + B \cos x + Ax \cos x - Bx \sin x$$
$$y_p''(x) = 2A \cos x - 2B \sin x - Ax \sin x - Bx \cos x$$

Substituting in the complete equation yields

$$2A \cos x - 2B \sin x = \sin x$$

Equating coefficients of like functions, we have $A = 0$, $B = \frac{1}{2}$.   The particular integral therefore is

$$y_p(x) = -\tfrac{1}{2}x \cos x$$

The general solution of the complete equation is

$$y(x) = c_1 \sin x + c_2 \cos x - \tfrac{1}{2}x \cos x$$

Example 4.   Find the general solution of

$$(D^2 - 2D + 1)y = e^x$$

The auxiliary equation has the equal roots 1, 1. The complementary function is

$$y_c(x) = c_1 e^x + c_2 x e^x$$

Since the right member of the complete equation is e^x, the first try for a particular integral would be $y_p(x) = A e^x$, but this function solves the reduced equation. In conformity with Example 3, we therefore try $y_p(x) = A x e^x$, but because of the equal roots of the auxiliary equation, this function, too, solves the reduced equation. We therefore multiply again by x and try

$$y_p(x) = A x^2 e^x$$

Then

$$y_p'(x) = A x^2 e^x + 2 A x e^x$$
$$y_p''(x) = A x^2 e^x + 4 A x e^x + 2 A e^x$$

and substituting in the complete equation yields

$$A x^2 e^x + 4 A x e^x + 2 A e^x - 2(A x^2 e^x + 2 A x e^x) + A x^2 e^x = e^x$$

or $A = \frac{1}{2}$.

The general solution of the complete equation is therefore

$$y(x) = c_1 e^x + c_2 x e^x + \tfrac{1}{2} x^2 e^x$$

From the above examples we see that the form of a particular integral may often be inferred from the form of the right member f of the complete equation. In general, one may say that such is the case if by indefinitely repeated differentiation of f there are generated but a finite number of linearly independent functions. The accompanying table illustrates the procedure for some familiar functions.

$f(x)$	Trial $y_p(x)$
$e^{\alpha x}$	$A e^{\alpha x}$
$\cos \beta x$ or $\sin \beta x$	$A \sin \beta x + B \cos \beta x$
x^n	$A_0 x^n + A_1 x^{n-1} + A_2 x^{n-2} + \cdots + A_n$
$x^n e^{\alpha x}$	$e^{\alpha x}(A_0 x^n + A_1 x^{n-1} + \cdots + A_n)$
$e^{\alpha x} \sin \beta x$ or $e^{\alpha x} \cos \beta x$	$e^{\alpha x}(A \sin \beta x + B \cos \beta x)$

If the trial y_p happens to have a component which solves the reduced equation, one should use the trial y_p multiplied by x. If this function also has a component which solves the reduced equation, multiply by x^2. This will be as far as one need go in the case of a second-order equation.†

† Every solution of the reduced equation is an exponential function (with possible complex exponents) or x times such a function. No solution of the reduced equation therefore contains x^2 as a factor; hence it will never be necessary to multiply a trial y_p by more than x^2.

Of course, if the right member f is a sum of several different functions, each function may be treated separately (see Prob. 2, Sec. 4).

PROBLEMS

1. Find general solutions for the following constant-coefficient equations:

(a) $(D^2 - 4)y = \sin 2x$

(b) $(D^2 - 4D + 3)y = 2e^{-x} - 2$

(c) $(D^2 + 2D - 8)y = 16x$

(d) $(D^2 - 2D + 2)y = e^x \sin x$

(e) $(D^2 + 4)y = \sin 2x + x$

(f) $(D^2 - 2D + 1)y = 3xe^x$

(g) $(D^2 + 2D + 1)y = a + 25 \sin 2x$

(h) $D^2y = a_0x^n + a_1x^{n-1} + \cdots + a_n$

(i) $(D^2 + 16)y = A \cos^2 2x$

(j) $(D^2 - 3D + 2)y = 2x^2 + 2x$

(k) $y'' + 2y' = 4x$

(l) $(D^2 + 4D + 5)y = A \sin 2x$

(m) $(D^2 - 4D + 4)y = 2e^{2x} + xe^{2x}$

(n) $(D^2 + D)y = \sin 2x$

(o) $(D^2 - 2D)y = 4x^2e^{2x}$

(p) $(D^2 + D - 2)y = (1 + e^{-x})^3$

(q) $(D^2 - D + 1)y = \sinh 2x$†

(r) $(D^2 - 9)y = \cosh 3x$

(s) $(D^2 + D - 2)y = x(\sinh x + \frac{1}{10}e^x)$

★(t) $(D^2 - 1)y = x^{2n}$ (n a positive integer)

★(u) $(D^2 + 1)y = (e^{nx} - 1)/(e^x - 1)$ (n a positive integer)

★(v) $(D^2 + 1)y = [\sinh (n + \frac{1}{2})x]/(2 \sinh \frac{1}{2}x)$ (n a positive integer)

2. Find solutions for the following equations, satisfying the initial conditions indicated:

(a) $y'' - 3y' + 2y = -5 + 12e^{-x}; y = \frac{7}{2}, y' = 9, x = 0$

(b) $y'' - 2y' = 2; y = 0, y' = 0, x = 0$

(c) $(D^2 - D - 2)y = 5 \sin x; y = 1, y' = -1, x = 0$

(d) $y'' + \lambda^2y = A \sin \omega x; y = 0, y' = 0, x = 0$ (A, ω, λ constants; $\omega \neq \lambda$)

(e) $y'' - 2y' - 3y = 2 \sin^2 x; y = -\frac{1}{3}, y' = 0, x = 0$

(f) $y'' - 2y' - 3y = 3x; y = 0, y' = 1, x = 0$

6. The Method of Variation of Parameters

This method of finding a particular integral is due to J. L. Lagrange (1736–1813). It consists in using the general solution of the reduced equation and replacing the arbitrary constants with functions so chosen that a particular integral is obtained. It is important to know

† The *hyperbolic functions* $\sinh x$, $\cosh x$ are defined as $\sinh x = \frac{1}{2}(e^x - e^{-x})$ $\cosh x = \frac{1}{2}(e^x + e^{-x})$. Hence $D \sinh x = \cosh x$ and $D \cosh x = \sinh x$.

that *this method is also applicable to linear equations with nonconstant coefficients.*

Consider the linear equation

(6.1) $y'' + P(x)y' + Q(x)y = f(x)$

and suppose that $y_1(x)$ and $y_2(x)$ are linearly independent solutions of the reduced equation

(6.2) $y'' + P(x)y' + Q(x)y = 0$

The general solution of (6.2) then is

$$y_c(x) = c_1 y_1(x) + c_2 y_2(x)$$

Now consider the function

(6.3) $y_p(x) = u_1(x)y_1(x) + u_2(x)y_2(x)$

where $u_1(x)$ and $u_2(x)$ are functions which are to be so chosen that (6.3) is a particular integral of (6.1). Differentiating (6.3), we obtain

(6.4) $y' = u_1 y_1' + u_2 y_2' + u_1' y_1 + u_2' y_2$

Since we seek a solution of (6.1) and have two functions u_1 and u_2 at our disposal, we are free to impose one restriction on u_1 and u_2. We do this by setting the last two terms in (6.4) equal to zero:

(6.5) $u_1' y_1 + u_2' y_2 = 0$

Note that these are just the terms that arise because u_1 and u_2 are not constant.

Differentiating (6.4) and remembering that (6.5) holds, we obtain

(6.6) $y'' = u_1 y_1'' + u_2 y_2'' + u_1' y_1' + u_2' y_2'$

Substituting in the differential equation (6.1), we have

$$u_1 y_1'' + u_2 y_2'' + u_1' y_1' + u_2' y_2' + P(u_1 y_1' + u_2 y_2') + Q(u_1 y_1 + u_2 y_2) = f$$

or

(6.7) $u_1(y_1'' + Py_1' + Qy_1) + u_2(y_2'' + Py_2' + Qy_2) + u_1' y_1' + u_2' y_2' = f$

Because y_1 and y_2 are solutions of the reduced equation, the expressions in parentheses in (6.7) are zero; hence (6.7) reduces to

(6.8) $u_1' y_1' + u_2' y_2' = f$

Equations (6.5) and (6.8) constitute two linear equations in u_1' and u_2':

$$u_1'y_1 + u_2'y_2 = 0$$
$$u_1'y_1' + u_2'y_2' = f$$

Solving for u_1' and u_2' yields†

$$(6.9) \qquad u_1' = \frac{-fy_2}{y_1y_2' - y_1'y_2} \qquad u_2' = \frac{fy_1}{y_1y_2' - y_1'y_2}$$

From Eqs. (6.9) we obtain u_1 and u_2 by quadratures, and our problem is solved.

We illustrate the method by solving an equation with constant coefficients.

Example 1. Solve

$$(D^2 + 5D + 6)y = x^2 + 2x$$

by the method of variation of parameters.

The reduced equation is

$$(D^2 + 5D + 6)y = 0$$

and has the general solution

$$y_c(x) = c_1e^{-2x} + c_2e^{-3x}$$

Replacing c_1, c_2 with functions u_1, u_2 and differentiating, we get

$$y' = -2u_1e^{-2x} - 3u_2e^{-3x} + (u_1'e^{-2x} + u_2'e^{-3x})$$

We set the term in parentheses equal to zero:

$$u_1'e^{-2x} + u_2'e^{-3x} = 0$$

Thus,

$$y' = -2u_1e^{-2x} - 3u_2e^{-3x}$$

and

$$y'' = 4u_1e^{-2x} + 9u_2e^{-3x} - 2u_1'e^{-2x} - 3u_2'e^{-3x}$$

Substitution in the differential equation yields

$$4u_1e^{-2x} + 9u_2e^{-3x} - 2u_1'e^{-2x} - 3u_2'e^{-3x} + 5(-2u_1e^{-2x} - 3u_2e^{-3x})$$
$$+ 6(u_1e^{-2x} + u_2e^{-3x}) = x^2 + 2x$$

or

$$-2u_1'e^{-2x} - 3u_2'e^{-3x} = x^2 + 2x$$

† Naturally $y_1'y_2 - y_1y_2'$ must not be identically zero. But this fact follows from the assumption that y_1 and y_2 are linearly independent. For suppose that $y_1 \neq 0$; then, if $y_1y_2' - y_2y_1' = 0$, we have $(y_1y_2' - y_2y_1')/y_1^2 \equiv 0$ or $(d/dx)(y_2/y_1) \equiv 0$ or $y_2/y_1 = $ constant $= c$, and $y_2 = cy_1$; so y_1 and y_2 are dependent on any interval in which y_1 is never zero.

Solving for u_1' and u_2' gives

$$u_1'(x) = (x^2 + 2x)e^{2x} \qquad u_2'(x) = -(x^2 + 2x)e^{3x}$$

These last equations are easily integrated to give†

$$u_1(x) = \tfrac{1}{2}e^{2x}(x^2 + x - \tfrac{1}{2})$$
$$u_2(x) = \tfrac{1}{3}e^{3x}(-x^2 - \tfrac{4}{3}x + \tfrac{4}{9})$$

A particular integral of the complete equation then is

$$y_p(x) = \tfrac{1}{2}(x^2 + x - \tfrac{1}{2}) + \tfrac{1}{3}(-x^2 - \tfrac{4}{3}x + \tfrac{4}{9})$$
$$= \tfrac{1}{6}x^2 + \tfrac{1}{18}x - \tfrac{11}{108}$$

and the general solution is

$$y(x) = c_1e^{-2x} + c_2e^{-3x} + \tfrac{1}{6}x^2 + \tfrac{1}{18}x - \tfrac{11}{108}$$

which agrees with the solution obtained by the method of undetermined coefficients in Example 1, Sec. 5.

Example 2. Find the general solution of

$$(D^2 + 1)y = \sec x$$

The reduced equation has the general solution

$$y_c(x) = c_1 \cos x + c_2 \sin x$$

We try for a particular integral

$$y_p(x) = u_1(x) \cos x + u_2(x) \sin x$$

Then

$$y_p'(x) = -u_1 \sin x + u_2 \cos x + u_1' \cos x + u_2' \sin x$$

and we set

$$u_1' \cos x + u_2' \sin x = 0$$

For the second derivative we get

$$y_p''(x) = -u_1 \cos x - u_2 \sin x - u_1' \sin x + u_2' \cos x$$

On substituting y_p'' and y_p in the differential equation and simplifying, we obtain

$$-u_1' \sin x + u_2' \cos x = \sec x$$

Solving for u_1' and u_2', we obtain

$$u_1'(x) = -\frac{\sin x}{\cos x} \qquad u_2'(x) = 1$$

† There is no need to add a constant of integration here, since we seek a particular integral, and any functions $u_1(x)$ and $u_2(x)$ satisfying the required conditions will do.

Integrating these equations gives

$$u_1(x) = \log |\cos x| \qquad u_2(x) = x$$

Then

$$y_p(x) = x \sin x + (\log |\cos x|) \cos x$$

The general solution of the complete equation is therefore

$$y(x) = c_1 \cos x + c_2 \sin x + x \sin x + (\log |\cos x|) \cos x$$

Observe that we could not have used the method of undetermined coefficients, as we could not determine a proper form for a trial y_p.

The method of variation of parameters enables us to find the general solution of *any* linear differential equations of second order whose complementary function is known. Since the two quadratures involved in getting u_1, u_2 from (6.9) are considered as elementary operations from the point of view of differential equations, we may state: *The solution of a linear second-order differential equation is accomplished by finding two linearly independent solutions of the reduced equation.*

PROBLEMS

1. Find the general solutions of the following equations by the method of variation of parameters:

(a) $(D^2 - D - 2)y = e^{2x}$
(b) $(D^2 + 2D + 1)y = e^{-x}/x$
(c) $(D^2 + 1)y = \sin x$
(d) $y'' + 4y = \tan 2x$
(e) $y'' - y = 1/(e^x - 1)$
(f) $(D^2 - D - 2)y = e^{-2x} \cos e^{-x}$
(g) $(D^2 + 4)y = \csc 2x$
(h) $(D^2 + 4)y = \sin^2 x$
(i) $y'' + 2y' = 5 + e^{-x}$
(j) $y'' + 4y = \tan^2 2x$
(k) $y'' + \sqrt{2}\, y' + 2y = 2 \sqrt{2} \log |x| - 2x^{-3}$

2. Find a particular integral of:

(a) $(D^2 + 1)y = \sec x \csc x$
(b) $(D^2 + 1)y = \cot 2x$
(c) $(D^2 + 2D + 2)y = e^{-x} \sin x$
(d) $(D^2 - 2D - 3)y = \frac{1}{2}x^2 e^{-x}$
(e) $(D^2 + 1)y = |x|$

3. Find general solutions of the following equations (for the complementary functions, see Prob. 7, Sec. 2):

(a) $x^2y'' + xy' - 4y = x^3$
(b) $x^2y'' - 2y = x^2$
(c) $x^2y'' + xy' - y = x^2e^{-x}$
(d) $x^2y'' + 2xy' - 2y = 3x + (\log |x|)^2$
(e) $x^2y'' - 2y = (1/x^2) \cos (1/x)$

4. If $y(x) = c_1x + c_2(2x^2 - 1)$ is the general solution of $(2x^2 + 1)y'' - 4xy' + 4y = 0$, find a particular integral of $(2x^2 + 1)y'' - 4xy' + 4y = 2(1 + 6x^2)x^{-3}$.

★5. Show that the variation-of-parameters method applied to the equation $y'' + y = f$ yields the particular integral $y_p(x) = \int_0^x f(s) \sin (x - s)\, ds$.

★6. Show that the denominator

$$\Delta = \begin{vmatrix} y_1 & y_2 \\ y_1' & y_2' \end{vmatrix}$$

in formulas (6.9) (the so-called *Wronskian* of the solutions y_1, y_2) is given by the formula

$$\Delta(x) = \Delta(x_0)e^{-\int_{x_0}^x P(s)\, ds}$$

where P is the coefficient of y' in Eq. (6.2). HINT: Form Δ' and use (6.2) to replace y_1'', y_2'', obtaining $\Delta' = -P\Delta$.

7. Oscillatory Systems

Second-order linear equations with constant coefficients are so intimately connected with vibration problems that the treatment of the former cannot be considered complete without some discussion of the latter. In vibration problems the independent variable is the time t. Accordingly, we adopt the "dot" notation of Newton and write our second-order equation as

(7.1) $\ddot{x} + a\dot{x} + bx = f$

We discuss a mechanical system which gives rise to an equation of the form (7.1). Consider a particle of mass m attached to a weightless spring (Fig. 1) and subjected to a force $F(t)$ in the x direction. The neutral (unstretched spring) position of the mass is at $x = 0$, and the spring force is given by Hooke's law; that is, it is proportional to the displacement x from the neutral position. If there is a frictional force retarding the motion proportional to the velocity $\dot{x}$, then Newton's law of motion asserts that

$$m\ddot{x} = -kx - r\dot{x} + F$$

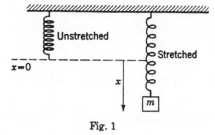

Fig. 1

where k is the spring constant (positive), and r the coefficient of friction (positive).   Then

$$m\ddot{x} + r\dot{x} + kx = F$$

or

(7.2)
$$\ddot{x} + \frac{r}{m}\dot{x} + \frac{k}{m}x = \frac{1}{m}F$$

Reference to (7.1) shows that in our problem $\ddot{x}$ arises from the inertia forces, $a\dot{x}$ from friction, and bx from the spring force.   The function on the right, f being in the nature of an impressed force, is called the *forcing function*.

In addition to the simple spring problem above, second-order equations with constant coefficients are also encountered in simple electric-circuit problems.   In Sec. 12, Chap. IV, we encountered the following equation:

(7.3)
$$\ddot{q} + \frac{R}{L}\dot{q} + \frac{1}{LC}q = \frac{1}{L}E$$

where R, L, and C are the resistance, inductance, and capacitance in the circuit of Fig. 18 of Chap. IV, and E is the impressed e.m.f., which is supposed known.   Thus, comparing Eqs. (7.2) and (7.3), we see that, in an electric circuit, inductance plays the role of mass in a mechanical system, resistance corresponds to coefficient of friction, the spring constant to the reciprocal of the capacitance, and the charge on the condenser to the displacement.

The analogy between electrical and mechanical systems renders the mathematical treatments of the two systems identical and extends to much more complicated systems than those we have considered.

8. The Superposition Principle

We have found, so far, two methods for solving the complete equation (7.1), namely, undetermined coefficients and variation of parameters. The theorem which follows enables us to write a particular integral whenever the right member of the complete equation is the sum of functions for which particular integrals are known. Equally important, the theorem often reflects a physical principle regarding the additivity of effects. For example, in a simple electrical circuit the effect of the sum of two impressed e.m.f.'s is equal to the sum of their individual effects.

Theorem (Principle of Superposition). *If $w_i(t)$ are solutions of*

$$\ddot{x} + a\dot{x} + bx = f_i$$

for $i = 1, \ldots, n$, then

$$x = w_1 + \cdots + w_n$$

is a solution of

$$\ddot{x} + a\dot{x} + bx = f_1 + \cdots + f_n$$

The proof of this theorem is a simple exercise and is left to the reader. It should be emphasized that the theorem is valid for linear equations whether the coefficients a and b are constant or not.

9. Free Vibrations

If the forcing function is identically zero, the differential equation (7.1) is homogeneous,

$$\ddot{x} + a\dot{x} + bx = 0$$

and we have the case of *free vibrations*. From the physical meaning of the coefficients, it follows that $a \geq 0$, $b \geq 0$. The character of the motion is determined by the nature of the roots of the auxiliary equation:

$$r_1 = \frac{-a + \sqrt{a^2 - 4b}}{2} \qquad r_2 = \frac{-a - \sqrt{a^2 - 4b}}{2}$$

There are three cases to consider.

Case 1. $a^2 - 4b > 0$. Here r_1 and r_2 are real and unequal, and if $b > 0$ (which we suppose), they are negative. The general solution is

$$x(t) = c_1 e^{r_1 t} + c_2 e^{r_2 t}$$

The motion is *aperiodic* and *overcritically damped*. The displacement can have at most one maximum, and it then decays to zero asymptotically. This type of motion is called *subsidence*.

Case 2. $a^2 - 4b = 0$. Here r_1 and r_2 are equal to $-\frac{1}{2}a$. The general solution is

$$x(t) = c_1 e^{-at/2} + c_2 t e^{-at/2}$$

The motion is *aperiodic* and *critically damped*.

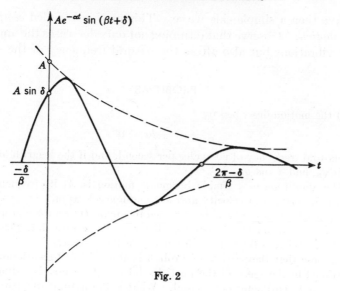

Fig. 2

Case 3. $a^2 - 4b < 0$. Here r_1 and r_2 are conjugate complex:

$$r_1 = -\alpha + i\beta \qquad r_2 = -\alpha - i\beta$$

where $\alpha = \frac{1}{2}a$ and $\beta = \frac{1}{2}\sqrt{4b - a^2}$. The general solution is

(9.1)
$$\begin{aligned} x(t) &= e^{-\alpha t}(c_1 \cos \beta t + c_2 \sin \beta t) \\ &= A e^{-\alpha t} \sin (\beta t + \delta) \end{aligned}$$

The motion has an *oscillatory* character and is *undercritically damped* by the factor $e^{-\alpha t} = e^{-at/2}$. The factor

$$c_1 \cos \beta t + c_2 \sin \beta t = A \sin (\beta t + \delta)$$

is a periodic function. Its period is $2\pi/\beta$, and its frequency $\beta/2\pi$ is called the *natural frequency* of the system—"natural" because the oscillations are not caused by any impressed force. A graph of the solution (9.1) appears in Fig. 2.

In any time interval equal to the *period* $2\pi/\beta$ the amplitude of the vibrations decreases in the constant ratio $e^{\alpha 2\pi/\beta}$. The logarithm of the amplitude thus decreases by the constant difference $\alpha 2\pi/\beta$. This difference is called the *logarithmic decrement*. The two numbers, natural frequency and logarithmic decrement, describe the character of the vibrations completely.

In the important case of *no damping*, $a = 0 = \alpha$, one has $\beta = \sqrt{b}$, and (9.1) becomes

$$x(t) = A \sin (\beta t + \delta)$$

We have then a simple sine wave. This motion is called *simple harmonic motion*. Observe that damping not only decreases the amplitude of the vibrations but also alters the natural frequency of the system.

PROBLEMS

1. If the motion described by

$$\ddot{x} + a\dot{x} + bx = 0$$

has a natural frequency of 60 cycles per second, and if the logarithmic decrement is $\frac{1}{10}$, find a and b.

2. The amplitude of a simple harmonic motion is A; its frequency is ν. What are its maximum velocity and maximum acceleration?

3. A particle of mass 1 gram is attracted to a point O by a force proportional to the distance from O. When the distance is 1 centimeter, the force is 100 dynes. What is the natural frequency of the system?

4. Suppose that the particle of Prob. 3 is also subject to a frictional force proportional to the speed of the particle and that this force is 5 dynes when the speed is 1 centimeter per second. What is the natural frequency of the system? The logarithmic decrement?

5. A weightless spring supports a weight of 20 pounds. The natural frequency of the system is found to be 1.27 cycles per second. Find the spring constant k.

6. A 5-pound weight stretches a weightless spring 2 inches. The natural frequency of the system is found to be $5/\pi$ cycles per second. If there is damping proportional to the velocity, find the time required for the amplitude of the oscillations to decrease to one-half its original value.

7. In a simple series electric circuit there are a condenser of capacitance 200×10^{-6} farad, a resistance of 1 ohm, and an inductance of 0.1 henry. What is the natural frequency of the system? How large must the resistance be in order that the system be critically damped?

8. The differential equation which governs the motion of the simple pendulum of Fig. 3, consisting of a mass m at the end of a weightless rod of length l, is

$$\frac{d^2\theta}{dt^2} = -\frac{g}{l}\sin\theta$$

(see Sec. 10, Chap. IV). Assuming θ is small, "linearize" this equation by replacing $\sin\theta$ with θ, and determine the period of the pendulum for small oscillations.

9. A cylindrical buoy 2 feet in diameter and weighing 100 pounds floats with its axis vertical in water (see Fig. 4). Find the period of oscillation when it is depressed slightly and released.

10. A cylindrical buoy 2 feet in diameter floats with its axis vertical in water. On being depressed lightly and released, it is found to bob with a period of 2 seconds. What is the weight of the buoy?

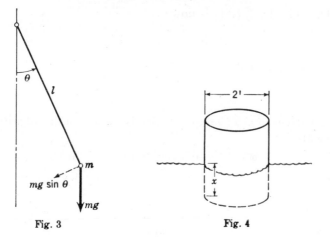

Fig. 3   Fig. 4

11. A cubical block of wood 28 inches on an edge floats in water with a face down. It is depressed slightly and released, whereupon it bobs with a period of 1.35 seconds. Find the specific gravity of the wood.

12. A 5-pound weight stretches a spring 6 inches. The weight is then pulled down 3 inches farther and released. Find the equation of motion, its period, and its frequency.

★13. In Prob. 12 suppose that the top of the spring is given the periodic motion $x(t) = \frac{1}{3} \sin \pi t$. Find the motion of the weight.

14. In the interior of the earth (if it is assumed spherical, of uniform density, and nonrotating) the gravitational force is directed toward the center and is proportional to the distance from the center. Show that a train in a straight tunnel joining two points on the earth would move by gravity alone (neglecting friction) in simple harmonic motion, and find its period. What would its maximum speed be if the tunnel is L miles long?

10. Simple Forcing Functions

In many oscillatory systems (7.1), the forcing function f is periodic. We therefore treat first the simplest periodic functions, namely, the simple harmonic forcing functions $f(t) = A \cos \omega t$ and $f(t) = A \sin \omega t$. Differential equation (7.1) is then

$$(10.1) \qquad \ddot{x} + a\dot{x} + bx = \begin{cases} A \cos \omega t \\ A \sin \omega t \end{cases}$$

Although we could seek particular integrals of (10.1) by the method of undetermined coefficients, it is far simpler in algebraic detail to find first the response to the complex exponential forcing function $f(t) = Ae^{i\omega t}$. The real and imaginary parts of this solution will then give solutions of (10.1).   The D.E. (7.1) is now

(10.2) $$\ddot{x} + a\dot{x} + bx = Ae^{i\omega t}$$

and we seek a particular integral

(10.3) $$x_p(t) = Ce^{i\omega t}$$

The derivatives $\dot{x}_p$, $\ddot{x}_p$ are immediately found, and substitution in (10.2) yields

$$-\omega^2 Ce^{i\omega t} + ai\omega Ce^{i\omega t} + bCe^{i\omega t} = Ae^{i\omega t}$$

Hence†

$$C = \frac{A}{(b - \omega^2) + ia\omega}$$

and therefore the particular integral is

(10.4) $$x_p(t) = \frac{A}{(b - \omega^2) + ia\omega} e^{i\omega t}$$

The real and imaginary parts of $Ae^{i\omega t}$ are $A \cos \omega t$ and $A \sin \omega t$, respectively.   Therefore, the real and imaginary parts of (10.4) must yield the corresponding particular integrals of Eqs. (10.1) with forcing functions $A \cos \omega t$ and $A \sin \omega t$.   To separate (10.4) into real and imaginary parts, we write the denominator in polar form:

$$(b - \omega^2) + ia\omega$$
$$= \sqrt{(b - \omega^2)^2 + a^2\omega^2} \left[\frac{b - \omega^2}{\sqrt{(b - \omega^2)^2 + a^2\omega^2}} + i \frac{a\omega}{\sqrt{(b - \omega^2)^2 + a^2\omega^2}} \right]$$
$$= \sqrt{(b - \omega^2)^2 + a^2\omega^2} \, (\cos \lambda + i \sin \lambda)$$
$$= \sqrt{(b - \omega^2)^2 + a^2\omega^2} \, e^{i\lambda}$$

where the constant λ is defined by

(10.5) $$\cos \lambda = \frac{b - \omega^2}{\sqrt{(b - \omega^2)^2 + a^2\omega^2}} \qquad \sin \lambda = \frac{a\omega}{\sqrt{(b - \omega^2)^2 + a^2\omega^2}}$$

Then the particular integral (10.4) becomes

$$x_p(t) = \frac{A}{\sqrt{(b - \omega^2)^2 + a^2\omega^2}} e^{-i\lambda} e^{i\omega t}$$

† If the denominator vanishes, there is no friction ($a = 0$), and $b = \omega^2$ or $\omega = \sqrt{b}$.   In other words there is no damping in the system, and the forcing function has the same frequency as the natural frequency of the system.   In this case our particular integral would have the form $Cte^{i\omega t}$.   We exclude this undamped "resonance" case from consideration.

or

(10.6) $x_p(t) = \dfrac{A}{\sqrt{(b - \omega^2)^2 + a^2\omega^2}} e^{i(\omega t - \lambda)}$

$= \dfrac{A}{\sqrt{(b - \omega^2)^2 + a^2\omega^2}} [\cos(\omega t - \lambda) + i \sin(\omega t - \lambda)]$

The particular integrals of D.E. (10.1) therefore are

(10.7) $x_p(t) = \begin{cases} \dfrac{A}{\sqrt{(b - \omega^2)^2 + a^2\omega^2}} \cos(\omega t - \lambda) \\[3mm] \dfrac{A}{\sqrt{(b - \omega^2)^2 + a^2\omega^2}} \sin(\omega t - \lambda) \end{cases}$

The general solutions of (10.1) are

(10.8) $x(t) = \begin{cases} Ce^{-\alpha t} \sin(\beta t + \delta) + \dfrac{A}{\sqrt{(b - \omega^2)^2 + a^2\omega^2}} \cos(\omega t - \lambda) \\[3mm] Ce^{-\alpha t} \sin(\beta t + \delta) + \dfrac{A}{\sqrt{(b - \omega^2)^2 + a^2\omega^2}} \sin(\omega t - \lambda) \end{cases}$

if we have positive damping less than critical. Then $-\alpha = -a/2 < 0$, and after a sufficiently long period of time the first term in (10.8) will be very small, owing to the damping factor $e^{-\alpha t}$. Hence, after a long time the only motion will be that of the forced vibrations given by (10.7). These vibrations have period $2\pi/\omega$, frequency $\omega/2\pi$, and amplitude $A/\sqrt{(b - \omega^2)^2 + a^2\omega^2}$ and lag the force by the *phase angle* λ.

The situation encountered here is described by saying that the first right-hand term in (10.8) represents the *transient phenomenon*, while the last term in (10.8) represents the *steady-state phenomenon*.

PROBLEMS

1. Find the steady-state solution for the current in the simple circuit of Fig. 18, Chap. IV, using $E(t) = E_0 \sin \omega t$. Show that the steady-state current may be written as

$$i_S(t) = \frac{E_0}{Z}\left(-\frac{X}{Z} \cos \omega t + \frac{R}{Z} \sin \omega t \right)$$

where $X = L\omega - 1/C\omega$ is called the *reactance*, and $Z = \sqrt{X^2 + R^2}$ is called the *impedance*. Thus show that the current lags the voltage by a time λ/ω, where λ is given by

$$\sin \lambda = \frac{X}{Z} \qquad \cos \lambda = \frac{R}{Z}$$

That is, the current maxima occur λ/ω seconds after the voltage maxima.

2. A simple circuit has an inductance of 0.1 henry, a resistance of 10 ohms, and a capacitance of 0.0002 farad. The impressed e.m.f. is the sum of two sinusoidal e.m.f.'s of equal phase, amplitudes 100 and 50 volts, and frequencies $200/\pi$ and $100/\pi$, respectively. Find the current as a function of time if $i = 0$ and $q = 0$ when the e.m.f. is zero.

3. A weightless coil spring is stretched 2 inches by a force of 1 pound. It is hung by one end, and a mass weighing 8 pounds is attached to the other. A force equal to $4 \sin t + 2 \sin 2t$ is applied to the mass. If the system is at rest when $t = 0$, find the motion.

4. Show that the steady-state solution for the current in the simple circuit of Fig. 18, Chap. IV, with the complex e.m.f. $E(t) = E_0 e^{i\omega t}$, can be written as

$$i_S(t) = \frac{E_0}{Y} e^{i\omega t}$$

where $Y = R + iX = Ze^{i\lambda}$ is called the *complex impedance* (R, X, Z, L as in Prob. 1).

5. Find a particular solution of Eq. (7.1) for the nonharmonic forcing function $f(t) = Ae^{\gamma t} \cos \omega t$. HINT: Observe that $f(t)$ is the real part of $Ae^{(\gamma+i\omega)t}$.

11. Superposition of Simple Solutions

Suppose now that the forcing function is periodic with period $2\pi/\omega$ and is the following sum of simple harmonic functions:

$$(11.1) \qquad f(t) = \sum_{k=1}^{n} (a_k \cos k\omega t + b_k \sin k\omega t)$$

In Sec. 10 we obtained particular integrals for simple harmonic forcing functions. Using (10.7), we see that particular integrals of

$$\ddot{x} + a\dot{x} + bx = \begin{cases} a_k \cos k\omega t \\ b_k \sin k\omega t \end{cases}$$

are, respectively,

$$x_p(t) = \frac{b - k^2\omega^2}{(b - k^2\omega^2)^2 + a^2k^2\omega^2} a_k \cos k\omega t$$

$$+ \frac{ak\omega}{(b - k^2\omega^2)^2 + a^2k^2\omega^2} a_k \sin k\omega t$$

and

$$x_p(t) = \frac{-ak\omega}{(b - k^2\omega^2)^2 + a^2k^2\omega^2} b_k \cos k\omega t$$

$$+ \frac{b - k^2\omega^2}{(b - k^2\omega^2)^2 + a^2k^2\omega^2} b_k \sin k\omega t$$

Application of the superposition principle yields, as a particular integral of

$$(11.2) \qquad \ddot{x} + a\dot{x} + b\dot{x} = f$$

where $f(t)$ is given by (11.1), the following function:

$$(11.3) \quad x_p(t) = \sum_{k=1}^{n} \frac{(b - k^2\omega^2)a_k - ak\omega b_k}{(b - k^2\omega^2)^2 + a^2k^2\omega^2} \cos k\omega t$$

$$+ \frac{ak\omega a_k + (b - k^2\omega^2)b_k}{(b - k^2\omega^2)^2 + a^2k^2\omega^2} \sin k\omega t$$

Example 1. Find, using (11.3), a particular integral of

$$\ddot{x} + \dot{x} + x = \sin 2\omega t + \cos 3\omega t$$

Here $a = 1, b = 1$ and $b_2 = 1, a_3 = 1$, while all other a_i, b_i are zero. Hence,

$$x_p(t) = \frac{0 - 2\omega}{(1 - 4\omega^2)^2 + 4\omega^2} \cos 2\omega t + \frac{0 + 1 - 4\omega^2}{(1 - 4\omega^2)^2 + 4\omega^2} \sin 2\omega t$$

$$+ \frac{1 - 9\omega^2 - 0}{(1 - 9\omega^2)^2 + 9\omega^2} \cos 3\omega t + \frac{3\omega + 0}{(1 - 9\omega^2)^2 + 9\omega^2} \sin 3\omega t$$

$$= \frac{-2\omega}{1 - 4\omega^2 + 16\omega^4} \cos 2\omega t + \frac{1 - 4\omega^2}{1 - 4\omega^2 + 16\omega^4} \sin 2\omega t$$

$$+ \frac{1 - 9\omega^2}{1 - 9\omega^2 + 81\omega^4} \cos 3\omega t + \frac{3}{1 - 9\omega^2 + 81\omega^4} \sin 3\omega t$$

Observe that the particular integrals we have obtained are (if there is damping) precisely the steady-state solutions. In addition, they are the only periodic solutions. The periodic particular integrals will (if there is damping) be referred to as *the* periodic solutions.

The sums (11.1) form a special class of periodic functions called *trigonometric polynomials*. They are as fundamental to the study of periodic functions as the familiar algebraic polynomials are to the study of nonperiodic functions. In particular, arbitrary periodic functions, restricted only by mild continuity conditions, can be approximated to any desired degree of accuracy by trigonometric polynomials. Moreover, the approximating trigonometric polynomials can be taken as the partial sums of an infinite series expansion of the function to be approximated. These expansions are known as *Fourier series*, and they form a most important tool of theoretical and applied mathematical analysis. A glimpse of their usefulness is caught in the observation that if the forcing function in Eq. (11.2) is represented (or approximated) by a sum similar to (11.1), then the periodic integral (which also is the steady-state solution in the case of damping) is immediately written down as a like sum [see (11.3)].

PROBLEMS

1. Find, using (11.3), a particular integral of
$$\ddot{x} + \dot{x} + 2x = \sin t + \tfrac{1}{2}\sin 2t + \tfrac{1}{3}\sin 3t$$

2. Find the periodic solution of
$$\ddot{x} + \tfrac{1}{2}\dot{x} - \tfrac{1}{2}x = \cos \tfrac{1}{2}t + \sin t$$

3. Find the periodic solution of
$$\ddot{x} + 2\dot{x} + 2x = 4\sin t \cos t$$

4. Find the general solution of
$$3\ddot{x} + 5x = 8\cos^2 \tfrac{3}{2}t \sin 2t$$

5. Find the periodic solution of
$$L\ddot{q} + R\dot{q} + \frac{1}{C}q = E(t)$$

where

$$E(t) = \tfrac{1}{2}a_0 + \sum_{k=1}^{n}(a_k \cos k\omega t + b_k \sin k\omega t)$$

★6. Use the result of Prob. 5 to calculate the integral

$$\frac{\omega}{2\pi}\int_0^{2\pi/\omega} i^2(t)\,dt \qquad i = \dot{q}$$

12. Connection with Systems; Existence and Uniqueness

Let us return to the general second-order equation

(12.1) $$y'' = g(x, y, y')$$

If we substitute z for y', then (12.1) becomes

(12.2) $$z' = g(x, y, z)$$

Equation (12.2) appears to be a first-order equation. Of course, (12.2) by itself cannot replace D.E. (12.1), since the relation between z and y is not expressed by (12.2). If, however, we add this relation, thus arriving at a *system of equations*

(12.3a) $$y' = z$$
(12.3b) $$z' = g(x, y, z)$$

then we have an equivalent formulation of D.E. (12.1). Indeed, by (12.3a) we have $z = y'$ and therefore $z' = y''$, and if these substitutions are made in (12.3b), the D.E. (12.1) is recovered.

Equations (12.3) form a system of two differential equations of the first order in the two unknowns y, z. System (12.3) is rather special; a quite general system (in normal form) is the following:

$$(12.4a) \qquad\qquad y' = f(x, y, z)$$
$$(12.4b) \qquad\qquad z' = g(x, y, z)$$

Even such a general system is related to a second-order equation as system (12.3) is related to (12.1). Indeed, if Eq. (12.4a) can be solved for z, say $z = h(x, y, y')$, then $z' = dh(x, y, y')/dx$, and when these expressions are substituted in (12.4b) a second-order equation for the function y results. Once this equation is solved, that is, y is known as a function of x, then z is also known, since $z(x) = h(x, y(x), y'(x))$. Thus the solution of system (12.4) is reduced to the solution of a single second-order equation.

Example 1. Eliminate z from the system

$$(12.5a) \qquad\qquad y'(x) = P(x, y)z + Q(x, y)$$
$$(12.5b) \qquad\qquad z'(x) = g(x, y, z)$$

Assuming that the solution $y(x)$ is twice differentiable, one can differentiate (12.5a) and obtain

$$(12.6) \qquad y'' = Pz' + \left(\frac{\partial P}{\partial x} + \frac{\partial P}{\partial y}y'\right)z + \frac{\partial Q}{\partial x} + \frac{\partial Q}{\partial y}y'$$

On the other hand, one has z from (12.5a): $z = (y' - Q)/P$; and z' from (12.5b): $z' = g[x, y, (y' - Q)/P]$. These expressions, substituted in (12.6), give

$$(12.7) \quad y'' = Pg\left(x, y, \frac{y' - Q}{P}\right) + \left(\frac{\partial P}{\partial x} + \frac{\partial P}{\partial y}y'\right)\frac{y' - Q}{P} + \frac{\partial Q}{\partial x} + \frac{\partial Q}{\partial y}y'$$
$$= f(x, y, y')$$

a second-order equation for y alone. When this equation is solved, z is found from the relation $z = (y' - Q)/P$. Thus, the solution of system (12.5) is reduced to that of the single equation (12.7).

By replacing the second-order equation (12.1) with the system (12.3), little is gained for the practical solution of (12.1). However, this replacement is of great heuristic importance. If one considers the two unknowns y, z in system (12.4) as the two components of one "vector" Y (no geometric meaning is implied in the use of this word), the derivatives y', z' as the two components of the derivative Y' of Y, and f, g

as the two components of a vector function F, then system (12.4) appears as a single equation of the first order in the one unknown Y:

$$(12.8) \qquad\qquad Y' = F(x, Y)$$

This is purely symbolical and does not solve anything, but it suggests how to extend results and methods known for first-order equations to systems of the form (12.4) and, therefore, to second-order equations similar to (12.1). The key is in the above interpretation of y, z as the two components of one quantity. For example, since prescribing the value of y at some initial x, say $y(x_0) = y_0$, specifies a particular solution of $y' = f(x, y)$, we expect that prescribing the value of Y at some initial x, say $Y(x_0) = Y_0$ [which amounts to $y(x_0) = y_0$, $z(x_0) = z_0$], singles out a particular solution of $Y' = F(x, Y)$ and, hence, of system (12.4). This is indeed the case, and for the second-order equation (12.1) this shows again that prescribing the values of y, y' at some x [$y(x_0) = y_0$, $y'(x_0) = y_0'$] specifies a particular solution.

In the next section we use the above heuristic device to extend the numerical methods developed in Chap. I for equations of the first order to systems and thereby to equations of the second order. Here we state existence and uniqueness theorems for (12.4) and (12.1). The proofs can be based on the convergence of the numerical methods in the same way as was done in Sec. 3, Chap. III, for single equations of the first order.

Theorem 1. *If $f(x, y, z)$, $g(x, y, z)$ and $\partial f/\partial y$, $\partial f/\partial z$, $\partial g/\partial y$, $\partial g/\partial z$ are continuous in some box R: $a_1 \leq x \leq a_2$, $b_1 \leq y \leq b_2$, $c_1 \leq z \leq c_2$, then through each point (x_0, y_0, z_0) interior to R passes a unique integral curve of the system $dy/dx = f(x, y, z)$, $dz/dx = g(x, y, z)$.*

It should be observed that "integral curve" in this theorem means a solution $y = y(x)$, $z = z(x)$, which in three-dimensional space with coordinates x, y, z represents a curve. That the curve "passes" through (x_0, y_0, z_0) means $y(x_0) = y_0$, $z(x_0) = z_0$.

We now specialize this theorem to apply to system (12.3) and, therefore, to the second-order equation (12.1). In this case we write p for $z = y'$ and speak of a region R in xyp space. It consists of a rectangle $a_1 \leq x \leq a_2$, $b_1 \leq y \leq b_2$ in the xy plane, together with an interval of values for the slope p: $c_1 \leq p \leq c_2$. A point (x_0, y_0, p_0) means a point (x_0, y_0) in the xy plane and a slope p_0. The function f is quite simple in this special case [compare (12.3) with (12.4)]: $f(x, y, p) = p$. This function is clearly continuous and has derivatives of all orders, so that no hypothesis need be formulated about it. We are now ready for our specialization of Theorem 1.

Theorem 2. *If $g(x, y, p)$, $\partial g/\partial y$, and $\partial g/\partial p$ are continuous in some region $a_1 \leq x \leq a_2$, $b_1 \leq y \leq b_2$, $c_1 \leq p \leq c_2$ of xyp space, and if (x_0, y_0, p_0) is a point of this region, then there is a unique integral curve of the equation $d^2y/dx^2 = g(x, y, dy/dx)$ which passes through (x_0, y_0) with slope p_0.*

PROBLEMS

1. Using the method of Example 1, find all solutions of the following systems:

(a) $y' = z - \dfrac{2}{x^2}$, $z' = y - \dfrac{2}{x}$

(b) $y' = e^{3x}z$, $4z' = 12z - 37e^{-3x}y$

(c) $y' = z \sec x$, $z' = \sin x - y \cos x - z \tan x$

(d) $y' = z + x^2$, $z' = 8y - 2z - 2x^2 + 16x$

(e) $xy' = z$, $xyz' = yz - z^2$

2. Find the solutions of the following systems which satisfy the given initial conditions:

(a) $e^x y' = -z$, $z' = 4e^x y - z$; $y = 3$, $z = 0$ at $x = 0$

(b) $2y' = z^2$, $2zz' = -4y + 3z^2$; $y = e^{-1}$, $z = 2e^{-\frac{1}{2}}$ at $x = -\frac{1}{2}$

(c) $e^{2y}y' = z$, $e^{2y}z' = 2z^2 + e^{2y}$; $y = z = 0$ at $x = -2$

(d) $y' = xz$, $xz' = -y - z + \sin x$; $y = 0$, $z = \frac{1}{2}$ at $x = \pi/2$

3. Which of the systems of Probs. 1 and 2 are (a) linear, (b) linear homogeneous, (c) linear with constant coefficients?

4. Is there an integral curve of the equation $xy'' = y'$ which passes through the point $(0, 1)$ with (a) slope 1, (b) slope 0?

★5. Formulate Lipschitz conditions analogous to (2.6), Chap. III, which can replace the hypotheses of existence and continuity of the partial derivatives of f and g in Theorems 1 and 2.

★6. Formulate a global existence theorem analogous to Theorem 3, Sec. 3, Chap. III, for the D.E. $y'' = g(x, y, y')$.

13. Numerical Solutions

Following the heuristic device developed in the preceding section, we extend the numerical methods of Sec. 7, Chap. I, to systems of two differential equations of the first order and thereby to differential equations of the second order. The device is to consider the two equations of the system

(13.1) $$y' = f(x, y, z) \qquad z' = g(x, y, z)$$

as the two components of one equation $Y' = F(x, Y)$, where Y is a vector whose components are y, z; Y' is the derivative of Y; F is a vector whose components are f, g. Likewise, the initial conditions

$$(13.2) \qquad\qquad y(x_0) = y_0 \qquad z(x_0) = z_0$$

are considered as the two components of the one equation $Y(x_0) = Y_0$.

Thus, to extend the most primitive Euler-Cauchy method [the E.C.M. I or polygonal method, Eq. (7.7), Chap. I] to system (13.1) with the I.C. (13.2), one writes $Y_k = Y_{k-1} + hF_{k-1}$ in place of $y_k = y_{k-1} + hf_{k-1}$ and transcribes this into

$$(13.3) \qquad\qquad y_k = y_{k-1} + hf_{k-1} \qquad z_k = z_{k-1} + hg_{k-1}$$

This is indeed a simple recursive formula for computing $y_1 = y(x_0 + h)$ and $z_1 = z(x_0 + h)$ from y_0 and z_0, $y_2 = y(x_0 + 2h)$ and $z_2 = z(x_0 + 2h)$ from y_1 and z_1, etc., with an error of order $O(h^2)$,† the same as in the case of a single equation. Of course, the notation used here and in the following is an extension of that used in Sec. 7, Chap. I:

$$(13.4) \qquad \begin{array}{lll} x_k = x_0 + kh & y_k = y(x_k) & z_k = z(x_k) \\ f_k = f(x_k, y_k, z_k) & g_k = g(x_k, y_k, z_k) \\ k = 0, \pm 1, \pm 2, \ldots \end{array}$$

We now translate this method into one for the second-order equation

$$(13.5) \qquad\qquad y'' = g(x, y, y')$$

with the initial conditions

$$(13.6) \qquad\qquad y(x_0) = y_0 \qquad y'(x_0) = p_0$$

By Sec. 12, this problem is equivalent to $y' = z$, $z' = g(x, y, z)$; $y(x_0) = y_0$, $z(x_0) = p_0$. Thus (13.3) applies, with $f(x, y, z) \equiv z$. If we write p for z, this gives

$$(13.7) \qquad\qquad y_k = y_{k-1} + hp_{k-1} \qquad p_k = p_{k-1} + hg_{k-1}$$

which is the E.C.M. I for D.E. (13.5). It should be observed that the quantities $p_0, p_1, \ldots$ [the computed slopes of $y(x)$ at $x_0, x_1, \ldots$] appear as auxiliary quantities which are used to compute $y_1, y_2, \ldots$.

---

† As in Sec. 7, Chap. I, $E = O(h^r)$ means $|E| \leq Mh^r$ for some constant M independent of h.

TABLE 1. $h = 0.2$

x_k	g_{k-1}	$p_k = p_{k-1} + hg_{k-1}$	$y_k = y_{k-1} + hp_{k-1}$
0.0	......	0.0000	1.0000
0.2	2.0000	0.4000	1.0000
0.4	2.4000	0.8800	1.0800
0.6	2.8800	1.4560	1.2560
0.8	3.4560	2.1472	1.5472
1.0	4.1472	2.9766	1.9766

TABLE 2. $h = 0.1$

x_k	g_{k-1}	$p_k = p_{k-1} + hg_{k-1}$	$y_k = y_{k-1} + hp_{k-1}$
0.0	......	0.0000	1.0000
0.1	2.0000	0.2000	1.0000
0.2	2.2000	0.4200	1.0200
0.3	2.4200	0.6620	1.0620
0.4	2.6620	0.9282	1.1282
0.5	2.9282	1.2210	1.2210
0.6	3.2210	1.5431	1.3431
0.7	3.5431	1.8974	1.4974
0.8	3.8974	2.2871	1.6871
0.9	4.2871	2.7158	1.9158
1.0	4.7158	3.1874	2.1874

TABLE 3. $y(x) = 2e^x - 2x - 1$

x_k	$y(x_k)$	x_k	$y(x_k)$
0.0	1.0000	0.6	1.4442
0.1	1.0104	0.7	1.6276
0.2	1.0428	0.8	1.8510
0.3	1.0998	0.9	2.1192
0.4	1.1836	1.0	2.4366
0.5	1.2974		

Example 1.   Compute $y(1)$ if $y'' + y' - 2y = 4x$; $y(0) = 1$, $y'(0) = 0$.
Tables 1 and 2 show the computations carried out according to (13.7) with
$h = 0.2$ and $h = 0.1$, respectively.   Table 3 gives the exact values calculated
from $y(x) = 2e^x - 2x - 1$ (in all cases the results are rounded off to five
decimal digits).

To illustrate further how the methods for first-order equations are
extended to second-order equations, we consider the E.C.M. II [see

Table 4

x_k	$\frac{1}{2}l_1 = \frac{1}{2}hg_{k-1}$	$x_{k-1} + \frac{1}{2}h$	$y_{k-1} + \frac{1}{2}hp_{k-1}$	$p_{k-1} + \frac{1}{2}l_1$	$l_2 = hg(x_{k-1} + \frac{1}{2}h, \; y_{k-1} + \frac{1}{2}hp_{k-1}, \; p_{k-1} + \frac{1}{2}l_1)$	$p_k = p_{k-1} + l_2$	$y_k = y_{k-1} + h(p_{k-1} + \frac{1}{2}l_1)$
0.0	.....	.....	.....	.....	.....	0.0000	1.0000
0.2	0.1000	0.1000	1.0000	0.1000	0.4600	0.4600	1.0200
0.4	0.2380	0.3000	1.0660	0.6980	0.5268	0.9868	1.1596
0.6	0.2932	0.5000	1.2583	1.2800	0.6473	1.6341	1.4156
0.8	0.3597	0.7000	1.5790	1.9938	0.7928	2.4269	1.8143
1.0	0.4402	0.9000	2.0570	2.8671	0.9694	3.3963	2.3877

Eq. (7.19), Chap. I]. The straightforward extension to system (13.1) is

$$(13.8) \quad \begin{aligned} k_1 &= hf_0 & l_1 &= hg_0 \\ k_2 &= hf(x_0 + \tfrac{1}{2}h, \; y_0 + \tfrac{1}{2}k_1, \; z_0 + \tfrac{1}{2}l_1) \\ l_2 &= hg(x_0 + \tfrac{1}{2}h, \; y_0 + \tfrac{1}{2}k_1, \; z_0 + \tfrac{1}{2}l_1) \\ y_1 &= y_0 + k_2 & z_1 &= z_0 + l_2 \end{aligned}$$

To apply this to D.E. (13.5), we use $f(x, y, z) \equiv z$ and write p for z. The auxiliary quantities k_1, k_2 need not be introduced, since $k_1 = hp_0$, $k_2 = h(p_0 + \tfrac{1}{2}l_1)$. Thus,

$$(13.9) \quad \begin{aligned} l_1 &= hg_0 \\ l_2 &= hg(x_0 + \tfrac{1}{2}h, \; y_0 + \tfrac{1}{2}hp_0, \; p_0 + \tfrac{1}{2}l_1) \\ y_1 &= y_0 + hp_0 + \tfrac{1}{2}hl_1 \\ p_1 &= p_0 + l_2 \end{aligned}$$

Since $l_1 = hg_0$, one also has $y_1 = y_0 + hp_0 + \tfrac{1}{2}h^2g_0$. Since, by (13.5), $g_0 = y''(x_0)$, it follows that y_1 in (13.9) is the second-degree Taylor polynomial for $y(x_1)$ and the error of this approximation is of the order $0(h^3)$. The auxiliary quantity l_2 in (13.9) is needed to calculate p_1 so that the same process can be carried on, now with x_1, y_1, p_1 replacing x_0, y_0, p_0, etc.

Example 2. The problem of Example 1 is to be done by the formula (13.9), with tabular difference $h = 0.2$.

The results are given in Table 4. Comparison with the correct values of Table 3 shows that the results are far better than those obtained by formulas (13.7), even with $h = 0.1$.

Below we give, for easy reference, the most important numerical methods for second-order equations that can be derived as above from those for first-order equations in Sec. 7, Chap. I. The error terms $0(h^r)$ refer to the discretization error in one step: in going from y_{k-1},

TABLE OF NUMERICAL METHODS

E.C.M. I:

$$g_{k-1} = g(x_{k-1}, y_{k-1}, p_{k-1})$$
$$p_k = p_{k-1} + hg_{k-1}$$
$$y_k = y_{k-1} + hp_{k-1} + 0(h^2)$$

E.C.M. II:

$$g_{k-1} = g(x_{k-1}, y_{k-1}, p_{k-1})$$
$$g_{k-\frac{1}{2}} = g(x_{k-1} + \tfrac{1}{2}h, y_{k-1} + \tfrac{1}{2}hp_{k-1}, p_{k-1} + \tfrac{1}{2}hg_{k-1})$$
$$p_k = p_{k-1} + hg_{k-\frac{1}{2}}$$
$$y_k = y_{k-1} + hp_{k-1} + \tfrac{1}{2}h^2 g_{k-1} + 0(h^3)$$

Runge-Kutta method (R.K.M.):

$$g_{k-1} = g(x_{k-1}, y_{k-1}, p_{k-1})$$
$$g_{k-\frac{1}{2}} = g(x_{k-1} + \tfrac{1}{2}h, y_{k-1} + \tfrac{1}{2}hp_{k-1}, p_{k-1} + \tfrac{1}{2}hg_{k-1})$$
$$g_{k-\frac{1}{2}}^* = g(x_{k-1} + \tfrac{1}{2}h, y_{k-1} + \tfrac{1}{2}hp_{k-1} + \tfrac{1}{4}h^2 g_{k-1}, p_{k-1} + \tfrac{1}{2}hg_{k-\frac{1}{2}})$$
$$g_k^* = g(x_{k-1} + h, y_{k-1} + hp_{k-1} + \tfrac{1}{2}h^2 g_{k-\frac{1}{2}}, p_{k-1} + hg_{k-\frac{1}{2}}^*)$$
$$p_k^* = p_{k-1} + \tfrac{1}{6}h(g_{k-1} + 2g_{k-\frac{1}{2}} + 2g_{k-\frac{1}{2}}^* + g_k^*)$$
$$y_k^* = y_{k-1} + hp_{k-1} + \tfrac{1}{6}h^2(g_{k-1} + g_{k-\frac{1}{2}} + g_{k-\frac{1}{2}}^*) + 0(h^5)$$

Milne's method (M.M.):

$$g_{k-3} = g(x_{k-3}, y_{k-3}, p_{k-3}) \qquad g_{k-2} = g(x_{k-2}, y_{k-2}, p_{k-2}) \qquad g_{k-1} = g(x_{k-1}, y_{k-1}, p_{k-1})$$
$$p_k^* = p_{k-4} + \tfrac{4}{3}h(2g_{k-3} - g_{k-2} + 2g_{k-1})$$
$$y_k^* = y_{k-4} + \tfrac{4}{3}h(2p_{k-3} - p_{k-2} + 2p_{k-1}) + 0(h^5)$$
$$g_k^* = g(x_k, y_k^*, p_k^*)$$
$$p_k = p_{k-2} + \tfrac{1}{3}h(g_{k-2} + 4g_{k-1} + g_k^*)$$
$$y_k = y_{k-2} + \tfrac{1}{3}h(p_{k-2} + 4p_{k-1} + p_k^*) + 0(h^5)$$

p_{k-1} to y_k, p_k. In the computation of $y(x_0 + L)$ for a fixed L by recursive application of a method with error term $0(h^r)$, the discretization error is of order $0(h^{r-1})$.

PROBLEMS

1. Compute by the indicated method and with the indicated tabular difference (carry at least four decimal digits throughout the calculations):

(a) $y(1)$ if $y'' - y' + y = 0$; $y(0) = 1$, $y'(0) = \frac{1}{2}$; E.C.M. I, $h = 0.1$ and $h = 0.05$.

(b) $y(-1)$ if $y'' + 2y' + 4y = x^2$; $y(0) = 1$, $y'(0) = 0$; E.C.M. I, $h = 0.1$; also with $h = 0.2$, modifying E.C.M. I by adding $\frac{1}{2}h^2 g_{k-1}$ to the expression for y_k.

(c) $y(2)$ if $y'' - y - \log_{10}(2x + y') = 0$; $y(\frac{1}{2}) = 0$, $y'(\frac{1}{2}) = 1$; E.C.M. II, $h = 0.25$.

(d) $y(2)$ if $y'' - y' - y^2 = x$; $y(0) = 0$, $y'(0) = 0$; R.K.M., $h = 0.25$.

(e) $y(1)$ if $y'' = \frac{1}{5}(1 + x^2)(1 + y'^2)^{\frac{3}{2}}$; $y(0) = 0$, $y'(0) = 0$. Use R.K.M. to obtain $y(0.1)$, $y(0.2)$, $y(0.3)$; then obtain $y(0.4)$, $y(0.5)$, . . . by Milne's method.

2. Derive the methods of Runge-Kutta and Milne for second-order equations from the corresponding methods for first-order equations.

3. Derive a method for second-order equations which corresponds to Heun's method for first-order equations (A.B.M. I; see table in Sec. 7, Chap. I).

4. Solve Prob. 1c by the method of Prob. 3.

5. Derive a method for the system $y' = f(x, y, z)$, $z' = g(x, y, z)$ which corresponds to the Euler-Cauchy method of order 2 for first-order equations (E.C.M. II; see table in Sec. 7, Chap. I).

★6. Derive the Euler-Cauchy method of order 2 for the equation $y'' = g(x, y, y')$ from that for systems (see Prob. 5).

7. Apply E.C.M. I with $h = 1/n$ to approximate $y(1)$ if $y'' = y$, $y(0) = y'(0) = 1$. Show that the exact value of $y(2)$ is approached as $n \to \infty$.

★8. The solution of $y'' = g(x)$, $y(0) = y'(0) = 0$ is given by the integral $y(h) = \int_0^h (h - x)g(x)\, dx$. What approximate value for this integral is obtained by application of the Runge-Kutta method? Compare with that obtained by Simpson's rule.

14. Boundary-value Problems

A general solution of a second-order differential equation contains two constants which—within limits—can take on arbitrary values. To single out a particular solution, additional specifications are required. The most important of them, next to the initial conditions which are used in the preceding sections, are *boundary conditions*, which prescribe the values of the solution $y(x)$ at two chosen abscissas, say $y(x_1) = y_1$, $y(x_2) = y_2$. Geometrically, this means that the integral curve passes through two given points (x_1, y_1), (x_2, y_2). Problems in which the solution of a differential equation is sought subject to boundary conditions are called *boundary-value problems*, and they are, from both the theoretical and practical points of view, more difficult than initial-value problems.

Example 1. Find an integral curve of $y'' + y = 1$ which passes through $(0, 0)$, $(\pi/2, -1)$.

The general solution is $y(x) = 1 + c_1 \sin x + c_2 \cos x$; $y(0) = 0$ gives $1 + c_2 = 0$; $y(\pi/2) = -1$ gives $1 + c_1 = -1$. Thus $c_1 = -2$ and $c_2 = -1$, and there is a unique solution of the problem: $y(x) = 1 - 2 \sin x - \cos x$.

The simplicity of this example must not deceive us, for it is not typical of boundary-value problems. First, in this example the general solution (comprising all possible solutions) was easily found, and, therefore, the problem of determining whether one or more integral curves pass through the given points was reduced to an algebraic one:

determining the numbers c_1, c_2 satisfying the system $1 + c_2 = 0$, $1 + c_1 = -1$. Second, the points were so chosen that the system for the unknowns c_1, c_2 had exactly one solution. If we had specified the two points $(0, 0)$, $(\pi, -1)$ in place of $(0, 0)$, $(\pi/2, -1)$, the conditions on c_1, c_2 would have been $1 + c_2 = 0$, $1 - c_2 = -1$, so no solution of the modified problem would have existed. If we had chosen the points $(0, 0)$, $(\pi, 2)$, the conditions on c_1, c_2 would have been $1 + c_2 = 0$, $1 - c_2 = 2$; this is solved by $c_2 = -1$, c_1 arbitrary, so the new problem has infinitely many solutions: $y(x) = 1 + c_1 \sin x - \cos x$, c_1 arbitrary.

One difficulty in boundary-value problems is that slightly different boundary conditions may lead to totally different results. From the data it is difficult to predict whether the problem has a unique solution, or none, or infinitely many solutions; it is even more difficult when no general solution is available. For initial-value problems these questions are satisfactorily answered by general theorems (see, for example, the existence and uniqueness theorem in Sec. 12) whose usefulness should be quite evident in the light of the present discussion. No such theorems of comparable generality exist for boundary-value problems. As a first introduction to the subject, it is more useful to get acquainted with a few typical examples and modes of attack than to consider theorems of restricted validity.

Example 2. Determine the values of the constant parameter λ for which the boundary-value problem

$$(14.1) \qquad y'' + \lambda y = 0 \qquad y(a) = y(a + \pi) = 0$$

has one, more than one, or no solution.

If $\lambda < 0$, the general solution of $y'' + y = 0$ is $y(x) = c_1 \cosh \sqrt{-\lambda}\, x + c_2 \sinh \sqrt{-\lambda}\, x$. The conditions $y(a) = y(a + \pi) = 0$ give

$$(14.2a) \qquad c_1 \cosh \sqrt{-\lambda}\, a + c_2 \sinh \sqrt{-\lambda}\, a = 0$$
$$(14.2b) \qquad c_1 \cosh \sqrt{-\lambda}\, (a + \pi) + c_2 \sinh \sqrt{-\lambda}\, (a + \pi) = 0$$

This is a linear algebraic system for the unknowns c_1, c_2, and it has the unique solution $c_1 = c_2 = 0$ (the so-called "trivial" solution) if and only if the determinant

$$(14.3) \quad \Delta(\lambda) = \cosh \sqrt{-\lambda}\, a \sinh \sqrt{-\lambda}\, (a + \pi)$$
$$- \sinh \sqrt{-\lambda}\, a \cosh \sqrt{-\lambda}\, (a + \pi)$$
$$= \sinh \sqrt{-\lambda}\, \pi$$

does not vanish. Such is the case for every $\lambda < 0$; therefore problem (14.1) has the unique solution $y(x) \equiv 0$ if $\lambda < 0$. For $\lambda = 0$ one easily confirms the same conclusion, since the general solution of the differential equation then is $y(x) = c_1 + c_2x$, and $y(a) = y(a + \pi) = 0$ if and only if $c_1 = c_2 = 0$.

For $\lambda > 0$ there is a more interesting result. Then $y(x) = c_1 \cos \sqrt{\lambda}\, x + c_2 \sin \sqrt{\lambda}\, x$ is the general solution, and the conditions $y(a) = y(a + \pi) = 0$ become

(14.4a) $$c_1 \cos \sqrt{\lambda}\, a + c_2 \sin \sqrt{\lambda}\, a = 0$$
(14.4b) $$c_1 \cos \sqrt{\lambda}\, (a + \pi) + c_2 \sin \sqrt{\lambda}\, (a + \pi) = 0$$

The determinant of this system is

(14.5) $$\Delta(\lambda) = \cos \sqrt{\lambda} \sin \sqrt{\lambda}\, (a + \pi) - \sin \sqrt{\lambda}\, a \cos \sqrt{\lambda}\, (a + \pi)$$
$$= \sin \sqrt{\lambda}\, \pi$$

and $\Delta(\lambda) \neq 0$ if $\sqrt{\lambda}$ is not an integer. Therefore, $y(x) \equiv 0$ is also, for $\lambda > 0$, the unique solution of (14.1) if $\sqrt{\lambda}$ is not an integer. However, if $\sqrt{\lambda}$ is an integer, that is, λ is one of the numbers 1, 4, 9, . . . , say $\lambda = \lambda_k = k^2$, then $\sin \sqrt{\lambda}\, (a + \pi)$ and $\cos \sqrt{\lambda}\, (a + \pi)$ differ from $\sin \sqrt{\lambda}\, a$, $\cos \sqrt{\lambda}\, a$ only by the factor $(-1)^k$, and (14.4b) is the same equation as (14.4a). Hence in this case there is but one condition on c_1, c_2:

(14.6) $$c_1 \cos ka + c_2 \sin ka = 0$$

If we write $-A \sin ka$ for c_1, then c_2 must be $A \cos ka$, and $y(x) = c_1 \cos kx + c_2 \sin kx$ becomes $y(x) = A \sin k(x - a)$.

In summary, problem (14.1) has a unique solution if and only if λ is not one of the integers 1, 4, 9, . . . , and this solution is $y(x) \equiv 0$. If $\lambda = \lambda_k = k^2$ ($k = 1, 2, . . .$), then the problem has the solutions $y(x) = A \sin k(x - a)$, with A an arbitrary constant.

Example 3. Let $f(x)$ be a given function defined and continuous on $a \leq x \leq \pi$. Determine the values of the parameter λ for which the problem

(14.7) $$y'' + \lambda y = f \qquad y(a) = y(a + \pi) = 0$$

has one, none, or more than one solution.

We start again with the general solution of $y'' + \lambda y = f$. It is

(14.8) $$y(x) = \begin{cases} c_1 \cosh \sqrt{-\lambda}\, x + c_2 \sinh \sqrt{-\lambda}\, x + y_p(x) & \text{if } \lambda < 0 \\ c_1 + c_2x + y_p(x) & \text{if } \lambda = 0 \\ c_1 \cos \sqrt{\lambda}\, x + c_2 \sin \sqrt{\lambda}\, x + y_p(x) & \text{if } \lambda > 0 \end{cases}$$

where $y_p(x)$ is a particular solution of the equation $y'' + \lambda y = f$ which need not be found at the moment. The conditions $y(a) = y(a + \pi) = 0$ result in a linear system of equations for the unknowns c_1, c_2, whose determinant $\Delta(\lambda)$ is the same as in Example 2. We conclude that this system has a unique solution [hence problem (14.7) has a unique solution] if and only if λ is not one of the numbers 1, 4, 9, ... If $\lambda = \lambda_k = k^2$ ($k = 1, 2, \ldots$), then the conditions $y(a) = y(a + \pi) = 0$ read

(14.9a) $$c_1 \cos ka + c_2 \sin ka + y_p(a) = 0$$
(14.9b) $$(-1)^k c_1 \cos ka + (-1)^k c_2 \sin ka + y_p(a + \pi) = 0$$

Since y_p is any particular solution of $y'' + k^2 y = f$, we may choose it so that $y_p(a) = 0$. Then one sees immediately that system (14.9) has no solution c_1, c_2 unless

(14.10) $$y_p(a + \pi) = 0$$

To see whether this condition is a restriction on our problem, we need to know y_p. Since f is some general function, y_p can be obtained only by the method of variation of parameters. One finds (see Prob. 5, Sec. 6)

(14.11) $$y_p(x) = \frac{1}{k} \int_a^x \sin k(x - s) f(s) \, ds$$

where we have used a as the lower limit so that $y_p(a) = 0$ will be satisfied. Condition (14.10) now becomes

(14.12) $$\int_a^{a+\pi} \sin k(a - s) f(s) \, ds = 0$$

Unless f satisfies this condition, there can be no solution of system (14.9), and hence none of (14.7). If, however, f satisfies (14.12) (there are many functions that do), then system (14.9) is identical with system (14.4) of Example 2, and its solution is given in (14.6), which gives for (14.7) the solution $y(x) = y_p(x) + A \sin k(x - a)$, with arbitrary A.

In summary: The problem (14.7) has a unique solution for every function f if and only if λ is not one of the integers 1, 4, 9, ... If $\lambda = \lambda_k = k^2$ ($k = 1, 2, \ldots$), then the problem has the solutions $y(x) = y_p(x) + A \sin k(x - a)$, where y_p is given by (14.11) if f satisfies (14.12).

The two preceding examples are typical of a class of very important boundary-value problems. They are linear (not necessarily with constant coefficients) and contain a parameter λ for whose different values different results are obtained. The problem may be homogeneous, as in Example 2 (both the equation and the boundary conditions are homogeneous); then $y = 0$ is always a solution (the trivial solution), and it is the only solution unless λ is one of a set of special numbers typical of the problem, called *characteristic* (or *proper*) *values*.[†] To such a characteristic value λ_k there belongs a nontrivial solution (called a *characteristic function*[‡]) y_k, and therefore infinitely many solutions, since $A y_k$ for any constant A also solves the homogeneous problem.

[†] They are also called *eigenvalues*, from the German adjective *eigen* = proper, characteristic.

[‡] Also called an *eigenfunction*.

The problem may be nonhomogeneous, as in Example 3. Then if λ is not one of the characteristic values of the reduced homogeneous problem, the problem has a unique solution; if λ is a characteristic value ($\lambda = \lambda_k$), then the nonhomogeneous problem has in general no solution, unless the forcing function f satisfies some condition typical of the problem and of the value λ_k. If so, then there are solutions of the nonhomogeneous problem which differ by a solution of the reduced homogeneous problem (i.e., by a characteristic function).

The characteristic values λ_k of the boundary-value problem (14.1) were found as the solutions of $\sin \lambda\pi = 0$ [see (14.5)]. In general, the characteristic values appear as the roots of a transcendental equation, which frequently is solved by graphical or numerical methods.

The boundary conditions for a second-order equation are not always of the form $y(x_1) = y_1$, $y(x_2) = y_2$. Other common types are

(14.13a) $y'(x_1) = p_1$ $y'(x_2) = p_2$

(14.13b) $y(x_1) = y_1$ $y'(x_2) = p_2$

(14.13c) $y(x_1) = y_1$ $\alpha y(x_2) + \beta y'(x_2) = \gamma$

(14.13d) $\alpha_1 y(x_1) + \alpha_2 y(x_2) = y_3$ $\beta_1 y'(x_1) + \beta_2 y'(x_2) = p_3$

All these conditions are linear. They are linear homogeneous if the right-hand terms are zero. The special case of (14.13d),

(14.14) $y(x_1) = y(x_2)$ $y'(x_1) = y'(x_2)$

is called a *periodicity condition*. When it is satisfied for a solution $y(x)$ of an "autonomous" differential equation $y'' = f(y, y')$ (independent variable absent), then $y''(x_1) = y''(x_2)$, and likewise for higher derivatives if they exist.

PROBLEMS

1. Solve the following boundary-value problems, which have unique solutions that can be found from the general solutions:

    (a) $y'' + 4y' + 5y = 8 \sin x$; $y(0) = 1$, $y(\pi/2) = 2$

    (b) $y'' - 2y' + 4y = 0$; $y(0) = 0$, $y(\pi/6 \sqrt{3}) = 1.353$

    (c) $y'' + y' + y = (2 + x) \cos x + \sin x$; $y(0) = 2$, $y(\frac{1}{3}\pi) = 0.846$

    (d) $y'' + 4y = \cos x + \sin 2x$; $y(-\frac{1}{2}\pi) = \frac{1}{8}\pi$, $y(\frac{1}{4}\pi) = \frac{1}{2}\sqrt{2}$

    (e) $y'' + ay' + by = 0$; a, b constants; $b - a^2/4 \neq \pi^2$; $y(0) = 0$, $y(1) = 0$

    (f) $\ddot{x} + 4\omega^2 x = 3\omega^2 \sin \omega t$; $\dot{x}(0) = 0$, $x(\pi/2\omega) = 1$

    (g) $\ddot{x} + x = \sin 2t$; $\dot{x}(0) = -0.4$, $x(\frac{1}{2}\pi) = 0.5$

    (h) $\ddot{x} + 2\dot{x} + 2x = 2 \sin 2t$; $x(0) = x(\pi)$, $\dot{x}(0) = \dot{x}(\pi)$

  ★(i) $y'' + y = |x|$; $y(-\frac{1}{2}\pi) = y(\frac{1}{2}\pi)$, $y'(-\frac{1}{2}\pi) = y'(\frac{1}{2}\pi)$

    (j) $yy'' + y'^2 - yy' = 0$; $y(- \log 2) = 0$, $y(0) = 1$

    (k) $(x + y')y'' + y' = 0$; $y(0) = \log 4$; $y'(1) = -\frac{2}{5}$

2. Find all the solutions of the following linear homogeneous boundary-value problems:

(a) $y'' + k^2y = 0$ $(k > 0)$; $y(0) = 0$, $y(\pi/k) = 0$
(b) $y'' + k^2y = 0$ $(k > 0)$; $y'(0) = 0$, $y'(\pi/k) = 0$
(c) $y'' + k^2y = 0$ $(k > 0)$; $y(0) = 0$, $y'(\pi/k) = 0$
(d) $y'' + k^2y = 0$ $(k > 0)$; $y(0) = 0$, $y'(\pi/2k) = 0$
(e) $y'' + k^2y = 0$ $(k > 0)$; $y(0) = y(2\pi)$, $y'(0) = y'(2\pi)$

3. For what values of $b > 0$ does the linear homogeneous boundary-value problem $y'' + 4y' + 13y = 0$, $y(0) = 0$, $y(b) = 0$ have nontrivial solutions, and what are these?

★4. Show that only for a special value of α does the boundary-value problem $y'' + 4y' + 8y = 2e^{-2x} + \alpha e^{3x}$, $y(0) = 0$, $y(\pi) = 0$ have solutions, and find these.

5. Find the characteristic values λ_k and characteristic functions y_k of each of the following linear homogeneous boundary-value problems:

(a) $y'' + \lambda y = 0$; $y(-L) = 0$, $y(L) = 0$
(b) $y'' + \lambda y = 0$; $y'(0) = 0$, $y(L) = 0$
(c) $y'' + \lambda y = 0$; $y(-L) = y(L)$, $y'(-L) = y'(L)$
(d) $y'' + ay' + \lambda y = 0$; $y(0) = 0$, $y(L) = 0$

6. Solve the nonlinear boundary-value problem $y'' = k\sqrt{1 + y'^2}$ (k constant, not equal to zero), $y'(0) = 0$, $y(L) = 0$.

★7. Show that the nonlinear boundary-value problem $y'' + 6yy'^3 = 0$, $y(0) = 0$, $y(1) = \eta$, has a unique solution if $0 \le \eta < 1$, but no solution if $\eta \ge 1$.

15. Static-equilibrium Problems

Certain simple problems of static equilibrium of one-dimensional structures (cables, beams, rods, columns, etc.) lead to boundary-value problems with second-order differential equations. Some of these will be taken up here.

A perfectly flexible cable (no elastic forces), loaded by its own weight or in some other way, hangs in a vertical plane (see Fig. 5). We choose a rectangular coordinate system in the plane with the x axis horizontal and assume that the position of the hanging cable can be represented as a curve $y = y(x)$. Let $P = P(x, y(x))$ be a point on the cable, $T = T(x)$ the tension in the cable at P (more precisely the force exerted on the part of the cable to the left of P),

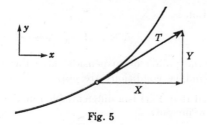

Fig. 5

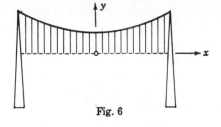

Fig. 6

and $X = X(x)$, $Y = Y(x)$ the horizontal and vertical components of T, respectively. Then, since T is tangent to the curve $y = y(x)$,

(15.1)
$$\frac{dy}{dx} = \frac{Y}{X}$$

To proceed from here, some knowledge of the load which results in the tension T is necessary. We assume that the loading force is vertical at all points. From this it follows that the horizontal tension X is constant. Then, differentiation of (15.1)† gives

(15.2)
$$\frac{d^2y}{dx^2} = \frac{1}{X}\frac{dY}{dx} = \frac{1}{X}q(x)$$

where $q(x) = dY/dx$ is the *density of the load* at x, and X is the *horizontal tension*. If $q(x)$ is given, then $y(x)$ is found from (15.2) simply by repeated quadratures. Less trivial differential-equation problems arise if the load $q(x)$ depends itself on the displacement $y(x)$.

Example 1. Determine the shape of a cable of given length that is suspended between two points lying in a horizontal line and carries a dense fringe of rods which are equally spaced horizontally. The ends of the rods lie in a horizontal line (see Fig. 6). The weight of the cable itself is to be neglected.

We choose the x axis along the lower edge of the fringe. The load density is $q(x) = ky(x)$, where k is a given constant (the weight of a square unit of the fringe). Then (15.2) becomes

(15.3)
$$y'' - \frac{k}{X}y = 0$$

and its general solution is

$$y(x) = c_1 e^{\sqrt{k/X}\,x} + c_2 e^{-\sqrt{k/X}\,x}$$

If we assume that the points of suspension have the coordinates $(-a, b)$, (a, b), then the boundary conditions are $y(a) = y(-a) = b$, and they give

---

† Here it is assumed that $Y(x)$ is a differentiable function. This is not true if concentrated loads are present.

$c_1 = c_2 = b/\cosh \sqrt{k/X}\, a$. Therefore, the cable hangs along the *catenary*

$$(15.4) \qquad y(x) = b\,\frac{\cosh \sqrt{k/X}\, x}{\cosh \sqrt{k/X}\, a}$$

The horizontal tension X can be determined from the given length of the cable, which we denote as $2l$. Using the calculus formula for arc length, we obtain

$$(15.5) \qquad l = \int_0^a \sqrt{1 + y'^2}\, dx = \int_0^a \sqrt{1 + b^2\,\frac{k}{X}\,\frac{\sinh^2 \sqrt{k/X}\, x}{\cosh^2 \sqrt{k/X}\, a}}\, dx$$

With numerical integration and inversion, X can be determined from this equation.

Example 2. Determine the shape of a uniform cable of given length that is suspended between two points lying in a horizontal line and hangs under its own weight.

Choose the x axis horizontal, with the y axis passing through the lowest point on the cable. The load density in this case is $q(x) = w\, ds/dx$, where $s(x)$ is the length of the cable from some fixed abscissa, and w is the weight of the cable per unit length. Equation (15.2) becomes

$$(15.6) \qquad y'' = \frac{w}{X} \sqrt{1 + y'^2}$$

This equation, although nonlinear, can easily be integrated, since y is absent (see Sec. 1). Setting $p = y'$ reduces the order of the equation:

$$\frac{dp}{dx} = \frac{w}{X} \sqrt{1 + p^2}$$

This gives, on separating variables and integrating,

$$\log (p + \sqrt{1 + p^2}) = \frac{wx}{X} + \text{constant}$$

or

$$p + \sqrt{1 + p^2} = Ae^{wx/X}$$

Since $p = 0$ at $x = 0$, we find $A = 1$. Thus,

$$(15.7) \qquad p = \tfrac{1}{2}e^{wx/X} - \tfrac{1}{2}e^{-wx/X} = \sinh \frac{wx}{X}$$

and another quadrature gives

$$y(x) = \frac{X}{w} \cosh \frac{wx}{X} + c$$

The curve is again a catenary.

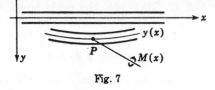

Fig. 7

The boundary conditions determine the value of c. If the coordinates of the points of suspension are $(\pm a, b)$, then the conditions are $y(a) = y(-a) = b$, and one finds easily that

$$(15.8) \qquad y(x) = b + \frac{X}{w}\left(\cosh\frac{wx}{X} - \cosh\frac{wa}{X}\right)$$

The horizontal tension X is again determined from the given length of the cable, which we denote as $2l$. By (15.7),

$$(15.9) \qquad \sqrt{1 + p^2} = \cosh\frac{wx}{X}$$

and therefore

$$(15.10) \qquad l = \int_0^a \cosh\frac{wx}{X}\, dx = \frac{X}{w}\sinh\frac{wa}{X}$$

This equation can readily be solved for X by numerical methods.

In the next two examples the structures considered are elastic beams and rods. In this case the deflection (bending or buckling) is determined by the balance of moments. We choose a rectangular coordinate system in the plane in which the beam is assumed to deflect, with the x axis parallel to the unde-flected beam, so that the position of the bent beam can be represented by a curve $y = y(x)$ (see Fig. 7). Let $P = P(x, y(x))$ be an arbitrary point on the beam. Let $M(x)$ be the bending moment at P of the external forces acting on the beam (more precisely the moment exerted on the part to the left of P). This moment must be balanced by the moment of the elastic forces at P, which can be shown to be EI/ρ. Here E is Young's modulus of elasticity for the material of the beam, $I = I(x)$ is an axial moment of inertia of the cross section at P, and $\rho = \rho(x)$ is the radius of curvature at P of the curve $y = y(x)$; that is, $\rho = (1 + y'^2)^{\frac{3}{2}}/y''$.† In the following examples the product EI (called the *flexural rigidity*) is assumed constant along the beam.

Balancing the moment gives the elastic beam equation

$$(15.11) \qquad EI\, \frac{y''}{(1 + y'^2)^{\frac{3}{2}}} = M$$

† These statements are somewhat imprecise, since on the one hand the beam is considered one-dimensional, and its position is represented as a curve $y = y(x)$, while on the other hand cross sections and their moments of inertia are considered. More precision is offered in treatises on elasticity theory.

If $M(x)$ is given, then the general solution of (15.11) can be found by the method of Sec. 1. If we set $y' = p$ and assume that $p = p_0$ for $x = x_0$, (15.11) gives

$$(15.12) \qquad EI \int_{p_0}^{p} (1 + u^2)^{-\frac{3}{2}} \, du = \int_{x_0}^{x} M(u) \, du$$

If the substitution $v = 1 + u^2$ is made in the first integral of (15.12), one obtains

$$(15.13) \qquad \tfrac{1}{2} EI \int_{1+p_0^2}^{1+p^2} \frac{dv}{\sqrt{v^4 - v^3}} = \int_{x_0}^{x} M(u) \, du$$

The integral on the left is not elementary; it is a typical elliptic integral, and the solution of (15.13) for p calls for the use of elliptic functions (see Ref. 3).

Usually, Eq. (15.11) is replaced with a linear equation. One assumes that the beam is only slightly bent, so that y' is small as compared with 1 all along the beam. If $1 + y'^2$ is then replaced with 1 in (15.11), one has the linear beam equation

$$(15.14) \qquad EIy'' = M$$

Example 3. A "weightless" beam resting on two supports in a horizontal position carries a single load at some point between the supports. Find the shape of the bent beam.

We take the x axis as passing through the points of support $S_1(-l, 0)$, $S_2(l, 0)$. Let $P_0(x_0, 0)$, $0 \le x_0 < l$, be the point at which the weight w is carried. The supports S_1, S_2 react with the forces $R_1 = [(l - x_0)/2l]w$, $R_2 = [(l + x_0)/2l]w$, respectively. The moment $M(x)$ exerted on the point to the left of $P(x, 0)$ is then $R_2(l - x)$ if $x \ge x_0$, and $R_2(l - x) - w(x_0 - x)$ if $x \le x_0$. It is convenient to have the same expression for $M(x)$ in the intervals $x \ge x_0$ and $x \le x_0$; otherwise the integration of (15.14) must be carried out separately in the two intervals. Using the absolute-value function, one can write the contribution to $M(x)$, which is zero for $x \ge x_0$ and $-w(x_0 - x)$ for $x \le x_0$, as $\tfrac{1}{2} w(x - x_0 - |x - x_0|)$. Thus,

$$M(x) = R_2(l - x) - \tfrac{1}{2} w(x - x_0 - |x - x_0|)$$
$$= \frac{w}{2l} (l^2 - x_0 x - l|x - x_0|)$$

Using this in Eq. (15.14) and integrating twice gives

$$(15.15) \qquad \frac{12EIl}{w} y(x) = 3l^2 x^2 - x_0 x^3 - l|x - x_0|^3 + c_1 x + c_2$$

The boundary conditions $y(-l) = y(l) = 0$ give the system

$$c_1 l + c_2 = x_0 l^3 - 3l^4 + l(l - x_0)^3$$
$$c_1 l - c_2 = x_0 l^3 + 3l^4 - l(l + x_0)^3$$

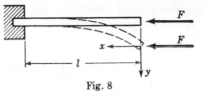

Fig. 8

from which c_1, c_2 are readily determined. It is seen from (15.15) that the curve $y = y(x)$ consists of two cubic parabolas which fit together at x_0 with a common tangent line.

The following classical example has contributed much to the understanding of characteristic values and functions.

Example 4. A "weightless" rod is clamped at one end and is subject to a single load attacking the other end in the direction of the rod. Does the rod buckle?

As before, one chooses the x axis parallel to the undeflected rod. It is convenient to put the origin at the loaded end of the buckling rod (see Fig. 8). Then the boundary conditions are

$$y(0) = 0 \qquad y'(l) = 0$$

where l is the abscissa of the clamped end. If F denotes the magnitude of the load (clearly it must be compressive if buckling is to occur), then the bending moment at x is $M(x) = -Fy(x)$; hence Eq. (15.14) becomes

$$EIy'' = -Fy$$

If we set

$$\frac{F}{EI} = \lambda$$

then we have the characteristic-value problem

(15.16) $$y'' + \lambda y = 0 \qquad y(0) = 0 \qquad y'(l) = 0$$

Proceeding as in Example 2, Sec. 5, one finds that there is always the trivial solution $y(x) \equiv 0$ (no buckling) but that for each of the values

$$\lambda = \lambda_k = \left[(2k - 1)\frac{\pi}{2l} \right]^2 \qquad k = 1, 2, 3, \ldots$$

there is a nontrivial solution

$$y = y_k(x) = A \sin \sqrt{\lambda_k}\, x \qquad A \text{ arbitrary}$$

Hence it seems that there is a sequence of loads

$$F_1 = \frac{\pi^2}{4}\frac{EI}{l^2} \qquad F_2 = \frac{9\pi^2}{4}\frac{EI}{l^2} \qquad \cdots \qquad F_k = \frac{(2k-1)^2\pi^2}{4}\frac{EI}{l^2} \qquad \cdots$$

Fig. 9

for which buckling takes place.   The corresponding buckling modes y_1, y_2, y_3 are sketched in Fig. 9.   Only their shapes, but not their amplitudes, are determined.   Of all these modes only the first, y_1, belonging to the load

(15.17) $$F_1 = EI \frac{\pi^2}{4l^2}$$

(the so-called *Euler buckling load*), is of practical significance.   All the others are unstable modes, difficult to produce experimentally.   Better approximations to the true physical behavior are the solutions of the nonlinear equation (15.11).   But (15.17), as the smallest buckling load, is also confirmed by the solution of the nonlinear problem.

PROBLEMS

1. Find the suspension curve of a weightless cable that is uniformly loaded; that is, $Y(x) = kx$ (if the left end of the cable is at $x = 0$).

2. A weightless cable has its ends fastened at $(-a, 0)$ and $(a, 0)$ and is uniformly loaded between $x = -\frac{1}{2}a$ and $x = \frac{1}{2}a$.   If the sag at $x = 0$ is δ, what is it at $x = \frac{1}{2}a$?

3. A cable has its ends fastened at $(-a, 0)$ and $(a, 0)$ and is of varying thickness so that any left endpiece of length s weighs ws^2.   Find its suspension curve.

4. An arch made of thin sheet steel supports a level pile of sand (see Fig. 10).   The stress at any point is due entirely to the weight of the sand.   What must be the shape of the arch if there are no bending stresses, i.e., if the resultant stress at any point is a pure compression.

5. A weightless beam resting on two supports at $(-l, 0)$ and $(l, 0)$ carries a load of weight w at each of the points $x = -\frac{1}{2}l$ and $x = \frac{1}{2}l$.   Find the maximum sag.

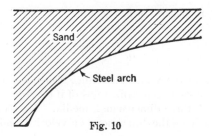

Fig. 10

6. A weightless beam resting on two supports at $(-l, 0)$ and $(l, 0)$ carries a load of density ρ uniformly distributed over the interval $-\frac{1}{2}l \leq x \leq \frac{1}{2}l$. Find the maximum sag.

7. A uniform cantilever beam (weight per unit length $= \rho$) is clamped horizontally at one end.   Find the sag of the free end.

8. A rope of length l and uniform density ρ, held tautly with constant tension X, spins about its axis at the constant angular velocity ω.   Does it bulge?

16. Some Dynamic Problems

As in the preceding section, we deal here with one-dimensional structures but consider time-dependent processes in place of equilibria.   Thus there are two independent variables involved, the space variable x and the time variable t, and the differential equations describing the processes are partial, not ordinary.   However, we study only special solutions of these equations— solutions which are products of a function of x and a function of t.   This restriction leads to boundary-value problems in ordinary differential equations, in particular to characteristic-value problems.   This is best illustrated by the classical problem of the vibrating string.

Example 1.   Consider a perfectly flexible string which is assumed to lie and vibrate in the xy plane, with its ends held fixed at the points $(0, 0)$ and $(l, 0)$. The string is assumed to be held taut so that the displacements are small and the distance l between the end points can be considered as the length of the string.   Let $y(x, t)$ be the displacement in the y direction at the abscissa x and the time t.   Since the string is structurally the same as a cable, we have, by Eq. (15.2),

$$\frac{\partial^2 y}{\partial x^2} = \frac{1}{X} q(x, t)$$

where X is the constant x component of the tension in the string, and $q(x, t)$ is the load density at x and t.   In this case the load is the dynamic reaction, which by Newton's law is mass times acceleration; hence $q(x, t) = \rho \, \partial^2 y/\partial t^2$, where ρ is the linear density (mass per unit length) of the string, presumed constant.   Thus,

$$(16.1) \qquad \frac{\partial^2 y}{\partial x^2} = \frac{\rho}{X} \frac{\partial^2 y}{\partial t^2}$$

If we set $X/\rho = c^2$, then Eq. (16.1) becomes

$$(16.2) \qquad \frac{\partial^2 y}{\partial t^2} = c^2 \frac{\partial^2 y}{\partial x^2}$$

This is the equation of the vibrating string, also called the one-dimensional *wave equation*, since obvious generalizations of it describe wave propagation in two-dimensional and three-dimensional media.   The constant $c = \sqrt{X/\rho}$ is seen from (16.2) to have the dimension of a velocity, and indeed its physical interpretation is that of a velocity. Since the string is fixed at its ends, we have, besides the D.E. (16.2), the boundary conditions

$$(16.3) \qquad y(0, t) = 0 \qquad y(l, t) = 0 \qquad \text{for all } t$$

Of all the myriad solutions of (16.2), (16.3), we seek and study only those which are of the form

$$(16.4) \qquad y(x, t) = u(x)v(t)$$

Physically, they correspond to motions of the string in which all its particles move in unison according to the time factor $v(t)$, with only the amplitude of the motion depending on x according to the space factor $u(x)$ (thus all particles reach their maximum displacement at the same time, pass through zero at the same time, etc.). Since $\partial^2 y/\partial x^2 = u''v$ and $\partial y^2/\partial t^2 = u\ddot{v}$ (a dot denotes differentiation with respect to t), Eq. (16.2) becomes

$$u\ddot{v} = c^2 u''v$$

or, with the variables separated,

$$(16.5) \qquad \frac{u''}{u} = \frac{1}{c^2}\frac{\ddot{v}}{v}$$

Now we use an argument which is employed again and again in similar partial-differential-equation problems. Since the left-hand term of (16.5) does not depend on t, and the right-hand term does not depend on x, both terms depend neither on t nor on x; that is, they are constant. If we write $-\lambda$ for this constant, we obtain two ordinary differential equations from (16.5):

$$(16.6) \qquad\qquad u'' + \lambda u = 0$$
$$(16.7) \qquad\qquad \ddot{v} + \lambda c^2 v = 0$$

We must now turn to the boundary conditions (16.3). For solutions of the form $y(x, t) = u(x)v(t)$, these conditions can be satisfied only if

$$(16.8) \qquad u(0) = 0 \qquad u(l) = 0$$

[the other alternative, $v(t) \equiv 0$, would make $y(x, t) \equiv 0$, that is, no motion]. Equations (16.6) and (16.8) constitute the characteristic-value problem of Example 2, Sec. 14. One concludes that $u(x) \equiv 0$ is the only solution for general λ. But $u(x) \equiv 0$ makes $y(x, t) \equiv 0$; again we have no motion. Only if λ is one of the characteristic values

$$(16.9) \qquad \lambda_k = \left(\frac{k\pi}{l}\right)^2 \qquad k = 1, 2, \ldots$$

is there a nontrivial solution

$$(16.10) \qquad u_k(x) = \sin\sqrt{\lambda_k}\, x = \sin k\pi\,\frac{x}{l}$$

Now (16.7) can also be solved. For $\lambda = \lambda_k$ it has the general solution

$$(16.11) \qquad v_k(t) = A \sin\left(k\pi \frac{ct}{l} + \delta\right) \qquad A, \delta \text{ arbitrary}$$

Thus we have found as nontrivial solutions of the problem (16.2), (16.3) the functions

$$(16.12) \quad y_k(x, t) = A \sin k\pi \frac{x}{l} \sin\left(k\pi \frac{ct}{l} + \delta\right) \qquad A, \delta \text{ arbitrary}$$
$$k = 1, 2, \ldots$$

The constants A, δ can be determined by initial conditions. For example, if the string is known to have its maximum displacement A_0 at time $t = 0$, then $\delta = \frac{1}{2}\pi$ and $A = A_0$, and (16.12) becomes

$$y_k(x, t) = A_0 \sin k\pi \frac{x}{l} \cos k\pi \frac{ct}{l}$$

For any fixed x, (16.12) represents a simple harmonic vibration of frequency

$$(16.13) \qquad\qquad\qquad \nu_k = k \frac{c}{2l}$$

We have shown that only for these frequencies do there exist harmonic vibrations of the string.   The lowest frequency, $\nu_1 = c/2l$, is called the *fundamental*, and the remaining ones, $\nu_2, \nu_3, \ldots$, in order, are called the first, second, $\ldots$ *harmonics*, or *overtones*. The corresponding amplitude functions, $u_k(x) = \sin(k\pi x/l)$, are shown in Fig. 11. If the meaning of c is recalled, the dependence of the characteristic frequencies on tension, density, and length of the string is seen from (16.13).

It can be shown that by taking infinite sums of the special solutions (16.12), all solutions of the problem (16.2), (16.3) [not only those of the form of (16.4)] can be found.

The next example is from thermodynamics.

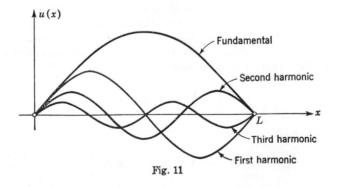

Fig. 11

Example 2. Consider a heat-conducting rod, so insulated that heat flows only in the direction of the axis of the rod, but not transversally to it. Such one-dimensional heat flow can also be realized by a slab of infinite cross section. Let the axis of the rod (or slab) coincide with the x axis between 0 and l, and let $\theta(x, t)$ denote the temperature at the abscissa x and the time t. By Sec. 6, Chap. IV, we know that the heat flux $Q(x, t)$ (that is, the quantity of heat flowing through a cross section at x in unit time) is proportional to the temperature gradient $\partial\theta/\partial x$ at x. The heat flux varies as x varies, and the local heat gain (or loss) per unit volume and unit time is $\partial Q/\partial x$ and hence is proportional to $\partial^2\theta/\partial x^2$. It is known that the heat gain results in a change of temperature proportional to it. Thus we have the partial differential equation

$$(16.14) \qquad \frac{\partial\theta}{\partial t} = \alpha^2 \frac{\partial^2\theta}{\partial x^2}$$

called the one-dimensional *heat* (or *diffusion*) *equation*. The constant α^2 in (16.14) can be calculated from the specific heat and thermal coductivity of the material of the rod.

Of all the solutions of (16.14), we seek again only those of the form

$$(16.15) \qquad \theta(x, t) = u(x)v(t)$$

Proceeding exactly as in the preceding example, we obtain the pair of equations

$$(16.16) \qquad u'' + \lambda u = 0$$
$$(16.17) \qquad \dot{v} + \lambda\alpha^2 v = 0$$

Nothing has been said yet about the end of the rod (or faces of the slab). Let it be specified in this example that the end $x = 0$ is kept at constant temperature and the end $x = l$ is thermally insulated. We may take the temperature at $x = 0$ as zero, since any temperature may be chosen as the zero point of the temperature scale;† insulation at $x = l$ means the heat flux, and therefore $\partial\theta/\partial x$, vanishes there. Thus, the boundary conditions are

$$(16.18) \qquad \theta(0, t) = 0 \qquad \frac{\partial\theta}{\partial x}(l, t) = 0 \qquad \text{for all } t$$

By (16.15), they imply

$$(16.19) \qquad u(0) = 0 \qquad u'(l) = 0$$

for the function u. As before, it is seen that only if λ is one of the characteristic values

$$(16.20) \qquad \lambda_k = \left[(2k - 1) \frac{\pi}{2l} \right]^2 \qquad k = 1, 2, \ldots$$

is there a nontrivial solution

$$(16.21) \qquad u_k(x) = \sin \sqrt{\lambda_k}\, x = \sin (2k - 1)\pi \frac{x}{2l}$$

† In the method we employ here, the boundary conditions must be homogeneous.

of problem (16.16), (16.19). The general solution of (16.17) for $\lambda = \lambda_k$ is

$$(16.22) \qquad v_k(t) = Ae^{-[(2k-1)\pi\alpha/2l]^2t} \qquad A \text{ arbitrary}$$

Thus we have found, as nontrivial solutions of the problem (16.14), (16.18),

$$(16.23) \quad \theta_k(x,\, t) = A \sin\left[(2k-1)\pi\frac{x}{2l}\right] e^{-[(2k-1)\pi\alpha/2l]^2t} \qquad A \text{ arbitrary}$$

$$k = 1, 2, \ldots$$

No other solutions of the form $\theta(x,\, t) = u(x)v(t)$ exist.

It can be shown that, by taking infinite sums of the special solutions (16.23), all solutions of the problem (16.14), (16.18) [not only those of the form of (16.15)] can be found.

PROBLEMS

1. Find the solutions of the vibrating-string equation of the form $y(x,\, t) = u(x)v(t)$ for which $y(0,\, t) = 0$, $(\partial y/\partial x)(\frac{1}{2}l,\, t) = 0$ (representing the harmonic vibrations of the string fastened at $x = 0$ and $x = l$ with maximum displacement at $x = \frac{1}{2}l$).

2. In a harmonic vibration the string passes through its neutral position at two instants T seconds apart. Show that there are nodes of the motion which are $T\sqrt{\rho/X}$ centimeters apart (if the tension X is in dynes, and the density ρ in grams).

3. Find the solutions of the heat equation of the form $\theta(x,\, t) = u(x)v(t)$ for which $(\partial\theta/\partial x)(0,\, t) = (\partial\theta/\partial x)(l,\, t) = 0$ (that is, both end faces of the slab are insulated).

4. Find the solutions of *Laplace's equation* $\partial^2 w/\partial x^2 + \partial^2 w/\partial y^2 = 0$ of the form $w(x,\, y) = u(x)v(y)$ for which $w(0,\, y) = 0$, $(\partial w/\partial x)(l,\, y) = 0$.

5. Find the solutions of Laplace's equation $\partial^2 w/\partial x^2 + \partial^2 w/\partial y^2 = 0$ of the form $w(x,\, y) = u(x)v(y)$ for which $w(0,\, y) = w(l,\, y)$, $(\partial w/\partial x)(0,\, y) = (\partial w/\partial x)(l,\, y)$.

6. The vibrations of a string which are damped by a force proportional to the velocity are described by the equation

$$\frac{\partial^2 y}{\partial t^2} + b\frac{\partial y}{\partial t} = c^2\frac{\partial^2 y}{\partial x^2}$$

Find the solutions of the form $y(x,\, t) = u(x)v(t)$ if $y(0,\, t) = y(l,\, t) = y(x,\, 0) = 0$.

7. Find the solutions of the heat equation of the form $\theta(x,\, t) = u(x)v(t)$ for which $\theta(0,\, t) = 0$, $(\partial\theta/\partial x)(l,\, t) = \kappa\theta(l,\, t)$ (that is, one end of a rod is kept at temperature 0, while at the other end there is heat transfer to a medium of temperature 0).

8. Find the solutions of the one-dimensional wave equation of the form $y(x,\, t) = u(x)v(t)$ for which $y(0,\, t) = 0$, $(\partial^2 y/\partial t^2)(l,\, t) = -\kappa(\partial y/\partial x)(l,\, t)$.

chapter **vi**

Linear Differential Equations of Higher Order; Constant Coefficients

1. Linear Operators

The general linear differential equation of order n (n may be any of the integers 1, 2, 3, . . .) is of the form

$$(1.1) \quad A_0(x) \frac{d^n y}{dx^n} + A_1(x) \frac{d^{n-1} y}{dx^{n-1}} + \cdots$$
$$+ A_{n-1}(x) \frac{dy}{dx} + A_n(x) y = F(x)$$

If $A_0(x) \neq 0$ we divide by $A_0(x)$ to obtain the *normal form*

$$(1.2) \quad \frac{d^n y}{dx^n} + a_1(x) \frac{d^{n-1} y}{dx^{n-1}} + \cdots + a_{n-1}(x) \frac{dy}{dx} + a_n(x) y = f(x)$$

where $a_1(x) = A_1(x)/A_0(x), \ldots, f(x) = F(x)/A_0(x)$. Isolated points at which $A_0(x) = 0$ are called *singular points* of the differential equation and are not dealt with in this chapter. Thus, it is no restriction

191

of generality to assume the equation to be cast in form (1.2). Both coefficient functions and solutions may be complex valued. An important special case is that in which $f(x) = e^{i\omega x}$.

The term $f(x)$ in Eq. (1.2) is isolated from the remaining terms of the equation and is written as the right member because it is the only term of the equation that is free from the unknown function y. If f is identically zero, the equation is said to be *homogeneous;* otherwise it is *nonhomogeneous*. The homogeneous case of (1.2) is

$$(1.3) \qquad \frac{d^n y}{dx^n} + a_1(x)\frac{d^{n-1}y}{dx^{n-1}} + \cdots + a_n(x)y = 0$$

In connection with the nonhomogeneous equation (1.2) one often studies the homogeneous equation that has the same left-hand member as (1.2). The latter is then referred to as the *reduced equation* to distinguish it from the former, the *complete equation*.

For the left-hand member of Eq. (1.2) we shall use the symbol $L[y(x)]$ or $L[y]$. Observe that if y is any n-times-differentiable function then L operates on y to give a new function $L[y]$:

$$(1.4) \qquad L[y] = y^{(n)} + a_1 y^{(n-1)} + \cdots + a_n y$$

It is an easy exercise (Prob. 4 below) to show that L operates linearly on functions, by which statement we mean that if y_1 and y_2 are functions, and c_1 and c_2 constants, then

$$(1.5) \qquad L[c_1 y_1 + c_2 y_2] = c_1 L[y_1] + c_2 L[y_2]$$

We therefore call L a *linear differential operator of the nth order*.

The problem posed by the differential equation (1.2) is the determination of those functions y for which

$$(1.6) \qquad L[y(x)] = f(x)$$

From the results in earlier chapters on differential equations of the first and second orders, it is to be expected that a general solution of Eq. (1.2) contains n essential constants. To single out a particular solution, additional conditions must be imposed. In this chapter the conditions will usually be *initial conditions* (I.C.) of the form

$$(1.7) \qquad \text{I.C.} \begin{cases} y(x_0) = y_0 \\ y'(x_0) = y_1 \\ y''(x_0) = y_2 \\ \cdots \cdots \\ y^{(n-1)}(x_0) = y_{n-1} \end{cases}$$

where y_0, y_1, y_2, . . . , y_{n-1} are *any given numbers* (real or complex). These conditions specify the value of the solution $y(x)$ and its first $n - 1$ derivatives at an initial point $x = x_0$.   If

$$y_0 = y_1 = y_2 = \cdots = y_{n-1} = 0$$

then the initial conditions are said to be *homogeneous*.

PROBLEMS

1. What is the linear differential operator L associated with the following equations?   Compute in each case $L[e^{\alpha x}]$, where α is a complex constant. Show, in each case, that $L[c_1y_1 + c_2y_2] = c_1L[y_1] + c_2L[y_2]$, where c_1 and c_2 are constants, and y_1 and y_2 are functions.

(a) $\dfrac{d^2y}{dx^2} + 3\dfrac{dy}{dx} - 4y = \sin x$

(b) $\dfrac{d^2y}{dx^2} + k^2y = x + 3,$ k constant

(c) $\dfrac{d^2u}{dx^2} + a\dfrac{du}{dx} + bu = \varphi(x),$ a, b constant

2. Let L_1, L_2 stand for the following differential operators:

$$L_1[y] \equiv \sin^2 x \frac{d^2y}{dx^2} + 2\frac{dy}{dx} + \frac{1}{1 + x}y$$

$$L_2[y] \equiv \cos^2 x \frac{d^2y}{dx^2} - 3\frac{dy}{dx} + \frac{1}{1 - x}y$$

Write in expanded form and simplify:

(a) $L_1[ay]$, where a is a constant
(b) $L_1[ay]$, where a is a function of x
(c) $L_2[a_1y_1 + a_2y_2]$, where a_1, a_2 are constants
(d) $L_1[y] + L_2[y]$
(e) $L_1[\log \sin x]$
(f) $L_1[y \log \sin x]$

3. If L is a differential operator as in the left-hand term of Eq. (1.2) and

$$L[y_1(x)] = f_1(x) \qquad L[y_2(x)] = f_2(x) \qquad \cdots \qquad L[y_k(x)] = f_k(x)$$

show that

$$L[y_1(x) + y_2(x) + \cdots + y_k(x)] = f_1(x) + f_2(x) + \cdots + f_k(x)$$

(This is the "principle of superposition"; see Sec. 9.)

4. If L is a differential operator as in the left-hand term of Eq. (1.2), and $c_1, c_2, \ldots, c_k$ are constants, show that

$$L[c_1 y_1(x) + c_2 y_2(x) + \cdots + c_k y_k(x)]$$
$$= c_1 L[y_1(x)] + c_2 L[y_2(x)] + \cdots + c_k L[y_k(x)]$$

2. Existence and Uniqueness of Solutions

No new idea is involved in extending Theorem 2 of Sec. 12, Chap. V, from differential equations of order 2 to equations of order n. One obtains

Theorem 1. *If $g(x, y, p_1, \ldots, p_{n-1})$, $\partial g/\partial y$, $\partial g/\partial p_1, \ldots, \partial g/\partial p_{n-1}$ are continuous in some region $a \leq x \leq b$, $c \leq y \leq d$, $c_1 \leq p_1 \leq d_1$, $\ldots, c_{n-1} \leq p_{n-1} \leq d_{n-1}$, of $xyp_1 \cdots p_{n-1}$ space, and if $(x_0, y_0, y_1, \ldots, y_{n-1})$ is a point inferior to this region, then there exists, in some neighborhood of x_0, a unique solution of the equation $y^{(n)} = g(x, y, y', \ldots, y^{(n-1)})$ which satisfies the initial conditions $y(x_0) = y_0$, $y'(x_0) = y_1, \ldots, y^{(n-1)}(x_0) = y_{n-1}$.*

For the linear equation (1.2) with coefficients which are continuous for $a \leq x \leq b$, the conditions of Theorem 1 are clearly satisfied if $a < x_0 < b$, with $y_0, y_1, \ldots, y_{n-1}$ arbitrary. Thus one can deduce the existence of a unique solution of D.E. (1.2) satisfying the I.C. (1.7) over the whole interval $a \leq x \leq b$ (for the necessary arguments concerning the global behavior see the proof of Theorem 3, Sec. 3, Chap. III). We formulate this result as

Theorem 2. *If $a_1(x), a_2(x), \ldots, a_n(x), f(x)$ are continuous† in the interval $a \leq x \leq b$ that includes the point $x = x_0$, then Eq. (1.2) has one and only one solution in $a \leq x \leq b$ that satisfies conditions (1.7).*

If a function y is to be a solution of Eq. (1.2), it obviously must have derivatives of order $1, 2, \ldots, n$. Since differentiability of a function implies its continuity, it follows that the derivatives of order $0, 1, 2, \ldots, n - 1$ are continuous. Moreover, by (1.2),

$$y^{(n)} = f - a_1 y^{(n-1)} - a_2 y^{(n-2)} - \cdots - a_n$$

and since the right-hand member of this equation is continuous, this is also the case for $y^{(n)}$.

Theorem 2 does not only assert that there exists an integral of Eq. (1.2) satisfying initial conditions (1.7), but also that there is but *one* such solution. There are many important applications of the uniqueness part of this theorem. Suppose two different methods are

---

† The continuity of f can be relaxed. Only *piecewise* continuity is required. See Sec. 14 for a discussion.

used to solve Eq. (1.2) with the given initial conditions. Then the two obtained expressions, although they may differ widely in form, must represent identical functions, for $a \leq x \leq b$. In this way power series, definite integrals, and other infinite expansions can often be "evaluated," that is, identified as expansions of known functions. The following examples serve to illustrate this point.

Example 1. The differential equation

$$3y'' - 2y' + y = 1$$

has the two solutions

$$y_1(x) = \sqrt{2}\, e^x (\cos \sqrt{2}\, x + \sin \sqrt{2}\, x) + 1$$

$$y_2(x) = \frac{1-i}{\sqrt{2}}\, e^{(1+\sqrt{2}i)x} + \frac{1+i}{\sqrt{2}}\, e^{(1-\sqrt{2}i)x} + 1$$

as may be readily verified. At $x = 0$ we have

$$y_1(0) = y_2(0) = 1 + \sqrt{2}$$

and

$$y_1'(0) = y_2'(0) = 2 + \sqrt{2}$$

Therefore y_1 and y_2 satisfy the same initial conditions, and $y_1(x) = y_2(x)$ for all x, by the uniqueness part of Theorem 2.

Example 2. By direct substitution it can be verified that each of the functions

$$y_1(x) = 2(x + \tfrac{1}{3}x^3 + \tfrac{1}{5}x^5 + \cdots)$$

$$y_2(x) = \log \frac{1+x}{1-x}$$

is, for $|x| < 1$, a solution of the equation

$$(1 - x^2)\frac{d^2y}{dx^2} - 2x\frac{dy}{dx} = 0$$

and satisfies the initial conditions

$$y(0) = 0 \qquad y'(0) = 2$$

Hence, by the uniqueness part of Theorem 2, these functions are identical.

PROBLEMS

1. What is the unique solution of the nth-order linear homogeneous D.E. $L[y] = 0$ which satisfies the I.C. $y(x_0) = y'(x_0) = \cdots = y^{(n-1)}(x_0) = 0$?

2. Show that both

$$y_1(x) = x + \frac{1}{2}\frac{x^3}{3} + \frac{1 \cdot 3}{2 \cdot 4}\frac{x^5}{5} + \frac{1 \cdot 3 \cdot 5}{2 \cdot 4 \cdot 6}\frac{x^7}{7} + \cdots$$

and

$$y_2(x) = \arcsin x$$

are, for $|x| < 1$, solutions of the equation

$$(1 - x^2)y'' - xy' = 0$$

satisfying the initial conditions $y(0) = 0$, $y'(0) = 1$. How does it follow that $y_1(x) = y_2(x)$?

3. Show that no integral curve of the equation

$$\frac{d^2y}{dx^2} + a_1(x)\frac{dy}{dx} + a_2(x)y = 0 \qquad a_1(x), a_2(x) \text{ continuous}$$

can be tangent to the x axis and go through $(1, 1)$.

4. Show that if $y = y_1(x)$, $y = y_2(x)$ are two integral curves of the equation

$$\frac{d^2y}{dx^2} + a_1(x)\frac{dy}{dx} + a_2(x)y = 0 \qquad a_1(x), a_2(x) \text{ continuous}$$

that intersect the x axis at the same point, then $y_1(x)$, $y_2(x)$ differ only by a constant factor. HINT: Suppose $y_1(x_0) = y_2(x_0) = 0$ and $y_1'(x_0) = m_1$, $y_2'(x_0) = m_2$. Then apply the result of Prob. 3 to the integral curve $y = m_2y_1(x) - m_1y_2(x)$.

★5. Show that both

$$y_1(x) = 1 - \frac{x^2}{2^2(1!)^2} + \frac{x^4}{2^4(2!)^2} - \frac{x^6}{2^6(3!)^2} + \cdots$$

and

$$y_2(x) = \frac{1}{\pi}\int_0^\pi \cos(x \cos \theta)\, d\theta$$

are solutions of the equation (Bessel's)

$$\frac{d^2y}{dx^2} + \frac{1}{x}\frac{dy}{dx} + y = 0$$

satisfying the initial conditions $y(0) = 1$, $y'(0) = 0$. These two functions are identical [equal to the Bessel function $J_0(x)$; see Sec. 5, Chap. X], but this fact cannot be deduced from Theorem 2. Why not?

★6. Verify that $y(x) = x \sin x$ is a solution of the equation

$$x^2\frac{d^2y}{dx^2} - 2x\frac{dy}{dx} + (x^2 + 2)y = 0$$

and of the initial conditions $y(0) = 0$, $y'(0) = 0$. Another solution is $y \equiv 0$. Is this a contradiction of Theorem 2 of Sec. 2?

7. Show that if $y_1(x)$ is a solution of the equation

$$\frac{d^n y}{dx^n} + a_1(x) \frac{d^{n-1} y}{dx^{n-1}} + \cdots + a_n(x) y = f(x)$$

and the functions $a_1, a_2, \ldots, a_n, f$ possess derivatives of every order in the interval $a \leq x \leq b$, then y_1 possesses derivatives of every order. HINT: Since y_1 is a solution of the equation, we have

$$y_1^{(n)} = -a_1 y_1^{(n-1)} - \cdots - a_n y_1 + f$$

Likewise, obtain $y_1^{(n+1)}, y_1^{(n+2)}, \ldots.$

8. Verify† that

$$z_1(x) = \int_{x_0}^{x} dx_4 \int_{x_0}^{x_4} dx_3 \int_{x_0}^{x_3} dx_2 \int_{x_0}^{x_2} f(x_1)\, dx_1$$

and

$$z_2(x) = \int_{x_0}^{x} \frac{(x - x_1)^3}{3!} f(x_1)\, dx_1$$

are both solutions of the D.E. $z^{(4)} = f$ satisfying the I.C. $z(x_0) = z'(x_0) = z''(x_0) = z'''(x_0) = 0$. Hence conclude that $z_1(x) \equiv z_2(x)$. Guided by this result, formulate a theorem by which n repeated integrations, all starting from the same abscissa x_0, can be replaced with one integration.

★9. Verify that

$$y_1(x) = \int_{x_0}^{x} dx_3 \int_{x_0}^{x} dx_2 \int_{x_0}^{x} e^{c(x-x_1)} f(x_1)\, dx_1$$

and

$$y_2(x) = \int_{x_0}^{x} \frac{(x - x_1)^2}{2!} e^{c(x-x_1)} f(x_1)\, dx_1$$

are both solutions of the D.E.

$$y''' - 3cy'' + 3c^2 y' - c^3 y = f \qquad c = \text{constant}$$

satisfying the I.C. $y(x_0) = y'(x_0) = y''(x_0) = 0$.

10. By writing Y for the n-tuple $(y_1, \ldots, y_n)$ and F for the n-tuple $(f_1, \ldots, f_n)$, formulate an existence and uniqueness theorem for the system of first-order equations $dY/dx = F(x, Y)$ and derive Theorem 1 from this theorem. HINT: Refer to Theorem 2, Sec. 3, Chap. III, and Theorem 1, Sec. 12, Chap. V.

† It is necessary to be able to differentiate a function φ given by

$$\varphi(x) = \int_{a}^{x} F(x, t)\, dt$$

The formula, which may be established from the definition of the derivative, is

$$\varphi'(x) = F(x, x) + \int_{a}^{x} \frac{\partial F}{\partial x}(x, t)\, dt$$

provided that F and $\partial F/\partial x$ are continuous.

3. Linear Combinations and Linear Independence

Before we consider the general solution of a linear differential equation, we must discuss some important preliminary notions.

Definitions. A sum of the form $c_1y_1 + c_2y_2 + \cdots + c_ky_k$, consisting of given functions $y_1, y_2, \ldots, y_k$ and arbitrary constants $c_1, c_2, \ldots, c_k$, is called a *linear combination* of the functions $y_1, y_2, \ldots, y_k$. It is understood that the constants $c_1, c_2, \ldots, c_k$ may be complex numbers. It is also understood that the functions are defined over a common interval I. The function y is said to be *linearly dependent* on the functions $y_1, y_2, \ldots, y_k$ if y can be represented as a linear combination of $y_1, y_2, \ldots, y_k$,

$$y(x) = c_1y_1(x) + \cdots + c_ky_k(x) \qquad \text{for all } x \text{ in } I$$

for some choice of the constants $c_1, \ldots, c_k$. If y is not linearly dependent on $y_1, \ldots, y_k$, then y is *linearly independent* of $y_1, \ldots, y_k$.

A finite number of functions $y_1, y_2, \ldots, y_k$ are said to be *linearly independent* (of one another) if no one of them can be represented as a linear combination of the remaining functions.

It is not always a simple matter to decide whether or not a given set of functions is linearly independent.† In this book we shall always rely on the definition and the properties of the functions being considered. We shall often make use of the following theorem.

Theorem 1. *In order that the functions* $y_1, \ldots, y_k$ *defined on a common interval I be linearly independent, it is necessary and sufficient that no linear combination of them is identically zero except the trivial one. In other words,* $y_1, \ldots, y_k$ *are linearly independent if and only if*

$$(3.1) \quad c_1y_1(x) + c_2y_2(x) + \cdots + c_ky_k(x) = 0 \qquad \text{for all } x \text{ in } I$$

implies $c_1 = c_2 = \cdots = c_k = 0$.

The proof of this theorem is left as an exercise.

Example 1. $3x^2 - 2x + 1$ is a linear combination of $(x^2 + x)$ and $(x^2 + 6x - 1)$, for $3x^2 - 2x + 1 = 4(x^2 + x) - 1(x^2 + 6x - 1)$.

Example 2. $\log(1 + \sqrt{2x - 1})$ is a linear combination of 1 and $\log(x + \sqrt{2x - 1})$, for

$$(3.2) \qquad \log(1 + \sqrt{2x - 1}) = (\tfrac{1}{2}\log 2)1 + \tfrac{1}{2}\log(x + \sqrt{2x - 1})$$

† A necessary and sufficient condition for the linear independence of k functions that are integrals of a linear differential equation of order k is the nonvanishing of the so-called *Wronskian determinant* (see Prob. 5, Sec. 4). As a general criterion for linear independence of sets of *arbitrary* functions, the Wronskian determinant is useless.

Example 3. The functions $1, x, x^2, \ldots, x^k$ are linearly independent. Assume that there is a linear combination of them that is identically zero, namely,

$$(3.3) \qquad c_0 + c_1 x + c_2 x^2 + \cdots + c_k x^k = 0$$

If not all the coefficients in Eq. (3.3) are zero, then it is an algebraic equation of degree no higher than k which can be satisfied by at most k values of x, but not identically. Therefore $c_1 = c_2 = \cdots = c_k = 0$.

The following theorem asserts that a certain large class of functions consists of linearly independent ones. These functions are precisely those which arise in solving linear differential equations with constant coefficients.

Theorem 2. *The functions*

$$e^{r_1 x} \qquad x e^{r_1 x} \qquad \cdots \qquad x^{n_1} e^{r_1 x} \qquad e^{r_2 x} \qquad x e^{r_2 x} \qquad \cdots \qquad x^{n_2} e^{r_2 x}$$

$$\cdots \qquad e^{r_k x} \qquad x e^{r_k x} \qquad \cdots \qquad x^{n_k} e^{r_k x}$$

where $n_1, n_2, \ldots, n_k$ are any nonnegative integers, and $r_1, r_2, \ldots, r_k$ are any distinct real or complex numbers, are linearly independent.

Proof. The theorem is true for $k = 1$ because if

$$(c_0 + c_1 x + \cdots + c_{n_1} x^{n_1}) e^{r_1 x} = 0 \qquad \text{for all } x$$

then, by Example 3, $c_0 = c_1 = \cdots = c_{n_1} = 0$.

Suppose the theorem is false. There is a *least* positive integer k for which it is false, and so there are polynomials $P_1, \ldots, P_k$ (none of them zero) and numbers $r_1, \ldots, r_k$ (all distinct) such that

$$(3.4) \qquad P_1(x) e^{r_1 x} + \cdots + P_k(x) e^{r_k x} = 0 \qquad \text{for all } x$$

where none of the P_i are zero because k is as small as possible. From (3.4) we obtain

$$(3.5) \qquad P_1(x) + P_2(x) e^{(r_2 - r_1) x} + \cdots + P_k(x) e^{(r_k - r_1) x} = 0$$

Differentiate (3.5) enough times (one more than the degree of P_1) so the first term vanishes. Then we have

$$(3.6) \qquad Q_2(x) e^{(r_2 - r_1) x} + \cdots + Q_k(x) e^{(r_k - r_1) x} = 0$$

with nonzero polynomials† $Q_2, \ldots, Q_k$ and distinct exponents

† It is left to the student to verify that the nth derivative of a function

$$y = (a x^n + b x^{n-1} + \cdots) e^{r x}$$

where $a \neq 0$ and $r \neq 0$, is of the form $y^{(n)} = (a r^n x^n + b_1 x^{n-1} + \cdots) e^{r x}$ (this holds also when $n = 0$, that is, $y = a e^{r x}$). Hence, none of the derivatives $y', y'', y''', \ldots$ can reduce to zero.

$r_2 - r_1, \ldots, r_k - r_1$. But (3.6) asserts the falsity of the theorem for $k - 1$. Since k was chosen as small as possible, we have a contradiction, and our proof is complete.

Example 4. The functions 1, x, xe^x, xe^{2x} are linearly independent because these are some of the functions of Theorem 2 with $k = 3$, $r_1 = 0$, $r_2 = 1$, $r_3 = 2$, and $n_1 = 1$, $n_2 = 1$, $n_3 = 1$.

PROBLEMS

1. Represent $\cos 2x$ as a linear combination of (a) $\sin^2 x$, $\cos^2 x$; (b) 1, $\cos^2 x$; (c) -3, $\sin^2 x$.

2. Represent $2x^2 + 8x + 3$ as a linear combination of (a) 1, x, x^2; (b) 1, $(x - 1)$, $(x - 1)^2$; (c) 5, $(x + 2)^2$; (d) 1, $x + 1$.

3. Show, by use of Theorem 1, that the functions x, x^2, e^x are linearly independent.

4. Determine, either directly from the definition or by use of Theorem 1, whether or not the following functions are linearly independent:

(a) 5, $x - 2$, $2x + 7$ (b) a, $ax + 3$, where constant $a \neq 0$

(c) $1 + x$, $1 - x$, $1 - x^2$ (d) 1, $x + 1$, x^2, $x^2 - x$

(e) $\sin x$, $\cos x$ (f) $\sin 2x$, $\sin x$, $\cos x$

(g) 1, e^x (h) 0, x

(i) e^x, e^{-x}, e^{2x} (j) π, e, $f(x)$

(k) 1, $x - x_0$, $(x - x_0)^2$, $\ldots$, $(x - x_0)^n$ $(x_0$ constant$)$

(l) 1, $\displaystyle\int_a^x f(x_1)\, dx_1$, $\displaystyle\int_b^x f(x_1)\, dx_1$ $(a, b$ constant$)$

5. Show that if y_1, y_2 are linear combinations of v_1, v_2, and v_1, v_2 are linear combinations of u_1, u_2, then y_1, y_2 are linear combinations of u_1, u_2.

6. Represent $A \sinh (ax + b)$ and $A \cosh (ax + b)$ as linear combinations of e^{ax}, e^{-ax}.

7. Represent e^{ax} and e^{-ax} as linear combinations of $\sinh ax$, $\cosh ax$.

★8. Represent $\cos^n x$ $(n = 1, 2, \ldots)$ as a linear combination of 1, $\cos x$, $\cos 2x$, $\ldots$, $\cos nx$. HINT: Use

$$\cos^n x = \left(\frac{e^{ix} + e^{-ix}}{2}\right)^n$$

★9. Can $\sin^n x$ be represented as a linear combination of $\sin x$, $\sin 2x$, $\ldots$, $\sin nx$ for every positive integer n?

★10. Show that if $y_1(x)$, $y_2(x)$, $y_3(x)$ are linearly dependent on the common interval I, then the determinant (the Wronskian of y_1, y_2, y_3)

$$\begin{vmatrix} y_1(x) & y_2(x) & y_3(x) \\ y_1'(x) & y_2'(x) & y_3'(x) \\ y_1''(x) & y_2''(x) & y_3''(x) \end{vmatrix}$$

vanishes for all x in I. Formulate the analogous result for n functions.

11. Use the method of Example 3 to show that the functions $1, x^{-1}, x^{-2}, \ldots$ x^{-k} are linearly independent.

12. Show that any set of functions is linearly dependent if (*a*) $y = 0$ is one of the functions; (*b*) two of the functions are identical; (*c*) one of the functions is a constant multiple of another; (*d*) a subset of these functions is linearly dependent.

13. Show, by use of Theorem 2, that the following sets of functions are linearly independent:

(*a*) $1, x, xe^x$
(*b*) $1, x, xe^x, xe^{2x}$
(*c*) $e^{(2+i)x}, e^{(2-i)x}, e^{3x}, e^{\pi x}$
(*d*) $1, x, x^2, e^{(\alpha+i\beta)x}, xe^{(\alpha+i\beta)x}, e^{(\alpha-i\beta)x}, xe^{(\alpha-i\beta)x}; \alpha^2 + \beta^2 > 0$

★14. By a proof similar to that of Theorem 2, show that the functions x^{r_1}, $x^{r_2}, \ldots, x^{r_k}$, where $r_1, \ldots, r_k$ are any distinct real numbers, are linearly independent.

4. Vector Spaces

The description of solutions of linear D.E. is greatly facilitated by use of the language of *linear algebra*. Although limitations of space do not permit an extended treatment of linear algebra, we shall use the language and give enough illustrations to convey the ideas.

The basic concept involved is that of a *linear vector space*. The reader is already familiar with *vectors* (or arrows) in Euclidean space. Recall that vectors can be added (by the parallelogram law) and multiplied by real numbers. Then, if $\mathbf{v}_1$, $\mathbf{v}_2$, and $\mathbf{v}_3$ are noncoplanar vector, every vector can be written as a sum of multiples of $\mathbf{v}_1$, $\mathbf{v}_2$, and $\mathbf{v}_3$, that is,

$$\mathbf{v} = c_1\mathbf{v}_1 + c_2\mathbf{v}_2 + c_3\mathbf{v}_3$$

where c_1, c_2, and c_3 are *real* numbers. The vectors $\mathbf{v}_1$, $\mathbf{v}_2$, $\mathbf{v}_3$ form a *basis* for the set of all vectors in space, and the latter is a three-dimensional vector space.

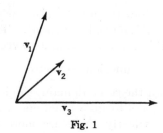

Fig. 1

The above situation generalizes to dimensions $n > 3$ and to vector spaces in which one can multiply vectors by complex numbers as well as real numbers.

Definition 1. A (linear) *vector space* V is a set V of entities called vectors with the following properties: Any two vectors $\mathbf{u}$ and $\mathbf{v}$ can be added to give another vector $\mathbf{w} = \mathbf{u} + \mathbf{v}$; any vector $\mathbf{u}$ can be multiplied by any complex number (scalar) c to give a vector $\mathbf{v} = c\mathbf{u}$. Addition of vectors is commutative and associative. Multiplication by scalars is associative. Furthermore, if c, c_1, and c_2 are scalars, and $\mathbf{v}$, $\mathbf{v}_1$, and $\mathbf{v}_2$ are vectors, then the following distributive laws are valid:

$$(c_1 + c_2)\mathbf{v} = c_1\mathbf{v} + c_2\mathbf{v} \qquad c(\mathbf{v}_1 + \mathbf{v}_2) = c\mathbf{v}_1 + c\mathbf{v}_2$$

There is a zero vector $\mathbf{0}$ such that, for all vectors $\mathbf{v}$,

$$\mathbf{v} + \mathbf{0} = \mathbf{v}$$

Finally, for any vectors $\mathbf{u}$ and $\mathbf{v}$,

$$1\mathbf{v} = \mathbf{v} \qquad (-1)\mathbf{v} = -\mathbf{v} \qquad \mathbf{v} + (-\mathbf{u}) = \mathbf{v} - \mathbf{u}$$

Definition 2. The vectors $\mathbf{v}_1, \ldots, \mathbf{v}_k$ are said to be *linearly independent* if $c_1\mathbf{v}_1 + c_2\mathbf{v}_2 + \cdots + c_k\mathbf{v}_k = 0$, where $c_1, \ldots, c_k$ are scalars, implies that $c_1 = c_2 = \cdots = c_k = 0$. If $\mathbf{v}_1, \ldots, \mathbf{v}_k$ are not linearly independent, they are linearly dependent.

The vector space V is said to have *dimension n* if V contains n linearly independent vectors but any $n + 1$ vectors in V are linearly dependent. Any set of n linearly independent vectors of the n-dimensional vector space V form a *linear basis* of V.

The following important theorem is an easy consequence of the definitions. Its proof is left to the reader.

Theorem 1. *If the vectors* $\mathbf{v}_1, \ldots, \mathbf{v}_n$ *form a linear basis of the n-dimensional vector space V, then every vector $\mathbf{v}$ in V is uniquely representable by a linear combination of* $\mathbf{v}_1, \ldots, \mathbf{v}_n$:

$$\mathbf{v} = c_1\mathbf{v}_1 + \cdots + c_n\mathbf{v}_n$$

It remains to be seen how the notion of linear vector space is related to the theory of linear differential equations. The idea is really quite simple. We merely think of a function as a vector:

$$\text{function} \leftrightarrow \text{vector}$$

Because functions (with the same domain) can be added and/or multiplied by complex numbers to give functions, one sees that functions form a vector space. Clearly there are more than n linearly independent functions for any fixed n.   Therefore, to obtain a vector space of functions of some finite dimension, one must select but "a few" from the set of all functions.   We shall see that a linear D.E. does, in effect, select such a set of functions.

The following theorem is an easy consequence of the definition of a vector space.

Theorem 2.   *The multitude of functions that are linear combinations of k fixed linearly independent functions y_1, y_2, $\ldots$, y_k form a vector space of functions of dimension k.   The functions y_1, y_2, $\ldots$, y_k are a basis of this space.*

We shall use the symbol $V[y_1, y_2, \ldots , y_k]$ to denote the vector space formed from the basis y_1, y_2, $\ldots$, y_k.

Example 1. $V[1, x, x^2, \ldots , x^n]$, the system of all polynomials of degrees $0, 1, 2, \ldots , n$, is of dimension $n + 1$.

Example 2.   All the harmonic vibrations $A \sin (\nu t + \delta)$ of fixed frequency ν, but arbitrary amplitude $A \geqq 0$ and arbitrary phase δ, form a two-dimensional vector space, with the *real* numbers as scalars.   As the basis of this system we may choose the two linearly independent functions $\sin \nu t$, $\cos \nu t$, for

$$A \sin (\nu t + \delta) = (A \cos \delta) \sin \nu t + (A \sin \delta) \cos \nu t$$

Conversely,

$$c_1 \sin \nu t + c_2 \cos \nu t = A \sin (\nu t + \delta)$$

where $A = \sqrt{c_1{}^2 + c_2{}^2}$, $\delta = \arctan (c_2/c_1)$.

Example 3.   Consider the vector space of all polynomials of degrees $0, 1, 2, \ldots , k$, for which the functions $1, x, x^2, \ldots , x^k$ form a basis (see Example 1 above).   Among all these polynomials are also the $k + 1$ linearly independent ones, namely, $1, (x - x_0), (x - x_0)^2, \ldots , (x - x_0)^k$.   Therefore,

$$V[1, x, x^2, \ldots , x^k] = V[1, (x - x_0), (x - x_0)^2, \ldots , (x - x_0)^k]$$

Example 4.   Another vector space of great importance in the theory of linear differential equations is

$$V[e^{(\alpha+\beta i)x}, e^{(\alpha-\beta i)x}]$$

As is well known,

$$e^{(\alpha \pm \beta i)x} = e^{\alpha x} e^{\pm i \beta x} = e^{\alpha x} \cos \beta x \pm i e^{\alpha x} \sin \beta x$$

Therefore, both $e^{(\alpha+\beta i)x}$ and $e^{(\alpha-\beta i)x}$ are linear combinations of $e^{\alpha x} \cos \beta x$, $e^{\alpha x} \sin \beta x$.   On the other hand, we also have the identities

$$e^{\alpha x} \cos \beta x = e^{\alpha x} \frac{e^{i\beta x} + e^{-i\beta x}}{2} = \frac{1}{2} e^{(\alpha+\beta i)x} + \frac{1}{2} e^{(\alpha-\beta i)x}$$

$$e^{\alpha x} \sin \beta x = e^{\alpha x} \frac{e^{i\beta x} - e^{i\beta x}}{2i} = -\frac{i}{2} e^{(\alpha+\beta i)x} + \frac{i}{2} e^{(\alpha-\beta i)x}$$

Therefore, both $e^{\alpha x} \cos \beta x$ and $e^{\alpha x} \sin \beta x$ are linear combinations of $e^{(\alpha+\beta i)x}$, $e^{(\alpha-\beta i)x}$. The two results may be stated in one equation:

$$V[e^{(\alpha+\beta i)x}, \; e^{(\alpha-\beta i)x}] = V[e^{\alpha x} \cos \beta x, \; e^{\alpha x} \sin \beta x]$$

PROBLEMS

1. Show that $V[1, x, x^2] = V[x + 2, x - 2, x^2 + 1]$.

2. Show that $V[e^{i\alpha x}, e^{-i\alpha x}] = V[\cos \alpha x, \sin \alpha x]$.

3. In the following linear spaces of dimension k, find k linearly independent functions different from the given basis functions:

(a) $V[1, x, x^2]$ (b) $V[x, e^x]$

(c) $V[1, x - x_0, (x - x_0)^2, (x - x_0)^3]$ (d) $V[e^x, e^{2x}, e^{3x}]$

(e) $V[e^{(2+3i)x}, e^{(2-3i)x}]$

4. The functions 2, $x - 3$, $x + 2$, $x^2 + 1$, $2x^2 - 3$ are linearly dependent. Find a basis for the space of all linear combinations of these functions. What is its dimension?

★5. In the text we have intentionally avoided finding any shortcut for deciding about the linear independence of solutions to homogeneous differential equations. We have done this in order to focus attention on the concept rather than on computational details. Nevertheless, there is a rather simple formal procedure for deciding about linear dependence. One has but to compute the Wronskian of the functions.

Definition. If $y_1, \ldots, y_n$ are n functions having derivatives of orders $1, 2, \ldots, n - 1$, the function W given by the determinant

$$W(x) = \begin{vmatrix} y_1(x) & y_2(x) & \cdots & y_n(x) \\ y_1^{(1)}(x) & y_2^{(1)}(x) & \cdots & y_n^{(1)}(x) \\ \cdots\cdots\cdots\cdots\cdots\cdots\cdots\cdots \\ y_1^{(n-1)}(x) & y_2^{(n-1)}(x) & \cdots & y_n^{(n-1)}(x) \end{vmatrix}$$

is called the *Wronskian* of the functions $y_1, \ldots, y_n$.

Theorem. *If $y_1, \ldots, y_n$ are solutions of the linear homogeneous nth-order equation $y^{(n)}(x) + a_1(x)y^{(n-1)}(x) + \cdots + a_n(x)y = 0$, where $a_1, \ldots, a_n$ are continuous functions on a common interval I, then $y_1, \ldots, y_n$ are linearly independent on I if and only if $W(x) \neq 0$ on I.*

Sketch of Proof. If $y_1, \ldots, y_n$ are dependent then there are constants $c_1, \ldots, c_n$—not all zero—such that $c_1 y_1(x) + \cdots + c_n y_n(x) = 0$; hence also $c_1 y_1^{(i)}(x) + \cdots + c_n y_n^{(i)}(x) = 0$ for $i = 1, \ldots, n - 1$. It follows from an elementary theorem of algebra that $W(x) = 0$.

If $W(x_0) = 0$ then constants $c_1, \ldots, c_n$—not all zero—can be found such that $c_1 y_1(x_0) + \cdots + c_n y_n(x_0) = 0$ and $c_1 y_1^{(i)}(x_0) + \cdots + c_n y_n^{(i)}(x_0) = 0$ for $i = 1, \ldots, n - 1$. The function $y = c_1 y_1 + \cdots + c_n y_n$ then satisfies a homogeneous D.E. and homogeneous I.C. By Theorem 2, Sec. 2, $y = 0$. This also shows that if $W(x_0) = 0$, then $W(x) = 0$ for all x in I.

Solve Prob. 4, Sec. 3, using the Wronskian. Assume, as is true, that the functions are solutions of linear homogeneous D.E.'s.

★6. Let $r_1, r_2, \ldots , r_n$ be any n distinct numbers. Using the fact that the Wronskian of the functions $e^{r_1 x}, e^{r_2 x}, \ldots , e^{r_n x}$ does not vanish, prove that the (so-called *Vandermond*) determinant

$$\begin{vmatrix} 1 & 1 & \cdots & 1 \\ r_1 & r_2 & \cdots & r_n \\ \cdots & \cdots & \cdots & \cdots \\ r_1^{n-1} & r_2^{n-1} & \cdots & r_n^{n-1} \end{vmatrix}$$

is different from zero.

5. General Solution of the Homogeneous Equation

The terminology of the preceding section makes it possible to characterize the multitude of solutions of a linear homogeneous differential equation in a very concise manner.

Theorem. *The integrals of the linear homogeneous differential equation of order n, $L[y] = 0$, form a linear vector space of dimension n.*

The proof will be carried out in three steps. First, we show that any linear combination of integrals is itself an integral. Then n special integrals $Y_0, Y_1, \ldots , Y_{n-1}$ are singled out and are shown to be linearly independent. Finally, it is proved that every integral is a linear combination of $Y_0, Y_1, \ldots , Y_{n-1}$.

The first step is the easiest. Assume that y is a linear combination of the integrals $y_1, y_2, \ldots , y_k$, namely,

$$(5.1) \qquad y(x) = c_1 y_1(x) + c_2 y_2(x) + \cdots + c_k y_k(x)$$

Because L is a linear operator,

$$\begin{aligned} L[y] &= c_1 L[y_1] + c_2 L[y_2] + \cdots + c_k L[y_k] \\ &= c_1 \cdot 0 + c_2 \cdot 0 + \cdots + c_k \cdot 0 \\ &= 0 \end{aligned}$$

Hence, every linear combination of integrals of the equation $L[y] = 0$ is itself an integral of this equation.

Next, we select n special integrals $Y_0, Y_1, \ldots , Y_{n-1}$, distinguished by the different initial conditions that they satisfy. At the initial point $x = x_0$, Y_k and its first $n - 1$ derivatives are to vanish, except the kth derivative, which is to be unity, or

$$(5.2) \qquad Y_k^{(i)}(x_0) = \begin{cases} 0 & \text{for } i \neq k \\ 1 & \text{for } i = k \end{cases}$$

By Theorem 2 of Sec. 2, there are such solutions and they are uniquely determined. It is readily seen that these solutions are linearly independent. Assume that one of them, say Y_k, is a linear combination of the remaining ones:

$$Y_k(x) = c_0 Y_0(x) + c_1 Y_1(x) + \cdots + c_{k-1} Y_{k-1}(x)$$
$$+ c_{k+1} Y_{k+1}(x) + \cdots + c_{n-1} Y_{n-1}(x)$$

If this equation is differentiated k times (here $k \leq n - 1$), and then the initial value x_0 is substituted for x, the impossible equation

$$1 = c_0 \cdot 0 + c_1 \cdot 0 + \cdots + c_{n-1} \cdot 0$$

results. Hence, the assumption that $Y_0, Y_1, \ldots, Y_{n-1}$ are not linearly independent must be rejected. Among the integrals of $L[y] = 0$ there are, *at least*, n linearly independent ones, in particular the integrals $Y_0, Y_1, \ldots, Y_{n-1}$.

To complete the proof, let us consider a linear combination of these particular integrals:

$$(5.3) \qquad Y(x) = c_0 Y_0(x) + c_1 Y_1(x) + \cdots + c_{n-1} Y_{n-1}(x)$$

where $c_0, c_1, \ldots, c_{n-1}$ are arbitrary constants. Because of the I.C. (5.2), the ith derivative of Y at x_0 is

$$Y^{(i)}(x_0) = c_0 \cdot 0 + c_1 \cdot 0 + \cdots + c_i \cdot 1 + \cdots + c_{n-1} \cdot 0$$
$$= c_i$$

Hence, Y is a solution of the equation $L[y] = 0$ satisfying the initial conditions

$$Y(x_0) = c_0 \qquad Y'(x_0) = c_1 \qquad \cdots \qquad Y^{(n-1)}(x_0) = c_{n-1}$$

and, because of Theorem 2 of Sec. 2, this is the only such solution. Since the numbers $c_0, c_1, \ldots, c_{n-1}$ are arbitrary, any solution whatsoever of $L[y] = 0$ can be obtained in the form (5.3). Hence the n particular integrals $Y_0, Y_1, \ldots, Y_{n-1}$ form a linear basis of all the solutions, and the theorem is proved.

It should be observed that the particular integrals $Y_0, Y_1, \ldots, Y_{n-1}$ considered in the above proof do not constitute the only basis of the vector space of integrals of $L[y] = 0$. Any other set of n linearly independent integrals, say $y_1, y_2, \ldots y_n$, form such a basis, and every solution of the equation can be obtained as a linear combination of n basis integrals. Hence, the content of the theorem may also be stated as follows:

Corollary. *Every solution of the homogeneous linear differential equation of order* n, $L[y] = 0$, *is given by*

$$(5.4) \qquad\qquad y = c_1 y_1 + c_2 y_2 + \cdots + c_n y_n$$

where y_1, y_2, $\ldots$, y_n *are any* n *linearly independent solutions.*

Since *every* integral of $L[y] = 0$ is given by (5.4), we are justified in calling (5.4) *the* general solution.

We are now in the following position: If we but knew n linearly independent solutions, then we would know all solutions. The problem, therefore, is to find, *in any way,* n linearly independent solutions. We now examine a few equations to illustrate the idea.

Example 1. The linear homogeneous differential equation of order n

$$(5.5) \qquad\qquad \frac{d^n y}{dx^n} = 0$$

obviously has the n integrals $1, x, x^2, \ldots, x^{n-1}$, which are linearly independent (see Example 3, Sec. 3). Hence, these functions form a basis of the linear space of all integrals of Eq. (5.5), and the vector space of all solutions is the class of polynomials of degrees $0, 1, 2, \ldots, n - 1$. The particular integrals satisfying conditions (5.2) are, in this case,

$$Y_0(x) = 1 \qquad Y_1(x) = \frac{x - x_0}{1!} \qquad \cdots \qquad Y_{n-1}(x) = \frac{(x - x_0)^{n-1}}{(n-1)!}$$

Thus, we have two expressions for the general integral of Eq. (5.5):

$$y(x) = c_0 + c_1 x + c_2 x^2 + \cdots + c_{n-1} x^{n-1}$$

and

$$y(x) = C_0 + C_1 \frac{x - x_0}{1!} + C_2 \frac{(x - x_0)^2}{2!} + \cdots + C_{n-1} \frac{(x - x_0)^{n-1}}{(n-1)!}$$

Example 2. The equation

$$x^3 y''' + 9x^2 y'' + 18xy' + 6y = 0$$

has three linearly independent solutions of the form x^r.

To find these solutions, we try $y = x^r$ in the equation and obtain

$$x^3 r(r-1)(r-2)x^{r-3} + 9x^2 r(r-1)x^{r-2} + 18xrx^{r-1} + 6x^r = 0$$

whence

$$r(r-1)(r-2) + 9r(r-1) + 18r + 6 = 0$$

or

$$r^3 + 6r^2 + 11r + 6 = 0$$

This equation determines the possible values of r. Since the equation has integer coefficients, any rational roots must be among the numbers ± 1, ± 2, ± 3, ± 6. By trial, one finds that the roots are $r = -1, -2, -3$, whence three solutions of the D.E. are x^{-1}, x^{-2}, x^{-3}; these are easily shown to be linearly independent. Therefore every solution is given, for suitable constants c_1, c_2, c_3, by

$$y(x) = c_1 x^{-1} + c_2 x^{-2} + c_3 x^{-3}$$

PROBLEMS

1. The following D.E.'s have linearly independent solutions of the form e^{rx}, where r is a constant. Find all solutions of each.

(a) $y''' + y'' - 10y' + 8y = 0$

(b) $y''' + 3y'' + y' - 2y = 0$

(c) $\dfrac{d^4y}{dx^4} + \dfrac{d^3y}{dx^3} - 2\dfrac{d^2y}{dx^2} - 2\dfrac{dy}{dx} = 0$

(d) $\dfrac{d^2y}{dx^2} + 2y = 0$

(e) $y'' + y' + y = 0$

(f) $\dfrac{d^4y}{dx^4} - \dfrac{d^2y}{dx^2} - 12y = 0$

2. The equation

$$x^3 \frac{d^3y}{dx^3} + x^2 \frac{d^2y}{dx^2} - 2x \frac{dy}{dx} + 2y = 0$$

has three linearly independent integrals of the form x^r. Determine these, and then establish the general solution.

3. The equation

$$\frac{d^4x}{dt^4} + 4a \frac{d^3x}{dt^3} + 6a^2 \frac{d^2x}{dt^2} + 4a^3 \frac{dx}{dt} + a^4x = 0$$

has four linearly independent integrals of the form $t^r e^{-at}$. Determine these, and then establish the general solution.

4. Show that both the functions

$$1 \qquad \sin x \qquad \cos x \qquad \sin 2x \qquad \cos 2x$$

and the functions

$$\sin x \qquad \cos x \qquad \sin^2 x \qquad \sin x \cos x \qquad \cos^2 x$$

form a basis of the vector space of solutions of the equation

$$\frac{d^5y}{dx^5} + 5\frac{d^3y}{dx^3} + 4\frac{dy}{dx} = 0$$

Hence represent the general solution of the D.E. in two ways.

6. Constant Coefficients; Differential Operators

The most important class of linear homogeneous differential equations consists of those with constant coefficients:

$$\frac{d^ny}{dx^n} + a_1 \frac{d^{n-1}y}{dx^{n-1}} + \cdots + a_ny = 0$$

where $a_1, \ldots, a_n$ are given constants. They arise in innumerable applications and, fortunately, are equations for which a simple technique gives n linearly independent solutions. A justification of the method is facilitated by a study of polynomial differential operators, and it is the purpose of this section to establish rules concerning these operators.

Definition 1. If the function $f(x)$ has a derivative of order k, it may be "multiplied" from the left by the operator D^k, and the result $D^kf(x)$ represents d^kf/dx^k. D^0 represents the "identity operator," that is, $D^0f(x) = f(x)$.

This symbolic multiplication must be carefully distinguished from the actual multiplication of numbers by numbers or functions by functions. Its usefulness lies in the fact that it shares many properties with ordinary multiplication.

Definition 2. Suppose $P(q)$ is the polynomial

$$P(q) = a_0q^n + a_1q^{n-1} + \cdots + a_n$$

A corresponding polynomial in the operator D is

$$P(D) = a_0D^n + a_1D^{n-1} + \cdots + a_{n-1}D + a_nD^0$$

and $P(D)$ operates on the function f by the equation

$$P(D)f = (a_0D^n + a_1D^{n-1} + \cdots + a_{n-1}D + a_nD^0)f$$
$$= a_0 \frac{d^nf}{dx^n} + a_1 \frac{d^{n-1}f}{dx^{n-1}} + \cdots + a_{n-1} \frac{df}{dx} + a_nf$$

Example 1
$$(D^3 + D^2 - D + 2D^0)f = f''' + f'' - f' + 2f$$

Example 2
$$P(D)e^{qx} = (a_0D^n + a_1D^{n-1} + \cdots + a_{n-1}D + a_nD^0)e^{qx}$$
$$= (a_0q^n + a_1q^{n-1} + \cdots + a_{n-1}q + a_n)e^{qx}$$
$$= P(q)e^{qx}$$

Thus, to each polynomial P there corresponds a differential operator $P(D)$. These operators share many of the properties of ordinary polynomials, thereby forming an algebra of differential operators. There are four rules, or properties, of this algebra which are essential for our needs.

Rule 1.   If c is a constant,

$$D^k(cf) = cD^kf$$

Rule 2

$$D^k(f_1 + f_2) = D^kf_1 + D^kf_2$$

Rule 3.   Suppose $P_1(q)$, $P_2(q)$ are two polynomials, and

$$P_1(q)P_2(q) = Q(q)$$

Then

$$P_1(D)[P_2(D)f] = Q(D)f$$

Rule 4 (Shifting Rule)

(a) $$P(D)(e^{rx}f) = e^{rx}P(D + r)f$$
(b) $$e^{-rx}P(D)(e^{rx}f) = P(D + r)f$$
(c) $$e^{-rx}P(D)f = P(D + r)(e^{-rx}f)$$

At this point a decisive difference between actual multiplication and the defined symbolic multiplication may be observed.   Whereas it is true that $D(cf) = cDf$ if c is a constant, it is not true that $D(gf) = gDf$ if g is a function of x.   For example,

$$D(e^xf) = \frac{d}{dx}(e^xf) = e^xDf + e^xf$$

whereas

$$e^xDf = e^xDf$$

Example 3.   Suppose $P(q) = q^3 - q^2 - q - 2$.   Then $P(q)$ factors:

$$P(q) = (q^2 + q + 1)(q - 2)$$

Rule 3 asserts that

$$(D^3 - D^2 - D - 2)f = (D^2 + D + 1)[(D - 2)f]$$
$$= (D - 2)[(D^2 + D + 1)f]$$

This is easily verified by direct computation.   For example,

$$(D^2 + D + 1)[(D - 2)f] = (D^2 + D + 1)(f' - 2f)$$
$$= D^2(f' - 2f) + D(f' - 2f) + (f' - 2f)$$
$$= f''' - f'' - f' - 2f$$
$$= (D^3 - D^2 - D - 2)f$$

Example 4.   The shifting rule enables one to compute certain derivatives rather quickly.   To find $D^3(e^{\alpha x} \cos \beta x)$, we apply rule 4a:

$$D^3(e^{\alpha x} \cos \beta x) = e^{\alpha x}(D + \alpha)^3 \cos \beta x$$
$$= e^{\alpha x}(D^3 + 3\alpha D^2 + 3\alpha^2 D + \alpha^3 D^0) \cos \beta x$$
$$= e^{\alpha x}(\beta^3 - 3\alpha^2\beta) \sin \beta x + (\alpha^3 - 3\alpha\beta^2) \cos \beta x$$

Example 5. Find $P(D)e^{rx}$ for any polynomial P. Let $P(q) = a_0 q^n + a_1 q^{n-1} + \cdots + a_n$. By the shifting rule 4a with $f(x) \equiv 1$,

$$
\begin{aligned}
P(D)e^{rx} &= e^{rx}P(D + r)1 \\
&= e^{rx}[a_0(D + r)^n + \cdots + a_n]1 \\
&= e^{rx}(a_0 r^n + \cdots + a_n)1 = e^{rx}P(r)
\end{aligned}
$$

Proofs of the Rules. Rules 1 and 2 follow immediately from Definition 1 and elementary properties of derivatives. They assert that the operators D^k are linear operators.

For rule 3 we shall prove a special case from which the general result follows. Suppose

$$
P_1(q) = a_1 q + b_1 \qquad P_2(q) = a_2 q + b_2
$$

Then

$$
Q(q) = a_1 a_2 q^2 + (a_1 b_2 + a_2 b_1)q + b_1 b_2
$$

On the other hand,

$$
\begin{aligned}
P_1(D)P_2(D)f &= (a_1 D + b_1)(a_2 Df + b_2 f) \\
&= (a_1 D + b_1)(a_2 f' + b_2 f) \\
&= a_1 D(a_2 f' + b_2 f) + b_1(a_2 f' + b_2 f) \\
&= a_1 a_2 f'' + (a_1 b_2 + a_2 b_1)f' + b_1 b_2 f \\
&= [a_1 a_2 D^2 + (a_1 b_2 + a_2 b_1)D + b_1 b_2]f \\
&= Q(D)f
\end{aligned}
$$

Since every polynomial can be written as a product of linear factors, one can give a proof of rule 3 by induction.

To prove rule 4a, we start again with a linear polynomial, namely, $P(D) = aD + b$. Then

$$
\begin{aligned}
P(D)(e^{rx}f) &= (aD + b)(e^{rx}f) \\
&= aD(e^{rx}f) + be^{rx}f \\
&= ae^{rx}Df + are^{rx}f + be^{rx}f \\
&= e^{rx}[a(D + r) + b]f \\
&= e^{rx}P(D + r)f
\end{aligned}
$$

Now assume that $P(D)$ is a product of two linear operators, namely, $P(D) = P_1(D)P_2(D)$. Then, by rule 3 and by what we have proved so far,

$$
\begin{aligned}
P(D)(e^{rx}f) = P_1(D)P_2(D)(e^{rx}f) &= P_1(D)[e^{rx}P_2(D + r)f] \\
&= e^{rx}P_1(D + r)[P_2(D + r)f] \\
&= e^{rx}P_1(D + r)P_2(D + r)f \\
&= e^{rx}P(D + r)f
\end{aligned}
$$

This can obviously be done for any number of linear factors; hence rule 4a is proved.

Rules 4b and c are simple variants of rule 4a.

PROBLEMS

1. Show that if c_1 and c_2 are constants, then

$$P(D)(c_1 f_1 + c_2 f_2) = c_1 P(D)f_1 + c_2 P(D)f_2$$

Hence conclude that $P(D)$ is a linear operator.

2. Show, by direct computation, that

(a) $(D - 1)\{(D + 1)[(D + 2)f]\} = (D^2 - 1)[(D - 2)f]$
(b) $(D + 2)[(D^2 - D - 1)f] = (D^2 - D - 1)[(D + 2)f]$
(c) $D[(D + a)y] = (D + a)(Dy)$
(d) $(D + a)^3(e^{-ax}f) = e^{-ax}D^3 f$

3. Compute by use of the shifting rule:

(a) $D^2(e^{-2x} \sin x)$
(b) $D^3(e^x \sin 2x)$
(c) $(D^3 + D^2 - D + 1)[e^{2x}(x^2 + x + 1)]$
(d) $(D - 2)^5(x^2 e^{2x})$
(e) $(D - a)^n(e^{ax}f)$
(f) $(D^4 + 12D^3 + 54D^2 + 108D + 81)(e^{-3x}x^3)$

4. Show that if $z = e^{2x}y$ is a solution of the D.E. $(D^3 - 2D^2 + 2)z = 0$, then y is a solution of $(D^3 + 4D^2 + 4D + 2)y = 0$.

5. Show, by factoring the operator polynomial, that if y is a solution of the D.E. $(D - 2)y = 0$, then y is also a solution of $(D^3 - 3D^2 + 3D - 2)y = 0$.

6. Show that if the polynomial equation $P(q) = 0$ has no real roots, then the D.E. $P(D)y = 0$ has no solution $y(x) = e^{ax}$ with a real.

7. Show that if the polynomial equation $P(q) = 0$ with real coefficients has a purely imaginary root, then the D.E. $P(D)y = 0$ has the solution $y(x) = A \sin(\nu x - \delta)$ for some real ν and arbitrary real A, δ.

7. Application to the Solution of Homogeneous Equations

Before solving the general homogeneous differential equation with constant coefficients we consider an example.

Example 1. Find the general solution of the equation

(7.1)
$$\frac{d^3y}{dx^3} - 2\frac{d^2y}{dx^2} + \frac{dy}{dx} = 0$$

The polynomial $P(q) = q^3 - 2q^2 + q$ can be factored as

$$P(q) = q(q^2 - 2q + 1) = q(q - 1)^2$$

Hence solutions of Eq. (7.1) can be found by solving the equations

$$(7.2) \qquad Dy = 0$$
$$(7.3) \qquad (D - 1)^2 y = 0$$

The equation $Dy = 0$ has the solution $y(x) = A$, where A is an arbitrary constant. Equation (7.3) can, by the shifting rule, be written as

$$e^x D^2 (e^{-x} y) = 0 \qquad \text{or} \qquad \frac{d^2}{dx^2} (e^{-x} y) = 0$$

whose general solution is

$$e^{-x} y(x) = Bx + C \qquad \text{or} \qquad y(x) = (Bx + C) e^x$$

where B, C are arbitrary constants. Since the sum of any two solutions of a linear homogeneous equation is again a solution, we have the solution

$$(7.4) \qquad y(x) = A + (Bx + C) e^x$$

Since (7.4) contains the three linearly independent solutions 1, e^x, xe^x, it is the general solution of the third-order differential equation (7.1).

We now turn to the general linear homogeneous equation with constant coefficients,

$$(7.5) \quad P(D)y = a_0 \frac{d^n y}{dx^n} + a_1 \frac{d^{n-1} y}{dx^{n-1}} + \cdots + a_{n-1} \frac{dy}{dx} + a_n y = 0$$

where $P(q)$ is the polynomial

$$a_0 q^n + a_1 q^{n-1} + \cdots + a_{n-1} q + a_n \qquad a_0 \neq 0$$

Let us assume this polynomial is separated into two factors, say

$$P(q) = P_1(q) P_2(q)$$

Then, by rule 3 of the preceding section, Eq. (7.5) may be replaced with either one of the equations

$$P_1(D) P_2(D) y = 0 \qquad P_2(D) P_1(D) y = 0$$

Now if $P_2(D)y = 0$, then $P_1(D) P_2(D) y = P_1(D)0 = 0$. Likewise, if $P_1(D)y = 0$, then $P_2(D) P_1(D) y = 0$. Hence, if $y(x)$ is a solution of either $P_1(D)y = 0$ or of $P_2(D)y = 0$, then $y(x)$ is a solution of the original equation $P(D)y = 0$. Thus, we have the following important result:

If the polynomial $P_1(q)$ is a factor of $P(q)$, and if $P_1(D)y = 0$, then $P(D)y = 0$.

The practical use of this result lies, of course, in the fact that the equation $P_1(D)y = 0$ is of lower order than $P(D)y = 0$. Thus, integrals of the original equation $P(D)y = 0$ are obtained by solving differential equations of lower order whose operators are factors of the operator polynomial $P(D)$.

In order to make this result on factorization of operator polynomials into an effective procedure, certain theorems of algebra must be used. We first take up the question of how to factor the polynomial $P(q)$. By the fundamental theorem of algebra, a polynomial $P(q)$ of degree n whose highest coefficient is a_0 can be factored as follows:

$$(7.6) \qquad P(q) = a_0(q - r_1)(q - r_2) \cdots (q - r_n)$$

where $r_1, r_2, \ldots, r_n$ are the roots of the equation $P(q) = 0$. Not all the roots are necessarily distinct, nor are all or any of them necessarily real numbers. If the same root c occurs k times in product (7.6), then the corresponding factors can be combined into the one factor

$$(7.7) \qquad (q - c)^k$$

If the polynomial $P(q)$ has *real coefficients* (as we shall always assume in the following), then if $a + bi$ is a complex root of $P(q) = 0$, so is $a - bi$, and the two factors $q - a - bi$ and $q - a + bi$ can be multiplied to give the one quadratic factor $(q - a)^2 + b^2$. If the same pair of conjugate complex roots $a + bi$, $a - bi$ occurs l times in product (7.6), the corresponding quadratic factors give the one factor

$$(7.8) \qquad [(q - a)^2 + b^2]^l$$

Therefore, the *polynomial $P(q)$ can be written as a product of factors of the form* (7.7) *and* (7.8), *where these factors correspond to real roots and pairs of conjugate complex roots, respectively.*

It should be observed that the algebraic problem of factoring $P(q)$, with real coefficients, into real linear and quadratic factors can be a formidable one. In applications the polynomial can be of high degree and can have awkward numbers for coefficients. There are efficient numerical methods for this purely algebraic problem, but we shall not pursue them here. We shall confine our attention to problems so chosen that the factorization problem can be handled quite simply. In some problems the factorization will be obvious from elementary algebra.

After $P(q)$ is factored, it remains to solve the differential equation corresponding to each of the factors of form (7.7) or (7.8), that is, differential equations of the form

$$(7.9) \qquad (D - c)^k y = 0 \qquad k = 1, 2, \ldots$$

and

$$(7.10) \qquad [(D - a)^2 + b^2]^l y = 0 \qquad l = 1, 2, \ldots$$

Applying the shifting rule to Eq. (7.9), we obtain

$$e^{cx} D^k (e^{-cx} y) = 0$$

or

$$\frac{d^k}{dx^k} (e^{-cx} y = 0$$

whose general solution is obtained by k-fold integration:

$$e^{-cx} y(x) = C_0 + C_1 x + C_2 x^2 + \cdots + C_{k-1} x^{k-1}$$

Then the general solution of (7.9) is

$$(7.11) \qquad y(x) = (C_0 + C_1 x + \cdots + C_{k-1} x^{k-1}) e^{cx}$$

where $C_0, C_1, \ldots, C_{k-1}$ are k arbitrary constants.

Equation (7.10) can be written as

$$[D - (a + bi)]^l [D - (a - bi)]^l y = 0$$

and, by the preceding paragraph, we have the following solutions of this equation:

$$(7.12) \qquad (\alpha_0 + \alpha_1 x + \cdots + \alpha_{l-1} x^{l-1}) e^{(a+bi)x}$$

and

$$(7.13) \qquad (\beta_0 + \beta_1 x + \cdots + \beta_{l-1} x^{l-1}) e^{(a-bi)x}$$

If we use the Euler relations

$$e^{(a+ib)x} = e^{ax} e^{\pm ibx} = e^{ax}(\cos bx \pm i \sin bx)$$

then the kth terms in (7.13) and (7.14) become

$$\alpha_k x^k e^{ax}(\cos bx + i \sin bx)$$
$$\beta_k x^k e^{ax}(\cos bx - i \sin bx)$$

Hence, the following linear combinations of these solutions are also solutions:

$$(7.14) \quad e^{ax}(A_0 + A_1 x + \cdots + A_{l-1} x^{l-1}) \cos bx$$
$$+ (B_0 + B_1 x + \cdots + B_{l-1} x^{l-1}) \sin bx$$

where $A_0, A_1, \ldots, A_{l-1}, B_0, B_1, \ldots, B_{l-1}$ are arbitrary constants.

In summary, *for each factor of $P(q)$ of the form (7.7) we have the solution (7.11), and for each factor of $P(q)$ of the form (7.8) we have the solution (7.14).* In each case the number of linearly independent integrals contained in a solution is equal to the degree of the corresponding factor. Hence, if for each factor of $P(q)$ the corresponding solution (7.11) or (7.14) is formed, and if these solutions are added, a solution of $P(D)y = 0$ is obtained which is a linear combination of n linearly independent solutions (see Theorem 2 of Sec. 4) and, therefore, constitutes the general solution of this equation. This completes the proof of the following basic theorem.

Theorem. *Let the polynomial $P(q)$ be the product of factors of the form*

$$(q - c_j)^{k_j}$$

and

$$[(q - a_j)^2 + b_j^2]^{l_j}$$

where the c_j are the distinct real roots, and the $a_j + ib_j$ are the distinct complex roots, of $P(q) = 0$. For each factor of the first kind, form the solution

$$(C_0 + C_1 x + \cdots + C_{k_j-1} x^{k_j-1}) e^{c_j x}$$

and for each factor of the second kind, form the solution

$$e^{a_j x} [(A_0 + A_1 x + \cdots + A_{l_{j-1}} x^{l_j-1}) \cos b_j x \\ + (B_0 + B_1 x + \cdots + B_{l_{j-1}} x^{l_j-1}) \sin b_j x]$$

where the A_i, B_i, C_i are arbitrary constants. Then the sum of all these particular solutions is the general solution of the linear homogeneous equation $P(D)y = 0$.

The algebraic equation $P(q) = 0$ is called the *auxiliary equation* belonging to the differential equation $P(D)y = 0$. By the foregoing theorem, the problem of finding the general solution of a linear homogeneous differential equation with constant coefficients is reduced to the problem of determining the roots of the auxiliary equation. To determine the solution of a D.E. subject to given I.C., one must evaluate the constants of integration.

Example 2. Find the solution of

$$(D^4 + 5D^3 + 9D^2 + 15D + 18)y = 0$$

which satisfies the I.C. $y(0) = \frac{3}{2}$, $y''(0) = -1$, $y''(0) = -1$, $y'''(0) = -4$. The auxiliary equation is

$$q^4 + 5q^3 + 9q^2 + 15q + 18 = 0$$

which has integer coefficients. One easily finds that -2 and -3 are rational roots. Therefore the polynomial factors as

$$q^4 + 5q^3 + 9q^2 + 15q + 18 = (q + 2)(q + 3)(q^2 + 3)$$

The general solution of the D.E. is

$$y(x) = c_1 e^{-2x} + c_2 e^{-3x} + c_3 \cos \sqrt{3}\, x + c_4 \sin \sqrt{3}\, x$$

To evaluate the constants of integration, we must use the I.C. If we evaluate $y(x)$ and its first three derivatives at $x = 0$, we get four linear equations in c_1, c_2, c_3, c_4:

$$\tfrac{3}{2} = c_1 + c_2 + c_3$$
$$-1 = -2c_1 - 3c_2 + \sqrt{3}\, c_4$$
$$-1 = 4c_1 + 9c_2 - 3c_3$$
$$-4 = -8c_1 - 27c_2 - 3\sqrt{3}\, c_4$$

Solution of this system yields $c_1 = \tfrac{1}{2}$, $c_2 = 0$, $c_3 = 1$, $c_4 = 0$. The desired solution of the D.E. is therefore

$$y(x) = \tfrac{1}{2}e^{-2x} + \cos 3x$$

The determination of the constants of integration in any particular problem can be a laborious algebraic task. Thus an nth-order equation would require the solution of n simultaneous linear equations. The reader should decide for himself why the system of equations for the constants of integration is always a determinate and consistent system. The key to the answer is found in the theorems of Secs. 2 and 5.

PROBLEMS

Find the general solutions of the following equations. Where given, find the solution satisfying the I.C.

1. $\dfrac{d^3 y}{dx^3} - 3\dfrac{d^2 y}{dx^2} = 0$; I.C.: $y(0) = 0$, $y'(0) = 3$, $y''(0) = -9$

2. $\dfrac{d^3 y}{dx^3} + 5\dfrac{d^2 y}{dx^2} + 4\dfrac{dy}{dx} = 0$

3. $D^4 y + 2D^3 y + D^2 y = 0$; I.C.: $y(0) = 0$, $y'(0) = 2$, $y''(0) = -2$, $y'''(0) = 3$

4. $(D^4 - 1)y = 0$; I.C.: $y(0) = 1$, $y'(0) = -\tfrac{1}{2}$, $y''(0) = 1$, $y'''(0) = -\tfrac{3}{2}$

5. $(D^4 + 1)y = 0$

6. $(D^4 - 2D^3 - 3D^2 + 4D + 4)y = 0$; I.C.: $y(0) = y'(0) = 0$, $y''(0) = 6$, $y'''(0) = -8$

7. $(D^4 - D^3 - 3D^2 + 5D - 2)y = 0$; I.C.: $y(1) = 0 = y'(1) = y''(1) = y'''(1)$

8. $(D^4 + 2D^2 + 1)y = 0$

9. $(D^5 + D^3 + D^2 + 1)y = 0$

10. $(D^6 + 3D^4 + 3D^2 + 1)y = 0$

11. $(D^n + aD^{n-1})y = 0$

12. $(D^2 + 2aD + 2a^2)^n y = 0$

13. $2y'''' + 7y''' + 8y'' + 5y' + 2y = 0$

14. $(4D^4 + D^2 + 3D + 1)z = 0$

15. $(D^5 - D^4 - 7D^3 + 11D^2 - 8D + 12)z = 0$

★16. $(D^5 + 5D^4 + 5D^3 - 5D^2 - 5D - 1)z = 0$

17. $(D^4 + 2\pi^2 D^2 + \pi^4)(D + \pi)z = 0$

18. Show that the solution of the equation $[(D - a)^2 + b^2]^k y = 0$ can be written in the form

$$y = e^{ax}[A_0 \sin (bx + \alpha_0) + A_1 x \sin (bx + \alpha_1) + \cdots$$
$$+ A_{k-1}x^{k-1} \sin (bx + \alpha_{k-1})]$$

where $A_0, \ldots, A_{k-1}, \alpha_0, \ldots, \alpha_{k-1}$ are arbitrary constants.

19. Show that the solution of the equation $[(D - a)^2 - b^2]^k y = 0$ can be written in the form

$$y = e^{ax}[A_0 \sinh (bx + a_0) + A_1 x \sinh (bx + a_1) + \cdots$$
$$+ A_{k-1}x^{k-1} \sinh (bx + a_{k-1})]$$

where $A_0, \ldots, A_{k-1}, a_0, \ldots, a_{k-1}$ are arbitrary constants.

20. Show that if all the roots of the auxiliary equation $P(q) = 0$ lie in the left half of the complex plane (i.e., have negative real parts), then every integral of $P(D)y = 0$ tends to zero as $x \to +\infty$. Is the converse true?

8. The General Nonhomogeneous Equation

We return now to linear equations, with possibly variable coefficients, which are not homogeneous:

$$(8.1) \quad L[y] \equiv \frac{d^n y}{dx^n} + a_1(x) \frac{d^{n-1}y}{dx^{n-1}} + \cdots + a_{n-1}(x) \frac{dy}{dx} + a_n(x)y = f(x)$$

For the nonhomogeneous equation (8.1) it is not true that a linear combination of solutions is a solution. Yet integrals of the *complete equation*

$$(8.2) \qquad\qquad L[y] = f$$

are closely related to solutions of the associated *reduced equation*

$$(8.3) \qquad\qquad L[y] = 0$$

To see how this is so, suppose that y_p is a particular integral of (8.2), and that y_c is an integral of the reduced equation (8.3); that is,

$$(8.4) \qquad\qquad L[y_p] = f \qquad L[y_c] = 0$$

Then, by adding Eqs. (8.4), we obtain

$$(8.5) \qquad\qquad L[y_p] + L[y_c] = L[y_p + y_c] = f$$

Equation (8.5) obviously means that $y_p + y_c$ is also a solution of Eq. (8.2). Hence, by adding integrals of the reduced equation to a particular integral of the complete equation, new integrals of the complete equation are obtained. The question arises whether, starting with one particular integral of the complete equation, one can obtain all of them just by adding integrals of the reduced equation.

This is indeed the case. For, let $\tilde{y}_p$ be any other integral of the complete equation. That is,

$$(8.6) \qquad\qquad L[\tilde{y}_p] = f$$

Then one obtains, by subtracting (8.6) from (8.4),

$$L[y_p - \tilde{y}_p] = 0$$

Hence, the difference of the two particular integrals of the complete equation is a solution of the reduced equation. In other words, the arbitrary integral $\tilde{y}_p$ of the complete equation can differ from the particular integral y_p of the same equation only by some integral of the reduced equation. We state this result as a theorem.

Theorem. *The general solution of the nonhomogeneous linear differential equation $L[y] = f$ is obtained from any particular integral of this equation by adding the general solution of the reduced equation $L[y] = 0$.*

The general solution of the reduced equation is called the *complementary function*. Hence, this theorem may be expressed by the symbolic equation

$$y = y_p + y_c$$

Example 1. Find all solutions of

$$x^3 y''' + 2x^2 y'' - 4xy' + 4y = x^{-1}$$

The reduced equation is

$$x^3 y''' + 2x^2 y'' - 4xy' + 4y = 0$$

We must find three linearly independent solutions of this homogeneous equation. It so happens that there are three such of the form x^r. Setting $y = x^r$ in the D.E. we obtain

$$x^3 r(r-1)(r-2)x^{r-3} + 2x^2 r(r-1)x^{r-2} - 4xr x^{r-1} + 4x^r = 0$$

which gives the equation determining r:

$$(r-1)(r^2 - 4) = 0$$

whence $r = 1, -2, 2$. Therefore,

$$y_c(x) = Ax + Bx^2 + Cx^{-2}$$

is the general solution of the homogeneous equation.

It remains to find a particular solution of the complete equation. It is not hard to verify that there is one of the form Ex^{-1}. Setting $y_p = Ex^{-1}$, we have

$$x^3(-1)(-2)(-3)Ex^{-4} + 2x^2(-1)(-2)Ex^{-3} - 4x(-1)Ex^{-2} + 4Ex^{-1} = x^{-1}$$

whence

$$-6E + 4E + 4E + 4E = 1 \qquad \text{or} \qquad E = \tfrac{1}{6}$$

Therefore,

$$y_p(x) = \tfrac{1}{6}x^{-1}$$

The general solution of the original D.E. is therefore

$$y(x) = Ax + Bx^2 + Cx^{-2} + \tfrac{1}{6}x^{-1}$$

Example 2. Consider the nonhomogeneous equation

$$\frac{d^n y}{dx^n} = Ae^x$$

It is easy to guess a particular integral, namely, $y = Ae^x$. The reduced equation is $y^{(n)} = 0$, whose general solution was found in Example 1, Sec. 5. Therefore, the general solution is

$$y(x) = Ae^x + c_0 + c_1 x + c_2 x^2 + \cdots + c_{n-1}x^{n-1}$$

Example 3. An example of general importance is supplied by the equation

$$(8.7) \qquad \frac{d^n y}{dx^n} = f(x)$$

where $f(x)$ is an unspecified continuous function. The problem of finding the general solution of this equation may be considered as an extension of the problem of finding the general solution of the equation

$$\frac{dy}{dx} = f(x)$$

which is solved by the indefinite integral of $f(x)$.

To solve Eq. (8.7), we may interpret it as a differential equation of the first order in the unknown function $y^{(n-1)}$:

$$\frac{d}{dx} y^{(n-1)} = f(x)$$

Hence

$$(8.8) \qquad y^{(n-1)}(x) = \int^x f(x_1)\, dx_1 + C_1 = F_1(x) + C_1$$

where $F_1(x)$ denotes an indefinite integral of $f(x)$. Proceeding with Eq. (8.8) as we proceed with Eq. (8.7), we find

$$y^{(n-2)}(x) = \int^x [F_1(x_1) + C_1]\, dx_1 = F_2(x) + C_1x + C_2$$

where $F_2(x)$ is an indefinite integral of $F_1(x)$, and therefore $F_2(x)$ is an iterated indefinite integral of $f(x)$. When this process is repeated n times, one obtains

(8.9) $y(x) = F_n(x) + c_0 + c_1x + c_2x^2 + \cdots + c_{n-1}x^{n-1}$

where $F_n(x)$ is an n-times-repeated indefinite integral of $f(x)$, and $c_0, c_1, \ldots, c_{n-1}$ are arbitrary constants. In expression (8.9), $F_n(x)$ is a particular integral, and $c_0 + c_1x + \cdots + c_{n-1}x^{n-1}$ is the complementary function.

Any n-times-repeated indefinite integral of $f(x)$ may be used as $F_n(x)$ in Eq. (8.9). An important special case is obtained if all the lower limits of the n integrals are chosen to be equal, say to x_0. Then we have the following particular solution of Eq. (8.7):

(8.10) $F_n(x) = \int_{x_0}^x dx_n \int_{x_0}^x dx_{n-1} \cdots \int_{x_0}^{x_3} dx_2 \int_{x_0}^{x_2} f(x_1)\, dx_1$

This particular integral is characterized by the fact that it satisfies the initial conditions

(8.11) $F_n(x_0) = F_n'(x_0) = F_n''(x_0) = \cdots = F_n^{(n-1)}(x_0) = 0$

We remark that the repeated integral (8.10) can be converted into a single integral (see Prob. 8, Sec. 2):

(8.12) $F_n(x) = \int_{x_0}^x \frac{(x - x_1)^{n-1}}{(n-1)!} f(x_1)\, dx_1$

PROBLEMS

Find the general solutions of the following equations:

1. $\dfrac{d^3y}{dx^3} = Ae^{ax}$

2. $\dfrac{d^2x}{dt^2} = At \cos \omega t$

3. $\dfrac{d^4y}{dx^4} = A \log x$

4. $\dfrac{d^2y}{dx^2} = (a^2 - x^2)^{-\frac{3}{2}}$

Find the general solutions of the following differential equations. Make use of the suggested functions, which by proper choice of the constants are integrals of the complete equation.

5. $\dfrac{d^2y}{dx^2} - 13\dfrac{dy}{dx} + 36y = 3 \sin 6x;\ y_p(x) = C \cos 6x$

6. $(D^3 - D^2 + 4D - 4)y = 4e^{2x};\ y_p(x) = Ae^{2x}$

7. $(D^3 - D^2 + 4D - 4)y = 2 \sin x; y_p(x) = A \sin x + B \cos x$

8. $(D^4 - 8D^2 + 16)y = e^{2x}; y_p(x) = Cx^2 e^{2x}$

9. $2\dfrac{d^3x}{dt^3} - \dfrac{d^2x}{dt^2} - 2\dfrac{dx}{dt} + x = \sin \omega t; x_p(t) = A \sin \omega t + B \cos \omega t$

10. $\dfrac{d^4y}{dx^4} + 8\dfrac{d^2y}{dx^2} + 16y = ke^{ax}; k, a$ real constants; $y_p(x) = Ee^{ax}$

Find general solutions of the following equations. The suggested functions are solutions of either the reduced or the complete equation for proper choices of the constants.

11. $x^2\dfrac{d^2y}{dx^2} + x\dfrac{dy}{dx} - 9y = \dfrac{5}{x^2}; y_1(x) = Ax^{-2}, y_2(x) = Bx^{-3}, y_3(x) = Cx^3$

12. $(x^2 + 1)\dfrac{d^2y}{dx^2} - 2x\dfrac{dy}{dx} + 2y = x(x^2 + 3); y_1(x) = Ax, y_2(x) = Bx^3,$

$y_3(x) = C + Dx^2$

13. $x^4\dfrac{d^3y}{dx^3} - x^3\dfrac{d^2y}{dx^2} + x^2\dfrac{dy}{dx} = k; y_1(x) = A + Bx + Cx^2; y_2(x) =$

$Dx^2 \log x, y_3(x) = Ex^{-1}$

9. Principle of Superposition

This principle is often helpful in the solution of a nonhomogeneous *linear* differential equation whose nonhomogeneous term is the sum of several distinct functions.

Assume that y_a, y_b, y_c, . . . are any integrals of the equations $L[y] = f_a$, $L[y] = f_b$, $L[y] = f_c$, . . . , respectively, i.e., of nonhomogeneous equations with the same homogeneous part but different nonhomogeneous terms. Then

$$(9.1) \qquad \begin{aligned} L[y_a] &= f_a \\ L[y_b] &= f_b \\ L[y_c] &= f_c \\ & \cdot \cdot \cdot \cdot \cdot \cdot \end{aligned}$$

and summation of these gives

$$L[y_a + y_b + y_c + \cdots] = f_a + f_b + f_c + \cdots$$

or, in other words, the function $y = y_a + y_b + y_c + \cdots$ is an integral of the equation

$$(9.2) \qquad L[y] = f_a + f_b + f_c + \cdots$$

whose homogeneous part is the same as that of Eqs. (9.1) and whose nonhomogeneous term is the sum of those of Eqs. (9.1). Conversely, in order to find a solution of Eq. (9.2), we may first find integrals of the various Eqs. (9.1) and then sum these integrals. This method goes by the name *principle of superposition.*

It should be remarked that this method is also made use of in the case of nonhomogeneous terms that are sums of *infinitely* many terms (power series, Fourier series, etc.), but in such cases additional conditions as to the convergence of these sums are necessary for the method to be valid.

Example 1. In a linear automatic control mechanism the value of the output (or response) variable $x_0(t)$ at the time t is related to the value of the input (or signal) variable $x_i(t)$ at the time t by an equation of the form

$$L[x_0(t)] = x_i(t)$$

where L is some linear differential operator. Hence, by the principle of superposition, the response to a composite signal is the sum of the responses to the components of the signal.

PROBLEMS

1. Find particular solutions of $(D^2 + 5)y = 1$ and $(D^2 + 5)y = \sin x$. Then find a particular solution of $(D^2 + 5)y = 2 + 4 \sin x$. What is the general solution?

2. The equation $x^2 y'' - xy' + y = x^2$ has a solution of the form Ax^2, and the equation $x^2 y'' - xy' + y = x^3$ has a solution of the form Ax^3. Find a particular solution of $x^2 y'' - xy' + y = x^2/2 - x^3/3$.

3. A linear automatic control system satisfies the third-order linear differential equation $L[\varphi] = S$, where φ is the response to a signal S. Suppose that φ_1 and φ_2 are responses to signals S_1 and S_2, each satisfying the I.C.

$$\varphi(0) = \varphi'(0) = \varphi''(0) = 0$$

Show that the response to the signal $c_1 S_1(t) + c_2 S_2(t)$ with the same I.C. is $\varphi(t) = c_1 \varphi_1(t) + c_2 \varphi_2(t)$.

4. Find a particular solution of the form $x(t) = A \cos \beta t + B \sin \beta t$ for the equation $d^4 x/dt^4 + cx = a \cos \beta t + b \sin \beta t$ $(-c \neq \beta^4)$, and use the result to find a particular solution for each of the following equations:

(a) $\dfrac{d^4 x}{dt^4} + x = \cos^2 \beta t$ $\qquad \beta^2 \neq \frac{1}{4}$

(b) $\dfrac{d^4 x}{dt^4} + x = \sin^2 \beta t \cos^2 \beta t$ $\qquad \beta^2 \neq \frac{1}{4}, \frac{1}{16}$

(c) $\dfrac{d^4 x}{dt^4} + cx = \frac{1}{2}a_0 + \sum_{k=1}^{n} (a_k \cos k\beta t + b_k \sin k\beta t); c < 0$

(d) $\dfrac{d^4 x}{dt^4} + 8x = 4 \sin t \sin 2t \sin 3t$

5. The equation $4x^2(d^2y/dx^2) + y = Ax^k$ has an integral of the form ax^k. Determine this and use the result to find a particular integral of the equation

$$4x^2 \frac{d^2y}{dx^2} + y = \frac{x^n - 1}{x - 1}$$

10. Nonhomogeneous, Constant Coefficients

It has been shown that one obtains the general solution of the equation

(10.1) $P(D)y = (D^n + a_1D^{n-1} + \cdots + a_n)y = f$

where $a_1, \ldots, a_n$ are constants, and f is a continuous function, by adding any particular solution to the general solution of the reduced equation. Since the latter is known (Sec. 7), it remains to study methods for finding particular integrals.

Before considering some of the methods available, we remark that the class of forcing functions (or inputs) f which one encounters in applications is rather restricted, many of them belonging to one of the following classes:

  1. Polynomials: $c_0x^m + c_1x^{m-1} + \cdots + c_m$
  2. Exponentials: e^{cx}, where c is a real or complex constant
  3. Exponentials times polynomials: $e^{cx}(c_0x^m + \cdots + c_m)$
  4. Special periodic functions: $\sin \omega x$, $\cos \omega x$
  5. Piecewise-continuous functions made up of "pieces" of the above functions

In the sections to follow we shall be concerned primarily with particular integrals for these special forcing functions. The methods considered here are:

  1. *Successive integrations.* Factorization of $P(D)$, use of the shifting rule, and reduction to quadratures.

  2. *Undetermined coefficients.* Applicable when the forcing function is a polynomial.

  3. *Cases reducible to method 2.* The shifting rule is used to reduce the forcing function to a polynomial.

  4. *Green's functions.* Calculation of the response to a "unit step function" permits the reduction of the general case to quadratures.

In Chap. VII we shall give other methods.

11. Method 1: Successive Integrations

We describe this method for finding a particular integral because it clearly establishes the existence of a solution and is always applicable even though not the most convenient. We start by factoring the operator polynomial $P(D)$. Then Eq. (10.1) takes the form

(11.1) $(D - c_1)^{k_1}(D - c_2)^{k_2} \cdots [(D - \alpha_1)^2 + \beta_1^2]^{l_1}$
$$\times [(D - \alpha_2)^2 + \beta_2^2]^{l_2} \cdots y = f$$

where $c_1, c_2, \ldots$ are the distinct real roots; $\alpha_1 \pm \beta_1 i, \alpha_2 \pm \beta_2 i, \ldots$ are the distinct complex roots of the auxiliary equation $P(q) = 0$; and $k_1, k_2, \ldots, l_1, l_2, \ldots$ are their respective multiplicities. Let us write Eq. (11.1) as

(11.2) $$(D - c_1)^{k_1} z_1 = f$$

where z_1 is the factor remaining of the left member of Eq. (11.1) after $(D - c_1)^{k_1}$ is split off; that is,

(11.3) $z_1 = (D - c_2)^{k_2} \cdots [(D - \alpha_1)^2 + \beta_1^2]^{l_1}$
$$\times [(D - \alpha_2)^2 + \beta_2^2]^{l_2} \cdots y$$

We first determine z_1 as a solution of Eq. (11.2) and then substitute it in Eq. (11.3). This equation is then similar to the original Eq. (11.1), but of lower order (its order is $n - k_1$). After z_1 has been determined, the above process may be applied to Eq. (11.3). We may, for example, rewrite (11.3) as

(11.4) $$[(D - \alpha_1)^2 + \beta_1^2]^{l_1} z_2 = z_1$$

where z_2 is the factor remaining of the left member of Eq. (11.3) after $[(D - \alpha_1)^2 + \beta_1)^2]^{l_1}$ is split off. Continuing in this way, we eventually obtain a particular integral.

It is seen that each step in this reductive process requires a particular integral of an equation like (11.2) or an equation like (11.4). We now consider these special equations, first an equation like (11.2):

(11.5) $$(D - c)^k z = f$$

We obtain, by the shifting theorem,

$$e^{cx} D^k e^{-cx} z = f$$

or

$$\frac{d^k}{dx^k} (e^{-cx} z) = e^{-cx} f$$

Hence,

$$e^{-cx} z(x) = \int^x dx_k \int^{x_k} dx_{k-1} \int^{x_{k-1}} dx_{k-2} \cdots \int^{x_2} e^{-cx_1} f(x_1)\, dx_1$$

and

(11.6) $$z(x) = \int^x dx_k \int^{x_k} dx_{k-1} \int^{x_{k-1}} dx_{k-2} \cdots \int^{x_2} e^{c(x-x_1)} f(x_1)\, dx_1$$

is a solution. If we choose, in particular, the same lower limits in all the integrals of (11.6), then the k-fold integral can be converted into a simple integral (see Example 3, Sec. 8):

$$(11.7) \qquad z(x) = \int_{x_0}^x \frac{(x - x_1)^{k-1}}{(k-1)!}\, e^{c(x-x_1)} f(x_1)\, dx_1$$

Furthermore, (11.7), or (11.6) with x_0 as the lower limit on the integrals, satisfies the I.C. $z(x_0) = z'(x_0) = \cdots = z^{(k-1)}(x_0) = 0$.

Formula (11.7) is particularly convenient for numerical quadrature if the function f is merely tabulated. In any case, (11.7) reduces the problem to one of quadrature.

We shall not derive the analogous procedure for equations of type (11.4). We merely observe that

$$[(D - \alpha_1)^2 + \beta_1^2]^{l_1} z_2(x) = z_1(x)$$

may be written as

$$(D - \alpha_1 - i\beta_1)^{l_1}(D - \alpha_1 + i\beta_1)^{l_1} z_2 = z_1$$

or

$$(11.8) \qquad (D - \alpha_1 - i\beta_1)^{l_1} z_3 = z_1$$

where $z_3 = (D - \alpha_1 + i\beta_1)^{l_1} z_2$. Since Eq. (11.8) is of the same form as (11.2) except that $c_1 = \alpha_1 + i\beta_1$ is complex, the solution once again can be reduced to quadratures.

Observe that the method of this section is quite general. The function f need not even be continuous, merely integrable. In particular, it would suffice for f to be piecewise continuous.

PROBLEM

1. Write, in terms of quadratures (but do not carry out the integrations), solutions of the following D.E.'s.

(a) $(D - 2)y = x + e^x$
(b) $(D - 2)^3 y = x + e^x$
(c) $(D + 3)^2 y = \sin \omega x$
(d) $(D + 1)(D + 2)y = \sin x$
(e) $(D^2 + 1)y = \cos \omega x$

12. Method 2: Undetermined Coefficients

We first deal with a D.E. of the form

$$(12.1) \quad \begin{aligned} P(D)y &\equiv (a_0 D^n + a_1 D^{n-1} + \cdots + a_{n-1}D + a_n)y \\ &= A_0 x^k + A_1 x^{k-1} + \cdots + A_k \end{aligned}$$

A little reflection leads one to expect that this equation has a polynomial among its solutions and that the degree of this polynomial is k, provided that $a_n \neq 0$.   Assume that $a_n \neq 0$, and put

$$(12.2) \qquad y(x) = C_0 x^k + C_1 x^{k-1} + \cdots + C_{k-1} x + C_k$$

We wish to determine the coefficients $C_0, C_1, \ldots, C_k$ so that (12.2) becomes a solution of Eq. (12.1).   This is done by substituting the derivatives of (12.2) in Eq. (12.1) and equating the coefficients of like powers of x.   An example will illustrate the procedure.

Example 1.   Find a particular integral of the equation

$$(12.3) \qquad \frac{d^4y}{dx^4} + \frac{d^2y}{dx^2} + 16y = 16x^2 + 258$$

Here $a_n = 16 \neq 0$.   Hence, we try a solution of the form

$$y(x) = C_0 x^2 + C_1 x + C_2$$

Substitution in (12.3) results in

$$16C_0 x^2 + 16C_1 x + 16C_2 + 2C_0 = 16x^2 + 258$$

Therefore,

$$16C_0 = 16 \qquad C_0 = 1$$
$$16C_1 = 0 \qquad C_1 = 0$$
$$16C_2 + 2C_0 = 258 \qquad C_2 = 16$$

Hence, $y(x) = x^2 + 16$ is the desired integral.

If $a_n \neq 0$, the above method always leads to a unique solution for the coefficients $C_0, \ldots, C_r$, as the following proof shows.   If D^{k+1} is applied to (12.1), one obtains

$$(12.4) \qquad D^{k+1} P(D) y = 0$$

The auxiliary equation for the homogeneous D.E. (12.4) is

$$(12.5) \qquad q^{k+1} P(q) \equiv q^{k+1}(a_0 q^n + a_1 q^{n-1} + \cdots + a_n) = 0$$

Since $a_n \neq 0$, $q = 0$ is a root of (12.5) of multiplicity exactly $k + 1$. Therefore *every* solution of (12.4), and of (12.1), is of the form

$$(12.6) \qquad y(x) = C_0 x^k + C_1 x^{k-1} + \cdots + C_k + y_c(x)$$

where y_c is a solution of $P(D)y = 0$.   This shows that there is a solution of (12.1) of the form (12.2).

However, if $a_n = 0$, the procedure must be modified slightly. Then Eq. (12.1) is written in the form

$$(12.7) \quad (a_0 D^{n-1} + a_1 D^{n-2} + \cdots + a_{n-1}) Dy$$
$$= A_0 x^k + A_1 x^{k-1} + \cdots + A_k$$

This is an equation similar to (12.1), but for the function Dy. Hence, if $a_{n-1} \neq 0$, then a solution

$$Dy = C_0 x^k + C_1 x^{k-1} + \cdots + C_k$$

is found as before, and $y(x)$ itself is obtained by a simple quadrature. If a_{n-1} is also zero, then Eq. (12.1) can be considered as an equation in $D^2 y$, and so forth.

Example 2. Find a particular integral of the equation

$$(12.8) \qquad \frac{d^4 y}{dx^4} - \frac{d^2 y}{dx^2} = x^6 - 360 x^2$$

and find the solution that satisfies the I.C.

$$(12.9) \qquad y(0) = 1 \qquad y'(0) = 2 \qquad y''(0) = 1 \qquad y'''(0) = 1$$

Equation (12.8) may be written as

$$(12.10) \qquad (D^2 - 1) D^2 y = x^6 - 360 x^2$$

Hence, there must be a particular solution for which

$$D^2 y = A_0 x^6 + A_1 x^5 + A_2 x^4 + A_3 x^3 + A_4 x^2 + A_5 x + A_6$$

Then,

$$(12.11) \quad (D^2 - 1)(D^2 y) = -A_0 x^6 - A_1 x^5 + (30 A_0 - A_2) x^4$$
$$+ (20 A_1 - A_3) x^3 + (12 A_2 - A_4) x^2 + (6 A_3 - A_5) x + (2 A_4 - A_6)$$

Equating the coefficients of the right-hand members of (12.10) and (12.11) yields

$$A_0 = -1 \qquad A_1 = 0 \qquad A_2 = -30 \qquad A_3 = A_4 = A_5 = A_6 = 0$$

Therefore,

$$D^2 y = -x^6 - 30 x^4$$

and two integrations give the particular solution of Eq. (12.8):

$$y(x) = -\tfrac{1}{56} x^8 - x^6$$

The general solution of (12.8) is then easily found to be

$$(12.12) \qquad y(x) = -\tfrac{1}{56} x^8 - x^6 + C_0 + C_1 x + C_2 e^x + C_3 e^{-x}$$

and we must find $C_0, \ldots, C_3$ so that y, as given by (12.12), will satisfy the I.C. (12.9). Calculation of the derivatives and evaluation at $x = 0$ yield $C_0 = C_3 = 0$, $C_1 = C_2 = 1$, whence the desired solution of (12.8) and (12.9) is

$$y(x) = -\tfrac{1}{56}x^8 - x^6 + x + e^x$$

PROBLEMS

1. Obtain, *by inspection*, particular solutions of the following D.E.'s.

(a) $(D^4 + D^2 + 1)y = A$ (b) $(D^2 + \omega^2)y = 5$, $\omega \neq 0$
(c) $(D^8 - D^3)y = 12$ (d) $(D^4 - 1)y = x$
(e) $(D^{12} - 8D^6 - \pi)y = 6x$

2. Find particular integrals of the following D.E.'s; where I.C.'s are given, find the solution satisfying them:

(a) $(D - 1)(D + 1)(D - 2)z = 1$; I.C.: $z(0) = z'(0) = 0$, $z''(0) = 1$
(b) $(D - 1)(D + 1)(D - 2)z = x$
(c) $(D^4 - 1)y = x^2$; I.C.: $y(0) = y'(0) = y''(0) = y'''(0) = 0$
(d) $(D^3 - D^2 + D - 1)z = x^2$
(e) $(D^5 - D^2)y = x^2$; I.C.: $y(0) = y'(0) = y''(0) = y'''(0) = 0$
(f) $(D^3 + D^2 - D - 1)y = x^4 + 4x^3$
(g) $(D^3 + D^2 - D)y = x^4 + 4x^3$
(h) $(a_0 D^n + a_1 D^{n-1} + \cdots + a_{n-3}D^3 + D^2 - 3D + 1)y = x^2 - 2$; I.C.: $y(1) = 21$, $y'(1) = 8$, $y''(1) = 2$, $y'''(1) = \cdots = y^{(n-1)}(1) = 0$; a_i constant
(i) $(D^6 + 8D^3)y = 960x^3$

13. Method 3: Reduction to Method 2

Another class of nonhomogeneous equations for which a particular integral can easily be determined is comprised of equations of the form

$$(13.1) \quad P(D)y(x) = (A_0 x^k + A_1 x^{k-1} + \cdots + A_{k-1}x + A_k)e^{cx}$$

where c is a real or complex constant. Multiplying Eq. (13.1) by e^{-cx} and applying the shifting rule, we get

$$(13.2) \qquad P(D + c)(e^{-cx}y) = A_0 x^k + A_1 x^{k-1} + \cdots + A_k$$

This is an equation of the form of (12.1) for the unknown function $e^{-cx}y(x)$. Therefore, it can be solved as (12.1) is solved.

If the right-hand member of the nonhomogeneous equation consists of several summands of the form $Q_i(x)e^{c_i x}$, where $Q_i(x)$ is a polynomial, then a solution is found for each summand, and the sum of the solutions thus obtained is, by the principle of superposition, a solution of the given equation.

Next, we turn to equations of the types

(13.3) $P(D)y = (A_0x^k + A_1x^{k-1} + \cdots + A_k)e^{ax} \cos bx$
(13.4) $P(D)y = (A_0x^k + A_1x^{k-1} + \cdots + A_k)e^{ax} \sin bx$

where $A_0, \ldots, A_k, a, b$ are real numbers. These equations can be written as

(13.3) $P(D)y = \text{Re } (A_0x^k + A_1x^{k-1} + \cdots + A_k)e^{(a+bi)x}$
(13.4) $P(D)y = \text{Im } (A_0x^k + A_1x^{k-1} + \cdots + A_k)e^{(a+bi)x}$

respectively. Therefore, if the equation

$$P(D)y = (A_0x^k + A_1x^{k-1} + \cdots + A_k)e^{cx} \qquad c = a + bi$$

is solved by the above method, the real part of this solution is an integral of Eq. (13.3), and the imaginary part is an integral of Eq. (13.4).

Example 1. Find a particular integral of

(13.5) $(D^6 + 8D^3)y = Ae^x$

Then find the integral that satisfies the I.C.

$$y(0) = y'(0) = y''(0) = y'''(0) = y^{(4)}(0) = 0 \qquad y^{(5)}(0) = -A$$

Dividing (13.5) by e^x, we obtain

$$e^{-x}(D^6 + 8D^3)y = A$$

and, by the shifting rule,

$$[(D + 1)^6 + 8(D + 1)^3](e^{-x}y) = A$$

Since the right-hand member is a polynomial of degree zero, there must be a solution of the form

$$e^{-x}y(x) = C$$

Substitution gives

$$9C = A \qquad C = \tfrac{1}{9}A$$

Hence, $y(x) = \tfrac{1}{9}Ae^x$ is a particular solution of Eq. (13.5).

Observe that we might have guessed that the original D.E. had a solution of the form e^x. However, it might have happened that e^x was a solution of the homogeneous equation. The method of the text avoids any doubt.

The roots of the auxiliary equation are $0, 0, 0, -2, 1 + i\sqrt{3}, 1 - i\sqrt{3}$. Hence, the general solution of (13.5) is

$$y(x) = C_0 + C_1x + C_2x^2 + C_3e^{-2x} + C_4e^{(1+i\sqrt{3})x} + C_5e^{(1-i\sqrt{3})x} + \frac{A}{9}e^x$$

The necessary differentiations are easier to perform if the above exponential form is used instead of the trigonometric form. Calculation of the five derivatives and application of the I.C. give

$$C_0 = C_1 = -\frac{A}{8} \qquad C_2 = -\frac{A}{24} \qquad C_3 = \frac{A}{12} \qquad C_4 = -C_5 = -\frac{i\sqrt{3}\,A}{144}$$

Therefore, the desired solution is

$$y(x) = -\frac{A}{8} - \frac{A}{8}x - \frac{A}{24}x^2 + \frac{A}{72}e^{-2x} + \frac{A}{9}e^x - \frac{i\sqrt{3}}{144}Ae^{(1+i\sqrt{3})x}$$
$$+ \frac{i\sqrt{3}}{144}Ae^{(1-i\sqrt{3})x}$$
$$= -\frac{A}{24}(x^2 + 3x + 3) + \frac{A}{72}e^{-2x} + \frac{A}{9}e^x + \frac{A\sqrt{3}}{72}e^x \sin\sqrt{3}\,x$$

Example 2. Find a particular integral of the equation

$$(13.6) \qquad\qquad (D^3 - D)y = A\sin bx \qquad b \neq 0$$

Since $\sin bx = \text{Im } e^{ibx}$, we consider the equation

$$(D^3 - D)z = Ae^{ibx}$$

Multiplication by e^{-ibx} and use of the shifting rule lead to

$$[(D + ib)^3 - (D + ib)](e^{-ibx}z) = A$$

There must be a solution of the form

$$e^{-ibx}z(x) = C$$

Substitution gives

$$C = \frac{A}{b(b^2 + 1)}\,i$$

Hence,

$$z(x) = \frac{A}{b(b^2 + 1)}\,ie^{ibx} = \frac{A}{b(b^2 + 1)}(i\cos bx - \sin bx)$$

and

$$y(x) = \text{Im } z(x) = \frac{A}{b(b^2 + 1)}\cos bx$$

is a particular integral of Eq. (13.6).

PROBLEMS

1. Find a particular solution for each of the following equations. Look for shortcuts.

(a) $(D^3 + 1)y = e^{-x} \sin x$

(b) $(D^3 + 1)y = x^3 e^{-x}$

(c) $(D^3 + 1)y = \sin \omega x$

(d) $(D^4 - 1)y = x e^x$

(e) $(D^4 - 1)y = e^x \cos x$

(f) $(D + r)^n y = A e^{sx}, r + s \neq 0$

(g) $(D^3 - D^2 + 4D - 4)y = e^{2x}$

(h) $(D^3 - 2D^2 + 4D - 8)y = \cos 2x$

(i) $(D^3 - D^2 + D - 1)y = 8 \cos x$

(j) $(D^3 + D^2 + 9D + 1)y = 6 \sin 3x$

(k) $(D^4 + 2D^2 + 1)y = x \sin x$

(l) $(D - a)(D - b)(D - c)y = A e^{ax}, a \neq b \neq c \neq a$

(m) $(D - a)^2(D - b)y = A e^{ax}, a \neq b$

(n) $(D - a)^2(D - b)^2 y = A e^{ax}, a \neq b$

(o) $(D - r_1)(D - r_2) \cdots (D - r_n)y = A e^{sx}, r_1, \ldots, r_n,$ and s distinct

(p) $(D^2 + a^2)(D^2 + b^2)y = A \sin ax; |a| \neq |b|$ and $a \neq 0, b \neq 0$

(q) $(D^2 + a^2)^2 y = A \sin ax, a \neq 0$

2. Sometimes there are shortcuts. Obtain particular solutions to the following equations by inspection. Then apply the method of this section to get the solution another way.

(a) $(D^4 + 4)y = \sin x$

(b) $(D^4 + 16)y = \sin 2x$

(c) $(D^3 - 2D)y = \cos \omega x$

3. For each of the following equations, find the particular solution satisfying the given initial conditions:

(a) $(D + 1)^3 y = x^3 e^{-x}; y = Dy = D^2 y = 0$ when $x = 0$

(b) $(D - 1)^3 y = x^{-3} e^x; y = Dy = D^2 y = 0$ when $x = 1$

(c) $(D^3 + 3D^2 - 4D - 12)y = x e^{2x}; y = Dy = D^2 y = 0$ when $x = 0$

(d) $(D + r)^n y = x^k e^{-rx}; y = Dy = D^2 y = \cdots = D^{n-1}y = 0$ when $x = 0$

(e) $(D + r)^n y = f; y = Dy = D^2 y = \cdots = D^{n-1}y = 0$ when $x = 0$

★(f) $(D + r)^2(D + s)^2 y = f, r \neq s; y = Dy = D^2 y = D^3 y = 0$ when $x = 0$

(g) $(D^3 - D)y = f; y = Dy = D^2 y = 1$ when $x = 0$

(h) $(D^3 + D)y = f; y = D^2 y = 0, Dy = 1$ when $x = 0$

★(i) $(D^n - aD^{n-1})y = f, a \neq 0; y = 1, Dy = D^2 y = \cdots = D^{n-1}y = 0$ when $x = 0$

14. Method 4: Green's Functions

In this section we consider general linear differential equations, with possibly nonconstant coefficients, and show that knowledge of the response to forcing functions which are unit "step functions" or unit "impulses" permits one to calculate by quadratures the response to an arbitrary forcing function. When the D.E. has constant coefficients, this method permits the ready

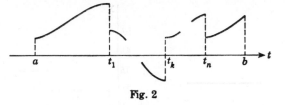

Fig. 2

calculation of the responses to these special inputs, so that in this case all the necessary functions can be calculated explicitly.

Because for the physical applications that we have in mind the independent variable is time, we shall change notation and use t for the independent variable and x for the dependent variable. The fundamental existence and uniqueness theorem of Sec. 2 states that the equation

$$(14.1) \qquad \frac{d^n x}{dt^n} + a_1(t) \frac{d^{n-1} x}{dt^{n-1}} + \cdots + a_{n-1}(t) \frac{dx}{dt} + a_n(t)x = f(t)$$

has one and only one solution $x(t)$ that is continuous, has continuous derivatives of order, 1, 2, . . . , n, and satisfies given initial conditions, provided that the given functions $a_1(t)$, . . . , $a_n(t)$, $f(t)$ are continuous.

The condition that the right-hand term $f(t)$ of Eq. (14.1) be continuous can readily be relaxed. This is of importance for theoretical reasons and because, in many applications in mechanical or electrical vibrations in which the right-hand term $f(t)$ represents an impressed force or voltage, this function is discontinuous. This is, in particular, the case when the force or voltage is of the switch-on or intermittent type.

The forcing functions we wish to consider are the *piecewise-continuous* ones. These are functions which have, in any interval, but a finite number of discontinuities at points t_1, . . . , t_n such that at these points the right- and left-hand limits of the function exist (see Fig. 2):

$$f(t_k+) = \lim f(t) \text{ as } t \to t_k \text{ from the right} = \lim_{t \to t_k^+} f(t)$$
$$f(t_k-) = \lim f(t) \text{ as } t \to t_k \text{ from the left} = \lim_{t \to t_k^-} f(t)$$

The piecewise-continuous function has a *jump discontinuity* of magnitude h at t_k if

$$h = f(t_k+) - f(t_k-)$$

The most elementary function possessing a jump discontinuity is the *unit step function,* defined by

$$(14.2) \qquad \mathbf{1}(t) = \begin{cases} 0 & \text{for } t < 0 \\ 1 & \text{for } t \geq 0 \end{cases}$$

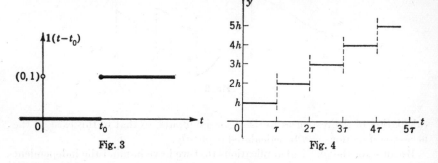

Fig. 3   Fig. 4

From this definition it follows that

$$\lim_{t \to 0-} \mathbf{1}(t) = 0 \qquad \lim_{t \to 0+} \mathbf{1}(t) = 1$$

The difference between these two one-sided limits is 1, which is the magnitude of the jump of the function at the point (or time) $t = 0$. At all other points the function $\mathbf{1}(t)$ is continuous. Moreover, $\mathbf{1}(t)$ is *continuous on the right* everywhere, including $t = 0$, since $\mathbf{1}(t+) = \mathbf{1}(t)$ for all t.

Obviously, $h\mathbf{1}(t)$ is a step function similar to $\mathbf{1}(t)$, except that the magnitude of the jump is h. It is also clear that $\mathbf{1}(t - t_0)$ is a unit step function similar to $\mathbf{1}(t)$, except that the jump occurs at the point $t = t_0$ (see Fig. 3):

$$(14.3) \qquad \mathbf{1}(t - t_0) = \begin{cases} 0 & \text{for } t < t_0 \\ 1 & \text{for } t \geq t_0 \end{cases}$$

More general functions can easily be formed by combinations of step functions. For example, the *escalator function* of Fig. 4 can be represented by the equation

$$y(t) = h[\mathbf{1}(t) + \mathbf{1}(t - \tau) + \mathbf{1}(t - 2\tau) + \cdots]$$

The *meander function* of Fig. 5 has the equation

$$y(t) = h[\mathbf{1}(t) - \mathbf{1}(t - \tau) + \mathbf{1}(t - 2\tau) - \cdots]$$

The *sawtooth function* of Fig. 6 has the equation

$$y(t) = h\left[\frac{t}{\tau}\mathbf{1}(t) - \mathbf{1}(t - \tau) - \mathbf{1}(t - 2\tau) - \cdots\right]$$

It is useful to note that every continuous or piecewise-continuous function f can be approximated by step functions. The method is apparent from the

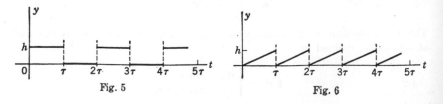

Fig. 5   Fig. 6

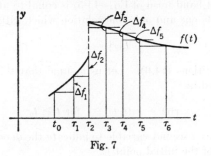

Fig. 7

example of Fig. 7. The equation for the approximating step function is

$$(14.4) \quad y(t) = f(t_0)\mathbf{1}(t - t_0) + \Delta f_1\,\mathbf{1}(t - \tau_1) + \Delta f_2\,\mathbf{1}(t - \tau_2) + \cdots$$

where

$$\Delta f_1 = f(\tau_1) - f(t_0) \qquad \Delta f_2 = f(\tau_2) - f(\tau_1) \qquad \cdots$$

The approximation is valid at all t_i if f is continuous on the right. We shall assume that all piecewise-continuous functions are continuous from the right. The reader can verify that this is no serious restriction. The assumption excludes, in particular, removable discontinuities, that is, points t^* where $f(t^*+) = f(t^*-) \neq f(t^*)$.

Now assume that we deal with a mechanical or electrical system whose vibrations are described by Eq. (14.1). Assume that the system is at rest up to the time $t = t_0$ and that at this time a force (or voltage) of constant magnitude 1 is impressed. The problem then is to find the solution of the differential equation

$$(14.5) \qquad L[x] \equiv \frac{d^n x}{dt^n} + a_1(t)\,\frac{d^{n-1}x}{dt^{n-1}} + \cdots + a_n(t)x = \mathbf{1}(t - t_0)$$

with the initial conditions

$$(14.6) \qquad x(t_0) = x'(t_0) = \cdots = x^{(n-1)}(t_0) = 0$$

The meaning of the initial conditions is that the values of the function $x(t)$ and its first $n - 1$ derivatives approach zero as t approaches t_0 both from the left and from the right.

Although Theorem 2 of Sec. 2 does not apply to this problem without changes because of the discontinuity of the forcing function, the basic results as to the existence and uniqueness of the solution can easily be derived from that theorem. Since the right-hand term of Eq. (14.5) vanishes for $t < t_0$, and since conditions (14.6) hold, it follows from that theorem that

$$x(t) = 0 \qquad \text{for } t \leqq t_0$$

For $t \geqq t_0$, the right-hand term of Eq. (14.5) is equal to unity. By the same theorem, there exists one and only one solution which satisfies the equation

$$L[x] = 1$$

and the initial conditions (14.6). Let us assume that this solution is found, and let it be denoted by

$$x(t) = x_1(t, t_0) \qquad \text{for } t \geqq t_0$$

where t_0 is written as a second variable to indicate the dependence of the solution on the choice of the initial point t_0.

In summary, we have found there is, for all values of t, a unique solution of Eq. (14.5) satisfying initial conditions (14.6), and it is

$$x(t) = K(t, t_0) = \begin{cases} 0 & \text{for } t \leqq t_0 \\ x_1(t, t_0) & \text{for } t \geqq t_0 \end{cases}$$

This composite function defines the *indicial function* belonging to the differential operator L. Observe that if L has constant coefficients, then finding $K(t, t_0)$ is a simple matter.

Example 1. Find the indicial function belonging to the differential operator

$$L[x] = \frac{d^4x}{dt^4} - k^4x \qquad k \neq 0$$

We must first find the solution of the D.E.

$$\frac{d^4x}{dt^4} - k^4x = 1$$

with the I.C.

$$x(t_0) = x'(t_0) = x''(t_0) = x'''(t_0) = 0$$

Obviously, $x = -1/k^4$ is a particular solution of the D.E. The complementary function of this equation can be written as

$$x(t) = A \cos k(t - \alpha) + B \cosh k(t - \beta)$$

where A, α, B, β are the constants of integration. Therefore, the general solution is

$$x(t) = -k^{-4} + A \cos k(t - \alpha) + B \cosh k(t - \beta)$$

The I.C. lead to the following equations for the constants A, α, B, β:

$$-k^{-4} + A \cos k(t_0 - \alpha) + B \cosh k(t_0 - \beta) = 0$$
$$- Ak \sin k(t_0 - \alpha) + Bk \sinh k(t_0 - \beta) = 0$$
$$- Ak^2 \cos k(t_0 - \alpha) + Bk^2 \cosh k(t_0 - \beta) = 0$$
$$Ak^3 \sin k(t_0 - \alpha) + Bk^3 \sinh k(t_0 - \beta) = 0$$

They are solved by

$$\alpha = \beta = t_0 \qquad A = B = \frac{1}{2k^4}$$

Therefore, the indicial function belonging to $L[x]$ is

$$K(t, t_0) = \begin{cases} 0 & \text{for } t \leq t_0 \\ \dfrac{1}{k^4}\left[-1 + \dfrac{1}{2}\cos k(t - t_0) + \dfrac{1}{2}\cosh k(t - t_0)\right] & \text{for } t \geq t_0 \end{cases}$$

In general, the indicial function and its first $n - 1$ derivatives are continuous for all values of t. This is obvious for $t \neq t_0$. It is also true for $t = t_0$ since, by construction, the solution $K(t, t_0)$ and its first $n - 1$ derivatives approach the limit zero as t approaches t_0 both from the left and from the right. However, the nth-order derivative of $K(t, t_0)$ is no longer continuous. From Eq. (14.5), we have, since $K(t, t_0)$ satisfies this equation for $t \neq t_0$,

$$\frac{\partial^n K}{\partial t^n} = -a_1(t)\frac{\partial^{n-1}K}{\partial t^{n-1}} - a_2(t)\frac{\partial^{n-2}K}{\partial t^{n-2}} - \cdots - a_n(t)K + \mathbf{1}(t - t_0)$$

The functions on the right-hand side of this equation are continuous for all values of t, except that $\mathbf{1}(t - t_0)$ has a jump of magnitude 1 at $t = t_0$. Thus the nth derivative of the indicial function $K(t, t_0)$ is continuous for all values of t except for $t = t_0$, where it has a jump of magnitude 1.

It is clear that if the forcing function in Eq. (14.5) were

$$h\mathbf{1}(t - t_0) \qquad h = \text{constant}$$

and nothing else were changed, the solution of the initial-value problem would be $x(t) = hK(t, t_0)$.

Now consider the equation

$$(14.7) \quad L[x] = \frac{d^n x}{dt^n} + a_1(t)\frac{d^{n-1}x}{dt^{n-1}} + \cdots + a_n(t)x = \begin{cases} 0 & \text{for } t < t_0 \\ f(t) & \text{for } t \geq t_0 \end{cases}$$

where $f(t)$ is an arbitrary function. Let us try to find a solution of this equation that satisfies the same initial conditions (14.6) that we had before. If we replace the right-hand term in Eq. (14.7) with the approximating step function (14.4), then the right-hand term becomes a sum of terms of the general form

$$\Delta f_k\, \mathbf{1}(t - \tau_k)$$

The solution for this forcing function satisfying initial conditions (14.6) is

$$\Delta f_k\, K(t, \tau_k)$$

Hence, by the principle of superposition, the solution of the equation whose right member is the step function (14.4) is

$$(14.8) \qquad f(t_0)K(t, t_0) + \Delta f_1\, K(t, \tau_1) + \Delta f_2\, K(t, \tau_2) + \cdots$$

As the points $\tau_1, \tau_2, \ldots$ at which the jumps of the approximating step functions occur move closer together, the sum in (14.8) tends to the integral

$$(14.9) \qquad x(t) = K(t, t_0)f(t_0) + \int_{t_0}^{t} K(t, \tau)\, df(\tau)$$

where the integral is a so-called *Stieltjes integral*. If it should happen that f is continuous with a piecewise-continuous derivative, then the Stieltjes integral in (14.9) is equal to a Riemann integral:

$$(14.10) \qquad \int_{t_0}^{t} K(t, \tau)\, df(\tau) = \int_{t_0}^{t} K(t, \tau)f'(\tau)\, d\tau$$

The function $x(t)$ in (14.9) is then given by

$$(14.11) \qquad x(t) = K(t, t_0)f(t_0) + \int_{t_0}^{t} K(t, \tau)f'(\tau)\, d\tau$$

From the construction we expect that the function $x(t)$ given by (14.9) or (14.11) is a solution of the D.E. (14.7) which satisfies the I.C. (14.6). That such is the case can be verified directly. The following steps are left as exercises for the reader. One obtains, for $t > t_0$, $k = 1, \ldots, n$, if t is a point of continuity† of $f(t)$,

$$\frac{d^k x}{dt^k} = \frac{\partial^k K}{\partial t^k}(t, t_0)f(t_0) + \int_{t_0}^{t} \frac{\partial^k K}{\partial t^k}(t, \tau)\, df(\tau)$$

Therefore,

$$L[x] = \left(\frac{\partial^n K}{\partial t^n} + a_1 \frac{\partial^{n-1} K}{\partial t^{n-1}} + \cdots + a_n K \right) f(t_0)$$
$$\qquad\qquad + \int_{t_0}^{t} \left(\frac{\partial^n K}{\partial t^n} + a_1 \frac{\partial^{n-1} K}{\partial t^{n-1}} + \cdots + a_n K \right) df(\tau)$$
$$= \mathbf{1}(t - t_0)f(t_0) + \int_{t_0}^{t} \mathbf{1}(t - \tau)\, df(\tau)$$
$$= f(t_0) + \int_{t_0}^{t} df(\tau) = f(t_0) + f(t) - f(t_0)$$
$$= f(t)$$

The integrals in (14.9) and (14.11) are called *Duhamel's integrals*.

The preceding results are summarized in the following theorem:

Theorem 1. *If f is piecewise continuous, then the solution of the D.E.*

$$L[x] \equiv \frac{d^n x}{dt^n} + a_1(t)\frac{d^{n-1}x}{dt^{n-1}} + \cdots + a_n(t)x = \begin{cases} 0 & \text{for } t < 0 \\ f(t) & \text{for } t \geq 0 \end{cases}$$

† At points of discontinuity of f, one cannot expect to have the D.E. satisfied. Thus, $y(t) = t\mathbf{1}(t)$ is the unique solution of $dy/dt = \mathbf{1}(t)$, $y(0) = 0$, but the D.E. is satisfied only for $t < 0$ and $t > 0$, not for $t = 0$.

which satisfies the I.C.

$$x(t_0) = x'(t_0) = \cdots = x^{(n-1)}(t_0) = 0$$

is given by

$$x(t) = K(t, t_0)f(t_0) + \int_{t_0}^{t} K(t, \tau) \, df(\tau)$$

If, in addition, f is continuous with a piecewise-continuous derivative, then

$$x(t) = K(t, t_0)f(t_0) + \int_{t_0}^{t} K(t, \tau)f'(\tau) \, d\tau$$

where $K(t, \tau)$ is the indicial function belonging to L.

The second integral in the theorem is less convenient than one could wish, for if f were given empirically, one would need first to compute f'. An integration by parts will remove this objection.

The usual formula for integration by parts is valid, whence

$$\int_{t_0}^{t} K(t, \tau) \, df(\tau) = K(t, \tau)f(\tau) \Big|_{t_0}^{t} - \int_{t_0}^{t} f(\tau) \, dK(t, \tau)$$

$$= -K(t, t_0)f(t_0) - \int_{t_0}^{t} \frac{\partial K}{\partial \tau} (t, \tau)f(\tau) \, d\tau$$

We therefore see that the solution $x(t)$ of the D.E. is

$$x(t) = -\int_{t_0}^{t} \frac{\partial}{\partial \tau} K(t, \tau)f(\tau) \, d\tau$$

If we put

$$G(t, \tau) = -\frac{\partial}{\partial \tau} K(t, \tau)$$

then $x(t)$ becomes

(14.12) $$x(t) = \int_{t_0}^{t} G(t, \tau)f(\tau) \, d\tau$$

Formula (14.12) does not involve the derivative of the function $f(t)$, and it holds true for any piecewise-continuous function $f(t)$.

The function $G(t, \tau) = -(\partial/\partial\tau)K(t, \tau)$ which occurs in the integral of formula (14.12) is called the *weighting function* or *Green's function* belonging to the differential expression $L[x]$.

By the definition of a derivative,

$$G(t, t_0) = -\frac{\partial K}{\partial \tau} (t, t_0)$$

$$= -\lim_{h \to 0} \frac{K(t, t_0 + h) - K(t, t_0)}{h}$$

$$= \lim_{h \to 0} \frac{K(t, t_0) - K(t, t_0 + h)}{h}$$

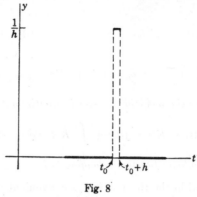

Fig. 8

Hence, for sufficiently small values of h, the function

$$(14.13) \qquad \frac{K(t, t_0) - K(t, t_0 + h)}{h}$$

may be considered as a good approximation to $G(t, t_0)$. If it is remembered that $K(t, t_0)$ is a solution of differential equation $L[x] = y$ with $y(t) = \mathbf{1}(t - t_0)$ as forcing function, then it is apparent that (14.13) is a solution of the same equation with

$$y(t) = \frac{\mathbf{1}(t - t_0) - \mathbf{1}(t - t_0 - h)}{h}$$

as forcing function. The graph of this function is shown in Fig. 8. Considered as a mechanical or electromotive force, it is an *impulse* of duration h and intensity $1/h$, hence of "moment" $h(1/h) = 1$. From this consideration we have the following interpretation of Green's function:

If the D.E. represents the excitation of a mechanical or electrical system, then the Green's function $G(t, t_0)$ belonging to it represents the excitation at time t due to an impulse at time t_0 of "infinitesimal" duration, of "infinite" intensity, and of unit moment.

Indicial and weighting functions are particularly useful in cases in which it is required to find the responses of an oscillating system to a variety of impressed forces. Once the indicial or weighting function for the system is known, the solution for any impressed force is found by evaluating the integral of formula (14.12), which may often most conveniently be done by numerical, graphical, or mechanical methods. In practical work, especially in problems that lead to difficult differential equations with variable coefficients, the indicial or weighting function is sometimes determined by experiment, namely, as the response of the system to a unit-step or unit-impulse force, respectively.

We have defined the Green's function in terms of the indicial function $K(t, \tau)$. It is of interest to obtain $G(t, \tau)$ directly from the D.E. Observe first that G satisfies the homogeneous D.E. We have

$$L[K(t, t_0)] = \mathbf{1}(t - t_0)$$

and so, taking the partial derivative of each side with respect to t_0, we obtain

(14.14) $$L\left[\frac{\partial K}{\partial t_0}(t, t_0)\right] = 0 \qquad t \neq t_0$$

Therefore G is a solution of $L[x] = 0$. It remains to determine the I.C. satisfied by G.

From Taylor's theorem we have

$$K(t, t_0) = K(t, t_0)\Big|_{t=t_0} + \frac{\partial K}{\partial t}(t, t_0)\Big|_{t=t_0} \frac{(t - t_0)}{1!} + \cdots$$
$$+ \frac{\partial^{n-1}K}{\partial t^{n-1}}(t, t_0)\Big|_{t=t_0} \frac{(t - t_0)^{n-1}}{(n - 1)!} + \frac{1}{(n - 1)!}\int_{t_0}^{t} (t - \tau)^{n-1} \frac{\partial^n K}{\partial t^n}(t, \tau)\, d\tau$$

and since $K(t, t_0)$ satisfies the homogeneous I.C. (14.6),

$$K(t, t_0) = \frac{1}{(n - 1)!}\int_{t_0}^{t} (t - \tau)^{n-1} \frac{\partial^n K(t, \tau)}{\partial t^n}\, d\tau$$

Now we get $-G(t, t_0)$ by differentiating this formula for $K(t, t_0)$ with respect to t_0. We obtain

(14.15) $$G(t, t_0) = \frac{(t - t_0)^{n-1}}{(n - 1)!} \frac{\partial^n K(t, t_0)}{\partial t^n}$$

From this new formula for the Green's function one sees, on differentiating (14.15), that $G(t, t_0)$ and its first $n - 2$ derivatives vanish at $t = t_0$. If we recall the jump discontinuity of $\partial^n K(t, t_0)/\partial t^n$ at $t = t_0$, we also obtain from this last equation the relation

$$\frac{\partial^{n-1}G(t, t_0)}{\partial t^{n-1}} = \begin{cases} 0 & \text{if } t < t_0 \\ 1 & \text{if } t = t_0 \end{cases}$$

We summarize these results in Theorem 2.

Theorem 2. *If $f(t)$ is piecewise continuous and $a_1, \ldots, a_n$ are continuous, the solution of*

$$L[x] = \frac{d^n x}{dt^n} + a_1(t) \frac{d^{n-1}x}{dt^{n-1}} + \cdots + a_n(t)x = \begin{cases} 0 & \text{if } t < t_0 \\ f(t) & \text{if } t > t_0 \end{cases}$$

which satisfies the I.C.

$$x(t_0) = x'(t_0) = \cdots = x^{(n-1)}(t_0) = 0$$

is given by

$$x(t) = \int_{t_0}^{t} G(t, \tau) f(\tau) \, d\tau$$

where $G(t, \tau)$ is the unique function which vanishes for $t < \tau$ and which, for $t > \tau$, is the solution of the initial-value problem

$$L[x] = 0$$
$$x(\tau) = x'(\tau) = \cdots = x^{(n-2)}(\tau) = 0 \qquad x^{(n-1)}(\tau) = 1$$

How do the problems of determining $K(t, \tau)$ and $G(t, \tau)$ compare? Both vanish for $t < \tau$. For $t \geq \tau$, $K(t, \tau)$ satisfies the nonhomogeneous equation $L[x] = 1$ and homogeneous I.C., whereas $G(t, \tau)$ satisfies the homogeneous equation $L[x] = 0$ and the nonhomogeneous I.C. of Theorem 2. Thus the two problems are of equal difficulty.

Example 2. In Example 1 we obtained $K(t, \tau)$ for $L[x] = x^{(4)} - k^4 x$:

$$K(t, \tau) = \frac{1}{k^4} [-1 + \tfrac{1}{2} \cos k(t - \tau) + \tfrac{1}{2} \cosh k(t - \tau)]$$

whence

$$-G(t, \tau) = \frac{\partial}{\partial \tau} K(t, \tau) = \frac{1}{2k^3} [\sin k(t - \tau) - \sinh k(t - \tau)]$$

We can also obtain $G(t, \tau)$ by solving the initial-value problem of Theorem 2. The general solution of the homogeneous equation $L[x] = 0$ is

$$x(t) = A \sin k(t - \alpha) + B \sinh k(t - \beta)$$

The I.C. give the following equations for A, B, α, β:

$$A \sin k(\tau - \alpha) + B \sinh k(\tau - \beta) = 0$$
$$k[A \cos k(\tau - \alpha) + B \cosh k(\tau - \beta)] = 0$$
$$k^2[-A \sin k(\tau - \alpha) + B \sinh k(\tau - \beta)] = 0$$
$$k^3[-A \cos k(\tau - \alpha) + B \cosh k(\tau - \beta)] = 1$$

which have the solution

$$\alpha = \beta = \tau \qquad A = \frac{-1}{2k^3} \qquad B = \frac{1}{2k^3}$$

Thus the same $G(t, \tau)$ is obtained.

PROBLEMS

1. Represent the functions graphed in Fig. 9 by the use of the unit step function.

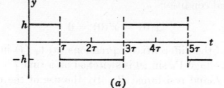

(a)

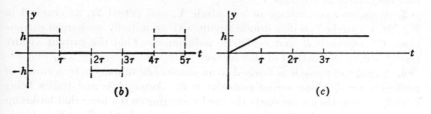

(b)   (c)

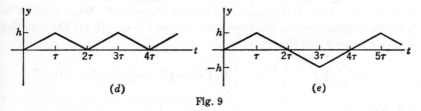

(d)   (e)

Fig. 9

2. Find the indicial and weighting functions belonging to the following differential expressions:

(a) $\dfrac{d^2x}{dt^2} + k^2x;\ k \neq 0$

(b) $\dfrac{d^2x}{dt^2} - k^2x;\ k \neq 0$

(c) $\dfrac{d^2x}{dt^2} + a\dfrac{dx}{dt};\ a \neq 0$

(d) $\dfrac{d^2x}{dt^2} + a\dfrac{dx}{dt} + bx;\ b \neq 0,\ a^2 - 4b \neq 0$

(e) $t^2\dfrac{d^2x}{dt^2} + at\dfrac{dx}{dt};\ a \neq 1$

(f) $t^2\dfrac{d^2x}{dt^2} + at\dfrac{dx}{dt} + bx;\ b \neq 0,\ (a-1)^2 - 4b \neq 0$

★(g) $\dfrac{d^2x}{dt^2} + at\dfrac{dx}{dt} + ax;\ a \neq 0.$ Hint: $\dfrac{d}{dt}\left(\dfrac{dx}{dt} + atx\right) = ?$

3. By the use of the results of Prob. 2, find the solution of the equation

$$L[x] = \begin{cases} f(t) & \text{for } t \geq 0 \\ 0 & \text{for } t < 0 \end{cases}$$

subject to the initial conditions

$$x(0) = x'(0) = 0$$

where $L[x]$ is any of the differential expressions (a) to (f) in Prob. 2.

4. A sinusoidal voltage $V_0 \sin \omega t$ is switched on a time $t = 0$ in a simple circuit of inductance L and resistance R. By the use of the results of Prob. 2, find the current at any time $t > 0$.

5. A square-wave voltage of amplitude V_0 and period 2τ, as graphed in Fig. 9a, is switched on in a simple circuit with an initially uncharged capacitance C, resistance R, and negligible inductance. Find the current at any time $t > 0$ by the method of this section.

★6. A trailer of mass M is hitched to an automobile of mass m by a spring of negligible mass, whose spring constant is k. Automobile and trailer being initially at rest, the engine starts the car by exerting on it a force that builds up linearly from the value 0 at time $t = 0$ to the maximal value F_0 at time $t = \tau$, as in Fig. 9c. What is the maximum force in the spring? What would it be if the driving force were applied suddenly at time $t = 0$? HINT: The equation for the extension x of the spring is

$$m \frac{d^2x}{dt^2} + k \frac{M + m}{M} x = \frac{t}{\tau} F_0[\mathbf{1}(t) - \mathbf{1}(t - \tau)] + F_0\mathbf{1}(t - \tau)$$

7. Show that

$$K(t, \tau) = K(t - \tau, 0)$$
$$G(t, \tau) = G(t - \tau, 0)$$

if these indicial and weighting functions belong to a differential expression that has constant coefficients. HINT: If $x(t)$ is a solution of a linear differential equation with constant coefficients satisfying certain initial conditions for $t = 0$, then $x(t - \tau)$ is a solution of the same differential equation and satisfies the same initial conditions for $t = \tau$.

chapter vii

Laplace Transforms and Operator Methods

The use of so-called operational methods in solving linear D.E. with constant coefficients goes back to Oliver Heaviside (1850–1925). Today these problems are often handled by the use of Laplace transforms. Though the Heaviside calculus is applicable to a somewhat broader class of functions, the two methods are equivalent for most practical cases. Because Laplace transforms are easy to apply, and because one can deduce physical properties related to solutions directly from the properties of their transforms, the use of Laplace transforms is widespread. In this chapter we shall describe both these methods.

1. The Laplace Transform

In transform methods the basic idea is to associate with each (suitable) function f another function Tf, called the transform of f:

$$(1.1) \qquad f \leftrightarrow Tf \qquad \text{one-to-one correspondence}$$

There is no necessity for a function and its transform to have the same domain, but it is essential that the correspondence (1.1) be *one to one*.

As applied to differential equations, transform methods usually have two characteristics:

1. The transform has desirable properties of smoothness not necessarily possessed by the original function.

245

Fig. 1   Fig. 2

2. The transform of the solution of a differential equation can be found using more elementary operations than those used in finding the solution itself.

There are many kinds of transforms, each of which is particularly suited to certain classes of problems. Among these are the Fourier and Laplace transforms, which are the best known and most widely used.

We shall be concerned with functions defined only for $0 \leqq t < \infty$, but for convenience we shall extend the domain of f to the whole line by defining $f(t) = 0$ for $t < 0$. All functions will be presumed to be at least piecewise continuous† in any interval, and as in Chap. VI we shall assume that at points of discontinuity the functions are continuous on the right. Thus (see Fig. 1), $f(t_0) = f(t_0{}^+) = \lim f(t)$ as $t \to t_0$ from the right. Unless explicitly stated otherwise, *all* functions vanish for $t < 0$.

Definition 1.   Suppose f is such that the improper integral

$$(1.2) \qquad F(s) = \int_0^\infty e^{-s\tau} f(\tau) \, d\tau = \lim_{t \to \infty} \int_0^t e^{-s\tau} f(\tau) \, d\tau$$

exists for $s \geqq c$, where c is some real number. Then the integral defines a function F called the *Laplace transform* of f and denoted by

$$\mathcal{L}f = F$$

The value of the transform at s is

$$\mathcal{L}f(s) = F(s)$$

Example 1.   If f is the unit step function 1 (see Fig. 2), then

$$\mathcal{L}f(s) = \int_0^\infty e^{-s\tau} \mathbf{1}(\tau) \, d\tau$$
$$= \lim_{t \to \infty} \int_0^t e^{-s\tau} \, d\tau$$
$$= \frac{1}{s} \quad \text{if} \quad s > 0$$

† See Sec. 14, Chap. VI.

Example 2.   If $f(t) = t$ for $t \geq 0$, then

$$\mathcal{L}f(s) = \int_0^\infty e^{-s\tau}\tau\, d\tau = \lim_{t \to \infty} \left(\frac{-te^{-st}}{s} - \frac{e^{-st}}{s^2} + \frac{1}{s^2} \right)$$

$$= \frac{1}{s^2} \qquad \text{if} \qquad s > 0$$

Example 3.   If $f(t) = \sin \omega t$ for $t \geq 0$, then

$$\mathcal{L}f(s) = \int_0^\infty e^{-s\tau} \sin \omega \tau\, d\tau$$

$$= \lim_{t \to \infty} \left[\frac{1}{s^2 + \omega^2} (-s \sin \omega \tau - \omega \cos \omega \tau)e^{-st} \right]_0^t$$

$$= \frac{\omega}{s^2 + \omega^2} \qquad \text{if} \qquad s > 0$$

Remark on Notation.   The variable s in (1.2) is often called the *transform variable*. One must be careful not to confuse it with the independent variable t of the original function. The two are quite unrelated. The value of $\mathcal{L}f(s)$ is a "smeared" average of the values of f over all $t > 0$. Different values of s give different smeared averages. We wish to avoid the precise but somewhat pedantic formulation of the examples, in which there is the introductory phrase, "If $f(t) = \ldots$." In many cases we wish to use the formula for f in place of f in $\mathcal{L}f$. Thus, the results of Examples 1 to 3 become

$$\mathcal{L}1(s) = \frac{1}{s}$$

$$\mathcal{L}\{t\}(s) = \frac{1}{s^2} \qquad\qquad \text{all for } s > 0$$

$$\mathcal{L}\{\sin \omega t\}(s) = \frac{\omega}{\omega^2 + s^2}$$

Observe that this notation conforms to the earlier one if we regard the expression in the curly brackets as the function. If there existed good functional symbols for the functions $t \to t$, $t \to \sin \omega t$, the variable symbol t would not be used in the last two examples.

It will also be convenient to consistently use corresponding capital letters for Laplace transforms, for example, $\mathcal{L}f = F$, $\mathcal{L}g = G$, $\mathcal{L}\varphi = \Phi$. With this convention it will be unnecessary, when speaking of F, to add the phrase, "where $F = \mathcal{L}f$."

Remark on the Domain of s.   The transform variable s can be a complex number, with the consequence that the Laplace transform is defined over a portion of the complex plane. As we shall see in Sec.

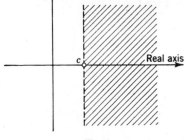

Fig. 3

2, if $\mathcal{L}f(s)$ exists for s real and $s > c$, then $\mathcal{L}f(s)$ exists in the half of the complex plane in which $\operatorname{Re} s > c$, as is illustrated in Fig. 3.

Example 4. If a is any complex number, then

$$\mathcal{L}\{e^{at}\}(s) = \int_0^\infty e^{-s\tau}e^{a\tau}\,d\tau$$

$$= \lim_{t \to \infty}\left[\frac{e^{-(s-a)\tau}}{-(s-a)}\right]_0^t$$

Now set $s - a = u + iv$, where u, v are real; then

$$\mathcal{L}\{e^{at}\}(s) = \lim_{t \to \infty}\left[\frac{e^{-ut}e^{-ivt}}{-(s-a)} + \frac{1}{s-a}\right]$$

$$= \frac{1}{s-a} \qquad \text{if} \qquad u = \operatorname{Re}(s-a) > 0$$

Thus the limit exists if $\operatorname{Re}(s-a) > 0$, and we say the domain of the transform is the half plane $\operatorname{Re} s > \operatorname{Re} a$.

We can use the above result to derive that of Example 3 in a different way. Suppose $a = i\omega$; then $\sin \omega t = \operatorname{Im} e^{i\omega t}$, and, for s real and positive,

$$\mathcal{L}\{\sin \omega t\}(s) = \mathcal{L}\{\operatorname{Im} e^{i\omega t}\}(s)$$
$$= \operatorname{Im} \mathcal{L}\{e^{i\omega t}\}(s)$$

$$= \operatorname{Im} \frac{1}{s - i\omega}$$

$$= \operatorname{Im} \frac{s + i\omega}{s^2 + \omega^2} = \frac{\omega}{s^2 + \omega^2}$$

For future use we shall need a short table of Laplace transforms of some of the elementary functions. Such a table is quite analogous to a table of integrals and will be used in much the same way. Not only shall we use this table to find transforms of functions, but we shall also

TABLE OF LAPLACE TRANSFORMS

---

1. $\mathcal{L}\{1\}(s) = \dfrac{1}{s}$ Re $s > 0$

2. $\mathcal{L}\{t\}(s) = \dfrac{1}{s^2}$ Re $s > 0$

3. $\mathcal{L}\{t^m\}(s) = \dfrac{m!}{s^{m+1}}$ Re $s > 0$ and $m = 0, 1, 2, \ldots$

4. $\mathcal{L}\{e^{at}\}(s) = \dfrac{1}{s - a}$ Re $s >$ Re a

5. $\mathcal{L}\{t^m e^{at}\}(s) = \dfrac{m!}{(s - a)^{m+1}}$ Re $s >$ Re a and $m = 0, 1, 2, \ldots$

6. $\mathcal{L}\{\sin \omega t\}(s) = \dfrac{\omega}{\omega^2 + s^2}$ Re $s > 0$

7. $\mathcal{L}\{\cos \omega t\}(s) = \dfrac{s}{s^2 + \omega^2}$ Re $s > 0$

8. $\mathcal{L}\{\sinh at\}(s) = \dfrac{a}{s^2 - a^2}$ Re $s > |a|$

9. $\mathcal{L}\{\cosh at\}(s) = \dfrac{s}{s^2 - a^2}$ Re $s > |a|$

10. $\mathcal{L}\{e^{at} \sin \omega t\}(s) = \dfrac{\omega}{(s - a)^2 + \omega^2}$ Re $s > a$

11. $\mathcal{L}\{e^{at} \cos \omega t\}(s) = \dfrac{s - a}{(s - a)^2 + \omega^2}$ Re $s > a$

12. $\mathcal{L}\{1(t - t_0)\}(s) = \dfrac{1}{s} e^{-st_0}$ Re $s > 0$

---

use it to find the original function when the transform is known. It is a simple exercise in the calculus to calculate the table above, and the details are left to the reader. We have incorporated the results of the above examples in the table.

2. Some Theorems on Transforms

We collect together in this section the basic theorems which permit one to use Laplace transforms to solve linear D.E. with constant coefficients.

Theorem 1. $\mathcal{L}$ *is a linear operator; that is,* $\mathcal{L}(c_1 f_1 + c_2 f_2)$ *exists, and* $\mathcal{L}(c_1 f_1 + c_2 f_2)(s) = c_1 \mathcal{L} f_1(s) + c_2 \mathcal{L} f_2(s)$ *for* Re $s > c$, *where* c_1 *and* c_2 *are constants, provided that* $\mathcal{L} f_1(s)$ *and* $\mathcal{L} f_2(s)$ *exist for* Re $s > c$.

The proof is left to the reader.

So far we have not shown that Laplace transforms actually exist for any class of functions. All we know is that the transforms of the elementary functions of the table on this page exist. In fact, not all functions possess Laplace transforms. For example, if $f(t) = e^{t^2}$ for

$t \geqq 0$, then the limit

$$\lim_{t \to \infty} \int_0^t e^{-s\tau} e^{\tau^2} \, d\tau$$

does not exist for any s. The function e^{t^2} "grows too rapidly." As a consequence of this fact, the Laplace-transform method is not as generally applicable for the solution of D.E. as the operator method to be described in Sec. 7. However, the functions that occur in practice do not grow too rapidly, and Laplace transforms are quite adequate. A large class of functions, sufficient for most applications, is described in the following definition.

Definition 1. If f is at least piecewise continuous, and if there is a real number c such that

$$(2.1) \qquad\qquad \lim_{t \to \infty} e^{-ct} f(t) = 0$$

then f is said to be of *exponential order*.

Theorem 2. *If f is of exponential order, then $\mathcal{L}f(s)$ exists for Re $s > c$, where c is the constant of* (2.1).

Proof. From calculus, in order to prove that the improper integral (1.2) converges for Re $s > c$, it suffices to prove that, given any $\epsilon > 0$, there is a positive number A such that, if $A \leqq t_1 < t_2$, then

$$I = \left| \int_{t_1}^{t_2} e^{-s\tau} f(\tau) \, d\tau \right| < \epsilon$$

Let $s = u + iv$, where u and v are real, and let $u = c + a$, where $a > 0$. Then

$$I \leqq \int_{t_1}^{t_2} |e^{-u\tau} e^{-iv\tau} f(\tau)| \, d\tau$$

$$= \int_{t_1}^{t_2} e^{-a\tau} e^{-c\tau} |f(\tau)| \, d\tau$$

But by (2.1) there is a number A such that $e^{-c\tau} |f(\tau)| < \epsilon a$ if $\tau \geqq A$. Therefore,

$$I \leqq \int_{t_1}^{t_2} e^{-a\tau} a\epsilon \, d\tau = (e^{-at_1} - e^{-at_2})\epsilon$$

$$< e^{-at_1}\epsilon < \epsilon \qquad \text{if} \qquad A \leqq t_1 < t_2$$

This completes the proof.

Remark on Theorem 2. Theorem 2 establishes the existence of $F(s) = \mathcal{L}f(s)$ in the half plane Re $s > c$ of Fig. 3. It may be shown that F not only exists but has derivatives of all orders, even though f may not. In fact, F is a so-called *analytic function* of a complex variable in the half plane Re $s > c$. Because of this, a deeper study of Laplace transforms requires some familiarity with the theory of analytic functions. (For a few facts concerning power-series representations of these functions, see Sec. 1, Chap. X.) It so happens that the analytic function F, when studied in the complex plane, reflects important properties of f. This is one of the attractive features of the Laplace transform—one can infer properties of solutions of differential equations by examining their transforms without ever obtaining the solutions. However, in this elementary development, we shall confine our attention mainly to real values of the transform variable s.

The next theorem establishes the one-to-one nature of the correspondence $f \leftrightarrow \mathcal{L}f$. It is the only difficult theorem of this section and is given here without proof (see, for example, Ref. 7, pp. 309, 317).

Theorem 3. *If f_1 and f_2 are piecewise continuous† and there is a real number c such that $\mathcal{L}f_1(s) = \mathcal{L}f_2(s)$ for $\operatorname{Re} s > c$, then $f_1(t) = f_2(t)$ for all t.*

Because the transformation $f \to \mathcal{L}f$ is one to one, we can speak of the inverse transformation. We shall use $\mathcal{L}^{-1}$ for this inverse:

$$\mathcal{L}^{-1}F = f$$

When we have a formula for F expressed in terms of s, then, just as for $\mathcal{L}$, we shall use curly brackets:

$$\mathcal{L}^{-1}\{F(s)\}(t) = f(t)$$

The linearity of $\mathcal{L}$ implies that $\mathcal{L}^{-1}$ is also linear.

Example 1. What is f if

$$\mathcal{L}f(s) = \frac{3}{s^2 + s - 2}$$

First rewrite $\mathcal{L}f(s)$ using partial fractions:

$$\frac{3}{s^2 + s - 2} = \frac{3}{(s-1)(s+2)} = \frac{A}{s-1} + \frac{B}{s+2}$$

An easy computation gives $A = -3$ and $B = 3$. Because $\mathcal{L}^{-1}$ is linear, we have

$$\mathcal{L}^{-1}\left\{\frac{-3}{s-1}\right\}(t) = -3e^t$$

$$\mathcal{L}^{-1}\left\{\frac{3}{s+2}\right\}(t) = 3e^{-2t}$$

† Here we assume again that all functions are continuous on the right (see Sec. 1).

from formula 4 of the table, whence

$$\mathcal{L}^{-1} \left\{ \frac{3}{s^2 + s - 2} \right\} (t) = -3e^t + 3e^{-2t} = f(t)$$

Example 2. Find f if

$$\mathcal{L}f(s) = \frac{-s^2 - 8s - 7}{(s^2 + 5)(s - 2)^2}$$

Express $F(s)$ as a sum of partial fractions:

$$\frac{-s^2 - 8s - 7}{(s^2 + 5)(s - 2)^2} = \frac{As + B}{s^2 + 5} + \frac{C}{(s - 2)^2} + \frac{D}{s - 2}$$

After a short calculation we find that $A = 0, B = 2, C = -3, D = 0$. Then formulas 5 and 6 of the transform table give

$$\mathcal{L}^{-1} \left\{ \frac{2}{s^2 + 5} \right\} (t) = \frac{2}{\sqrt{5}} \mathcal{L}^{-1} \left\{ \frac{\sqrt{5}}{s^2 + 5} \right\} (t) = \frac{2}{\sqrt{5}} \sin \sqrt{5}\, t$$

$$\mathcal{L}^{-1} \left\{ \frac{-3}{(s - 2)^2} \right\} (t) = -3\mathcal{L}^{-1} \left\{ \frac{1}{(s - 2)^2} \right\} (t) = -3te^{-2t}$$

In order to apply Laplace transforms to D.E., we must have a connection between the transform of a function and the transform of its derivative. The necessary link is supplied by the next theorem and its corollaries. In the following we shall use the phrase "$\mathcal{L}f$ exists" without specifying for what values of s the integral $\int_0^\infty e^{-s\tau} f(\tau)\, d\tau$ exists. In each case it is meant that there is some real number c such that $\mathcal{L}f(s)$ exists for $s > c$, and the context shows how to find such a number c.

Theorem 4. *If f is continuous, is of exponential order, and has a piecewise-continuous derivative, then $\mathcal{L}f'$ exists, and*

$$(2.2) \qquad \mathcal{L}f'(s) = s\mathcal{L}f(s) - f(0) = sF(s) - f(0)$$

Proof. Integrating by parts, we find that

$$(2.3) \qquad \int_0^t e^{-s\tau} f'(\tau)\, d\tau = f(\tau)e^{-s\tau} \Big|_0^t + s \int_0^t e^{-s\tau} f(\tau)\, d\tau$$

Now, if c is the constant of Definition 1, and if Re $s > c$, then when we let $t \to \infty$ in (2.3) we get (2.2).

Corollary 1. *If f is of exponential order, and if $f, f', \ldots, f^{(m-1)}$ are continuous and $f^{(m)}$ is at least piecewise continuous, then $\mathcal{L}f^{(m)}$ exists, and*

$$(2.4) \quad \mathcal{L}f^{(m)}(s) = s^m F(s) - s^{m-1}f(0) - s^{m-2}f'(0) - \cdots - f^{(m-1)}(0)$$

The proof is by induction and is left to the reader.

Corollary 2. *If y is a solution of the linear D.E. with constant coefficients*

$$(2.5) \qquad (\alpha_0 D^n + \alpha_1 D^{n-1} + \cdots + \alpha_n)y = f$$

where f is piecewise continuous and of exponential order, then $\mathcal{L}y^{(k)}$ exists for $k = 0, 1, \ldots, n$, and

$$\mathcal{L}y^{(k)}(s) = s^k \mathcal{L}y(s) - s^{k-1}y(0) - \cdots - sy^{(k-1)}(0) - y^{(k-1)}(0)$$

Proof. If we but knew that y was of exponential order, then Corollary 2 would be an immediate consequence of Corollary 1. That such actually is the case follows from the results of Secs. 4 and 11, Chap. VI. For the present we assume y is of exponential order and proceed. Observe that all one needs to know is that every solution of the homogeneous equation is of exponential order and that at least *one* solution of (2.5) is of exponential order. For, suppose that y and $\tilde{y}$ are solutions of (2.5), and $\tilde{y}$ is known to be of exponential order. Then $y_c = y - \tilde{y}$ is a solution of the homogeneous equation (presumed to be of exponential order), and so $y = \tilde{y} + y_c$, as a sum of functions of exponential order, is also such a function.

The final theorem of this section concerns the decay of the transform for large values of s.

Theorem 5. *If f is piecewise continuous and of exponential order, then*

$$\lim_{s \to \infty} \mathcal{L}f(s) = 0 \qquad s \to \infty \text{ through real values}$$

Proof. Since f is of exponential order, there are a real number c and a positive number M such that $e^{-ct}|f(t)| \leq M$ for all t. Then, for $s > c$,

$$|F(s)| = \left| \int_0^\infty e^{-s\tau}f(\tau)\,d\tau \right| = \left| \int_0^\infty e^{-(s-c)\tau}e^{-c\tau}f(\tau)\,d\tau \right|$$

$$\leq \int_0^\infty e^{-(s-c)\tau} M\,d\tau = \frac{M}{s-c}$$

Therefore, as $s \to \infty$, $M/(s-c) \to 0$ and $F(s) \to 0$.

PROBLEMS

1. Each of the functions F is the Laplace transform of a function f. Find f by using the transform table.

(a) $F(s) = \dfrac{3}{s} - \dfrac{1}{s+1} + \dfrac{2}{s^2+1}$

(b) $F(s) = \dfrac{\frac{1}{2}}{s-a} - \dfrac{\frac{1}{2}}{s+a} = \dfrac{a}{s^2 - a^2}$ (two methods)

(c) $F(s) = \dfrac{A}{s} - \dfrac{2s}{s^2 - 4} = \dfrac{A}{s} - \dfrac{1}{s-2} - \dfrac{1}{s+2}$ (two methods)

(d) $F(s) = \dfrac{A\omega + Bs}{\omega^2 + s^2}$

(e) $F(s) = \dfrac{4}{16 + s^2} - \dfrac{8}{s^2 - 4s + 20}$

(f) $F(s) = \dfrac{\omega}{2i}\dfrac{1}{s - i\omega} - \dfrac{\omega}{2i}\dfrac{1}{s + i\omega} = \dfrac{\omega^2}{s^2 + \omega^2}$ (two methods)

(g) $F(s) = \dfrac{1}{2}\dfrac{1}{s - i\omega} + \dfrac{1}{2}\dfrac{1}{s + i\omega} = \dfrac{s}{s^2 + \omega^2}$ (two methods)

(h) $F(s) = \dfrac{2}{(3s - 2)^2}$

(i) $F(s) = \dfrac{5}{s^3 - s^2 - s + 1}$

(j) $F(s) = \dfrac{5}{s^2 + 2s + 17}$

(k) $F(s) = \dfrac{s + 2}{2(s^2 + 4s - 5)}$

(l) $F(s) = \dfrac{1}{s^2 - s + 2}$

(m) $F(s) = \dfrac{1}{s^3 - 1}$

(n) $F(s) = \dfrac{1}{2s^3 - s^2 + s}$

(o) $F(s) = \dfrac{12}{s^4 + s^3 - 3s^2 - s + 2}$

2. Prove Theorem 1.

3. Establish Corollary 1 of Theorem 4 for $m = 2$.

4. Prove Corollary 1.

5. If $f(t) = t^3$ for $t \geq 0$, obtain $\mathcal{L}f'''$ from Theorem 4. Then find $\mathcal{L}f''$ directly from f'' and Definition 1.

6. Show that the following functions are of exponential order, and find a real number c satisfying (2.1) for each.

(a) $\sin t^2$

(b) e^{at}, a real

(c) t^2

(d) $\log (1 + t)$

(e) $P(t) = \alpha_0 t^n + \alpha_1 t^{n-1} + \cdots + \alpha_n$

(f) $\int_0^t e^{-\tau^2}\, d\tau$

(g) $\sqrt{1 + e^{at}}$, a real

(h) $\tanh at$, a real

★7. Suppose that f_1 and f_2 are of exponential order and satisfy (2.1) with constants c_1 and c_2, respectively. Prove that (a) $\alpha_1 f_1 + \alpha_2 f_2$ is of exponential order if α_1 and α_2 are constants; (b) $f_1 f_2$ is of exponential order; (c) $\int_0^t f_1(\tau)\, d\tau$ is of exponential order.

8. Describe the functions of exponential order whose Laplace transforms are rational functions.

★9. The *gamma function* Γ is defined by $\Gamma(\alpha) = \int_0^\infty t^\alpha e^{-t}\, dt$ for $\alpha > -1$. Show that (a) if $\alpha = n$, a positive integer, then $\Gamma(n) = (n-1)!$; (b) $\mathcal{L}\{t^\alpha\}(s) = \Gamma(\alpha)/s^{\alpha+1}$.

3. Application to Differential Equations with Constant Coefficients

To see how Laplace transforms can provide solutions to linear differential equations with constant coefficients, we first examine two examples.

Example 1. Solve $(D^3 + 2D^2 - D - 2)y = \sin t$ subject to the I.C. $y(0) = y'(0) = y''(0) = 0$.

The sine function is of exponential order, so if y is the desired solution, then Corollary 2, Sec. 2, applies. We have, taking Laplace transforms of both members of the D.E.,

$$\mathcal{L}y''' + 2\mathcal{L}y'' - \mathcal{L}y' - 2\mathcal{L}y = \mathcal{L}\{\sin t\}$$

$$(s^3 + 2s^2 - s - 2)Y(s) = \frac{1}{s^2 + 1}$$

and so

$$Y(s) = \frac{1}{(s^2 + 1)(s^3 + 2s^2 - s - 2)} = \frac{1}{(s^2 + 1)(s - 1)(s + 1)(s + 2)}$$

$$= \frac{1}{12}\frac{1}{s - 1} - \frac{1}{4}\frac{1}{s + 1} + \frac{1}{15}\frac{1}{s + 2} + \frac{1}{10}\frac{s - 2}{s^2 + 1}$$

after decomposition into partial fractions. Therefore, from the table of transforms we get

$$y(t) = \tfrac{1}{12}e^t - \tfrac{1}{4}e^{-t} + \tfrac{1}{15}e^{-2t} + \tfrac{1}{10}\cos t - \tfrac{1}{5}\sin t$$

Example 2. Find y if

$$(D^2 - D - 6)y = \cos 2t$$

and $y(0) = 0$, $y'(0) = 1$.

Taking the transforms of both members of the D.E., we have

$$\mathcal{L}y'' - \mathcal{L}y' - 6\mathcal{L}y = \mathcal{L}\{\cos 2t\}$$

and

$$s^2 Y(s) - 1 - sY(s) - 6Y(s) = \frac{s}{s^2 + 4}$$

$$Y(s) = \frac{1}{s^2 - s - 6}\left(\frac{s}{s^2 + 4} + 1\right) = \frac{s^2 + s + 4}{(s - 3)(s + 2)(s^2 + 4)}$$

$$= \frac{16}{65}\frac{1}{s - 3} - \frac{3}{20}\frac{1}{s + 2} - \frac{5}{52}\frac{s}{s^2 + 4} - \frac{1}{26}\frac{1}{s^2 + 4}$$

From the table of transforms we obtain the solution

$$y(t) = \tfrac{16}{65}e^{3t} - \tfrac{3}{20}e^{-2t} - \tfrac{5}{52}\cos 2t - \tfrac{1}{52}\sin 2t$$

These two examples illustrate not only the technique of solving problems, but also the general result which we now state.

Theorem 1. *The solution y of the linear D.E. with constant coefficients,*

(3.1) $$P(D)y = (\alpha_0 D^n + \cdots + \alpha_n)y = f$$

which satisfies the I.C.

(3.2) $y(0) = y_0$ $y'(0) = y_1$ $\cdots$ $y^{(n-1)}(0) = y_{n-1}$

where f is of exponential order, has for its Laplace transform

(3.3) $$Y(s) = \frac{F(s) + \alpha_0 y_0 s^{n-1} + (\alpha_0 y_1 + \alpha_1 y_0)s^{n-2} + \cdots + (\alpha_0 y_{n-1} + \cdots + \alpha_{n-1} y_0)}{\alpha_0 s^n + \alpha_1 s^{n-1} + \cdots + \alpha_n}$$

Proof. By Corollary 2 of Theorem 4, Sec. 2, and by taking Laplace transforms of both members of (3.1), we obtain

$$\alpha_0(s^n Y - s^{n-1}y_0 - \cdots - sy_{n-2} - y_{n-1})$$
$$+ \alpha_1(s^{n-1}Y - s^{n-2}y_0 - \cdots - sy_{n-3} - y_{n-2})$$
$$+ \cdots + \alpha_n Y = F(s)$$

whence, solving for Y, we obtain (3.3).

In many applications $F(s)$ is a rational function of s, in which case the right member of (3.3) is a rational function and so is of the form

(3.4) $$Y(s) = \frac{b_0 s^m + b_1 s^{m-1} + \cdots + b_m}{c_0 s^r + c_1 s^{r-1} + \cdots + c_r}$$

Since, by Theorem 5, Sec. 2, $Y(s) \to 0$ as $s \to \infty$, it follows that the degree m of the numerator in (3.4) is less than the degree of the denominator. Therefore $Y(s)$ may be written as a sum of partial fractions of the form

(3.5) $$\frac{A_k}{(s - \alpha)^k} + \frac{A_{k-1}}{(s - \alpha)^{k-1}} + \cdots + \frac{A_1}{s - \alpha}$$

where α is a root of multiplicity k of $c_0 s^r + c_1 s^{r-1} + \cdots + c_r = 0$ and may be real or complex. Each term in (3.5), and so each term in the complete partial-fraction decomposition of Y given by (3.4), is the Laplace transform of an elementary function. Therefore $Y(s)$ is easily found if $F(s)$ is a rational function. However, the solution requires knowledge of the zeros of the denominator of (3.4) and partial-fraction expansions of (3.4).

Formula (3.3) becomes particularly simple if the initial conditions are homogeneous: $y_0 = y_1 = \cdots = y_{n-1} = 0$. Then

$$(3.6) \qquad Y(s) = \frac{F(s)}{\alpha_0 s^n + \cdots + \alpha_n} = \frac{1}{P(s)} F(s)$$

The function $1/P(s)$ is especially important and is given a name.

Definition 1.   The function T defined by

$$T(s) = \frac{1}{P(s)} = \frac{1}{\alpha_0 s^n + \alpha_1 s^{n-1} + \cdots + \alpha_n}$$

is called the *transfer function* of the D.E. (3.1).

With this notation,

$$(3.7) \qquad Y(s) = T(s)F(s)$$

and

$$y = \mathcal{L}^{-1} T F$$

is the solution of the D.E. with homogeneous I.C.

It is easy to show that T itself is the transform of a solution of an initial-value problem.

Theorem 2.   *If y is the solution of the problem*

$$P(D)y = 0$$

with I.C.

$$y(0) = 0 = \cdots = y^{(n-2)}(0) \qquad y^{(n-1)}(0) = \frac{1}{\alpha_0}$$

then $\mathcal{L}y(s) = T(s)$.

Proof.   From (3.3),

$$Y(s) = \frac{1}{\alpha_0 s^n + \cdots + \alpha_n} = T(s)$$

PROBLEMS

1. Use Laplace transforms to solve the following initial-value problems:

(a) $y'' + y' - 12y = 0$; $y(0) = y'(0) = 0$
(b) $y'' + y' - 12y = 0$; $y(0) = 1$, $y'(0) = 0$

(c) $y'' + y' - 12y = 0$; $y(0) = 0$, $y'(0) = 1$

(d) $y'' + y' - 12y = e^t$; $y(0) = y'(0) = 0$

(e) $y'' + y' - 12y = e^{-4t}$; $y(0) = y'(0) = 0$

(f) $y'' + y' - 12y = 1$; $y(0) = y'(0) = 0$

(g) $(D^3 - 3D^2)y = 0$; $y(0) = 0$, $y'(0) = 3$, $y''(0) = -9$

(h) $(D^4 + 2D^3 + D^2)x = 0$; $x(0) = 0$, $x'(0) = 2$, $x''(0) = -2$, $x'''(0) = 3$

(i) $(D^4 - 2D^3 - 3D^2 + 4D + 4)x = 0$; $x(0) = x'(0) = x'''(0) = 0$, $x''(0) = -4$

(j) $(D^2 - 1)(D - 2)Z = 1$; $Z(0) = Z'(0) = 0$, $Z''(0) = 1$

(k) $(D^4 - 1)y = t^2$; homogeneous I.C. at 0

(l) $(D^4 - 2D^2)y = t^2$; homogeneous I.C. at 0

(m) $(D + 1)^3 y = t^3 e^{-t}$; homogeneous I.C. at 0

(n) $(D^3 + 3D^2 - 4D - 12)y = (40t + 18)e^{2t}$; homogeneous I.C. at 0

(o) $(D^3 + D^2 + D + 1)y = \sin \omega t$, $\omega \neq 1$; homogeneous I.C. at 0

(p) $(D^3 + D^2 + D + 1)y = \sin \omega t$, $\omega \neq 1$; $y(0) = y'(0) = 1$, $y''(0) = 0$

★2. Prove that $\mathcal{L}\{f(t - t_0)\}(s) = e^{-st_0}\mathcal{L}f(s)$, where $t_0 > 0$ and as always $f(t) = 0$ for $t < 0$.

3. Solve $y'' + y' - 12y = \mathbf{1}(t - t_0)$ with homogeneous I.C. at t_0.

4. Solve $(D^2 + \omega^2)y = \sin \omega t$ with homogeneous I.C. at 0. Then solve $(D^2 + \omega^2)y = \sin \omega(t - \pi/2\omega)\mathbf{1}(t - \pi/2\omega)$ with homogeneous I.C. at $\pi/2\omega$.

5. Let $T(s)$ be the transfer function of D.E. (3.1) with $f = 0$. Which initial-value problem has the solution $y = \mathcal{L}^{-1}\{s^k T(s)\}$ ($k = 0, 1, \ldots, n - 1$)?

4. Convolutions

In Theorem 2 of Sec. 3 we have an interpretation of the transfer function. In this section we provide the basis for a second interpretation which will connect the transfer function with the Green's function of Sec. 14, Chap. VI.

Theorem 1. *If f and g are piecewise continuous, then the integral*

$$(4.1) \qquad C_{fg}(t) = \int_0^t f(\tau)g(t - \tau) \, d\tau$$

represents a continuous function of t.

Proof Sketch. A few remarks may reveal the underlying reasons for the continuity of C_{fg}. If f and g were continuous, the continuity of C_{fg} would be easy to prove. Any piecewise-continuous function is the sum of a continuous function and a number of step functions $h_1\mathbf{1}(t - t_1)$, $h_2\mathbf{1}(t - t_2)$, . . . ; hence to complete the proof it suffices to prove the continuity of C_{fg}, where either f or g (or both) is a step function. This latter proof is quite easy. For example, if $0 < t_1 < t$, then

$$\int_0^t f(\tau)\mathbf{1}(t - \tau - t_1) \, d\tau = \int_0^{t - t_1} f(\tau) \, d\tau$$

and the integral on the left is zero if $t < t_1$. The resulting function is seen to be continuous.

Definition 1. The function C_{fg} of Theorem 1 is called the *convolution* of f and g and is denoted by $f * g$.

Remark. If g is a *fixed* function, then the operation of taking the convolution of f with g transforms f into another function. Often this is called the *convolution transform*. The convolution operator has a number of properties, most of which cannot be pursued here. The elementary ones are given in the next theorem.

Theorem 2. *If f and g are piecewise continuous, then*

$$(a) \qquad f * g = g * f$$
$$(b) \qquad f * cg = (cf) * g \qquad c \text{ constant}$$
$$(c) \qquad f * (g + h) = f * g + f * h$$
$$(d) \qquad f * (g * h) = (f * g) * h$$

The simple proofs are left to the reader. We remark that, because of (d), parentheses may be omitted in a multiple convolution.

From this theorem it is seen that the operation $*$ has many of the properties of ordinary multiplication. Indeed, much more is true. At this point we merely remark that this "$*$-multiplication" has no *unit*. In other words, there is no function u such that

$$f * u = f$$

for all functions f. We shall see in the next section how to adjoin such a unit (which will not be a function) to our system.

Theorem 3. *If f and g are piecewise continuous and of exponential order, then $f * g$ has a Laplace transform, and*

$$(4.2) \qquad \mathcal{L}f * g = \mathcal{L}f \, \mathcal{L}g$$

Proof. We calculate $\mathcal{L}f * g$ directly. (However, we shall not justify our formal interchange of order of integration in the improper integral.)

$$(4.3) \qquad \mathcal{L}f * g(s) = \int_0^\infty e^{-st} \, dt \int_0^t f(\tau)g(t - \tau) \, d\tau$$
$$= \int_0^\infty f(\tau) \, d\tau \int_\tau^\infty e^{-st}g(t - \tau) \, dt$$

Each iterated integral in (4.3) is equal to the double integral of $e^{-st}f(\tau)g(t - \tau)$ over the shaded region of Fig. 4.

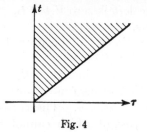

Fig. 4

Now if we make the change of variable $t - \tau = v$, the second integral in (4.3) becomes

$$\mathcal{L}f * g(s) = \int_0^\infty f(\tau)\, d\tau \int_0^\infty e^{-s(\tau+v)} g(v)\, dv$$

$$= \int_0^\infty e^{-s\tau} f(\tau)\, d\tau \int_0^\infty e^{-sv} g(v)\, dv$$

$$= F(s)G(s)$$

Example 1. We calculate the Laplace transform of $\{e^{at}\} * \{e^{-at}\}$ two ways. First we find the convolution

$$\{e^{at}\} * \{e^{-at}\} = \int_0^t e^{a\tau} e^{-a(t-\tau)}\, d\tau$$

$$= e^{-at} \int_0^t e^{2a\tau}\, d\tau$$

$$= \frac{1}{a} \frac{e^{at} - e^{-at}}{2} = \frac{1}{a} \sinh at$$

Then

$$\mathcal{L}\{e^{at}\} * \{e^{-at}\} = \mathcal{L}\left\{\frac{1}{a} \sinh at\right\} = \frac{1}{a} \frac{a}{s^2 - a^2} = \frac{1}{s^2 - a^2}$$

from the transform table.

On the other hand, from Theorem 2,

$$\mathcal{L}\{e^{at}\} * \{e^{-at}\}(s) = \mathcal{L}\{e^{at}\}\mathcal{L}\{e^{-at}\}$$

$$= \frac{1}{s - a} \frac{1}{s + a} = \frac{1}{s^2 - a^2}$$

PROBLEMS

1. Find the following convolutions:

(a) $\{e^{i\omega t}\} * \{e^{-i\omega t}\}$
(b) $\{t\} * \{t\}$
(c) $\{e^t\} * \{\sin \omega t\}$
(d) $\{e^{3t}\} * \{e^t\}$

(e) $\mathbf{1} * \mathbf{1}$

(f) $\{\sin \omega t\} * \{\cos \omega t\}$

(g) $\{\mathbf{1}(t - t_1)\} * \{\mathbf{1}(t - t_2)\}, \, 0 < t_1 < t_2$

(h) $\{\mathbf{1}(t - t_0)\} * \{f(t)\}, \, t_0 \geq 0$

(i) $\{t\} * \{t\} * \cdots * \{t\}$ (k factors)

2. In each of the following, calculate the convolution and its Laplace transform. Then use Theorem 3, and verify that the same result is achieved.

(a) $\mathcal{L}\{e^{at}\} * \{e^{bt}\}, \, a \neq b$

(b) $\mathcal{L}\{e^{at}\} * \{e^{at}\}$

(c) $\mathcal{L}\{\mathbf{1}(t)\} * \{\mathbf{1}(t - t_0)\}, \, t_0 > 0$

(d) $\mathcal{L}\{e^t\} * \{\cos t\}$

3. Use Theorem 3 to find y if

(a) $\mathcal{L}y(s) = \dfrac{1}{(s + 1)^2} = \dfrac{1}{s + 1}\dfrac{1}{s + 1}$

(b) $\mathcal{L}y(s) = \dfrac{1}{(s^2 + \omega^2)^2}$

(c) $\mathcal{L}y(s) = \dfrac{1}{s^2}\, e^{-st_0} = \dfrac{1}{s}\dfrac{1}{s}\, e^{-st_0} \qquad t_0 > 0$

4. Use Theorem 3 to find the convolutions

(a) $\{t^k\} * \{t^l\}; \, k, l = 0, 1, 2, \ldots$

(b) $\{e^{at}\} * \{e^{bt}\} * \{e^{ct}\}, \, a \neq b \neq c \neq a$

(c) $\{e^{at}\} * \{\sin \omega t\}$

5. Let $F = \mathcal{L}f$. Use Theorem 3 to obtain two different expressions for $\mathcal{L}^{-1}\{s^n F(s)\} = \mathcal{L}^{-1}\{s \cdot s \cdots F(s)\}$. Thus obtain a new proof for the identity of Example 3, Sec. 8, Chap. VI.

5. The δ Function and Green's Function

Consider the forcing function $\delta_h(t) = (1/h)[\mathbf{1}(t) - \mathbf{1}(t - h)]$, where $h > 0$, shown in Fig. 5.

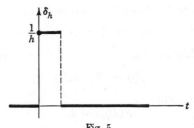

Fig. 5

We calculate the convolution $f * \delta_h$ for any f:

$$f * \delta_h(t) = \int_0^t f(\tau) \delta_h(t - \tau) \, d\tau$$

$$= \frac{1}{h} \int_t^{t+h} f(\tau) \, d\tau = f(\bar{\tau})$$

where $t < \bar{\tau} < t + h$ if h is sufficiently small and if f is continuous on the right. Then

(5.1) $$\lim_{h \to 0+} f * \delta_h(t) = f(t)$$

Because of (5.1), it is tempting to consider the limit δ_h as a function.   But if $t \neq 0$,

$$\lim_{h \to 0+} \delta_h(t) = 0$$

and if $t = 0$,

$$\lim_{h \to 0+} \delta_h(0) = \infty$$

Clearly this limit is not a proper function.   Nevertheless, although this limit is not a function, we can consider the "limit convolution operator."   We denote this operator by δ.   It has the fundamental property that for all functions f which are piecewise continuous and continuous on the right,

(5.2) $$f * \delta = f$$

Though δ is not a function, it is customary in the literature to refer to it as such.   Thus one speaks of the δ *function* (also *Dirac function*, after the physicist Dirac), or the *unit impulse function*.

Now that δ has been defined, we can ask what its Laplace transform ought to be.   Since δ is a "limit" of δ_h, we define the transform of δ as a limit:

$$\mathcal{L}\delta = \lim_{h \to 0+} \mathcal{L}\delta_h = \lim_{h \to 0+} \int_0^\infty e^{-st} \delta_h(t) \, dt$$

$$= \lim_{h \to 0+} \frac{1}{h} \int_0^h e^{-st} \, dt$$

$$= \lim_{h \to 0+} \frac{1 - e^{-sh}}{sh} = 1$$

Finally, we define what is meant by the response of a linear D.E. when the forcing function is the δ function: The solution of the problem

(5.3) $$P(D)y = (\alpha_0 D^n + \cdots + \alpha_n)y = \delta$$

with homogeneous initial conditions $y_0 = 0 = \cdots = y_{n-1}$, is

(5.4) $$g(t) = \lim_{h \to 0+} y_h(t)$$

where y_h solves the problem

$$P(D)y_h = \delta_h$$

with the same I.C.

Theorem 1. *The transfer function is the Laplace transform of the response to the δ function for homogeneous I.C.*

Proof. If $g(t)$ is the solution of (5.3), so that g is given by (5.4), then

$$\mathcal{L}g = \mathcal{L} \lim_{h \to 0+} y_h$$
$$= \lim_{h \to 0+} \mathcal{L}y_h$$
$$= \lim_{h \to 0+} T\mathcal{L}\delta_h = T \lim_{h \to 0+} \mathcal{L}\delta_h = T$$

(We have not, in the above formal argument, justified the interchange of $\mathcal{L} \lim_{h \to 0}$ and $\lim_{h \to 0} \mathcal{L}$, but, using well-known theorems on uniform convergence, this can easily be done.)

The function $g = \mathcal{L}^{-1}T$ is closely related to the Green's function of Sec. 14, Chap. VI. Suppose we seek the solution of

$$P(D)y = f$$

with homogeneous I.C.: $y_0 = y_1 = \cdots = y_{n-1} = 0$. Then

$$\mathcal{L}y(s) = T(s)F(s)$$

But $T = \mathcal{L}g$ and $F = \mathcal{L}f$, whence y is the convolution of f and g:

$$y(t) = f * g(t) = \int_0^t f(t)g(t - \tau) \, d\tau$$

In other words,

(5.5) $$g(t - \tau) = G(t, \tau)$$

where $G(t, \tau)$ is the Green's function belonging to the differential operator $P(D)$. Incidentally, we see from (5.5) that, for linear D.E. with constant coefficients, $G(t, \tau) = G(t - \tau, 0)$ (see Prob. 7, Sec. 14, Chap. VI). In other words, the Green's function is a function only of the difference $t - \tau$. With (5.5) and Theorem 1, this proves the following theorem.

Theorem 2. *In the case of linear differential operators with constant coefficients, the transfer function is the Laplace transform of the Green's function.*

PROBLEMS

1. Find T and $\mathcal{L}^{-1}T$ for the D.E. $(D^2 - 3D + 2)y = 0$. Then find the Green's function and solve the D.E. $(D^2 - D - 2)y = f(t)$ with homogeneous I.C.

2. Find the Green's function for the differential operator $(D^2 + \omega^2)y$. Then solve, with homogeneous I.C. at 0, $(D^2 + \omega^2)y = \sin \omega t$.

3. Find, by the method of variation of parameters, the particular solution of $(D^2 + \omega^2)y = f(t)$ satisfying the I.C. $y(0) = y'(0) = 0$. Show that one gets the Green's function in the integrand of the solution.

4. Find, by the method of variation of parameters, the solution of $(D^2 + 2aD + b)y = f(t)$ $(a^2 \neq b)$ satisfying homogeneous I.C. Show that one gets the Green's function in the integrand of the solution.

5. Find the solution of $(D^2 + 2aD + b)y = 1(t - t_0)$ $(a^2 \neq b, t_0 \geqq 0)$ with homogeneous I.C. at $t = t_0$. Let this solution be $y(t) = K(t, t_0)$. Show that the Green's function $\mathfrak{L}^{-1}T$ is equal to $-\partial K(t, t_0)/\partial t_0$.

6. Find the solution of $(D^4 - \alpha^4)y = 1(t - t_0)$ with homogeneous I.C. at t_0. Denote this solution by $y(t) = K(t, t_0)$. Show that the Green's function $\mathfrak{L}^{-1}T$ is equal to $-\partial K(t, t_0)/\partial t_0$.

★7. Put $\eta_h(t) = (1/h)e^{-t/h}$ $(h > 0)$. Calculate $\lim\limits_{h \to 0+} \mathfrak{L}(\eta_h * f)$, and show that $\lim\limits_{h \to 0+} \eta_h * f = f$ for all piecewise-continuous f continuous on the right. This shows that δ may also be considered as $\lim\limits_{h \to 0+} \eta_h$.

6. Steady State; Stability

Linear physical systems, mechanical, electrical, and others, are usually made up of elements that are invariant in time or change in a periodic rhythm. These systems are described by differential equations whose coefficients are constants or functions of time that have a common period τ. Their nonhomogeneous parts correspond to the external sources of mechanical or electric energy. In general, such systems dissipate energy and, therefore, cannot sustain excitations indefinitely without a continually functioning external source of energy. We shall refer to this common type as *dissipative systems*.

Mathematically speaking, a system is dissipative if every solution of the reduced equation describing it tends to zero as time increases indefinitely. In particular, the reduced equation can have no nontrivial periodic solution. Consequently a dissipative system can sustain, for a given impressed energy source of period τ, one and only one excitation of period τ, called the *steady state* of the system. If the initial conditions are not those of this one periodic solution, then the steady state will, at least theoretically, never be attained. However, every dissipative system, no matter what its initial state happens to be, will, when driven by a periodic force, tend to the steady state asymptotically. For this reason, any other state can be considered as temporary and is called a *transient state*. Then if y is any solution of the linear D.E., and if y_S is the steady-state or periodic solution, the transient y_T is defined by

$$y = y_T + y_S$$

Thus y_T is some solution of the reduced equation (no outside energy source), and y_S is the periodic particular solution of the complete equation (driven by a periodic forcing function).

If we have the D.E. (3.1) with constant coefficients and the periodic forcing function $Ae^{i\omega t}$,

$$P(D)y(t) = Ae^{i\omega t}$$

then the periodic solution is

$$y(t) = \frac{1}{P(i\omega)} A e^{i\omega t}$$

The function $1/P(i\omega)$ is called *the frequency-response function*. Its absolute value is the *amplification factor*. The frequency-response function is essentially the transfer function, since $1/P(i\omega) = T(i\omega)$. Thus, the value of the frequency-response function at the frequency ω is the value of the transfer function at $s = i\omega$.

Because they return to the steady state from any initial condition, dissipative systems are also said to be *stable*. One can easily determine whether systems that are described by equations with constant coefficients are stable or not. The general solution of a reduced equation with constant coefficients is of the form

$$C_1 e^{r_1 t} + C_2 e^{r_2 t} + \cdots + C_n e^{r_n t}$$

where the numbers $r_1, r_2, \ldots, r_n$ are the roots of the corresponding auxiliary equation. If the complex number $r = a + bi$ is one of these roots, then

$$e^{rt} = e^{at} e^{bit} = e^{at}(\cos bt + i \sin bt)$$

Hence, it is seen that the solution converges to zero as $t \to \infty$ for every choice of the constants $C_1, C_2, \ldots, C_n$ if and only if the real parts of all the roots $r_1, r_2, \ldots, r_n$ are negative.

The general solution of a homogeneous linear differential equation with constant coefficients has the above form only if the corresponding auxiliary equation has no repeated roots. If $r = a + bi$ is a k-fold repeated root, then the corresponding term in the general solution is

$$e^{rt}(c_0 + c_1 t + c_2 t^2 + \cdots + c_{k-1} t^{k-1})$$
$$= e^{at}(c_0 + c_1 t + c_2 t^2 + \cdots + c_{k-1} t^{k-1})(\cos bt + i \sin bt)$$

It is seen that in this case, too, the solution converges to zero as $t \to \infty$ if and only if $a < 0$. This proves the next theorem.

Theorem. *A physical system described by a linear differential equation with constant coefficients is stable if and only if the real parts of all the roots of the corresponding auxiliary equation are negative.*

Frequently, one will simply want to know whether a system is stable or not without ever actually finding the solution. There are a number of criteria for determining stability, of which we mention here only two, those due to Nyquist and Hurwitz-Routh. For proofs, see Ref. 7, pages 405 and 415. It should be emphasized that these criteria are of a purely algebraic nature, since they are concerned only with the location of the roots of the auxiliary equation.

The Nyquist Criterion. *Consider a large contour C in the s plane, consisting of a segment from $-i\omega_0$ to $i\omega_0$ along the imaginary axis and a semicircular arc, as shown in Fig. 6. All roots of the equation $P(s) = 0$ have negative real parts if and only if the image of C does not encircle the origin in the $z = P(s)$ plane.*

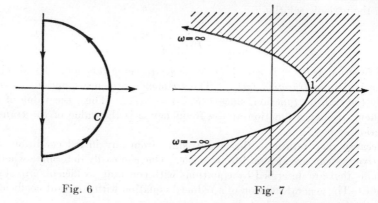

Fig. 6   Fig. 7

Usually one can simply graph the curve $z = P(i\omega)$, which is the image of the straight part of C, because large circles in the s plane map (maybe multiply) into large "near circles" in the z plane.

Example 1. The equation $(D^2 + D + 1)y = 0$ is easily seen to be stable if one finds its solution. We shall verify that the Nyquist criterion gives the same result.

We have $P(s) = s^2 + s + 1$ and $P(i\omega) = (1 - \omega^2) + i\omega$. The graph of this curve is shown in Fig. 7, where the image in the z plane of the right half plane Re $s > 0$ is shaded.

The Hurwitz-Routh Criterion. *All roots of the algebraic equation with real coefficients*

$$P(s) = a_n s^n + a_{n-1} s^{n-1} + \cdots + a_1 s + a_0 = 0$$

where it is assumed that $a_0 > 0$, have negative real parts if and only if the n determinants

$$a_1 \qquad \begin{vmatrix} a_1 & a_0 \\ a_3 & a_2 \end{vmatrix} \qquad \begin{vmatrix} a_1 & a_0 & 0 \\ a_3 & a_2 & a_1 \\ a_5 & a_4 & a_3 \end{vmatrix} \qquad \cdots \qquad \begin{vmatrix} a_1 & a_0 & 0 & \cdots & 0 \\ a_3 & a_2 & a_1 & \cdots & 0 \\ \cdots & \cdots & \cdots & \cdots & \cdots \\ a_{2n-1} & a_{2n-2} & & \cdots & a_n \end{vmatrix}$$

are positive.

It is understood that coefficients with subscripts greater than n in these determinants are to be replaced by zero.

As an example, the general cubic equation with real coefficients

$$a_3 x^3 + a_2 x^2 + a_1 x + a_0 = 0$$

which is first multiplied by ± 1 so as to make $a_0 > 0$, has only roots with negative real parts if and only if

$$a_1 > 0 \qquad a_1 a_2 - a_0 a_3 > 0 \qquad a_3(a_1 a_2 - a_0 a_3) > 0$$

In this case, the last condition may be replaced by $a_3 > 0$.

PROBLEMS

1. Use both the Nyquist and Hurwitz criteria to determine the stability of the following equations. Then check by determining whether all roots of the auxiliary equation have negative real parts.

(a) $(D^3 + 1)y = 0$
(b) $(D^4 - \alpha^4)y = 0, \alpha > 0$
(c) $(D^4 + D^2 + 1)y = 0$
(d) $(D^2 + bD + b^2)y = 0, b > 0$

2. The following equations describe linear physical systems. Verify that they are stable, and find their steady states.

(a) $a\dfrac{d^2x}{dt^2} + b\dfrac{dx}{dt} + cx = A \sin \omega t; \ a > 0, b > 0, c > 0$

(b) $\dfrac{d^3x}{dt^3} + a\dfrac{d^2x}{dt^2} + b\dfrac{dx}{dt} + \dfrac{ab}{2}x = A \cos \sqrt{b}\, t; \ a > 0, b > 0$

(c) $\dfrac{d^4x}{dt^3} + a\dfrac{d^3x}{dt^3} + (b + 2)\dfrac{d^2x}{dt^2} + a\dfrac{dx}{dt} + bx = A \sin t + B \cos t; \ a > 0,$
$b > 0$

3. Show that in the Hurwitz criterion the condition

$$\begin{vmatrix} a_1 & a_0 & 0 & \cdots & 0 \\ a_3 & a_2 & a_1 & \cdots & 0 \\ \cdots & \cdots & \cdots & \cdots & \cdots \\ a_{2n-1} & a_{2n-2} & \cdots & \cdots & a_n \end{vmatrix} > 0$$

can be replaced by $a_n > 0$.

4. Prove without the use of the Hurwitz criterion that the two roots of

$$a_2x^2 + a_1x + a_0 = 0 \qquad a_0 > 0$$

have negative real parts if and only if $a_1 > 0, a_2 > 0$.

5. Prove that if the equation

$$a_nx^n + a_{n-1}x^{n-1} + \cdots + a_1x + a_0 = 0 \qquad a_0 > 0$$

has only roots with negative real parts, then all the coefficients are positive. HINT: Factor the equation into real factors; i.e., use linear factors for real roots and quadratic factors for pairs of conjugate complex roots. Then use the result of Prob. 4.

7. Inverse Operators

In this section the algebra of differential operators introduced in the previous chapter is further developed. Whereas in the preceding chapter only positive integral powers and polynomials of the differential operator were considered, we now take up negative powers and rational functions of operators.

In Sec. 11, Chap. VI, we found that the differential equation

$$(7.1) \qquad\qquad (D - c)^k y = f$$

has the particular solution

$$(7.2) \qquad\qquad y(x) = \int_{x_0}^{x} \frac{(x - x_1)^{k-1}}{(k - 1)!} e^{c(x-x_1)} f(x_1) \, dx_1$$

where x_0 can be arbitrarily chosen. This solution satisfies the homogeneous I.C. $y(x_0) = y'(x_0) = \cdots = y^{(k-1)}(x_0) = 0$. The symbolic form of Eq. (7.1) suggests a symbolic solution:

$$(7.3) \qquad\qquad y = \frac{1}{(D - c)^k} f = (D - c)^{-k} f$$

We are free to identify the thus far undefined symbol $(D - c)^{-k} f$ with the expression given by the right-hand term of (7.2), and we shall then be able to say that differential equation (7.2) is solved like an algebraic equation.

Definition 1. The *inverse, or integral, operator*

$$(D - c)^{-k} \qquad \text{or} \qquad \frac{1}{(D - c)^k} \qquad k = 1, 2, \ldots$$

is defined as the integral

$$(7.4) \qquad (D - c)^{-k} f(x) = \int_{x_0}^{x} \frac{(x - x_1)^{k-1}}{(k - 1)!} e^{c(x-x_1)} f(x_1) \, dx_1$$

where x_0 is an arbitrary but fixed number.

In particular, if $c = 0$, then (7.4) becomes

$$(7.5) \qquad D^{-k} f(x) = \int_{x_0}^{x} \frac{(x - x_1)^{k-1}}{(k - 1)!} f(x_1) \, dx_1$$
$$= \int_{x_0}^{x} dx_k \int_{x_0}^{x_k} dx_{k-1} \cdots \int_{x_0}^{x_3} dx_2 \int_{x_0}^{x_2} f(x_1) \, dx_1$$

(see Example 3, Sec. 8, Chap. VI), that is, $D^{-k} f$ is a k-times-repeated integral of f, which is as it should be since $D^k f$ is the kth derivative of f.

The fact that (7.2) is a solution of Eq. (7.1) can be expressed by the equation

$$(D - c)^k (D - c)^{-k} f = f$$

i.e., the original function f is restored if operated upon in succession by the operators $(D - c)^{-k}$ and $(D - c)^k$. In other words, the operator consisting of the integrations indicated by $(D - c)^{-k}$ followed by the differentiations indicated by $(D - c)^k$ is the "identity operator" which leaves every function unchanged:

$$(7.6) \qquad (D - c)^k(D - c)^{-k} = (D - c)^0 = 1$$

Equation (7.6) expresses the fundamental property of the operator $(D - c)^{-k}$, whose definition was designed so as to make this equation valid.

From Eq. (7.6) one might expect the equation

$$(7.7) \qquad (D - c)^{-k}(D - c)^k = 1$$

to hold; that is,

$$(7.8) \qquad (D - c)^{-k}(D - c)^k f = f$$

That this is, in general, not true can be seen from an example. Let $c = 0$ and $k = 1$; then Eq. (7.8) states that

$$f(x) - f(x_0) = \int_{x_0}^{x} f'(x_1)\, dx_1 = f(x)$$

which is true if and only if $f(x_0) = 0$. In general, Eq. (7.8) holds (for functions f with a piecewise-continuous derivative of kth order) if and only if

$$f(x_0) = f'(x_0) = \cdots = f^{(k-1)}(x_0) = 0$$

Hence, Eq. (7.7) cannot be accepted as universally valid. Therefore, the combination of a differential operator with an integral operator, although it has the appearance of an ordinary product, is not commutative, as is the ordinary product of numbers. Clearly, conclusions by analogy are not reliable, and a careful examination of all operations is necessary.

Equation (7.4) may also be written in the form

$$(7.9) \qquad (D - c)^{-k}f(x) = e^{cx} \int_{x_0}^{x} \frac{(x - x_1)^{k-1}}{(k - 1)!}\, e^{-cx_1} f(x_1)\, dx_1$$
$$= e^{cx} D^{-k}[e^{-cx}f(x)]$$

Hence the *shifting rule* (rule 4, Sec. 6, Chap. VI) *applies to integral operators in the same way it applies to differential operators.*

We now discuss the result of applying two operators $(D + r)^{\pm k}$, $(D + r)^{\pm l}$ ($k, l = 1, 2, \ldots$) in succession. It suffices to do this for the operators $D^{\pm k}$, $D^{\pm l}$. By use of the shifting rule the results can then easily be extended to the more general operators.

From the definition of D it is clear that $D^k D^l = D^{k+l}$. It is also true that $D^k D^{-l} = D^{k-l}$, for

$$D^k D^{-l} f(x) = \frac{d^k}{dx^k} \int_{x_0}^{x} dx_l \int_{0}^{x_l} dx_{l-1} \cdots \int_{x_0}^{x_2} f(x_1) \, dx_1$$

The k-times-repeated differentiation reduces the l integrals to $l - k$ integrals if $l > k$, to $f(x)$ if $l = k$, and to $f^{(k-l)}(x)$ if $k > l$. Hence, in all cases, $D^k D^{-l} f = D^{k-l} f$. The equation $D^{-k} D^{-l} = D^{-k-l}$ is also true, for the $(k + l)$-times-repeated integral of a function f can be obtained by integrating the l-times-repeated integral k times. The remaining equation $D^{-k} D^{l} = D^{-k+l}$ is, in general, not true, as shown above for the special case $k = l$. But if

$$f(x_0) = f'(x_0) = \cdots = f^{(l-1)}(x_0) = 0$$

then $D^{-l} D^{l} f = f$, as was observed above. Hence, under these conditions,

$$D^{-k+l} f = D^{-k+l} (D^{-l} D^{l} f) = D^{-k+l-l} (D^{l} f) = D^{-k} (D^{l} f)$$

By applying the shifting rule twice in succession, we obtain

$$
\begin{aligned}
(D + r)^{\pm k} (D + r)^{\pm l} f(x) &= (D + r)^{\pm k} [e^{-rx} D^{\pm l} (e^{rx} f(x))] \\
&= e^{-rx} D^{\pm k} \{ e^{+rx} [e^{-rx} D^{\pm l} (e^{rx} f(x))] \} \\
&= e^{-rx} D^{\pm k} D^{\pm l} (e^{rx} f(x))
\end{aligned}
$$

Hence, the case of the operators $(D + r)^{\pm k}$, $(D + r)^{\pm l}$ is reduced to the case of the operators $D^{\pm k}$, $D^{\pm l}$ treated above.

The results may be summarized in the following rule:

Theorem 1. *If k, l are positive integers, then*

$$
\begin{aligned}
(D + r)^{k} (D + r)^{l} &= (D + r)^{k+l} \\
(D + r)^{k} (D + r)^{-l} &= (D + r)^{k-l} \\
(D + r)^{-k} (D + r)^{-l} &= (D + r)^{-k-l}
\end{aligned}
$$

The equation $(D + r)^{-k+l} f = (D + r)^{-k} (D + r)^{l} f$ also holds true if $f(x_0) = f'(x_0) = \cdots = f^{(l-1)}(x_0) = 0$.

Even more general operators than the differential and integral operators considered so far may now be defined. Let $R(q)$ be a *rational function* of the variable q; that is, $R(q)$ is the quotient of two polynomials in q:

$$R(q) = \frac{B(q)}{A(q)} = \frac{b_0 q^m + b_1 q^{m-1} + \cdots + b_{m-1} q + b_m}{a_0 q^n + a_1 q^{n-1} + \cdots + a_{n-1} q + a_n}$$

The difference $m - n$ of the degrees of the numerator and denominator is said to be the *degree of the rational function* $R(q)$. The degree may be positive, zero, or negative. If the degree is positive or zero, then the numerator $B(q)$ may be divided by the denominator $A(q)$, the quotient being a polynomial of degree $m - n$ (a constant if $m = n$), and the remainder being a rational function of negative degree. Now a rational function of negative degree can be decomposed into a sum of partial fractions of the form

$$\frac{C_k}{(q - \alpha)^k} + \frac{C_{k-1}}{(q - \alpha)^{k-1}} + \cdots + \frac{C_1}{q - \alpha}$$

with such a sum for each zero α (of multiplicity k) of the denominator polynomial $A(q)$.

Summarizing, we may say that every rational function $R(q)$ may be cast in the form

$$(7.10) \qquad R(q) = P(q) + \sum \frac{C}{(q - \alpha)^k}$$

where $P(q)$ is a polynomial whose degree is equal to the degree of $R(q)$ if this degree is nonnegative [if $R(q)$ is of negative degree, then $P(q)$ is absent in (7.10)], and the other term is a sum of partial fractions. This decomposition can be made in one way only.

Equation (7.10), together with the earlier definitions of differential and integral operators, suggest the following:

Definition 2. If $R(q)$ is a rational function whose decomposition is

$$R(q) = P(q) + \sum \frac{C}{(q - \alpha)^k}$$

then the operator $R(D)$, where $D = d/dx$, is defined by the equation

$$R(D)f = P(D)f + \Sigma C(D - \alpha)^{-k} f$$

It should be observed that this definition is in agreement with the definition of differential operators and that of integral operators; as a matter of fact, it includes these definitions as special cases.

The following example illustrates the use of Definition 2.

Example 1. Evaluate

$$\frac{D^3 + 2D^2 + 3}{D^2 + D - 2} e^{3x} \qquad \text{for} \qquad x_0 = 0$$

The decomposition of $(q^3 + 2q^2 + 3)/(q^2 + q - 2)$ is

$$\frac{q^3 + 2q^2 + 3}{q^2 + q - 2} = q + 1 + \frac{2}{q - 1} - \frac{1}{q + 2}$$

Hence,

$$\frac{D^3 + 2D^2 + 3}{D^2 + D - 2}\, e^{3x} = [D + 1 + 2(D - 1)^{-1} - (D + 2)^{-1}]e^{3x}$$

$$= \frac{d}{dx}\, e^{3x} + e^{3x} + 2\int_0^x e^{(x - x_1)}e^{3x_1}\, dx_1 - \int_0^x e^{-2(x - x_1)}e^{3x_1}\, dx_1$$

$$= 3e^{3x} + e^{3x} + 2e^x\left(\frac{e^{2x}}{2} - \frac{1}{2}\right) - e^{-2x}\left(\frac{e^{5x}}{5} - \frac{1}{5}\right)$$

$$= \tfrac{24}{5}e^{3x} - e^x + \tfrac{1}{5}e^{-2x}$$

To complete our operator algebra, it now remains to study the result of the successive application of two operators $R_1(D)$, $R_2(D)$, where $R_1(q)$, $R_2(q)$ are rational functions. We want to compare

$$R_1(D)[R_2(D)f] \qquad \text{and} \qquad [R_1(D)R_2(D)]f$$

Since $R_1(q)$ is a sum of terms similar to $(q - \alpha)^k$ and $(q - \alpha)^{-k}$, and $R_2(q)$ is a sum of terms similar to $(q - \beta)^l$ and $(q - \beta)^{-l}$ ($k, l = 0, 1, 2, \ldots$), it suffices to consider the combinations $(D - \alpha)^{\pm k}(D - \beta)^{\pm l}$. A lengthy examination of all cases (which we omit here, but see Probs. 8 to 10) will establish the following theorem:

Theorem 2

$$R_1(D)[R_2(D)f] = [R_1(D)R_2(D)]f$$

if the degree of the rational function $R_2(q)$ is negative or zero. The equation is also true if the degree l of $R_2(D)$ is positive, provided that

$$f(x_0) = f'(x_0) = \cdots = f^{(l-1)}(x_0) = 0$$

As a corollary we have the important special case in which $R_2(D) = R(D)$ is of negative degree: $-n$ and $R_1(D) = D^k$, $k = 0, \ldots, n - 1$; thus $D^k[R(D)f] = [D^kR(D)]f$. Now $[D^kR(D)]f$ consists of a sum of integrals all having the same lower limit x_0. If x_0 is substituted for x in this sum, it vanishes. Hence, we have proved the following theorem:

Theorem 3. *If $R(q)$ is a rational function of negative degree $-n$, then $R(D)f(x)$ is a function whose derivatives of order $0, 1, 2, \ldots, n - 1$ vanish for $x = x_0$.*

Thus, it follows from Theorems 2 and 3 that $y = [1/P(D)]f$ is the solution of the equation $P(D)y = f$ which satisfies the initial conditions

$$y(x_0) = y'(x_0) = y''(x_0) = \cdots = y^{(n-1)}(x_0) = 0$$

The following example will illustrate the nontrivial character of Theorem 2.

Example 2. Evaluate

$$\frac{D}{D+1}\left(\frac{D}{D-1}f\right) \quad \text{and} \quad \frac{D^2}{D^2-1}f$$

and compare the results.

Here $R_2(D) = D(D-1)$ and is of degree zero. Thus, by Theorem 2, the two expressions should be equal.

The decompositions of the rational functions are

$$\frac{q}{q-1} = 1 + \frac{1}{q-1} \qquad \frac{q}{q+1} = 1 - \frac{1}{q+1}$$

$$\frac{q^2}{q^2-1} = 1 + \frac{\frac{1}{2}}{q-1} - \frac{\frac{1}{2}}{q+1}$$

Therefore,

$$\frac{D}{D+1}\left(\frac{D}{D-1}\right)f(x) = \frac{D}{D+1}\left[\left(1 + \frac{1}{D-1}\right)f(x)\right]$$

$$= \frac{D}{D+1}\left(f(x) + \int_{x_0}^{x} e^{(x-x_1)}f(x_1)\,dx_1\right)$$

$$= \left(1 - \frac{1}{D+1}\right)\left(f(x) + \int_{x_0}^{x} e^{(x-x_1)}f(x_1)\,dx_1\right)$$

$$= f(x) + \int_{x_0}^{x} e^{(x-x_1)}f(x_1)\,dx_1 - \int_{x_0}^{x} e^{-(x-x_1)}f(x_1)\,dx_1$$

$$- \int_{x_0}^{x} e^{-(x-x_2)}\,dx_2 \int_{x_0}^{x_2} e^{(x_2-x_1)}f(x_1)\,dx_1$$

Through integration by parts,

$$\int_{x_0}^{x} e^{2x_2}\,dx_2 \int_{x_0}^{x_2} e^{-x_1}f(x_1)\,dx_1 = \left[\frac{e^{2x_2}}{2}\int_{x_0}^{x_2} e^{-x_1}f(x_1)\,dx_1\right]_{x_2 = x_0}^{x_2 = x}$$

$$- \int_{x_0}^{x} \frac{e^{2x_1}}{2} e^{-x_1}f(x_1)\,dx_1$$

$$= \frac{e^{2x}}{2}\int_{x_0}^{x} e^{-x_1}f(x_1)\,dx_1 - \frac{1}{2}\int_{x_0}^{x} e^{x_1}f(x_1)\,dx_1$$

Hence,

$$\frac{D}{D+1}\left(\frac{D}{D-1}\right)f(x) = f(x) + \frac{1}{2}\int_{x_0}^{x} e^{(x-x_1)}f(x_1)\,dx_1 - \frac{1}{2}\int_{x_0}^{x} e^{-(x-x_1)}f(x_1)\,dx_1$$

On the other hand,

$$\frac{D^2}{D^2-1}f(x) = \left(1 + \frac{\frac{1}{2}}{D-1} - \frac{\frac{1}{2}}{D+1}\right)f(x)$$

$$= f(x) + \frac{1}{2}\int_{x_0}^{x} e^{(x-x_1)}f(x_1)\,dx_1 - \frac{1}{2}\int_{x_0}^{x} e^{-(x-x_1)}f(x_1)\,dx_1$$

It is seen that the results are identical although they were arrived at in different ways.

PROBLEMS

1. Show that

$$(D + r)^{-k}(D + r)^k f = f$$

if and only if $f(x_0) = f'(x_0) = \cdots = f^{(k-1)}(x_0) = 0$.

Evaluate, using $x_0 = 0$, the following expressions:

2. $\dfrac{2D^2 - 5D - 1}{D^3 - D} (1 + xe^x)$ **3.** $\dfrac{D^3 - D^2 - 5D - 2}{D^4 + 3D^3 + 2D^2} \sin x$

4. $\dfrac{D^4}{D^4 - 1} \cosh x$ **5.** $\dfrac{D^3}{D^2 + 1} \cos 2x$

6. Solve Probs. 1k to o of Sec. 3 by the operator method.

★7. Suppose that $P_1(q)$, $P_2(q)$ are polynomials of degree n_1, n_2, respectively. Show that if y_1 is a particular solution of the equation $P_1(D)y = f$ satisfying the initial conditions $y = Dy = \cdots = D^{n_1-1}y = 0$ when $x = x_0$, then $y_2 = [1/P_2(D)] y_1$ solves the equation $P_1(D)P_2(D)y = f$ and satisfies the conditions $y = Dy = \cdots = D^{(n_1+n_2-1)}y = 0$.

★8. Prove $(D - \alpha)^k[(D - \beta)^{-l}f] = [(D - \alpha)^k(D - \beta)^{-l}]f$ (k, $l = 0$, 1, 2, . . .). HINT: Expand $(D - \alpha)^k$ in powers of $D - \beta$.

★9. Prove $(D - \alpha)^{-k}[(D - \beta)^{-l}f] = [(D - \alpha)^{-k}(D - \beta)^{-l}]f$ (k, l, = 0, 1, 2, . . .). HINT: Writing F for the right-hand term, first show $F = (D - \alpha)^{-k}(D - \alpha)^k F$. Then, by the result of Prob. 8, $F = (D - \alpha)^{-k}[(D - \beta)^{-l}f]$.

★10. Prove $(D - \alpha)^{-k}[(D - \beta)^l f] = [(D - \alpha)^{-k}(D - \beta)^l]f$ (k, $l = 0$, 1, 2, . . .), provided that $f(x_0) = f'(x_0) = f^{(l-1)}(x_0) = 0$. HINT: Expand $(D - \beta)^l$ in powers of $D - \alpha$, and use Theorem 1.

8. Comparison of Operator and Transform Methods

The linear D.E. with constant coefficients

$$P(D)y(t) = f(t) \qquad D = \frac{d}{dt}$$

has the solution

$$(8.1) \qquad y(t) = \frac{1}{P(D)} f(t) = \sum \frac{C}{(D - \alpha)^k} f(t)$$

$$= \sum C \int_{t_0}^{t} \frac{(t - t_1)^{k-1}}{(k - 1)!} e^{\alpha(t-t_1)} f(t_1) \, dt_1$$

$$(8.2) \qquad y(t) = \int_{t_0}^{t} \left[\sum C \frac{(t - t_1)^{k-1}}{(k - 1)!} e^{\alpha(t-t_1)} \right] f(t_1) \, dt_1$$

which satisfies homogeneous I.C. at t_0. From (8.2) we see that the function in brackets under the integral sign must be the Green's function belonging to the operator $P(D)$. All that is required here of the function f is that it be integrable over any finite interval, for example, piecewise continuous. The Green's function then is

$$G(t, t_1) = \sum C \frac{(t - t_1)^{k-1}}{(k - 1)!} e^{\alpha(t-t_1)}$$

Turning to Laplace transforms, we first note that we are restricted to functions that vanish for $t < 0$. But this is not an essential difficulty, for we can always shift the time scale. But with transforms we must restrict the growth rate of $f(t)$, for example, by requiring f to be of exponential order. Then if y satisfies the homogeneous I.C. at $t_0 = 0$,

(8.3)
$$Y(s) = \frac{1}{P(s)} F(s)$$

$$y = \mathcal{L}^{-1} Y = \mathcal{L}^{-1} \left\{ \frac{1}{P} F \right\}$$

(8.4)
$$y = \left(\mathcal{L}^{-1} \frac{1}{P} \right) * f$$

In Sec. 5 we saw that

$$\mathcal{L}^{-1} \frac{1}{P} (t) = \mathcal{L}^{-1} T(t) = g(t)$$

where g is the response to the δ function, and

$$g(t - t_1) = G(t, t_1)$$

is the Green's function. Therefore, by (8.4)

(8.5)
$$y(t) = \int_0^t f(t_1) g(t - t_1) \, dt_1$$

and this is precisely the same as (8.2) with $t_0 = 0$.

Thus the two techniques are closely related. Observe the strong analogy between (8.1) and (8.3). Computationally, the two techniques are also about the same, since both the evaluation of $[1/P(D)]f$ and that of $[\mathcal{L}^{-1}(1/P)] * f$ require partial-fraction expansion of $1/P$. Although nonhomogenous I.C. can be handled by the operator method, the transform method supplies a formula applicable to all cases.

chapter viii

Systems of Differential Equations

In this chapter we shall be concerned primarily with systems of simultaneous linear D.E. with constant coefficients. Such systems arise frequently in many fields of applied science, especially in the analysis of vibrating mechanical systems with several degrees of freedom and in multiloop electrical networks. Furthermore, systems have mathematical importance in themselves, for, as we shall see in Sec. 5, each nth-order equation is equivalent to a system of n first-order equations. Consequently, the theory of first-order systems comprises the whole theory of ordinary D.E.

1. Systems of Simultaneous Linear Differential Equations

A system of simultaneous linear D.E. in the unknown functions $x, y, z, \ldots$ is a set of linear equations in these variables and some of their derivatives. The system is *linear* if all the equations of the set are of the form (where t is the independent variable and $D = d/dt$)

$$(1.1) \quad (a_0 D^k + a_1 D^{k-1} + \cdots + a_k)x \\ + (b_0 D^l + b_1 D^{l-1} + \cdots + b_l)y + \cdots = f$$

The coefficients $a_0, a_1, \ldots, a_k, b_0, b_1, \ldots, b_l, \ldots$ may be functions of t. But in the following we shall only consider *linear systems with constant coefficients.* If all the right-member terms are zero, the system is said to be *linear homogeneous.*

In operator notation, the coefficient of x in Eq. (1.1) may be written as an operator polynomial $P(D)$, the coefficient of y as some other operator polynomial $Q(D)$, and so forth. To distinguish the several equations of the system, subscripts 1, 2, . . . may be employed. The system then takes the form

(1.2)
$$P_1(D)x + Q_1(D)y + \cdots = f_1$$
$$P_2(D)x + Q_2(D)y + \cdots = f_2$$
$$\cdot \quad \cdot \quad \cdot \quad \cdot \quad \cdot \quad \cdot \quad \cdot \quad \cdot \quad \cdot \quad \cdot \quad \cdot$$

By an *integral* (or *solution*) of the system we mean a set of functions $x, y, z, \ldots$ which, when substituted in the equations of the system, transform these equations into identities. As in the case of a single differential equation, there exist, in general, many integrals of the same system, and initial (or other) conditions are used to single out a particular one. But as to the number of required conditions no such simple rules as for single differential equations can be given. This will become apparent from an examination of a few examples.

Example 1
$$(D^2 - 1)x - D^2y = -2 \sin t$$
$$(D^2 + 1)x + D^2y = 0$$

Adding these equations we eliminate y and find for x the equation

$$2D^2x = -2 \sin t$$

whose general solution is

$$x(t) = \sin t + A_1 t + A_2$$

where A_1, A_2 are arbitrary constants. When this is substituted in the first equation, we obtain

$$D^2y = -A_1 t - A_2$$

whose general solution is

(1.3)
$$y(t) = \frac{-A_1}{6} t^3 - \frac{A_2}{2} t^2 + B_1 t + B_2$$

where B_1, B_2 are additional arbitrary constants. It is immediately checked that the second equation of the system is also satisfied by these functions. Hence, we have found a solution with four arbitrary constants. From the form of this solution it is apparent that a particular integral is obtained by specifying

$$x = x_0 \qquad Dx = x_1 \qquad y = y_0 \qquad Dy = y_1 \qquad \text{when} \qquad t = t_0$$

where x_0, x_1, y_0, y_1 are arbitrary numbers. Another possible set of initial conditions is

$$y = y_0 \qquad Dy = y_1 \qquad D^2y = y_2 \qquad D^3y = y_3 \qquad \text{when} \qquad t = t_0$$

with no conditions for x, Dx, ... For then A_1, A_2, B_1, B_2 can be determined from (1.3) and its first three derivatives. On the other hand, it would not do to specify initial values only for the function x and its derivatives, since x involves only the constants A_1, A_2.

Example 2

$$(D^2 - 1)x + D^2y = -2 \sin t$$
$$(D^2 + 1)x + D^2y = 0$$

To eliminate y, we subtract the first equation from the second, obtaining

$$2x = 2 \sin t$$

or

$$x(t) = \sin t$$

On substituting this in the first equation, we obtain

$$D^2y = 0$$

Hence,

$$y(t) = B_1t + B_2$$

where B_1, B_2 are arbitrary constants.

Although the system is quite similar to that of the preceding example (only a sign is changed), we see that in this case the general solution contains but two arbitrary constants. A particular solution is singled out by the initial conditions

$$y = y_0 \qquad Dy = y_1 \qquad \text{when} \qquad t = t_0$$

No initial conditions can be imposed on x.

Example 3

$$(D^2 - 1)x + (D^2 - 2)y = -2 \sin t$$
$$(D^2 + 1)x + D^2y = 0$$

By subtracting the first equation from the second, we find

(1.4) $$x + y = \sin t$$

Substitution of this result in the second equation yields

$$x(t) = \sin t$$

and, because of (1.4),

$$y(t) = 0$$

There are no arbitrary constants in this solution. Therefore, no initial conditions can be imposed on either x or y.

Example 4

$$(D^2 - 1)x + (D^2 - D)y = -2 \sin t$$
$$(D^2 + D)x + D^2 y = 0$$

By subtracting the first equation from the second, one finds

$$(D + 1)x + Dy = 2 \sin t$$

This equation, when differentiated, yields

$$(D^2 + D)x + D^2 y = 2 \cos t$$

This last equation is inconsistent with the second of the equations of the system. Hence, this system has no solution whatsoever.

The four examples discussed above show that, as far as the number of possible solutions is concerned, systems of differential equations may vary widely, although there appears to be little difference in their form. Because of this, the formal appearance of the equations in a system is not much of a clue as to how many constants of integration there are in the general solution or by what sort of initial conditions they can be determined.

There is a general criterion concerning the number of arbitrary constants in the general solution of a system, and we shall discuss this in Sec. 2. Furthermore, there is a simple algorithm, which we shall also take up in Sec. 2, that supplies *the* solution, if any, in each particular case. At present we shall treat each problem as a separate challenge and be guided only by our experience with linear algebraic systems.

In the algebraic case one successively eliminates the unknowns. In dealing with differential systems such as (1.2), in which the coefficients are operator polynomials, elimination of unknowns is done by forming linear combinations of the equations of the system using operator polynomials as factors. For example, if the unknown x is to be eliminated from the first two equations of system (1.2), one may "multiply" the first equation by $P_2(D)$, multiply the second equation by $P_1(D)$, and then subtract the two equations. It should be kept in mind that "multiplication" by operator polynomials actually involves differentiations of the equations. For this reason the resulting equations, although derived from the given equations and, therefore, necessarily satisfied by any solution of the given system, *may* have more solutions with more constants of integration than the original equations. What is needed, therefore, is a method that will produce at each step a new system *equivalent* to the original one. We shall describe such a method in Sec. 2. For the present, in order to eliminate any extraneous arbitrary constants, *it is necessary to substitute the general solution of the derived equations in all the equations of the original system.* This usually leads to a reduction of the number of arbitrary constants in the solution.

Example 5. Find the general solution of the system

$$(D^2 - 2D + 3)x + (D - 1)y + Dz = 0$$
$$(3D + 1)x - 3Dy - Dz = 1$$
$$2x - 2y - z = -4$$

We may first solve the last equation for z, obtaining

$$z = 2x - 2y + 4$$

When this is substituted in the first two equations, there results the system

$$(D^2 + 3)x - (D + 1)y = 0$$
$$(D + 1)x - Dy = 1$$

To eliminate y from these equations, we operate with D on the first equation, and with $-(D + 1)$ on the second, and then add. (Note that, because we have differentiated, it is quite possible that the solution we get will have too many constants of integration.) We obtain

$$(D^3 - D^2 + D - 1)x + 0y = D0 - (D + 1)1$$

or

$$(D - 1)(D^2 + 1)x = -1$$

The general solution of this equation is

$$x(t) = 1 + c_1 \sin t + c_2 \cos t + c_3 e^t$$

To determine y, one may similarly eliminate x from the above two equations, or one may substitute the established solution for x in one of the equations, thus obtaining an equation for y alone. The latter method is preferable, since the same substitution must also be made for the purpose of eliminating extraneous solutions. On substitution for x, the second of the above equations becomes

$$Dy = (D + 1)x - 1$$
$$= (c_1 + c_2) \cos t + (c_1 - c_2) \sin t + 2c_3 e^t$$

whose general solution is

$$y(t) = (c_1 + c_2) \sin t - (c_1 - c_2) \cos t + 2c_3 e^t + c_4$$

If these tentative solutions for x and y are substituted in the first of the above equations, one finds

$$(-c_1 + 3c_1 - c_1 + c_2 - c_1 - c_2) \sin t$$
$$+ (-c_2 + 3c_2 - c_1 - c_2 + c_1 - c_2) \cos t$$
$$+ (c_3 + 3c_3 - 2c_3 - 2c_3)e^t + 3 - c_4 = 0$$

Hence c_4 is not an arbitrary constant, but $c_4 = 3$.   Since

$$z = 2x - 2y + 4$$

the general solution of the system is

$$x(t) = 1 + c_1 \sin t + c_2 \cos t + c_3 e^t$$
$$y(t) = 3 + (c_1 + c_2) \sin t - (c_1 - c_2) \cos t + 2c_3 e^t$$
$$z(t) = -2c_2 \sin t + 2c_1 \cos t - 2c_3 e^t$$

containing the three arbitrary constants c_1, c_2, c_3.

PROBLEMS

The general solution of each of the following systems can be easily determined by trial or by elimination of unknowns.   Discuss the number of arbitrary constants of integration and possible initial conditions.

1. $(D + 1)x = 2e^t$, $Dx - y = e^t$

2. $(D - 2)x + (D - 2)y = 2t^2 - 2t$, $(D + 1)x - (D + 1)y = t^2 + 2t$

3. $(D + 1)x + y = \dfrac{1}{t}$, $(D - 1)x + y = -\dfrac{1}{t} + 2e^{-t}$

4. $(D + 1)x + y = \dfrac{1}{t}$, $(D + 1)x - y = -\dfrac{1}{t} + e^{-t}$

5. $(D^2 + 4)x = 3 \sin t$, $Dx - (D^2 - 1)y = 2 \cos t$

6. $(D^2 - 1)x + (D^2 + 1)y = f(t)$, $(D - 1)x + (D - 1)y = 0$

7. $(D - 1)x = 0$, $3x + 2(D + 1)y = 0$, $2y + (2D - 3)z = 0$

8. $(D^2 + D + 1)x + (D^2 + 1)y = e^{2t}$, $(D + 1)x + Dy = 1$

9. $(D^2 + D + 1)x + (D^2 - D + 1)y + Dz = t^2$, $Dx + (D + 1)y = t$, $x - 2y + z = 0$

★10. Show that the system

$$x + Q_1(D)y = f_1$$
$$P_2(D)x + Q_2(D)y = f_2$$

has one and only one solution satisfying the initial conditions

$$y = Dy = D^2y = \cdots = D^ky = 0 \qquad \text{when} \qquad t = t_0$$

where k is the degree of the polynomial $Q_2(q) - Q_1(q)P_2(q)$ (which we assume to be not identically vanishing).   What is this solution if $f_1 = f_2 \equiv 0$?

11. Show that the (triangular) system

$$P_1(D)x = f_1$$
$$Q_2(D)y + P_2(D)x = f_2$$
$$R_3(D)z + Q_3(D)y + P_3(D)x = f_3$$
$$\cdots \cdots \cdots \cdots \cdots \cdots \cdots \cdots$$

has one and only one solution satisfying the initial conditions

$$x = Dx = \cdots = D^{k_1-1}x = 0$$
$$y = Dy = \cdots = D^{k_2-1}y = 0 \qquad \text{when } t = t_0$$
$$z = Dz = \cdots = D^{k_3-1}z = 0$$
$$\cdots \cdots \cdots \cdots \cdots \cdots \cdots$$

where k_1, k_2, k_3, ... are the degrees of the polynomials $P_1(q)$, $Q_2(q)$, $R_3(q)$, ..., respectively. What is this solution if $f_1 = f_2 = \cdots \equiv 0$?

2. Reduction to Triangular Form

The method of solving a system of differential equations by reducing it to a triangular form is quite general and applies to any system of simultaneous linear differential equations with constant coefficients. There is no restriction as to the number of unknowns, number of equations, or order of equations, nor is there any need for the hypothesis that the number of unknowns be equal to the number of equations.

Definition 1. Two systems of simultaneous D.E. are *equivalent* if each solution of one system is also a solution of the other, and conversely.

The method of this section provides a new system, equivalent to the given system, for which the equations can be solved one by one, in order. These are systems in triangular form.

Definition 2. A system of linear D.E. is said to be in *triangular form* if each equation contains at least one unknown not in the preceding equations.

Example 1. The system

$$(D + 1)x - y = 0$$
(2.1) $$x + (D - 1)y + (D + 2)z = 0$$
$$Dy + Dz - u = 0$$

is in triangular form. The second equation contains z, which is not in the first; the third contains u, which is not in the second. Observe that for no other arrangement would the system be in triangular form.

The first equation can now be solved without regard for the remaining equations. Since it contains two unknowns, one of them, say x, may be chosen arbitrarily. Hence, we put

$$x(t) = f(t) \qquad \text{arbitrary}$$

Then

$$y(t) = (D + 1)f(t)$$

Substitution of these expressions in the second of equations (2.1) yields for z the equation

$$(D + 2)z = -f - (D - 1)(D + 1)f$$
$$= -D^2 f$$

Hence,

$$z(t) = - \int^t e^{2(t_1-t)} D^2 f(t_1) \, dt_1 + A e^{-2t}$$

where A is an arbitrary constant. Finally, u is obtained by substitution in the last of the above equations:

$$u(t) = D(D+1)f(t) + D\left[-\int^t e^{2(t_1-t)} D^2 f(t_1) \, dt_1 + A e^{-2t} \right]$$

$$= (D^2 + D)f(t) - D^2 f(t) + 2\int^t e^{2(t_1-t)} D^2 f(t_1) \, dt_1 - 2A e^{-2t}$$

$$= Df(t) + 2\int^t e^{2(t_1-t)} D^2 f(t_1) \, dt_1 - 2A e^{-2t}$$

There is no need to check for extraneous constants of integration, because no differentiations have been performed.

We now show how a pair of equations containing the same unknown, say x, can be transformed into an equivalent pair, one of which is free from x. Let the two equations be

$$(2.2) \qquad P_1(D)x = F_1 \qquad P_2(D)x = F_2$$

where F_1, F_2 are free of x, and P_1, P_2 are operator polynomials. If we operate on the equations of (2.2) with $P_2(D)$ and $P_1(D)$, respectively, and subtract, we can eliminate x:

$$(2.3) \qquad P_2(D)P_1(D)x - P_1(D)P_2(D)x = P_2(D)F_1 - P_1(D)F_2$$

But Eq. (2.3) and either one of Eqs. (2.2), say the first,

$$(2.4) \qquad \begin{aligned} P_1(D)x &= F_1 \\ 0 &= P_2(D)F_1 - P_1(D)F_2 \end{aligned}$$

will not always be a system equivalent to (2.2). This is so because (2.3) is generally of higher order than either of Eqs. (2.2), so that the system (2.4) will have more solutions than does (2.2). The proper procedure is first to determine the least common multiple $P(q)$ of the two polynomials $P_1(q)$, $P_2(q)$ [that is, the polynomial of lowest degree that contains $P_1(q)$, $P_2(q)$ as factors]. Then there must be factors $Q_1(q)$, $Q_2(q)$ such that

$$Q_1(q)P_1(q) = Q_2(q)P_2(q) = P(q)$$

Therefore, the equation

$$(2.5) \qquad Q_1(D)P_1(D)x - Q_2(D)P_2(D)x = 0 = Q_1(D)F_1 - Q_2(D)F_2$$

is free of x. What is needed is a second equation which, with (2.5), will form a system equivalent to (2.2).

The polynomials $Q_1(q)$, $Q_2(q)$ were chosen to have no common factor of positive degree. For a pair of such polynomials it is possible† to find two other polynomials $Q_1^*(q)$, $Q_2^*(q)$ such that

$$(2.6) \qquad Q_1(q)Q_2^*(q) - Q_2(q)Q_1^*(q) \equiv 1$$

With the operator polynomials $Q_1^*(D)$, $Q_2^*(D)$ we can derive another equation from (2.2):

$$(2.7) \quad [Q_1^*(D)P_1(D) - Q_2^*(D)P_2(D)]x = Q_1^*(D)F_1 - Q_2^*(D)F_2$$

Equations (2.5) and (2.7) give us the system

$$(2.8) \quad \begin{aligned} [Q_1(D)P_1(D) - Q_2(D)P_2(D)]x &= 0 = Q_1(D)F_1 - Q_2(D)F_2 \\ [Q_1^*(D)P_1(D) - Q_2^*(D)P_2(D)]x &= Q_1^*(D)F_1 - Q_2^*(D)F_2 \end{aligned}$$

which we assert is equivalent to (2.2). Clearly, every solution of (2.2) is a solution of (2.8), for the latter was derived from (2.2). It remains therefore to derive (2.2) from (2.8). If we operate on the first of (2.8) with $Q_2^*(D)$ and on the second with $-Q_2(D)$ and add, we obtain

$$[Q_1(D)Q_2^*(D)P_1(D) - Q_2(D)Q_1^*(D)P_1(D)]x$$
$$= Q_1(D)Q_2^*(D)F_1 - Q_2(D)Q_1^*(D)F_1$$

or, because of (2.6),

$$P_1(D)x = F_1$$

If we operate on the first of (2.8) with $Q_1^*(D)$ and on the second with $-Q_1(D)$, we get

$$P_2(D)x = F_2$$

This completes the proof that (2.8) is equivalent to (2.2).

Thus we have a method of transforming a pair of equations containing the same unknown, say x, into an equivalent pair of equations, one of which is free of x. We use operators $Q_1(D)$, $Q_2(D)$, which have no common factor, to derive the equation free of x, and another pair of operators $Q_1^*(D)$, $Q_2^*(D)$, which we may call *adjoint operators* and which are related to $Q_1(D)$, $Q_2(D)$ by identity (2.6),‡ to derive the other equation. By this method any system can be reduced to an equiva-

---

† For a proof, see A. A. Albert, "College Algebra," p. 102, McGraw-Hill Book Company, New York, 1946. In most cases the polynomials $Q_1(q)$, $Q_2(q)$ are so simple that the polynomials $Q_1^*(q)$, $Q_2^*(q)$ satisfying identity (2.6) can be guessed. In other cases the method of undetermined coefficients can be used to find $Q_1^*(q)$, $Q_2^*(q)$.

‡ It is clear that in place of unity we may choose any constant different from zero as the right member of identity (2.6).

lent triangular system which has the property that each of its equations contains at least one unknown that does not occur in the preceding equations.†

Definitions.   If the system in its triangular form is such that the first equation contains one unknown and each succeeding equation contains exactly one more unknown, then the unknowns can be determined one by one from these equations.   The system is then *determinate*, since the unknowns are, except for arbitrary constants of integration, uniquely determined.

If, however, the first equation of the triangular system contains more than one unknown, or if any of the other equations contains more than one unknown more than the number occurring in the preceding equation, then some of the unknowns remain arbitrary, and the remaining ones are expressed in terms of these arbitrary unknowns.   The system is *indeterminate*.

Finally, it may happen that the first or some of the first equations of the triangular system contain no unknowns at all.   In this case we say the system is *dependent*.   There are two possibilities.   (1) The equations free of unknowns are identities and can be disregarded.   The system then is *consistent* and can be either determinate or indeterminate. (2) The equations free of unknowns are not identities.   The system then is *inconsistent* and has no solution.

Example 2.   Find the general solution of the system

(a) $$(D^2 - 1)x + 2(D + 1)y + (D + 1)z = 0$$
(b) $$(D - 1)^2x + 4Dy + (2D - 1)z = 0$$
(c) $$(D - 1)x + 2y - (D - 1)z = 0$$

The unknown y is easily eliminated from Eqs. (b) and (c) by applying the operators 1, $2D$, which are $Q_1(D)$ and $Q_2(D)$, respectively, for this pair of equations.   The adjoints are obviously $Q_1^*(D) = 0$ and $Q_2^*(D) = 1$, for then

$$Q_1(D)Q_2^*(D) - Q_2(D)Q_1^*(D) = 1 \cdot 1 - 2D \cdot 0 = 1$$

The new system equivalent to (b) and (c) is, symbolically,

$$Q_1(D)(b) - Q_2(D)(c) = 0$$
$$Q_1^*(D)(b) - Q_2^*(D)(c) = 0$$

or, if we keep (a) unchanged, the system equivalent to (a), (b), and (c) is

(a) $$(D^2 - 1)x + 2(D + 1)y + (D + 1)z = 0$$
(b') $$-(D^2 - 1)x + (2D^2 - 1)z = 0$$
(c) $$(D - 1)x + 2y - (D - 1)z = 0$$

† It may happen that one or more of the first equations contains no unknowns at all.

Now y is eliminated from Eqs. (a) and (c) by applying the operators 1, $(D+1)$. The adjoint operators are 0, 1, and we obtain

(a') $$(D^2 + D)z = 0$$
(b') $$-(D^2 - 1)x + (2D^2 - 1)z = 0$$
(c) $$2y + (D - 1)x - (D - 1)z = 0$$

Observe that (a') is simpler than anticipated. We anticipated for (a') an equation in both x and z, but x is fortunately missing. Had x been present in (a'), we would have had to apply our process once more to eliminate either x or z from (a') and (b'). As it is, the system is already in triangular form and is seen to be a determinate system. The general solution of (a') is

$$z(t) = C_1 + C_2 e^{-t}$$

Substitution in (b') leads to the following equation for x:

$$(D^2 - 1)x = -C_1 + C_2 e^{-t}$$

whose general solution is

$$x(t) = C_1 - \frac{C_2}{2} te^{-t} + A_1 e^t + A_2 e^{-t}$$

Finally, from Eq. (c),

$$y(t) = \left[A_2 - \frac{C_2}{2}\left(t + \frac{3}{2}\right) \right] e^{-t}$$

Example 3. How must the function h be chosen to make the following system consistent, and what is then its general solution?

(a) $$(D^2 - 1)x - (D^2 - D)y = h$$
(b) $$(D^2 + D)x - D^2 y = 0$$

The coefficients of y have the common factor D. Hence, the operators used to eliminate y from Eqs. (a) and (b) are D, $(D - 1)$, and the adjoint operators are 1, 1. The transformed equations are

(a') $$0x + 0y = Dh$$
(b') $$-(D + 1)x + Dy = h$$

Since Eq. (a') contains neither x nor y, system (a), (b) is dependent. Equation (a') is an identity only if $Dh(t) \equiv 0$; hence system (a), (b) is consistent if and only if $h(t)$ is constant, say $h(t) = k$. Then only Eq. (b') remains to be satisfied. Since this equation contains two unknowns, one of them can be chosen arbitrarily, say

$$x(t) = f(t) \qquad \text{arbitrary}$$

Then we have, for y, the equation

$$Dy = k + (D + 1)f$$

whose general solution is

$$y(t) = kt + f(t) + \int^t f(t_1)\, dt_1 + A$$

where A is an arbitrary constant.

We finally remark that from the triangular form we can see at once the number of arbitrary constants in the solution. Suppose the system is in triangular form and is *determinate*. The first equation is of degree n_1, say, in x, and its solution will involve n_1 constants. If the second equation involves y and is of degree n_2, then its solution will add n_2 new constants. There will be, in all, $n = n_1 + n_2 + \cdots + n_k$ constants if there are k variables. Now n is the degree in D of the determinant of the coefficients of $x, y, z, \ldots$ and is invariant under transformations leading to the triangular form. This proves the following theorem:

Theorem. *Let $\Delta(D)$ be the determinant of the coefficients of the unknowns in a system of k equations in k unknowns, and assume $\Delta(D) \neq 0$. Then the system is determinate, and the number of arbitrary constants in the solution of the system is equal to the degree of $\Delta(D)$.*

If the system in triangular form is *indeterminate*, then it may be interpreted as a system containing as many equations as unknowns, but with at least one coefficient along the diagonal equal to zero. Therefore, the determinant of the coefficients is zero. *Conversely, if this determinant is zero, then the system is indeterminate.*

Example 4. Consider the five examples of Sec. 1. In Example 1, $\Delta(D) = 2D^4$, of degree 4. There are four constants.
In Example 2, $\Delta(D) = -2D^2$, of degree 2. There are two constants.
In Example 3, $\Delta(D) = 2$, of degree 0. There are no constants.
In Example 4, $\Delta(D) = 0$. The system is indeterminate—more specifically, inconsistent.
In Example 5, $\Delta(D) = D^3 - D^2 + D - 1$, of degree 3. There are three constants.

PROBLEMS

Reduce to triangular systems and solve:

1. $(D^2 + 1)x + Dy = h(t)$, $D^3x + (D^2 - 1)y = 0$
2. $(D^2 - 3D)x + (2D - 1)y = 0$, $(D + 1)x - Dy = e^{\frac{1}{2}t}$
3. $Dx = y - z$, $Dy = z - x$, $Dz = x - y$
4. $(D^2 - 1)x + (D + 1)y + (D + 1)z = 0$, $(D - 1)^2x + 2Dy + (2D - 1)z = 0$, $(D - 1)x + y - (D - 1)z = 0$, $D(D + 1)z = 0$

5. $D^2x + y = 0$, $(D^2 - 1)y + D^2z = 0$, $x + y + z = h$

6. $(D^2 + D)x + Dz - u = 0$, $Dx - Dy - (D + 2)z = 0$, $x - y + 2z + u = 0$

7. $Dx + 4y = 2e^t$, $(2D - 3)x + (D^2 - D)y = 0$

8. $(D^2 + 3)x + 2Dy = 2e^{-t}$, $(D - 1)x + y = -e^{-t}$

9. $(D^3 + 1)x + Dy = \cos 2t$, $(D^2 - 1)x + y = -\cos 2t$

10. $(D^2 + 2)x + Dy + Dz = 0$, $Dx + y = 0$, $2x - Dy - Dz = 0$

Solve the following systems with the given initial conditions:

11. $(D - 1)x + 2y = 0$, $3x + (D - 2)y = 0$. (a) $x = 1$, $y = 0$ when $t = 0$; (b) $x = 0$, $y = 1$ when $t = 0$

12. $Dx + (D - 1)y = 3e^t$, $2Dx + (D + 2)y = 0$; $x = 1$, $y = 0$ when $t = 0$

13. $(D + a)x - by = A$, $bx + (D - a)y = B$, $a^2 - b^2 = 1$; $x = y = 0$ when $t = 0$ a, b, A, B constants

14. $(D + 3)x + 16y + 14z = 0$, $12x - (D - 40)y + 33z = 0$, $12x + 38y + (D + 31)z = 0$; $x = 1$, $y = z = 0$ when $t = 0$

15. $(D^2 - D)x + Dy = e^t$, $(D^2 - 1)x + D^2y = e^t$; $x = Dx = y = Dy = 1$ when $t = 0$

16. $(D^2 + 2)x + 3y = \cos 3t$, $7x + (D^2 + 6)y = -\cos 3t$; $x = Dx = y = Dy = 0$ when $t = 0$

17. $D^2x + a\,Dy = A \cos at$, $-a\,Dx + D^2y = 0$, $a \neq 0$; $x = Dx = y = Dy = 0$ when $t = 0$ a, A constants

18. $D^2x + y = 2 \cos t$, $(D^2 - 1)y + D^2z = 0$, $(D^2 - 1)x + D^2z = 0$; $x = Dx = y = Dy = 0$, $z = z_0$, $Dz = z_1$ when $t = 0$

19. How must the constant a be chosen so as to make the following system consistent, and what is then its general solution?

$$(D^4 - 1)x + (D^2 + 1)y = 2e^t$$
$$(D^2 - 1)^2x + (D^2 - 1)y = ae^t$$

20. Decide, for each of the systems of Probs. 1 to 10, without solving, how many constants of integration the solution has.

3. The Laplace-transform Method

The technique is in essence the same as that for a single equation. Consider an example.

Example 1. Find the solution (if any) of the system

$$(3.1) \qquad \begin{aligned} (D + 2)x + y &= 1 \\ (D - 1)y + (D + 2)z &= 0 \\ (D - 1)x + Dz &= -1 \end{aligned}$$

which satisfies the I.C. $x(0) = 1$, $y(0) = z(0) = 0$.

Assume that a solution exists and that each function has a Laplace transform. Then, with the notation of Chap. VII,

$$sX - 1 + 2X + Y = \frac{1}{s}$$

$$sY - 0 - Y + sZ - 0 + 2Z = 0$$

$$sX - 1 - X + sZ - 0 = -\frac{1}{s}$$

or

(3.2)
$$(s + 2)X + Y = \frac{s + 1}{s}$$

$$(s - 1)Y + (s + 2)Z = 0$$

$$(s - 1)X + sZ = \frac{s - 1}{s}$$

Equations (3.2) are linear algebraic equations in the transforms X, Y, Z. The determinant of the coefficients is

$$\Delta(s) = (s - 1)(s + 1)(s + 2)$$

which is of degree 3. Thus, by the theorem of Sec. 2, there are three arbitrary constants in the general solution. Solving (3.2), we get

(3.3)
$$X(s) = \frac{s^2 + 2s + 2}{s(s + 1)(s + 2)} = \frac{1}{s} - \frac{1}{s + 1} + \frac{1}{s + 2}$$

$$Y(s) = \frac{-1}{s(s + 1)} = -\frac{1}{s} + \frac{1}{s + 1}$$

$$Z(s) = \frac{s - 1}{s(s + 1)(s + 2)} = -\frac{\frac{1}{2}}{s} + \frac{2}{s + 1} - \frac{\frac{3}{2}}{s + 2}$$

The inverse transforms give x, y, z:

(3.4) $x(t) = 1 - e^{-t} + e^{-2t}$ $y(t) = -1 + e^{-t}$

$$z(t) = -\tfrac{1}{2} + 2e^{-t} - \tfrac{3}{2}e^{-2t}$$

Now consider the above procedure. What we have shown is that if there is a solution having a Laplace transform then it must be given by (3.4). But the steps to (3.4) can be reversed. From (3.4) we get (3.3), which is equivalent to (3.2), and this in turn implies (3.1). Hence we have proved that there is a solution and that any solution which has a Laplace transform must be (3.4). That no other solution exists (i.e., one with no Laplace transform) requires a uniqueness theorem which we could obtain from the triangulation method of Sec. 2 (see also Sec. 4). Compare with Corollary 2, Sec. 2, Chap. VII.

Now let us turn to the general situation. In order to avoid cumbersome notation, we shall discuss only systems of three equations with three unknowns; the generalization to the case of n equations with n unknowns is trivial and requires no further elaboration. The system to be considered is

$$
\begin{array}{l}
P_1(D)x + Q_1(D)y + R_1(D)s = f_1 \\
P_2(D)x + Q_2(D)y + R_2(D)z = f_2 \\
P_3(D)x + Q_3(D)y + R_3(D)z = f_3
\end{array}
\tag{3.5}
$$

where P_i, Q_i, R_i are polynomials in D. We shall suppose that the *characteristic determinant*

$$
\Delta(D) = \begin{vmatrix}
P_1(D) & Q_1(D) & R_1(D) \\
P_2(D) & Q_2(D) & R_2(D) \\
P_3(D) & Q_3(D) & R_3(D)
\end{vmatrix}
\tag{3.6}
$$

is different from zero. This prevents the system (3.5) from being indeterminate. From the theorem of Sec. 2, we know that the degree of $\Delta(D)$ is equal to the number of arbitrary constants in the general solution.

As in the example, we begin by assuming that we have a solution which has a Laplace transform and that this solution has at $t = 0$ the initial values

$$
\begin{array}{lll}
x(0) = x_0 & x'(0) = x_1 & \cdots \\
y(0) = y_0 & y'(0) = y_1 & \cdots \\
z(0) = z_0 & z'(0) = z_1 & \cdots
\end{array}
\tag{3.7}
$$

The Laplace transform of $P_1(D)x$ is

$$
\begin{aligned}
(3.8) \quad \mathcal{L}P_1(D)x(s) &= P_1(s)X + \alpha_0(s^{n_1-1}x_0 + s^{n_1-2}x_1 + \cdots) \\
&\qquad + \alpha_1(s^{n_1-2}x_0 + \cdots) + \cdots + \alpha_{n_1-1}x_0 \\
&= P_1(s)X + I_1(s)
\end{aligned}
$$

where n_1 is the degree of $P_1(s)$:

$$
P_1(s) = \alpha_0 s^{n_1} + \alpha_1 s^{n_1-1} + \cdots + \alpha_{n_1-1}s + \alpha_{n_1}
$$

and where I_1 is the polynomial which occurs in (3.8) and which involves the coefficients of P_1 and the initial values (3.7).

From (3.5) and equations similar to (3.8) we obtain, after taking Laplace transforms,

$$
\begin{array}{l}
P_1(s)X + Q_1(s)Y + R_1(s)Z = F_1(s) + C_1(s) \\
P_2(s)X + Q_2(s)Y + R_2(s)Z = F_2(s) + C_2(s) \\
P_3(s)X + Q_3(s)Y + R_3(s)Z = F_3(s) + C_3(s)
\end{array}
\tag{3.9}
$$

where the polynomials C_i involve the I.C. of x, y, z. Observe that $C_1 = C_2 = C_3 = 0$ if the initial values are all zero. These equations are linear algebraic equations in X, Y, Z and are solved by Cramer's rule if $\Delta(s) \neq 0$.

(3.10)
$$X = \frac{\begin{vmatrix} F_1 + C_1 & Q_1 & R_1 \\ F_2 + C_2 & Q_2 & R_2 \\ F_3 + C_3 & Q_3 & R_3 \end{vmatrix}}{\Delta} \qquad Y = \frac{\begin{vmatrix} P_1 & F_1 + C_1 & R_1 \\ P_2 & F_2 + C_2 & R_2 \\ P_3 & F_3 + C_3 & R_3 \end{vmatrix}}{\Delta}$$

$$Z = \frac{\begin{vmatrix} P_1 & Q_1 & F_1 + C_1 \\ P_2 & Q_2 & F_2 + C_2 \\ P_3 & Q_3 & F_3 + C_3 \end{vmatrix}}{\Delta}$$

Then x, y, z are obtained by finding the inverse transforms of X, Y, Z. Thus we see that if we but knew the correct initial values of our solution, Eqs. (3.10) would determine that solution.   What will happen in particular problems is that once we have obtained (3.10), we shall see from its form what initial conditions we must impose on x, y, z.   Usually many of the initial values x_0, y_0, z_0, x_1, y_1, z_1, . . . will drop out, leaving just as many initial values as the degree of $\Delta(s)$.   In practice one is given initial values imposed by the physical problem.   Then one simply computes (3.10) using these initial values and makes a check to see whether the inverse transforms of (3.10) satisfy the given I.C.   In the next section a few special systems are taken up for which one can tell what I.C. are the proper ones.

Example 2.   We solve, using transforms, the problem of Example 1, Sec. 1:

$$(D^2 - 1)x - D^2y = -2 \sin t$$
$$(D^2 + 1)x + D^2y = 0$$

Note that $\Delta(s) = 2s^4$, which is of degree 4.   Thus we must have four constants in the solution, and we try the I.C. $x(0) = x_0$, $x'(0) = x_1$, $y(0) = y_0$, $y'(0) = y_1$.   Taking Laplace transforms, we have

$$s^2X - sx_0 - x_1 - X - s^2Y + sy_0 + y_1 = -\frac{2}{s^2 + 1}$$

$$s^2X - sx_0 - x_1 + X + s^2Y - sy_0 - y_1 = 0$$

or

$$(s^2 - 1)X - s^2Y = sx_0 + x_1 - sy_0 - y_1 - \frac{2}{s^2 + 1}$$

$$(s^2 + 1)X + s^2Y = sx_0 + x_1 + sy_0 + y_1$$

Solving these equations yields

$$X(s) = \frac{-1}{s^2(s^2+1)} + \frac{x_0}{s} + \frac{x_1}{s^2} = \frac{-1}{s^2} + \frac{1}{s^2+1} + \frac{x_0}{s} + \frac{x_1}{s^2}$$

$$Y(s) = \frac{y_0}{s} + \frac{y_1}{s^2} + \frac{1-x_1}{s^4} - \frac{x_0}{s^3}$$

The inverse transforms yield x and y:

$$x(t) = \sin t + (x_1 - 1)t + x_0$$
$$y(t) = y_0 + y_1 t + \tfrac{1}{6}(1 - x_1)t^3 - \tfrac{1}{2}x_0 t^2$$

These are seen to be the same expressions as obtained previously, except for different notation for the constants. An easy check shows that this solution satisfies the I.C.

Example 3. In some problems there are relations among the initial values that one cannot foresee. Suppose we look for the solution of

$$(D^2 - 1)x + Dy = \sin \omega t$$
$$Dx + y = \cos \omega t$$

satisfying the I.C. $x(0) = x_0$, $x'(0) = x_1$, $y(0) = y_0$. Then

(3.11)
$$(s^2 - 1)X + sY = \frac{\omega}{s^2+\omega^2} + sx_0 + x_1 + y_0$$

$$sX + Y = \frac{s}{s^2+\omega^2} + x_0$$

Observe that $\Delta(s) = -1$, which is of degree 0, so that there are no constants in the solution. If we solve (3.11) for X, we get

$$X(s) = \frac{-\omega}{s^2+\omega^2} + \frac{s^2}{s^2+\omega^2} - x_1 - y_0$$

$$= \frac{-(\omega+\omega^2)}{s^2+\omega^2} + 1 - x_1 - y_0$$

The first term in this last expression is recognized as the transform of $-(1+\omega)\sin \omega t$. The second term, $1 - x_1 - y_0$, must be zero, as is seen by putting $t = 0$ in the second of the given equations. Therefore,

$$x(t) = -(1+\omega)\sin \omega t$$
$$y(t) = (1+\omega+\omega^2)\cos \omega t$$

PROBLEMS

Solve, using transforms, the following systems with the given I.C.:

1. $(D-1)x + 2y = 0$, $3x + (D-2)y = 0$. (a) $x = 1$, $y = 0$ when $t = 0$; (b) $x = 0$, $y = 1$ when $t = 0$

2. $Dx + (D-1)y = 3e^t$, $2Dx + (D+2)y = 0$; $x = 1$, $y = 0$ when $t = 0$

3. $(D + a)x - by = A,$ $bx + (D - a)y = B,$ $a^2 - b^2 = 1;$ $x = y = 0$
when $t = 0$ a, b, A, B constants

4. $(D + 3)x + 16y + 14z = 0, 12x - (D - 40)y + 33z = 0, 12x + 38y +$
$(D + 31)z = 0;$ $x = 1, y = z = 0$ when $t = 0$

5. $(D^2 - D)x + Dy = e^t,$ $(D^2 - 1)x + D^2y = e^t;$ $x = Dx = y = Dy = 1$
when $t = 0$

6. $(D^2 + 2)x + 3y = \cos 3t,$ $7x + (D^2 + 6)y = - \cos 3t;$ $x = Dx = y =$
$Dy = 0$ when $t = 0$

7. $D^2x + aDy = A \cos at,$ $-aDx + D^2y = 0;$ $a \neq 0;$ $x = Dx = y =$
$Dy = 0$ when $t = 0$ a, A constants

8. $D^2x + y = 2 \cos t,$ $(D^2 - 1)y + D^2z = 0,$ $(D^2 - 1)x + D^2z = 0;$ $x =$
$Dx = y = Dy = 0, z = z_0, Dz = z_1$ when $t = 0$

Find the general solutions of the following systems.   Make use of $x(0) =$
$x_0, x'(0) = x_1,$ etc., as needed.

9. $(D^3 + 1)x + Dy = \cos 2t,$ $(D^2 - 1)x + y = - \cos 2t$

10. $(D^2 + 3)x + 2Dy = 2e^{-t},$ $(D - 1)x + y = -e^{-t}$

11. $(D^2 + 2)x + Dy + Dz = 0,$ $Dx + y = 0, 2x - Dy - Dz = 0$

12. $Dx + 4y = 2e^t,$ $(2D - 3)x + (D^2 - D)y = 0$

13. $Dx + ay - bz = 0,$ $-ax + Dy + cz = 0,$ $bx - cy + Dz = 0;$ $a^2 +$
$b^2 + c^2 = 1$ a, b, c constants

14. $(D + 1)x + (D + 1)y + (D^2 - 1)z = 0, (D + 1)x - (D + 1)y +$
$(D + 1)^2z = \sinh t, x + y - (D - 1)z = 0$

15. Solve Example 2 of Sec. 1 using transforms.

16. Solve Example 3 of Sec. 1 using transforms.

17. Show, using transforms, that the system of Example 4 of Sec. 1 is inconsistent.

4. Special Systems; Existence and Uniqueness

If every D.E. of a system is of order ≤ 1, the system is a *first-order
system*.   Generally, but not always, such a system can be put in the
normal form

$$\frac{dx_i}{dt} = f_i(t, x_1, \ldots, x_n) \qquad i = 1, \ldots, n$$

in which the derivative of each unknown x_i appears only once, as the
left-hand term of the ith equation.   We are interested here only in
normal first-order systems that are linear with constant coefficients,
and, in order to avoid cumbersome notation, we confine ourselves to
three equations in three unknowns.   If the unknowns are denoted as
x, y, z and the independent variable as t, the system takes the form

$$
\begin{aligned}
Dx &= a_1x + b_1y + c_1z - f_1 \\
Dy &= a_2x + b_2y + c_2z - f_2 \\
Dz &= a_3x + b_3y + c_3z - f_3
\end{aligned}
$$

(4.1)

where the a_i, b_i, c_i are constants, the f_i are functions of t, and $D = d/dt$.
Suitable initial conditions for (4.1) are

$$(4.2) \qquad x(t_0) = x_0 \qquad y(t_0) = y_0 \qquad z(t_0) = z_0$$

where x_0, y_0, z_0 are prescribed.   The formulas to be derived will take a simpler form if we assume *homogeneous* I.C., that is,

$$(4.3) \qquad x(t_0) = 0 \qquad y(t_0) = 0 \qquad z(t_0) = 0$$

This is not a restriction, since the general I.C. (4.2) can be reduced to (4.3) by a simple trick.   Let us make the substitution

$$x^*(t) = x(t) - x_0 \qquad y^*(t) = y(t) - y_0 \qquad z^*(t) = z(t) - z_0$$

in (4.1).   We find that x^*, y^*, z^* satisfy the same D.E. (4.1), except that $f_i(t)$ is replaced by

$$f_i^*(t) = f_i(t) - a_i x_0 - b_i y_0 - c_i z_0 \qquad i = 1, 2, 3$$

and the I.C. (4.2) are replaced by $x^*(t_0) = y^*(t_0) = z^*(t_0) = 0$.
Let us rewrite the system (4.1) in the form

$$(4.4) \qquad \begin{aligned} (-D + a_1)x + b_1 y + c_1 z &= f_1 \\ a_2 x + (-D + b_2)y + c_2 z &= f_2 \\ a_3 x + b_3 y + (-D + c_3)z &= f_3 \end{aligned}$$

If we disregard for the moment the fact that some of the coefficients of system (4.4) are operators and treat them as ordinary numbers, then (4.4) appears to be an algebraic system.   By Cramer's rule its solution is

$$x = \frac{\begin{vmatrix} f_1 & b_1 & c_1 \\ f_2 & b_2 - D & c_2 \\ f_3 & b_3 & c_3 - D \end{vmatrix}}{\begin{vmatrix} a_1 - D & b_1 & c_1 \\ a_2 & b_2 - D & c_2 \\ a_3 & b_3 & c_3 - D \end{vmatrix}} \qquad y = \frac{\begin{vmatrix} a_1 - D & f_1 & c_1 \\ a_2 & f_2 & c_2 \\ a_3 & f_3 & c_3 - D \end{vmatrix}}{\begin{vmatrix} a_1 - D & b_1 & c_1 \\ a_2 & b_2 - D & c_2 \\ a_3 & b_3 & c_3 - D \end{vmatrix}}$$

$$z = \frac{\begin{vmatrix} a_1 - D & b_1 & f_1 \\ a_2 & b_2 - D & f_2 \\ a_3 & b_3 & f_3 \end{vmatrix}}{\begin{vmatrix} a_1 - D & b_1 & c_1 \\ a_2 & b_2 - D & c_2 \\ a_3 & b_3 & c_3 - D \end{vmatrix}}$$

which can also be written as

(4.5)
$$x = \frac{\Delta_{a_1}(D)}{\Delta(D)} f_1 + \frac{\Delta_{a_2}(D)}{\Delta(D)} f_2 + \frac{\Delta_{a_3}(D)}{\Delta(D)} f_3$$

$$y = \frac{\Delta_{b_1}(D)}{\Delta(D)} f_1 + \frac{\Delta_{b_2}(D)}{\Delta(D)} f_2 + \frac{\Delta_{b_3}(D)}{\Delta(D)} f_3$$

$$z = \frac{\Delta_{c_1}(D)}{\Delta(D)} f_1 + \frac{\Delta_{c_2}(D)}{\Delta(D)} f_2 + \frac{\Delta_{c_3}(D)}{\Delta(D)} f_3$$

where

$$\Delta(D) = \begin{vmatrix} a_1 - D & b_1 & c_1 \\ a_2 & b_2 - D & c_2 \\ a_3 & b_3 & c_3 - D \end{vmatrix}$$

$[\Delta(D)$ is the so-called *characteristic determinant* of system (4.4)] and $\Delta_{a_i}(D)$, $\Delta_{b_i}(D)$, $\Delta_{c_i}(D)$ are the cofactors in $\Delta(D)$ of the elements identified by the subscripts. For example,

$$\Delta_{a_2}(D) = -\begin{vmatrix} b_1 & c_1 \\ b_3 & c_3 - D \end{vmatrix} = (c_1 b_3 - b_1 c_3) + b_1 D$$

Equations (4.5) were tentatively derived by handling the symbol D as a number, but they were put in a form that makes a correct interpretation possible. Since each of the fractions in (4.5) is of degree ≤ -1 in D, it is a sum of integrals extended over the interval (t_0, t). We now assert that (4.5), thus interpreted, represents the unique solution of system (4.4) with the I.C. (4.3).

Theorem 1. *If f_1, f_2, f_3 are continuous (or piecewise continuous) in an interval containing t_0, then the first-order normal system (4.4) has a unique solution satisfying the I.C. (4.3), and it is given by expressions (4.5) obtained by formally applying Cramer's rule to (4.4).*

Proof. It is a well-known property of determinants that if the cofactors of a row are multiplied by the corresponding elements of a row, then the sum of the products gives either zero or the determinant, depending on whether the cofactors and elements are taken from different rows or from the same row. Thus,

(4.6)
$$(a_1 - D)\Delta_{a_1}(D) + b_1\Delta_{b_1}(D) + c_1\Delta_{c_1}(D) = \Delta(D)$$
$$(a_1 - D)\Delta_{a_2}(D) + b_1\Delta_{b_2}(D) + c_1\Delta_{c_2}(D) = 0$$
. . . .

Therefore, if (4.5) is substituted in (4.4), one obtains

$$(a_1 - D) \sum_{i=1}^{3} \frac{\Delta_a(D)}{\Delta(D)} f_i + b_1 \sum_{i=1}^{3} \frac{\Delta_{b_i}(D)}{\Delta(D)} f_i + c_1 \sum_{i=1}^{3} \frac{\Delta_{c_i}(D)}{\Delta(D)} f_i$$

$$= \frac{\Delta(D)}{\Delta(D)} f_1 + 0 f_2 + 0 f_3 = f_1$$

and so on. Here we have made use of Theorem 2, Sec. 7, Chap. VII, according to which

$$(a_1 - D) \sum_{i=1}^{3} \frac{\Delta_{a_i}(D)}{\Delta(D)} = \sum_{i=1}^{3} \frac{(a_1 - D)\Delta_{a_i}(D)}{\Delta(D)}$$

and so on. Since the right-hand members of (4.5) are sums of integrals extended over the interval (t_0, t), it is clear that

$$x(t_0) = y(t_0) = z(t_0) = 0$$

Thus it has been proved that (4.5) solves (4.4) and satisfies (4.3).

It remains to show that the solution is unique. Assume that x_1, y_1, z_1 is any solution of (4.4) satisfying the I.C. (4.3) [possibly differing from solution (4.5)], and write u, v, w for the differences $x - x_1, y - y_1, z - z_1$. Then u, v, w is a solution of the homogeneous system

(4.7)
$$\begin{aligned}
(-D + a_1)u + b_1 v + c_1 w &= 0 \\
a_2 u + (-D + b_2)v + c_2 w &= 0 \\
a_3 u + b_3 v + (-D + c_3)w &= 0
\end{aligned}$$

satisfying the homogeneous I.C. (4.3). If we operate with $\Delta_{a_1}(D)/\Delta(D)$, $\Delta_{a_2}(D)/\Delta(D)$, $\Delta_{a_3}(D)/\Delta(D)$ on the three equations (4.7), sum, and use Theorem 2, Sec. 7, Chap. VII, and the relations (4.6), we obtain $u = 0$. In the same way $v = 0$ and $w = 0$ are obtained. Thus, uniqueness is proved.

We observe that the solution of system (4.4) with I.C. (4.3) can also be obtained with the Laplace transform provided that the Laplace transforms F_1, F_2, F_3 of the right-hand terms of (4.4) exist. Indeed, if the Laplace transform is applied to each of Eqs. (4.4) and the resulting algebraic linear system is solved by Cramer's rule, one obtains

(4.8)
$$X(s) = \frac{\Delta_{a_1}(s)}{\Delta(s)} F_1(s) + \frac{\Delta_{a_2}(s)}{\Delta(s)} F_2(s) + \frac{\Delta_{a_3}(s)}{\Delta(s)} F_3(s)$$

$$Y(s) = \frac{\Delta_{b_1}(s)}{\Delta(s)} F_1(s) + \frac{\Delta_{b_2}(s)}{\Delta(s)} F_2(s) + \frac{\Delta_{b_3}(s)}{\Delta(s)} F_3(s)$$

$$Z(s) = \frac{\Delta_{c_1}(s)}{\Delta(s)} F_1(s) + \frac{\Delta_{c_2}(s)}{\Delta(s)} F_2(s) + \frac{\Delta_{c_3}(s)}{\Delta(s)} F_3(s)$$

where $\Delta(s)$, $\Delta_{a_1}(s)$, etc., are the same polynomials as the above $\Delta(D)$, $\Delta_{a_1}(D)$, etc., but now formed with the variable s in place of the operator D. Comparison of (4.8) and (4.5) reveals again the equivalence of the operator and Laplace-transform methods.

Example 1. Find the solution of the system

$$(D + 2)x + y = f$$
$$3x + Dy + 2z = 0$$
$$-3x - y + Dz = 0$$

satisfying the I.C. $x(0) = y(0) = z(0) = 0$.

This is a normal linear system with homogeneous I.C. By (4.8), we need only the determinant Δ and the cofactors $\Delta_{a_1}, \Delta_{b_1}, \Delta_{c_1}$. One finds easily

$$\Delta(s) = (s + 2)(s^2 - 1)$$
$$\Delta_{a_1}(s) = s^2 + 2 \qquad \Delta_{b_1}(s) = -s \qquad \Delta_{c_1}(s) = 2$$

and then the partial-fraction expansions

$$\frac{\Delta_{a_1}(s)}{\Delta(s)} = \frac{2}{s + 2} - \frac{\frac{3}{2}}{s + 1} + \frac{\frac{1}{2}}{s - 1}$$

$$\frac{\Delta_{b_1}(s)}{\Delta(s)} = \frac{\frac{2}{3}}{s + 2} - \frac{\frac{1}{2}}{s + 1} - \frac{\frac{1}{6}}{s - 1}$$

$$\frac{\Delta_{c_1}(s)}{\Delta(s)} = \frac{\frac{2}{3}}{s + 2} - \frac{1}{s + 1} + \frac{\frac{1}{3}}{s - 1}$$

Thus, by (4.8), if $\mathcal{L}f = F$, the Laplace transforms of the solution are

$$X(s) = \left(\frac{2}{s + 2} - \frac{\frac{3}{2}}{s + 1} + \frac{\frac{1}{2}}{s - 1} \right) F(s)$$

$$Y(s) = \left(\frac{\frac{2}{3}}{s + 2} - \frac{\frac{1}{2}}{s + 1} - \frac{\frac{1}{6}}{s - 1} \right) F(s)$$

$$Z(s) = \left(\frac{\frac{2}{3}}{s + 2} - \frac{1}{s + 1} + \frac{\frac{1}{3}}{s - 1} \right) F(s)$$

With the aid of the table in Sec. 1, Chap. VII, and the convolution theorem, the inversion is easily accomplished, giving

$$x(t) = \int_0^t \left(2e^{-2(t-\tau)} - \tfrac{3}{2}e^{-(t-\tau)} + \tfrac{1}{2}e^{t-\tau} \right) f(\tau)\, d\tau$$

$$y(t) = \int_0^t \left(\tfrac{2}{3}e^{-2(t-\tau)} - \tfrac{1}{2}e^{-(t-\tau)} - \tfrac{1}{6}e^{t-\tau} \right) f(\tau)\, d\tau$$

$$z(t) = \int_0^t \left(\tfrac{2}{3}e^{-2(t-\tau)} - e^{-(t-\tau)} + \tfrac{1}{3}e^{t-\tau} \right) f(\tau)\, d\tau$$

One observes that it was not necessary to determine the Laplace transform $F = \mathcal{L}f$. Indeed, $\mathcal{L}f$ need not even exist. Formulas (4.8) are only a different form of formulas (4.5), and the latter make no use of Laplace transforms.

The form of the general solution of the first-order normal system (4.1) is easily described. Let x_p, y_p, z_p be any particular solution of (4.1). One sees immediately that any other solution x, y, z differs from x_p, y_p, z_p by a solution u, v, w of the homogeneous system (4.7) which in this context is called the *reduced system*. The general solution of the reduced system can be obtained from three linearly independent solutions by forming all linear combinations. Indeed if u_1, v_1, w_1; u_2, v_2, w_2; u_3, v_3, w_3 are the three solutions of the system (4.7) satisfying the special I.C.

$$\text{(4.9)} \qquad \begin{aligned} u_1(t_0) &= 1 & v_1(t_0) &= 0 & w_1(t_0) &= 0 \\ u_2(t_0) &= 0 & v_2(t_0) &= 1 & w_2(t_0) &= 0 \\ u_3(t_0) &= 0 & v_3(t_0) &= 0 & w_3(t_0) &= 1 \end{aligned}$$

(that such solutions exist is guaranteed by Theorem 1), then $u = \alpha_1 u_1 + \alpha_2 u_2 + \alpha_3 u_3$, $v = \alpha_1 v_1 + \alpha_2 v_2 + \alpha_3 v_3$, $w = \alpha_1 w_1 + \alpha_2 w_2 + \alpha_3 w_3$ is also a solution of (4.7) for any choice of the constants α_1, α_2, α_3. This is immediately verified by substituting in (4.7). From (4.9) it follows that

$$u(t_0) = \alpha_1 \cdot 1 + \alpha_2 \cdot 0 + \alpha_3 \cdot 0 = \alpha_1$$

$v(t_0) = \alpha_2$, $w(t_0) = \alpha_3$, and since α_1, α_2, α_3 can be chosen arbitrarily, every solution of (4.7) is obtained. We have proved the following theorem:

Theorem 2. *The general solution of the first-order normal system (4.1) can be written in the form*

$$x = x_p + u \qquad y = y_p + v \qquad z = z_p + w$$

where x_p, y_p, z_p is any particular solution, and u, v, w is the general solution of the reduced system (4.7). The latter can be formed from the three special solutions u_i, v_i, w_i ($i = 1, 2, 3$) by taking all linear combinations with constant coefficients:

$$\begin{aligned} u &= \alpha_1 u_1 + \alpha_2 u_2 + \alpha_3 u_3 \\ v &= \alpha_1 v_1 + \alpha_2 v_2 + \alpha_3 v_3 \\ w &= \alpha_1 w_1 + \alpha_2 w_2 + \alpha_3 w_3 \end{aligned}$$

We now show that the homogeneous system (4.7) always has solutions of the simple form

$$\text{(4.10)} \qquad u(t) = A e^{rt} \qquad v(t) = B e^{rt} \qquad w(t) = C e^{rt}$$

where A, B, C are constants not all zero, and r is a constant. Solutions of the form (4.10) are called *normal modes* in vibration theory, and r is the *characteristic exponent* of the normal mode. To find such solutions, we substitute (4.10) in (4.7) and cancel the factor e^{rt}, obtaining

$$\begin{aligned}
(a_1 - r)A + b_1 B + c_1 C &= 0 \\
a_2 A + (b_2 - r)B + c_2 C &= 0 \\
a_3 A + b_3 B + (c_3 - r)C &= 0
\end{aligned}$$

(4.11)

This linear homogeneous system for the unknowns A, B, C has a non-trivial solution (i.e., one in which $|A| + |B| + |C| > 0$) if and only if the determinant of the system vanishes. Hence, r must be a root of the *characteristic equation*

$$\Delta(r) = 0 \tag{4.12}$$

and the three equations (4.11) become dependent. Then A, B, C can be determined from (4.11), for example, by ignoring one of the equations. If the cubic equation (4.12) happens to have three distinct roots r_1, r_2, r_3, then for each of them a normal mode can be found, and the three normal modes can be used to obtain the general solution of (4.7) by taking all linear combinations. This is true even in some cases in which the characteristic equation (4.12) does not have distinct roots.

One should observe that the normal modes cannot be found by the transform or operator method, since one does not know what the initial conditions are that specify the normal modes.

Example 2. Find the general solution of the system of Example 1.

Since we found a particular solution in Example 1, it remains to determine the general solution of the reduced system

$$\begin{aligned}
(D + 2)u + v &= 0 \\
3u + Dv + 2w &= 0 \\
-3u - v + Dw &= 0
\end{aligned}$$

We look for normal modes. The characteristic equation

$$\Delta(r) = (r + 2)(r^2 - 1) = 0$$

has the distinct roots $r_1 = 1$, $r_2 = -1$, $r_3 = -2$. Therefore, there are three normal modes. The one belonging to r_1 is of the form

$$u(t) = Ae^t \qquad v(t) = Be^t \qquad w(t) = Ce^t$$

and substitution in (4.11) gives the system

$$3A + B = 0 \qquad 3A + B + 2C = 0 \qquad -3A - B + C = 0$$

which has the solution $A = 1$, $B = -3$, $C = 0$. Thus we have one normal mode:

$$u_1(t) = e^t \qquad v_1(t) = -3e^t \qquad w_1(t) = 0$$

Similarly, one finds the other two modes:

$$u_2(t) = e^{-t} \qquad v_2(t) = -e^{-t} \qquad w_2(t) = -2e^{-t}$$
$$u_3(t) = e^{-2t} \qquad v_3(t) = 0 \qquad w_3(t) = -\tfrac{3}{2}e^{-2t}$$

The general solution of the reduced system is now

$$u(t) = \alpha_1 e^t + \alpha_2 e^{-t} + \alpha_3 e^{-2t}$$
$$v(t) = -3\alpha_1 e^t - 3\alpha_2 e^{-t} \qquad \alpha_1, \alpha_2, \alpha_3 \text{ arbitrary}$$
$$w(t) = -2\alpha_2 e^{-t} - \tfrac{3}{2}\alpha_3 e^{-2t}$$

We finally turn to more general systems of the form

$$
\begin{aligned}
P_1(D)x + Q_1(D)y + R_1(D)z &= f_1 \\
(4.13) \qquad P_2(D)x + Q_2(D)y + R_2(D)z &= f_2 \\
P_3(D)x + Q_3(D)y + R_3(D)z &= f_3
\end{aligned}
$$

Here we assume that the polynomials P_i, Q_i, R_i are all of degree $\leq p$ (some positive integer) and that the determinant (the *characteristic determinant*)

$$
\Delta(D) = \begin{vmatrix} P_1(D) & Q_1(D) & R_1(D) \\ P_2(D) & Q_2(D) & R_2(D) \\ P_3(D) & Q_3(D) & R_3(D) \end{vmatrix}
$$

is of degree $3p$. Clearly it could not be of higher degree, but what is essential here is that it should not be of lower degree either. The normal first-order system (4.4) is a special case in which $p = 1$ and $\Delta(D)$ is of degree 3.

The initial conditions appropriate for (4.13) prescribe the values of x, y, z together with their derivatives of order $\leq p - 1$ at some initial t_0. In order not to encumber the formulas, we shall assume again that the prescribed values are zero (homogeneous I.C.).

By a proof similar to that for Theorem 1, one now establishes:

Theorem 3. *If the operator polynomials in system (4.13) are all of degree $\leq p$, and if the determinant $\Delta(D)$ formed from them is of degree $3p$, then system (4.13) has a unique solution satisfying the I.C.*

$$x(t_0) = Dx(t_0) = \cdots = D^{p-1}x(t_0) = 0$$
$$y(t_0) = Dy(t_0) = \cdots = D^{p-1}y(t_0) = 0$$
$$z(t_0) = Dz(t_0) = \cdots = D^{p-1}z(t_0) = 0$$

This solution is given by the expressions

$$x = \frac{\Delta_{P_1}(D)}{\Delta(D)} f_1 + \frac{\Delta_{P_2}(D)}{\Delta(D)} f_2 + \frac{\Delta_{P_3}(D)}{\Delta(D)} f_3$$

$$y = \frac{\Delta_{Q_1}(D)}{\Delta(D)} f_1 + \frac{\Delta_{Q_2}(D)}{\Delta(D)} f_2 + \frac{\Delta_{Q_3}(D)}{\Delta(D)} f_3$$

$$z = \frac{\Delta_{R_1}(D)}{\Delta(D)} f_1 + \frac{\Delta_{R_2}(D)}{\Delta(D)} f_2 + \frac{\Delta_{R_3}(D)}{\Delta(D)} f_3$$

where the Δ_{P_i}, Δ_{Q_i}, Δ_{R_i} are the cofactors of $P_i(D)$, $Q_i(D)$, $R_i(D)$ in the determinant $\Delta(D)$.

Example 3.   Find the solution of the system

$$x + D^2 y + z = 1$$
$$(D^2 - 2)x + 6y = 1$$
$$6y + (D^2 + 2)z = 0$$

for which

$$x = 1 \qquad Dx = y = Dy = z = Dz = 0 \qquad \text{when} \qquad t = t_0$$

With the transformation $x(t) = 1 + x^*(t)$, the system becomes

$$x^* + D^2 y + z = 0$$
$$(D^2 - 2)x^* + 6y = 2$$
$$6y + (D^2 + 2)z = 0$$

The characteristic determinant is

$$\Delta = \begin{vmatrix} 1 & D^2 & 1 \\ D^2 - 2 & 6 & 0 \\ 0 & 6 & D^2 + 2 \end{vmatrix} = -D^2(D^4 - 16)$$

Since it is of degree 6, Theorem 3 applies.   Therefore,

$$x^* = \frac{\Delta_{P_2}}{\Delta} 2 \qquad y = \frac{\Delta_{Q_2}}{\Delta} 2 \qquad z = \frac{\Delta_{R_2}}{\Delta} 2$$

But

$$\frac{\Delta_{P_2}}{\Delta} = \frac{D^4 + 2D^2 - 6}{D^2(D^4 - 16)} = \frac{\frac{3}{8}}{D^2} + \frac{\frac{9}{16}}{D^2 - 4} + \frac{\frac{1}{16}}{D^2 + 4}$$

$$\frac{\Delta_{Q_2}}{\Delta} = -\frac{D^2 + 2}{D^2(D^4 - 16)} = \frac{\frac{1}{8}}{D^2} - \frac{\frac{3}{16}}{D^2 - 4} + \frac{\frac{1}{16}}{D^2 + 4}$$

$$\frac{\Delta_{R_2}}{\Delta} = \frac{6}{D^2(D^4 - 16)} = \frac{-\frac{3}{8}}{D^2 - 4} + \frac{\frac{3}{16}}{D^2 - 4} + \frac{\frac{3}{16}}{D^2 + 4}$$

Hence,

$$x^*(t) = \tfrac{3}{8}t^2 + \tfrac{9}{32}(\cosh 2t - 1) - \tfrac{1}{32}(\cos 2t - 1)$$

and

$$x(t) = \tfrac{3}{4} + \tfrac{3}{8}t^2 + \tfrac{9}{32}\cosh 2t - \tfrac{1}{32}\cos 2t$$
$$y(t) = \tfrac{1}{8} + \tfrac{1}{8}t^2 + \tfrac{3}{32}\cosh 2t - \tfrac{1}{32}\cos 2t$$
$$z(t) = -\tfrac{3}{8}t^2 + \tfrac{3}{32}\cosh 2t - \tfrac{3}{32}\cos 2t$$

PROBLEMS

1. Find the normal modes of the reduced systems and the general solutions of the following systems:

(a) $(D - 1)x + 2y = 0,\ 3x + (D - 2)y = 0$

(b) $(D + a)x - by = A,\ bx + (D - a)y = B;\ a^2 - b^2 = 1$ a, b, A, B constants

(c) $(D + 3)x + 16y + 14z = 0,\ 12x - (D - 40)y + 33z = 0,$
$12x + 38y + (D + 31)z = 0$

(d) $Dx = x + f,\ Dy = y + z + g,\ Dz = 2z$

(e) $Dx = x - 4y - 4z,\ Dy = -9y - 10z,\ Dz = 8y + 9z$

(f) $Dx + ay - bz = 0,\ -ax + Dy + cz = 0,\ bx - cy + Dz = 0;\ a^2 + b^2 + c^2 = 1$ a, b, c constants

2. Find the solution of the following system:

$$(D + 2)x + y = 1$$
$$(D - 1)y + (D + 2)z = 0$$
$$(D - 1)x + Dz = -1$$

with I.C. $x = 1,\ y = z = 0$ at $t = 0$.

3. Find the solution of the system of Example 3 using Laplace transforms.

4. Suppose $a_{11}, a_{12}, \ldots, a_{33}$ are constants. Use Theorem 1 to show that the first-order homogeneous system

$$Dx_1 = a_{11}x_1 + a_{12}x_2 + \cdots + a_{1n}x_n$$
$$\cdots \cdots \cdots \cdots \cdots \cdots \cdots \cdots \cdots$$
$$Dx_n = a_{n1}x_1 + a_{n2}x_2 + \cdots + a_{nn}x_n$$

has a unique solution satisfying the I.C. $x_1(t_0) = \xi_1, \ldots, x_n(t_0) = \xi_n$. Give the operational form of the solution.

5. Let $(D^n + a_1D^{n-1} + \cdots + a_n)x = f$ be a linear nth-order equation with constant coefficients. Establish an equivalent normal first-order system in the functions $x_k = D^{k-1}x$ $(k = 1, \ldots, n)$. Using this device, formulate the conclusions of Theorems 1 and 2 for the nth-order equation.

6. Formulate the analogue of Theorem 2 for the system (4.13).

7. Extend the statements of Theorems 2 and 3 to systems of n equations in n unknown functions.

8. Find the Laplace transforms X, Y, Z of the solution of (4.13) that satisfies homogeneous I.C., assuming that the transforms F_1, F_2, F_3 of f_1, f_2, f_3 exist. Compare with the operator solution of the system.

★9. In system (4.13) assume that the degree p of P_1 is greater than the degrees of P_2 and P_3, that the degree q of Q_2 is greater than the degrees of Q_1 and Q_3, and that the degree r of R_3 is greater than the degrees of R_1 and R_2. Prove that the system has a unique solution for prescribed initial values of x, Dx, $\ldots$, $D^{p-1}x$; y, Dy, $\ldots$, $D^{q-1}y$; z, Dz, $\ldots$, $D^{r-1}z$, at some initial t_0. HINT: Set up a first-order normal system equivalent to (4.13) in the $p + q + r$ unknown functions $x_k = D^{k-1}x$ $(k = 1, \ldots , p)$, $y_k = D^{k-1}y$ $(k = 1, \ldots , q)$, $z_k = D^{k-1}z$ $(k = 1, \ldots , r)$. Then apply the conclusion of Prob. 7.

5. Applications to Mechanical Systems

We consider mechanical systems in which the motion is restricted either to translations along fixed straight lines (*translational systems*) or to rotations about fixed axes (*rotational systems*). We assume that the moving bodies are rigid and that the guides constraining the motion are of negligible mass.

The elementary components of the *translational* systems to be considered are masses constrained to move along fixed lines, springs, dampers, and sources of force (acceleration) or of velocity. Each of these elements results in a force acting along the line of motion.

Masses provide *reaction* or *inertia* forces. If x is the displacement of mass m with respect to a reference frame that is at rest or in uniform motion, and $v = Dx$ is the velocity, then the force necessary to impart the acceleration D^2x to mass m is $mDv = mD^2x$. The negative of this force, that is, $-mD^2x$, is the reaction force resulting from the motion of the inert mass.

Springs provide *restoring forces*. If x is the displacement difference of the ends of the spring, then the restoring force is assumed to be $-kx$, where k is independent of x (that is, the spring is "linear") and is called the *stiffness constant* of the spring.

Dampers provide *resistance forces*. If $v = Dx$ is the velocity difference of the parts of the damper that are in frictional contact, then the resistance force is assumed to be $-bv$, where b is independent of v (that is, the damper is "linear") and is called the *resistance constant* of the damper.

The masses m, stiffness constants k, and resistance constants b are assumed to be invariant in time. With these assumptions the equations of motion of the mechanical systems to be considered are linear differential equations with constant coefficients.

The equations of motion may be established by use of *D'Alembert's principle* (Jean le Rond d'Alembert, 1717–1783), which may be expressed as follows:

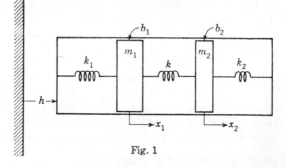

Fig. 1

The sum of all the instantaneous forces acting on a body, including the reaction force due to inertia, is zero.

This is but another version of Newton's second law of motion. By this principle the equations of dynamics are formally the same as those of statics, the difference consisting only in the inclusion of reactive forces.

An example will illustrate the proper use of the introduced concepts.

Example 1. A mechanical system (see Fig. 1) consists of two masses m_1, m_2 connected by a spring of stiffness k. The masses are constrained by a frame to move only in a horizontal direction. There is viscous friction between the masses and the frame, the respective resistance constants being b_1, b_2. Mass m_1 is attached to one end of the frame through a spring of stiffness k_1; mass m_2 is attached to the other end through a spring of stiffness k_2. Determine the motion of the masses resulting from a given horizontal motion of the frame, assuming that at time $t = 0$ the springs are not stressed and the masses are at rest.

Let $h(t)$, $x_1(t)$, $x_2(t)$ be the displacements of the frame and the masses, at time t, from fixed reference lines which are chosen such that when $h = x_1 = x_2 = 0$ there is no stress in the springs. Then the elongations of the springs k_1, k, k_2 at time t are, respectively, $x_1(t) - h(t)$, $x_2(t) - x_1(t)$, $h(t) - x_2(t)$. Therefore, the restoring forces acting on m_1, m_2 are, respectively,

$$k(x_2 - x_1) - k_1(x_1 - h) \qquad k_2(h - x_2) - k(x_2 - x_1)$$

Since the velocities of the masses with respect to the frame at time t are $D[x_1(t) - h(t)]$, $D[x_2(t) - h(t)]$, the resistance forces acting on m_1, m_2 are, respectively,

$$-b_1 D(x_1 - h) \qquad -b_2 D(x_2 - h)$$

Hence, by D'Alembert's principle, the equations of motion are

$$-m_1 D^2 x_1 - b_1 D(x_1 - h) + k(x_2 - x_1) - k_1(x_1 - h) = 0$$
$$-m_2 D^2 x_2 - b_2 D(x_2 - h) + k_2(h - x_2) - k(x_2 - x_1) = 0$$

or

$$(m_1D^2 + b_1D + k + k_1)x_1 - kx_2 = (b_1D + k_1)h$$
$$-kx_1 + (m_2D^2 + b_2D + k + k_2)x_2 = (b_2D + k_2)h$$

If we denote the known right members of these equations by f_1, f_2, and their transforms by F_1, F_2, then the solution of this system for which $x_1 = Dx_1 = x_2 = Dx_2 = 0$ when $t = 0$ has Laplace transforms X_1 and X_2 satisfying

$$(m_1s^2 + b_1s + k + k_1)X_1 - kX_2 = F_1(s)$$
$$-kX_1 + (m_2s^2 + b_2s + k + k_2)X_2 = F_2(s)$$

whence

$$X_1(s) = \frac{(m_2s^2 + b_2s + k + k_2)F_1(s) + kF_2(s)}{\Delta(s)}$$

$$X_2(s) = \frac{kF_1(s) + (m_1s^2 + b_1s + k + k_1)F_2(s)}{\Delta(s)}$$

where $\Delta(s) = (m_1s^2 + b_1s + k + k_1)(m_2s^2 + b_2s + k + k_2) - k^2$. Then x_1 and x_2 are found by finding the inverse transforms.

The solution, using operator methods as in Sec. 4, is

$$x_1 = \frac{m_2D^2 + b_2D + k + k_2}{\Delta(D)} f_1 + \frac{k}{\Delta(D)} f_2$$

$$x_2 = \frac{k}{\Delta(D)} f_1 + \frac{m_1D^2 + b_1D + k + k_1}{\Delta(D)} f_2$$

We next consider *rotational* systems. Their elementary components are masses constrained to rotate about fixed axes, torsional springs, dampers, and sources of torque (angular acceleration) and of angular velocity. Each of these elements results in a torque acting about the axis of rotation.

Masses provide *reaction* or *inertia* torques. If θ is the angular displacement of mass m about the axis of rotation from a reference line that is fixed or in uniform rotation, and if $\omega = D\theta$ is the angular velocity, then the torque necessary to impart the angular acceleration $D^2\theta = D\omega$ to mass m is $ID\omega = ID^2\theta$, where I is the polar moment of inertia of mass m with respect to the axis of rotation. The negative of this torque, that is, $-ID^2\theta$, is the torque resulting from the rotation of the inert mass.

Torsional springs provide *restoring torques*. If θ is the angular displacement difference of the ends of the spring, then the restoring torque is assumed to be $-k\theta$, where k is independent of θ and is called the *torsional stiffness constant* of the spring.

Dampers provide *resistance torques*. If $\omega = D\theta$ is the angular velocity difference of the surfaces of the damper that are in frictional contact, then the resistance torque is assumed to be $-b\omega$, where b is

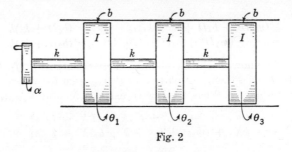

Fig. 2

independent of ω and is called the *torsional resistance constant* of the damper.

As for translational systems, the equations of motion for rotational systems are linear differential equations with constant coefficients if we assume the inertia moments I, the stiffness constants k, and the resistance constants b to be invariant in time. D'Alembert's principle, stated above for translational systems, applies to rotational systems too, provided that in its statement forces are replaced with torques.

Example 2. A shaft (see Fig. 2) carries three flywheels of the same polar moment of inertia I. One of its ends is free; the other end carries a driving wheel. The three parts of the shaft between the driving wheel and flywheels are of the same torsional stiffness k. The flywheels are in frictional contact with a stationary surface, the torsional resistance constant for each being b. Determine the angular motion of the flywheels resulting from a given angular motion of the driving wheel, assuming that at time $t = 0$ the shaft is not twisted and the flywheels are at rest.

Let $\alpha(t)$, $\theta_1(t)$, $\theta_2(t)$, $\theta_3(t)$ be the angular displacements, at time t, of the driving wheel and flywheels from fixed reference lines which are such that when $\alpha = \theta_1 = \theta_2 = \theta_3 = 0$ there is no torsion in the shaft. Then the twists of the three parts of the shaft at time t are $\theta_1(t) - \alpha(t)$, $\theta_2(t) - \theta_1(t)$, $\theta_3(t) - \theta_2(t)$. Therefore, the restoring torques acting on the three rotors are

$$k[(\theta_2 - \theta_1) - (\theta_1 - \alpha)] \qquad k[(\theta_3 - \theta_2) - (\theta_2 - \theta_1)] \qquad -k(\theta_3 - \theta_2)$$

The resistance torques are

$$-bD\theta_1 \qquad -bD\theta_2 \qquad -bD\theta_3$$

Therefore, the equations of motion are

$$-ID^2\theta_1 - bD\theta_1 + k(\theta_2 - 2\theta_1 + \alpha) = 0$$
$$-ID^2\theta_2 - bD\theta_2 + k(\theta_3 - 2\theta_2 + \theta_1) = 0$$
$$-ID^2\theta_3 - bD\theta_3 - k(\theta_3 - \theta_2) = 0$$

or

$$(ID^2 + bD + 2k)\theta_1 - k\theta_2 = k\alpha$$
$$-k\theta_1 + (ID^2 + bD + 2k)\theta_2 - k\theta_3 = 0$$
$$-k\theta_2 + (ID^2 + bD + k)\theta_3 = 0$$

The Laplace transforms Θ_1, Θ_2, Θ_3 of the solution satisfying the I.C. $\theta_1 = D\theta_1 = \theta_2 = D\theta_2 = \theta_3 = D\theta_3 = 0$ at $t = 0$ will satisfy the equations

$$(Is^2 + bs + 2k)\Theta_1 - k\Theta_2 = kA(s)$$
$$-k\Theta_1 + (Is^2 + bs + 2k)\Theta_2 - k\Theta_3 = 0$$
$$k\Theta_2 + (Is^2 + bs + k)\Theta_3 = 0$$

where $A = \mathcal{L}\alpha$. Solving for Θ_1, Θ_2, Θ_3 and taking inverse transforms will give the solution. The solution can also be written symbolically using operators as in Sec. 4.

PROBLEMS

1. A train is made up of a locomotive of mass m_1 and one car of mass m_2. The connecting coupling is a spring of stiffness constant k together with a shock absorber that is a viscous friction damper of resistance constant b. Determine the Laplace transforms of the motions of locomotive and car if the train starts from rest at $t = 0$ and the driving force of the locomotive is $f(t)$. Also write the solution using the integral operators of Sec. 4.

2. Determine the Laplace transforms of the motions of Prob. 1 if the velocity of the locomotive is v_0 at time $t = 0$ and there is no driving force. What is the smallest value of the resistance constant b such that the relative motion of locomotive and car is not oscillatory?

3. A train is made up of a locomotive and two cars, each having a mass m. The connecting couplings are springs of stiffness constant k, together with shock absorbers of resistance constant b. Determine the Laplace transforms of the motions of the three units if the locomotive has velocity v_0 at time $t = 0$ and there is no driving force. What is the smallest value of the resistance constant b such that the relative motion of the units is not oscillatory?

4. A uniform shaft free to rotate in bearings carries three disks. The polar moment of inertia of each of the two end disks is I; that of the center disk is $2I$. The torsional stiffness constant of the shaft between each two disks is k. Determine the motion of one of the end disks if the shaft starts from rest and an alternating torque $T_0 \sin \omega t$ is applied to the center disk.

5. A shaft is fixed at the point O and carries disks of the same polar moment of inertia at the points A, B, C. If the torsional stiffness constants of the portions OA, AB, BC of the shaft are $k_1 = 11k$, $k_2 = 8k$, $k_3 = 19k$, respectively, determine the natural frequencies of the vibrating shaft.

6. A shaft carries at one end a disk whose polar moment of inertia is I_1. At the other end it carries a vibration damper consisting of a drum that is rigidly attached to the shaft and an inner flywheel, whose rotation relative to the drum produces damping represented by the torsional resistance constant b. The polar moments of inertia of drum and flywheel are I_2 and I_3, respectively, and the torsional stiffness constant of the shaft is k. Determine the motion of the disk if a torque $T(t)$ is applied to it, assuming that the shaft is at rest when $t = 0$. What is the frequency of the free damped oscillations (i.e., with no torque applied) if in a system of consistent units $I_1 = 111$, $I_2 = 1$, $I_3 = 8$, $k = 111$, $b = 16$.

7. A mechanical system consists of two pendulums of equal length l carrying equal masses m suspended from points A, B lying on a horizontal. The pendulums are connected by a spring $A'B'$ of stiffness constant k, where $AA' = BB' = h$. Determine the natural frequencies of small vibrations of the system. HINT: For small angles the sine can be replaced by the angle itself, and the cosine by unity. In this way the problem is "linearized."

6. Applications to Electrical Systems

The electrical systems we shall consider are one-dimensional networks whose physical dimensions are small as compared with the main wavelengths of the currents under consideration. With this restriction we may assume that all current and voltage changes take place practically instantaneously throughout the system, and hence we may disregard their dependence on space variables. The elements of the network appear then as "lumped" rather than "distributed."

The elementary components of the networks to be considered are resistors, capacitors, inductors, and sources of voltage (electromotive force) or of current.

Resistors cause voltage drops. If i is the current flowing through a resistor, then the voltage drop across the resistor is Ri, where R is independent of i (that is, the resistor is "linear") and is called the *resistance*. Since i is the rate of change of the charge q flowing through any cross section of the resistor ($i = Dq$), the voltage drop across the resistor may also be written as RDq. Capacitors, when charged, act as voltage sources. If q is the charge on the capacitor, then the voltage drop across the capacitor is assumed to be $(1/C)q$, where C is independent of q and is called the *capacitance*. Inductors tend to resist current changes. The voltage necessary to induce the rate of change Di in the inductor is assumed to be LDi, where L is independent of Di and is called the (*self-*) *inductance*.

The resistances R, capacitances C, and inductances L are assumed to be invariant in time. With these assumptions the network equations of the electrical systems to be considered are linear differential equations with constant coefficients.

The network equations are readily established by the use of Kirchhoff's laws:

1. The sum of the instantaneous branch currents flowing to or from a junction point (node) in the network is zero.

2. Around any closed circuit in the network the sum of the instantaneous voltage drops in a specific direction is zero.

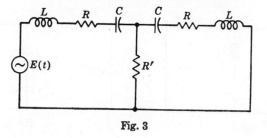

Fig. 3

For branches that contain capacitors, one uses the charge flowing through any cross section as the dependent variable; for branches without capacitors, one preferably uses the current as the dependent variable since the equation in the current is of lower order than that in the charge.

Example 1. Determine the currents through the inductance coils of the network of Fig. 3 if these currents and the charges on the capacitors are zero at time $t = 0$.

As the unknowns we choose the charges q_1, q_2 on the two capacitors. Then the currents through the inductance coils are Dq_1, Dq_2, and the current through the resistor R' is, by the first of the Kirchhoff laws, $D(q_1 - q_2)$. Hence, using the second Kirchhoff law, we obtain the following network equations:

$$\left(LD^2 + RD + \frac{1}{C}\right) q_1 + R'D(q_1 - q_2) = E$$

$$\left(LD^2 + RD + \frac{1}{C}\right) q_2 - R'D(q_1 - q_2) = 0$$

or

$$\left[LD^2 + (R + R')D + \frac{1}{C}\right] q_1 - R'Dq_2 = E$$

$$- R'Dq_1 + \left[LD^2 + (R + R')D + \frac{1}{C}\right] q_2 = 0$$

We seek the solution for which

$$q_1 = Dq_1 = q_2 = Dq_2 = 0 \quad \text{when} \quad t = 0$$

Taking Laplace transforms and solving for Q_1, Q_2, one obtains

(6.1)
$$Q_1(s) = \frac{Ls^2 + (R + R')s + C^{-1}}{\Delta(s)} \mathcal{L}E(s)$$

$$Q_2(s) = \frac{R's}{\Delta(s)} \mathcal{L}E(s)$$

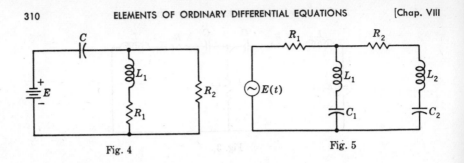

Fig. 4   Fig. 5

where $\Delta(s) = (Ls^2 + Rs + C^{-1})[Ls^2 + (R + 2R')s + C^{-1}]$. Since current $i = Dq$, the Laplace transforms of the currents are obtained from (6.1):

$$I_1(s) = \frac{Ls^3 + (R + R^1)s^2 + C^{-1}s}{\Delta(s)} \, \mathfrak{L}E(s)$$

$$I_2(s) = \frac{R's^2}{\Delta(s)} \, \mathfrak{L}E(s)$$

PROBLEMS

1. If in the network represented by Fig. 4 there is, at time $t = 0$, no charge on the capacitor and no current flowing, determine the charge as a function of time, using $C = 10^{-5}$ farad, $L_1 = 0.1$ henry, $R_1 = 50$ ohms, $R_2 = 200$ ohms, and $E = 100$ volts.

2. If in the network represented by Fig. 5 there are, at time $t = 0$, no charges on the capacitors and no currents flowing, determine the Laplace transforms of the currents through the coils L_1, L_2.

3. Each side of a triangular circuit contains a capacitance C, and each vertex is connected to a common central point by an inductance L. Show that the natural frequency of the oscillations of this network is $1/2\pi \sqrt{3LC}$. Also consider the network with capacitances and inductances interchanged.

4. Assuming there is initially no charge on the capacitor of the symmetric T network of Fig. 6, and initially no currents flow, determine the voltage $v(t)$

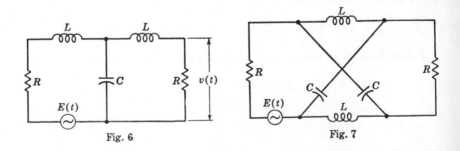

Fig. 6   Fig. 7

across the terminal resistance R if $L = 0.01$ henry, $C = 2 \times 10^{-6}$ farad, and $R = 100$ ohms.

5. Assuming there are initially no charges on the capacitors of the symmetric lattice network of Fig. 7, and initially no currents flow, show that the sum of the charges at time t is

$$\frac{1}{R} \int_0^t e^{(t_1 - t)/RC} E(t_1) \, dt_1$$

chapter *ix*

Linear Equations with Variable Coefficients

In this chapter a few methods are taken up that apply to the solution of linear differential equations with variable coefficients. The methods are, of necessity, restricted as to both scope and practicality. A more general treatment of this subject would require the use of advanced parts of the theory of functions, whose knowledge is not assumed in this elementary exposition.

It should be recalled at this point that the results established in Secs. 1 to 5, 8, and 9 of Chap. VI are quite general and apply to linear equations with variable coefficients as well as to those with constant coefficients. A brief summary of the most important of these results follows:

1. Where the coefficients of

$$y^{(m)} + A_1(x)y^{(m-1)} + \cdots + A_m(x)y = F(x)$$

are continuous, there is a unique solution satisfying given I.C.

2. The set of all solutions of the homogeneous equation of order m forms a vector space of dimension m.

3. The general solution of a nonhomogeneous equation is the sum of a particular solution and the general solution of the reduced equation.

4. The superposition principle holds.

1. Equations of Euler-Cauchy

These equations are closely related to those with constant coefficients. They are of the form

$$(1.1) \quad x^n \frac{d^n y}{dx^n} + a_1 x^{n-1} \frac{d^{n-1} y}{dx^{n-1}} + \cdots + a_{n-1} x \frac{dy}{dx} + a_n y = f(x)$$

where $a_1, a_2, \ldots, a_n$ are constants.

In order to solve Eq. (1.1), we introduce a new independent variable t defined by

$$(1.2) \qquad x = e^t \qquad t = \log x \qquad y(x) = Y(t) \qquad f(x) = F(t)$$

Since $\log x$ is real only when $x > 0$, this substitution is, strictly speaking, valid only for $x > 0$. For $x < 0$ one may employ the substitution

$$-x = e^t \qquad t = \log(-x)$$

and then proceed as with substitution (1.2).

To examine the effect of substituting $x = e^t$ in an equation of the above type, consider the equation of second order

$$(1.3) \qquad x^2 \frac{d^2 y}{dx^2} + a_1 x \frac{dy}{dx} + a_2 y = f(x)$$

By the chain rule of differentiation,

$$(1.4) \qquad \frac{dy}{dx} = \frac{dY}{dt} \frac{dt}{dx} = \frac{1}{x} \frac{dY}{dt}$$

$$\frac{d^2 y}{dx^2} = \frac{d}{dt}\left(\frac{1}{x} \frac{dY}{dt}\right) \frac{dt}{dx}$$

$$= \frac{1}{x} \frac{d}{dt}\left(\frac{dY}{dt}\right) \frac{dt}{dx} - \frac{1}{x^2} \frac{dY}{dt}$$

or

$$(1.5) \qquad \frac{d^2 y}{dx^2} = \frac{1}{x^2} \frac{d^2 Y}{dt^2} - \frac{1}{x^2} \frac{dY}{dt}$$

Hence, Eq. (1.3) becomes

$$\frac{d^2 Y}{dt^2} - \frac{dY}{dt} + a_1 \frac{dY}{dt} + a_2 Y = F$$

or

$$(1.6) \qquad \frac{d^2 Y}{dt^2} + (a_1 - 1) \frac{dY}{dt} + a_2 Y = F$$

Equation (1.6) is a linear equation with constant coefficients and can be dealt with by the methods developed in Chaps. V and VI. If

$t = \log x$ is substituted in the resulting solution, the solution of Eq. (1.3) is obtained.

Thus it is seen that the substitution $x = e^t$ has the effect of transforming Eq. (1.3) into one with constant coefficients. The same is true for the general Euler-Cauchy equation (1.1). We omit the proof.

Example 1. Find the general solution of the equation

$$(1.7) \qquad x^4 \frac{d^4y}{dx^4} + 4x^3 \frac{d^3y}{dx^3} + x^2 \frac{d^2y}{dx^2} + x \frac{dy}{dx} - y = -\log x \qquad x > 0$$

From (1.2), (1.4), and (1.5) we have dy/dx and d^2y/dx^2. We find two more derivatives using the chain rule.

$$\frac{d^3y}{dx^3} = \frac{d}{dt}\left(\frac{1}{x^2}\frac{d^2Y}{dt^2} - \frac{1}{x^2}\frac{dY}{dt} \right)\frac{dt}{dx}$$

$$= \frac{-2}{x^3}\frac{d^2Y}{dt^2} + \frac{1}{x^2}\frac{d^3Y}{dt^3}\frac{dt}{dx} + \frac{2}{x^3}\frac{dY}{dt} - \frac{1}{x^2}\frac{d^2Y}{dt^2}\frac{dt}{dx}$$

$$= \frac{1}{x^3}\frac{d^3Y}{dt^3} - \frac{3}{x^3}\frac{d^2Y}{dt^2} + \frac{2}{x^3}\frac{dY}{dt}$$

Similarly,

$$\frac{d^4y}{dx^4} = \frac{1}{x^4}\frac{d^4Y}{dt^4} - \frac{6}{x^4}\frac{d^3Y}{dt^3} + \frac{11}{x^3}\frac{d^2Y}{dt^2} - \frac{6}{x^4}\frac{dY}{dt}$$

Then the D.E. (1.7) becomes

$$(1.8) \qquad (D^4 - 2D^3 + 2D - 1)y = -t$$

where $D = d/dt$.

The roots of the auxiliary equation of (1.8) are 1, 1, 1, -1. A particular integral of (1.8) is easily seen to be $Y(t) = t + 2$. Hence the general solution of (1.8) is

$$Y(t) = Ae^{-t} + (B + Ct + Dt^2)e^t + t + 2$$

and the general solution of Eq. (1.7) is

$$y(x) = \frac{A}{x} + (B + C \log x + D \log^2 x)x + \log x + 2$$

In this example it is almost more laborious to check the solution than to derive it.

To transform the general Euler-Cauchy differential equation (1.1) into one with constant coefficients, one uses the formula

$$(1.9) \qquad \frac{d^ky}{dx^k} = x^{-k}D(D-1) \cdots (D-k+1)Y \qquad k = 1, 2, \ldots$$

which is readily established by mathematical induction.   The auxiliary equation of the resulting D.E. with constant coefficients is

$$(1.10) \quad r(r-1) \cdots (r-n+1) + a_1 r(r-1)$$
$$\cdots (r-n+2) + \cdots + a_{n-1}r + a_n = 0$$

Equations of the type

$$(1.11) \quad (Ax+B)^n \frac{d^n y}{dx^n} + a_1 (Ax+B)^{n-1} \frac{d^{n-1}y}{dx^{n-1}}$$
$$+ \cdots + a_{n-1}(Ax+B)\frac{dy}{dx} + a_n y = f(x)$$

where A, B, a_1, a_2, . . . , a_n are constants, are not essentially different from equations of type (1.1).   The transformation

$$Ax + B = e^t$$

reduces Eq. (1.11) to one with constant coefficients.

PROBLEMS

Find the general solutions of the following equations for $x > 0$:

1. $x^2 \dfrac{d^2y}{dx^2} + 2x \dfrac{dy}{dx} - 6y = 0$

2. $2x^2 \dfrac{d^2y}{dx^2} + 5x \dfrac{dy}{dx} + y = Ax + B$

3. $x^2 \dfrac{d^2y}{dx^2} + 3x \dfrac{dy}{dx} + y = Ax^2 + Bx + C$

4. $x^2 \dfrac{d^2y}{dx^2} + 3x \dfrac{dy}{dx} + y = x \log x$

5. $x^3 \dfrac{d^3y}{dx^3} + 2x^2 \dfrac{d^2y}{dx^2} - x \dfrac{dy}{dx} + y = (1 - \log x)^2$

6. $x^4 \dfrac{d^4y}{dx^4} + 5x^3 \dfrac{d^3y}{dx^3} + x^2 \dfrac{d^2y}{dx^2} + 2x \dfrac{dy}{dx} - 2y = 2 \sin (2 \log x)$
$+ 11 \cos (2 \log x)$

7. $x^3 \dfrac{d^3y}{dx^3} + (3 - 3m)x^2 \dfrac{d^2y}{dx^2} + (3m^2 - 3m + 1)x \dfrac{dy}{dx} - m^3 y = 0$

8. $(2x - 1)^2 \dfrac{d^2y}{dx^2} + (2 - 4x)\dfrac{dy}{dx} - 12y = 6(x^2 - x + 1)$ $(x > \tfrac{1}{2})$

9. Establish the Euler-Cauchy equation of third order whose general solution is $y = Ax + Bx^2 + Cx^3$.

10. Establish the Euler-Cauchy equation of third order whose general solution is $y = Ax + Bx \log x + Cx(\log x)^2$.

11. Write the general solution of the reduced equation (1.1) using the distinct roots $r_1, \ldots, r_m$ of the auxiliary equation (1.10).

*12. Show that every solution of the reduced D.E. (1.1) tends to 0 as x approaches 0 from the right, if and only if the roots of (1.10) lie in the right half plane.

2. Reduction by Known Integrals

The order of a linear differential equation can be reduced if any nonidentically vanishing solution of the reduced equation is known. This corresponds to the well-known device in algebra by which the degree of an equation can be reduced if one of its roots is known.

Consider first the linear equation of second order

$$(2.1) \qquad \frac{d^2y}{dx^2} + a_1(x)\frac{dy}{dx} + a_2(x)y = f(x)$$

and assume y_0 is a known integral of the reduced equation, i.e.,

$$(2.2) \qquad \frac{d^2y_0}{dx^2} + a_1(x)\frac{dy_0}{dx} + a_2(x)y_0 = 0$$

Suppose the substitution

$$(2.3) \quad y(x) = y_0(x)u(x) \qquad u(x) = \frac{y(x)}{y_0(x)} \qquad \text{wherever } y_0(x) \neq 0$$

is made, where u is the new unknown function that is to replace y in Eq. (2.1). Differentiating (2.3), one has

$$(2.4) \qquad \begin{aligned} y' &= y_0'u + y_0u' \\ y'' &= y_0''u + 2y_0'u' + y_0u'' \end{aligned}$$

On substituting (2.3) and (2.4) in Eq. (2.1), one obtains

$$y_0u'' + (2y_0' + a_1y_0)u' + (y_0'' + a_1y_0' + a_2y_0)u = f$$

But, because of (2.2), the coefficient of u vanishes, and this equation becomes

$$y_0u'' + (2y_0' + a_1y_0)u' = f$$

This can be considered as a *first-order equation* in the unknown u'. When this equation is solved, u is found by a quadrature, and then y is found by (2.3).

The procedure for the general linear equation of order n,

$$(2.5) \quad \frac{d^ny}{dx^n} + a_1(x)\frac{d^{n-1}y}{dx^{n-1}} + \cdots + a_{n-1}(x)\frac{dy}{dx} + a_n(x)y = f(x)$$

is the same. The substitution (2.3) transforms (2.5) into a D.E. in the derivatives of u but not involving u itself; hence it is a D.E. of order $(n - 1)$ in u'.

Observe that the substitution (2.3) will lead to all solutions of the transformed D.E. in u'. Therefore, if y_1 is another solution (linearly independent of y_0) of the reduced equation, then

$$(2.6) \qquad\qquad u_1' = \left(\frac{y_1}{y_0}\right)'$$

is a (nontrivial) solution of the reduced transformed equation. So, in general, if we know k linearly independent solutions of the original reduced equation, then we shall know $k - 1$ linearly independent solutions of the reduced transformed equation. Therefore the method can be continued, with the eventual result being a D.E. of order $n - k$.

As a special result of the method of reduction by known integrals we have the important conclusion that if n linearly independent integrals of the reduced linear equation of order n are known, then the general solution of the complete equation can be obtained by quadratures alone. If only $n - 1$ linearly independent solutions of the reduced equation are known, the complete equation can be reduced to a linear equation of order $n - (n - 1) = 1$. From Chap. II it is known that a linear equation of the first order can always be solved by quadratures alone. Hence, we have the following theorem:

Theorem 1. *If $n - 1$ linearly independent integrals of the reduced linear differential equation of order n are known, then the general solution of the complete equation can be found by quadratures alone.*

Example Suppose it is required to find the general solution of the equation

$$(2.7) \qquad\qquad \sin x \frac{d^3y}{dx^3} + \cos x \frac{d^2y}{dx^2} + \sin x \frac{dy}{dx} + (\cos x)y = 0$$

In order to exclude points at which the coefficient of the highest derivative vanishes, let x be limited to the interval $0 < x < \pi$.

The equation may be written as

$$\sin x(y''' + y') + \cos x(y'' + y) = 0$$

or

$$\sin x \frac{d}{dx}(y'' + y) + \cos x(y'' + y) = 0$$

or

$$\left(\sin x \frac{d}{dx} + \cos x\right)(y'' + y) = 0$$

Hence, it is seen that $y_0(x) = \sin x$ and $y_1(x) = \cos x$ are linearly independent solutions of this equation. Putting

$$y(x) = y_0(x)u(x) = (\sin x)u(x)$$

one has

$$y' = (\cos x)u + (\sin x)u'$$
$$y'' = -(\sin x)u + 2(\cos x)u' + (\sin x)u''$$
$$y''' = -(\cos x)u - 3(\sin x)u' + 3(\cos x)u'' + (\sin x)u'''$$

and Eq. (2.7) becomes

$$(\sin^2 x)u''' + 4(\sin x \cos x)u'' + 2(\cos^2 x - \sin^2 x)u' + 0u = 0$$

or

(2.8) $$u''' + 4(\operatorname{ctn} x)u'' + 2(\cot^2 x - 1)u' = 0$$

Since $y_1(x) = \cos x$ is a solution of Eq. (2.7),

$$u_1(x) = \frac{y_1(x)}{\sin x} = \cot x$$

must be a solution of Eq. (2.8). Then $u_1' = -\csc^2 x$, and to repeat the above procedure one puts

(2.9) $u'(x) = u_1'(x)v(x) = -(\csc^2 x)v(x)$ $v(x) = -(\sin^2 x)u'(x)$

Then

$$u'' = 2(\csc^2 x \cot x)v - (\csc^2 x)v'$$
$$u''' = -(4 \csc^2 x \cot^2 x + 2 \csc^4 x)v + 4(\csc^2 x \cot x)v' - (\csc^2 x)v''$$

and Eq. (2.8) becomes

$$-(\csc^2 x)v'' + 0v' + 0v = 0$$

(that the coefficient of v is zero is a necessary result of the method; this is not so for the coefficient of v'; its vanishing is fortuitous). Hence,

$$v'' = 0$$
$$v(x) = A + Bx$$

Then, by (2.9),

$$u'(x) = -(A + Bx) \csc^2 x$$

and integration gives

$$u(x) = (A + Bx) \cot x - B \log \sin x + C$$

Therefore,

$$y(x) = A \cos x + C \sin x + B(x \cos x - \sin x \log \sin x)$$

and this is the general solution of Eq. (2.7).

PROBLEMS

For each of the following equations, one or more particular integrals of the corresponding reduced equation are given. Find the general solutions of the complete equations.

1. $x \dfrac{d^2y}{dx^2} - (1 + x) \dfrac{dy}{dx} + y = 0; 1 + x \qquad (x > 0)$

2. $4x(1 - x) \dfrac{d^2y}{dx^2} + (6 - 8x) \dfrac{dy}{dx} - y = 0; x^{-\frac{1}{2}} \qquad (0 < x < 1)$

3. $x^2 \dfrac{d^2y}{dx^2} + x \dfrac{dy}{dx} - y = 2x^2; x^{-1} \qquad (x > 0)$

4. $x^2 \dfrac{d^2y}{dx^2} + x \dfrac{dy}{dx} + \left(x^2 - \dfrac{1}{4} \right) y = 0; x^{-\frac{1}{2}} \sin x \qquad (x > 0)$

5. $(1 - x^2) \dfrac{d^2y}{dx^2} - 2x \dfrac{dy}{dx} + 6y = 0;$ polynomial of degree 2 $\qquad (-1 < x < 1)$

6. $x^3 \dfrac{d^3y}{dx^3} + x \dfrac{dy}{dx} - y = \dfrac{1}{x}; x, x \log x \qquad (x > 0)$

7. $x^2y'' + 3xy' - 3y = \sin x; x, x^{-3} \qquad (x > 0)$. Leave the answer as a quadrature.

3. Method of Variation of Parameters

As shown in the preceding section, the order of a linear equation can be reduced if some integrals of the reduced equation are known. The procedure described there consisted in reducing the order step by step through successive substitutions, each of which employs another of the known integrals. An alternative method will be described now in which only one substitution is made. All k known integrals are used, and the order of the equation is reduced by the number k at once. The method is essentially the same as that of Sec. 6, Chap. V.

Not to complicate matters by cumbersome notation, assume that three linearly independent integrals $y_1(x)$, $y_2(x)$, $y_3(x)$ of the reduced equation are known; hence

$$(3.1) \quad \frac{d^ny_i}{dx^n} + a_1(x) \frac{d^{n-1}y_i}{dx^{n-1}} + \cdots + a_{n-1}(x) \frac{dy_i}{dx} + a_n(x)y_i = 0$$

$$i = 1, 2, 3$$

We introduce three unknown functions u_1, u_2, u_3 and make the substitution

$$(3.2) \qquad y = y_1u_1 + y_2u_2 + y_3u_3$$

Then

$$(3.3) \qquad y' = y_1'u_1 + y_2'u_2 + y_3'u_3 + \underline{y_1u_1' + y_2u_2' + y_3u_3'}$$

This derivative will be simplified if we put the underlined part equal to zero, i.e.,

$$(3.4) \qquad y_1u_1' + y_2u_2' + y_3u_3' = 0$$

Since there are three functions u_1, u_2, u_3 at our disposal which replace the one function y, it is possible to impose two conditions on these functions, and (3.4) is one of them.

Now (3.3) becomes

$$y' = y_1'u_1 + y_2'u_2 + y_3'u_3$$

and another differentiation gives

$$(3.5) \qquad y'' = y_1''u_1 + y_2''u_2 + y_3''u_3 + (y_1'u_1' + y_2'u_2' + y_3'u_3')$$

where the terms in parentheses can be omitted if we impose on u_1, u_2, u_3 the further condition

$$(3.6) \qquad y_1'u_1' + y_2'u_2' + y_3'u_3' = 0$$

Then, from (3.5),

$$y'' = y_1''u_1 + y_2''u_2 + y_3''u_3$$

and higher derivatives are found:

$$y''' = y_1'''u_1 + \cdots \qquad y^{(4)} = y_1^{(4)}u_1 + \cdots \qquad \cdots$$
$$y^{(n)} = y_1^{(n)}u_1 + \cdots$$

In these derivatives no more simplifications like those above are possible; otherwise too many equations would be obtained for the three unknowns u_1, u_2, u_3.

When all these derivatives are substituted in the D.E. and use is made of (3.1), a transformed equation is obtained that contains u_1', u_2', u_3', u_1'', u_2'', . . . , $u_1^{(n-2)}$, $u_2^{(n-2)}$, $u_3^{(n-2)}$, but not the functions u_1, u_2, u_3 themselves. From the previously established Eqs. (3.4) and (3.6), two of the functions u_1', u_2', u_3' can be eliminated, i.e., two of them, for example, u_2', u_3', can be expressed in terms of the third, in this case u_1'. When these expressions are substituted in the transformed equation, a linear equation results that contains only u_1', u_1'', . . . , $u_1^{(n-2)}$. Hence it is a linear differential equation of order $n - 3$ in the unknown u_1', and thus the order of the original equation is reduced by 3. When the transformed equation is solved, u_1 is obtained by a quadrature, and u_2, u_3 by two more quadratures. The solution y itself is then given by (3.2).

If $y_1, \ldots, y_k$ are k linearly independent integrals of (3.1), then $c_1 y_1 + \cdots + c_k y_k$ is also an integral for any choice of the constants $c_1, \ldots, c_k$. Our method of transforming the given equation into one of order $n - k$ is based on the substitution

$$y = u_1 y_1 + u_2 y_2 + \cdots + u_k y_k$$

Because of the formal replacement of the constants $c_1, \ldots, c_k$ by the variables $u_1, \ldots, u_k$, this method is known as *variation of parameters*.

Let the right-hand term of (3.1) be f. If n solutions of the reduced equation are found, the variation-of-parameters method enables us to find the general solution of the complete equation by quadratures alone.

Example 1. To illustrate this method, we apply it to the equation

$$(3.7) \quad (\sin x)y''' + (\cos x)y'' + (\sin x)y' + (\cos x)y = 0 \qquad (0 < x < \pi)$$

that was solved by a different method in the example of the preceding section. The equation has the integrals $\cos x$, $\sin x$. Hence we put

$$(3.8) \qquad y(x) = (\cos x)u_1 + (\sin x)u_2$$

Then

$$(3.9) \quad \begin{aligned} y' &= -(\sin x)u_1 + (\cos x)u_2 \\ y'' &= -(\cos x)u_1 - (\sin x)u_2 - (\sin x)u_1' + (\cos x)u_2' \\ y''' &= (\sin x)u_1 - (\cos x)u_2 - 2(\cos x)u_1' - 2(\sin x)u_2' \\ &\qquad\qquad - (\sin x)u_1'' + (\cos x)u_2'' \end{aligned}$$

and

$$(3.10) \qquad (\cos x)u_1' + (\sin x)u_2' = 0$$

Substitution of (3.8) and (3.9) in (3.7) gives

$$(3.11) \quad -(\sin^2 x)u_1'' + (\sin x \cos x)u_2'' - 3(\sin x \cos x)u_1' \\ + (\cos^2 x - 2\sin^2 x)u_2' = 0$$

From (3.10) we have

$$(3.12) \qquad u_2' = -(\cot x)u_1'$$

and, therefore,

$$(3.13) \qquad u_2'' = (\csc^2 x)u_1' - (\cot x)u_1''$$

Substitution of (3.12) and (3.13) in (3.11) gives

$$-(\sin^2 x + \cos^2 x)u_1'' + (\cot x - 3\sin x \cos x - \cos^2 x \cot x \\ + 2\sin x \cos x)u_1' = 0$$

or

$$u_1'' = 0$$

Hence,

(3.14) $$u_1(x) = A + Bx$$

and, by (3.12),

(3.15)
$$u_2' = -B \cot x$$
$$u_2(x) = -B \log \sin x + C$$

Substitution of (3.14) and (3.15) in (3.8) leads to the general solution

$$y(x) = A \cos x + C \sin x + B(x \cos x - \sin x \log \sin x)$$

PROBLEMS

For each of the following equations, some particular integrals of the corresponding reduced equation are given. Find, by the method of this section, the general solutions of the complete equations.

1. $(1 + x^2)^2 \dfrac{d^2y}{dx^2} + 2x(1 + x^2) \dfrac{dy}{dx} + y = A \arctan x; \; \dfrac{1}{\sqrt{1 + x^2}}, \; \dfrac{x}{\sqrt{1 + x^2}}$

2. $x^3 \dfrac{d^3y}{dx^3} + x \dfrac{dy}{dx} - y = \dfrac{1}{x}; \; x, \; x \log x \qquad (x > 0)$

3. $\dfrac{d^3y}{dx^3} - \left(\dfrac{3}{x} + 2x\right) \dfrac{d^2y}{dx^2} + \left(\dfrac{3}{x^2} + 2 - 4x^2\right) \dfrac{dy}{dx} + 8x^3y = x^3(x^2 - 1); \; e^{-x^2},$
$e^{x^2}, \; x^2 e^{x^2}$

4. $(\sin x)y''' + (\cos x)y'' + (\sin x)y' + (\cos x)y = f(x); \; \sin x, \; \cos x,$
$0 < x < \pi$

4. Transformation of Variables

In all the classes of differential equations treated in this chapter, the solutions are based on some transformation of the variables involved. Thus, in the case of Euler-Cauchy equations, the transformation used is $x = e^t$, which is a transformation of the independent variable. To reduce the order when one integral $y_0(x)$ is known, the transformation is $y = y_0 u$, or $u = y/y_0$, which is a transformation of the dependent variable. In Secs. 5 and 7 we shall encounter other transformations.

Many other transformations are used to convert differential equations to forms in which their solutions become apparent. General rules as to which transformation is to be used in any given case cannot be given here. In this section a few rules concerning the proper use of substitutions are presented. The only thing to remember is the chain rule for differentiation.

If a new *independent* variable is introduced according to

$$x = \varphi(t) \qquad t = \psi(x) \qquad y(x) = y^*(t)$$

then

$$\frac{dy}{dx} = \frac{dy^*}{dt}\frac{dt}{dx} = \psi'\,\frac{dy^*}{dt} \qquad \frac{d^2y}{dx^2} = \psi'^2\,\frac{d^2y^*}{dt^2} + \psi''\,\frac{dy^*}{dt} \qquad \cdots$$

If a new unknown for y is introduced according to

$$y = \psi(x, u) \qquad y(x) = \psi(x, u(x))$$

then

$$\frac{dy}{dx} = \psi_x + \psi_u\,\frac{du}{dx} \qquad \frac{d^2y}{dx^2} = \psi_{xx} + 2\psi_{xu}\,\frac{du}{dx} + \psi_{uu}\left(\frac{du}{dx}\right)^2$$
$$+ \psi_u\,\frac{d^2u}{dx^2} \qquad \cdots$$

where we have used subscripts to denote partial derivatives.

From these formulas it is seen that a change of the independent variable transforms a linear equation into another linear equation. A change of the dependent variable, however, transforms a linear equation into a nonlinear equation unless the substitution itself is linear in the new variable (that is, $\psi_{uu} \equiv 0$). In either case the order of the differential equation remains unchanged.

However, if the substitution involves the derivative of the old dependent variable or the derivative of the new dependent variable, the order of the differential equation may be decreased or increased (compare the transformation of a linear equation of order 2 into a Riccati equation in Sec. 7).

Example 1

$$(\sin^2 x)\,\frac{d^2y}{dx^2} + (\tan x)\,\frac{dy}{dx} - k^2(\cos^2 x)y = 0 \qquad 0 < x < \pi$$

Here the substitution

$$\sin x = t \qquad y(x) = y^*(t)$$

suggests itself. Then

$$\frac{dy}{dx} = (\cos x)\,\frac{dy^*}{dt} \qquad \frac{d^2y}{dx^2} = (\cos^2 x)\,\frac{d^2y^*}{dt^2} - (\sin x)\,\frac{dy^*}{dt}$$

and the differential equation becomes

$$(\sin^2 x \cos^2 x)\,\frac{d^2y^*}{dt^2} + (\sin x - \sin^3 x)\,\frac{dy^*}{dt} - k^2(\cos^2 x)y^* = 0$$

or, after dropping the factor $\cos^2 x$,

$$t^2 \frac{d^2 y^*}{dt^2} + t \frac{dy^*}{dt} -- k^2 y^* = 0$$

This is an Euler-Cauchy equation. Its solution is easily found to be

$$y^*(t) = A t^k + B t^{-k}$$

Hence, the general solution of the D.E. is

$$y(x) = A \sin^k x + B \sin^{-k} x$$

Example 2

(4.1) $$x \frac{d^2 y}{dx^2} + (x + 3) \frac{dy}{dx} + 2y = 0$$

If the two summands xy'' and $3y'$ were xy''' and $3y''$ instead, then their sum would be the third derivative of xy. Hence, the substitution

$$y = \frac{du}{dx}$$

is suggested. Then Eq. (4.1) becomes

$$x \frac{d^3 u}{dx^3} + (x + 3) \frac{d^2 u}{dx^2} + 2 \frac{du}{dx} = 0$$

which can be written as

$$\frac{d^3}{dx^3} (xu) + \frac{d^2}{dx^2} (xu) = 0$$

The general solution of this equation with constant coefficients is

$$A + Bx + Ce^{-x}$$

Hence,

$$u(x) = \frac{A}{x} + B + \frac{C}{x} e^{-x}$$

and

$$y(x) = \frac{A_1}{x^2} + C_1 \left(\frac{1}{x} + \frac{1}{x^2} \right) e^{-x}$$

By checking this solution, we verify that the substitution $y = u'$ has not introduced any extraneous solutions.

Example 3. The D.E. of Example 2 can also be solved by the substitution

$$u(x) = x^2 y(x) \qquad y(x) = \frac{u(x)}{x^2}$$

Then

$$y' = \frac{1}{x^2} u' - \frac{2}{x^3} u \qquad y'' = \frac{1}{x^2} u'' - \frac{4}{x^3} u' + \frac{6}{x^4} u$$

and D.E. (4.1), $xy'' + (x + 3)y' + 2y = 0$, becomes

$$\frac{1}{x} u'' + \left(\frac{1}{x} - \frac{1}{x^2}\right) u' = 0$$

which is a first-order equation for u' with the variables separable. Solving for u', we get

$$u'(x) = Cxe^{-x}$$

whence

$$u(x) = C \int^x xe^{-x}\,dx = -Cxe^{-x} - Ce^{-x} + A$$

and

$$y(x) = \frac{A}{x^2} - C\left(\frac{1}{x} + \frac{1}{x^2}\right)e^{-x}$$

which is the result of Example 2.

PROBLEMS

In the following problems transformations are suggested that will simplify the equations. Find the general solutions $(x > 0)$.

1. $x\dfrac{d^2y}{dx^2} - \dfrac{dy}{dx} + x^3y = 0; t = x^2$

2. $x(1 + x^2)^2\dfrac{d^2y}{dx^2} - (1 - 3x^2)(1 + x^2)\dfrac{dy}{dx} - 8x^3y = 4x^3(1 + x^2); t = 1 + x^2$

3. $x^2\dfrac{d^2y}{dx^2} + 2x^2 \tan y \left(\dfrac{dy}{dx}\right)^2 + x\dfrac{dy}{dx} - \sin y \cos y = 0; u = \tan y$

4. $x(x + 1)^2\dfrac{d^2y}{dx^2} + (3x + 2)(x + 1)\dfrac{dy}{dx} + y = \log(x + 1); u = xy$

5. $x\dfrac{d^2y}{dx^2} + x\left(\dfrac{dy}{dx}\right)^2 + \dfrac{1}{2}\dfrac{dy}{dx} = \dfrac{1}{4}; t = \sqrt{x}, u = e^y$

6. $(1 + x^2)x\dfrac{d^2y}{dx^2} + 2(1 + x)^2\dfrac{dy}{dx} + 4y = 0; u = y + x\dfrac{dy}{dx}$

7. $x^3\dfrac{d^3y}{dx^3} - 36x\dfrac{dy}{dx} - 48y = 0; y = \dfrac{du}{dx}, x^2u = v$

8. Show that a transformation of the form $t = ax + b$ $(a \neq 0)$ transforms a linear equation with constant coefficients into another such equation.

9. Show that a transformation of the form $t = x^r$ $(r \neq 0)$ transforms an Euler-Cauchy equation into another such equation.

10. The special Riccati equation (see Sec. 7)

$$\frac{dy}{dx} + y^2 = A^2 x^{-4}$$

can be transformed by the substitutions

$$x = t^{-1} \qquad y = x^{-1} - ux^{-2}$$

into a special Riccati equation with constant right-hand term. Find its general solution.

11. What transformation of y transforms the equation

$$\frac{d^2y}{dx^2} - x\frac{dy}{dx} + ay = 0$$

into the equation

$$\frac{d^2u}{dx^2} + \left(a + \tfrac{1}{2} - \frac{x^2}{4}\right)u = 0$$

HINT: See the method of Sec. 5.

5. Removal of the Second Highest Derivative

The transformation

(5.1) $$\qquad\qquad y(x) = y_0(x)u(x) \qquad u(x) = \frac{y(x)}{y_0(x)}$$

used when y_0 is a known integral of the reduced equation, is often useful even if y_0 is not an integral. In particular, by such a transformation it is always possible to remove the second highest derivative term from a linear differential equation.

Let the given differential equation be

(5.2) $$\qquad y^{(n)} + a_1(x)y^{(n-1)} + \cdots + a_{n-1}(x)y' + a_n(x)y = f(x)$$

When the substitution (5.1) is made, a new equation in u of the same order is obtained. Its $u^{(n-1)}$ term will originate from $y^{(n)}$ and $y^{(n-1)}$, since none of the lower derivatives can result in a $u^{(n-1)}$ term. But

$$y^{(n)} = y_0 u^{(n)} + ny_0' u^{(n-1)} + \cdots$$
$$y^{(n-1)} = y_0 u^{(n-1)} + \cdots$$

Hence, the coefficient of $u^{(n-1)}$ in the transformed equation is

$$ny_0' + a_1 y_0$$

If this is to vanish, we must have

$$\frac{y_0'}{y_0} = -\frac{1}{n}a_1$$

or, integrated,

$$y_0(x) = \exp\left[-\frac{1}{n}\int^x a_1(x')\,dx'\right]$$

Hence, by the substitution

(5.3) $$y(x) = u(x)\exp\left[-\frac{1}{n}\int^x a_1(x')\,dx'\right]$$

Eq. (5.2) is transformed into a linear equation of the same order with the derivative of order $n-1$ absent. This, by itself, need not make the solution any easier, but sometimes the transformed equation is of a "solvable" type.

Example 1. To find the general solution of the equation

(5.4) $$\frac{d^2y}{dx^2} + 2\frac{dy}{dx} + \left[1 + \frac{2}{(1+3x)^2}\right]y = 0$$

one may try the substitution

$$y(x) = u(x)\exp\left[-\tfrac{1}{2}\int^x a_1(x')\,dx'\right]$$

$$= u(x)e^{-x}$$

Then

$$y' = (-u + u')e^{-x}$$
$$y'' = (u - 2u' + u'')e^{-x}$$

and Eq. (5.4) becomes

(5.5) $$u'' + \frac{2}{(1+3x)^2}\,u = 0$$

This is an Euler-Cauchy equation. Hence, putting

(5.6) $$1 + 3x = e^t \qquad t = \log(1+3x) \qquad u(x) = U(t)$$

Eq. (5.5) becomes

$$9\frac{d^2U}{dt^2} - 9\frac{dU}{dt} + 2U = 0$$

The general solution of this equation with constant coefficients is

$$Ae^{\frac{1}{3}t} + Be^{\frac{2}{3}t}$$

Hence, by (5.6)

$$u(x) = A(1+3x)^{\frac{1}{3}} + B(1+3x)^{\frac{2}{3}}$$

and

$$y(x) = [A(1+3x)^{\frac{1}{3}} + B(1+3x)^{\frac{2}{3}}]e^{-x}$$

PROBLEMS

The following equations can be simplified by removal of the second highest derivative.   Obtain the general solutions.

1. $x^2 \dfrac{d^2y}{dx^2} - 2x \dfrac{dy}{dx} + (x^2 + 2)y = 0$

2. $\dfrac{d^2y}{dx^2} + \dfrac{2}{x} \dfrac{dy}{dx} - \dfrac{2}{(x+1)^2} y = 0$

3. $x^2 \dfrac{d^4y}{dx^4} + 8x \dfrac{d^3y}{dx^3} + 12 \dfrac{d^2y}{dx^2} + x^2y = 2e^x$

4. $(\sin x) \dfrac{d^3y}{dx^3} + 3(\cos x) \dfrac{d^2y}{dx^2} - 6(\sin x) \dfrac{dy}{dx} + (2 \sin x - 4 \cos x)y = \sin x$
$- 3 \cos x$

5. Show that in the case of linear differential equations of *first* order, the method of this section is identical with the method of the integrating factor (see Sec. 5, Chap. II).

6. The equation

$$\frac{d^2x}{dt^2} + b(t) \frac{dx}{dt} + k(t)x = f(t)$$

represents the motion of a vibrating system with variable damping coefficient $b(t)$, variable spring coefficient $k(t)$, and forcing function $f(t)$.   Show that $x(t) = e^{-B(t)}X(t)$, where $B(t) = \frac{1}{2} \displaystyle\int^t b(t') \, dt'$, and where $X(t)$ is the motion of an undamped vibrating system with spring coefficient $K = k - \frac{1}{4}b^2 - \frac{1}{2}b'$ and forcing function $F = e^B f$.

6. Exact Differential Equations and Integrating Factors

A differential equation

$$f(x, y, y', \ldots, y^{(n)}) = 0$$

is said to be *exact* if there is a function $g(x, y, y', \ldots, y^{(n-1)})$ such that

$$f(x, y, y', \ldots, g^{(n)}) = \frac{d}{dx} g(x, y, y', \ldots, y^{(n-1)})$$

is an identity.

Example 1.   The D.E.

(6.1) $$y''' + \sin x \, y'' + \cos x \, y' + y' = f(x)$$

is exact because it is obtained by differentiating

(6.2) $$y'' + \sin x \, y' + y = \int^x f(x_1) \, dx_1 + C$$

When a differential equation is recognized as an exact equation, it is readily integrated, and the result, which contains one arbitrary constant of integration, is said to be a *first integral* of the differential equation. Thus, Eq. (6.2) is a first integral of Eq. (6.1). A first integral is *not* itself a solution of the differential equation, but it is an important step toward the solution, since it is a differential equation of order one lower than the original equation. In many applications, first integrals represent by themselves significant results. For example, the equations in mechanics expressing conservation of energy and momentum are first integrals of the corresponding equations of motion.

For linear D.E. there is a simple criterion for exactness.

Theorem.   *The D.E.*

$$(6.3) \qquad \alpha_0(x)y^{(m)} + \alpha_1(x)y^{(m-1)} + \cdots + \alpha_m(x)y = f(x)$$

is exact if and only if

$$(6.4) \qquad \alpha_0{}^{(m)} - \alpha_1{}^{(m-1)} + \alpha_2{}^{(m-2)} \cdots + (-1)^m \alpha_m = 0$$

Proof.   To simplify the exposition, we shall give a proof for the case $m = 3$. The D.E. is

$$\alpha_0 y''' + \alpha_1 y'' + \alpha_2 y' + \alpha_3 y = f$$

The left member can be rewritten as

$$(6.5) \quad \alpha_0 y''' + \alpha_1 y'' + \alpha_2 y' + \alpha_3 y = \frac{d}{dx}(\alpha_0 y'') + \frac{d}{dx}[(-\alpha_0' + \alpha_1)y']$$

$$+ \frac{d}{dx}[(\alpha_0'' - \alpha_1' + \alpha_2)y] + (-\alpha_0''' + \alpha_1'' - \alpha_2' + \alpha_3)y$$

as may be seen if the differentiations are performed. The last term in (6.5) is a derivative if and only if

$$(6.6) \qquad \alpha_0''' - \alpha_1'' + \alpha_2' - \alpha_3 = 0$$

Therefore (6.3) is exact if and only if (6.6) is valid, which completes the proof.

Example 2.   To illustrate the use of first integrals, the equation

$$(6.7) \quad (\sin x)\frac{d^3y}{dx^3} + (\cos x)\frac{d^2y}{dx^2} + (\sin x)\frac{dy}{dx} + (\cos x)y = 0 \qquad (0 < x < \pi)$$

which was treated in Secs. 2 and 3, is taken up again. Criterion (6.4) is seen to be satisfied; hence this equation is exact. The sum $(\sin x)y''' + (\cos x)y''$ is the derivative of $(\sin x)y''$, and the sum $(\sin x)y' + (\cos x)y$ is the derivative of $(\sin x)y$; hence a first integral of Eq. (6.7) is

$$(\sin x)(y'' + y) = B$$

or

$$y'' + y = B \csc x$$

The general solution of this equation with constant coefficients is readily found to be

$$y(x) = A \cos x + C \sin x + B(\cos x - \sin x \log \sin x)$$

If a differential equation is not exact, it is possible at times to find an *integrating factor*, i.e., a factor that renders the equation exact. Suppose that $\mu(x)$ is such a factor for Eq. (6.3). Then the equation

$$(6.8) \qquad a_0\mu y^{(n)} + a_1\mu y^{(n-1)} + \cdots + a_n\mu y = \mu f$$

must be exact. By the theorem above this is true if and only if

$$(6.9) \qquad \frac{d^n}{dx^n}(a_0\mu) - \frac{d^{n-1}}{dx^{n-1}}(a_1\mu) + \cdots + (-1)^n a_n\mu = 0$$

This equation may be used to check whether or not a suggested function μ is an integrating factor. However, in most cases it would be impractical to try to solve Eq. (6.9) so as to find an integrating factor, since (6.9) is itself a differential equation of order n and, in general, is no less difficult to solve than the original equation. Equation (6.9) is said to be the *adjoint equation* of the reduced equation. It has many applications other than as a criterion for integrating factors.

No general treatment of the subject of integrating factors can be given here, and this method is suggested here only for those cases in which an integrating factor can be found by inspection or by a few systematic trials.

Example 3. In the case of the equation

$$(6.10) \qquad x^3 \frac{d^2y}{dx^2} + 2x \frac{dy}{dx} - 2y = 0$$

one may conjecture a power of x to be an integrating factor. Trying $\mu(x) = x^k$, we must have, by (6.9),

$$\frac{d^2}{dx^2}(x^{3+k}) - \frac{d}{dx}(2x^{1+k}) - 2x^k = 0$$

or

$$(3 + k)(2 + k)x^{1+k} - 2(2 + k)x^k = 0$$

This equation is satisfied if $k = -2$. Hence, x^{-2} is an integrating factor for Eq. (6.10), and the multiplied equation

$$x \frac{d^2y}{dx^2} + \frac{2}{x} \frac{dy}{dx} - \frac{2}{x^2} y = 0$$

is exact. This last equation is now written as

$$\frac{d}{dx}(xy') + \frac{d}{dx}\left[\left(\frac{2}{x} - 1\right)y\right] + \left(\frac{2}{x^2} - \frac{2}{x^2}\right)y = 0$$

from which it follows that

$$xy' + \left(\frac{2}{x} - 1\right)y = A$$

is a first integral. This is a linear equation of the first order, and its general solution is readily found:

$$y(x) = A_1 x + Bxe^{2/x}$$

PROBLEMS

Show that the following equations are exact, and find their general solutions. (In several cases the first integrals are also exact equations.)

1. $(1 + x^2)\dfrac{d^2y}{dx^2} - 2y = 2x$

2. $(x + x^3)\dfrac{d^2y}{dx^2} + (1 + 7x^2)\dfrac{dy}{dx} + 8xy = 0$

3. $(x - 2y)\dfrac{d^2y}{dx^2} + 2\dfrac{dy}{dx}\left(1 - \dfrac{dy}{dx}\right) = 12x^2$

4. $y\dfrac{d^2y}{dx^2} + \left(\dfrac{dy}{dx}\right)^2 + 1 = 0$

5. $\dfrac{1}{x}\dfrac{d^3y}{dx^3} + \left(1 - \dfrac{3}{x^2}\right)\dfrac{d^2y}{dx^2} + \dfrac{6}{x^3}\dfrac{dy}{dx} - \dfrac{6}{x^4}y = 0$

6. Show that the linear equation with constant coefficients

$$(a_0 D^n + a_1 D^{n-1} + a_2 D^{n-2} + \cdots + a_{n-1}D + a_n)y = f$$

is exact if and only if $a_n = 0$.

7. Show that the Euler-Cauchy equation

$$(a_0 x^n D^n + a_1 x^{n-1} D^{n-1} + \cdots + a_{n-1}xD + a_n)y = f(x)$$

is exact if and only if

$$a_0 - \frac{a_1}{n} + \frac{a_2}{n(n-1)} - \frac{a_3}{n(n-1)(n-2)} + \cdots + (-1)^n\frac{a_n}{n!} = 0$$

8. Show that the equation

$$(a_0 x^{m_0} D^n + a_1 x^{m_1} D^{n-1} + \cdots + a_{n-1}D)y = f(x)$$

where $m_k < n - k$ $(k = 0, 1, \ldots)$, is always exact.

★**9.** The equation

$$x^6\frac{d^2y}{dx^2} + (3x^5 - 16x)\frac{dy}{dx} - (3x^4 - 16)y = 0$$

has an integrating factor of the form x^m. Determine m, and then find the general solution of the equation.

10. The equation of motion of a particle of mass m moving along the x axis under the influence of a force $f(x)$ that depends only on the displacement of the particle from the fixed point 0 ("central force") is

$$m \frac{d^2x}{dt^2} = f(x)$$

Show that dx/dt is an integrating factor of this equation and that the corresponding first integral is the equation for conservation of energy.

★11. Show that the adjoint of the adjoint of a homogeneous linear equation is the equation itself. How does it follow from this that every integrating factor of the adjoint equation is an integral of the original equation, and vice versa?

7. Equations of Riccati

The equations of Riccati (J. F. Riccati, 1676–1754) are special nonlinear first-order D.E. that are closely related to linear *homogeneous* second-order D.E. The general Riccati equation is

$$(7.1) \qquad \frac{du}{dx} + b_0(x)u^2 + b_1(x)u + b_2(x) = 0$$

where $b_0(x)$ is not identically zero (otherwise the equation would be linear).

Theorem. *The homogeneous linear second-order D.E.*

$$(7.2) \qquad y'' + \alpha_1(x)y' + \alpha_2(x)y = 0$$

is transformed into a Riccati equation by the substitution

$$(7.3) \qquad u(x) = \frac{y'(x)}{b_0(x)y(x)} \qquad \text{or} \qquad y(x) = \exp\left[\int^x b_0(x_1)u(x_1)\, dx_1 \right]$$

Conversely, (7.3) *transforms the Riccati equation* (7.1) *into a second-order linear homogeneous D.E.*

Proof. Before starting the proof, we remark that the function b_0 can be chosen arbitrarily if we start with the linear D.E. (7.2). Different choices for b_0 will give different Riccati equations. Of course one must have $b_0(x) \neq 0$.
From (7.3),

$$y' = b_0 y u$$
$$y'' = b_0 y u' + b_0' y u + b_0 y' u = (b_0 u' + b_0' u + b_0^2 u^2)y$$

Substituting these derivatives in (7.2), we obtain

$$u' + b_0 u^2 + \left(\alpha_1 + \frac{b_0'}{b_0} \right) u + \frac{\alpha_2}{b_0} = 0$$

which we recognize as a Riccati equation with

$$b_1 = \alpha_1 + \frac{b_0'}{b_0} \quad \text{and} \quad b_2 = \frac{\alpha_2}{b_0}$$

The proof that, conversely, one transforms a Riccati equation into a second-order linear equation by (7.3) is left to the reader.

Since the general solution of the second-order equation (7.2) contains two arbitrary constants, it appears that the relation $u = y'/y$ would result in a solution of the first-order equation in u which also contains two arbitrary constants. This, of course, cannot be true. The apparent paradox is easily dispelled. Since (7.2) is a homogeneous linear equation, its general solution is of the form

$$y = c_1 y_1 + c_2 y_2$$

where y_1, y_2 are two linearly independent integrals. Therefore,

$$u = \frac{y'}{y} = \frac{c_1 y_1' + c_2 y_2'}{c_1 y_1 + c_2 y_2} = \frac{y_1' + (c_2/c_1) y_2'}{y_1 + (c_2/c_1) y_2}$$

and this expression contains essentially one constant c_2/c_1.

It should not be assumed that, by converting a homogeneous linear equation of the second order into a first-order equation of Riccati's type, the former is brought closer to its solution. There exists no general method for the solution of a Riccati equation. Even the so-called *special Riccati equation*

(7.4) $$\frac{du}{dx} + u^2 + ax^m = 0 \qquad a = \text{constant}$$

cannot be solved by quadratures alone unless m is a number that can be written in the form

$$-\frac{4k}{2k \pm 1}$$

where k is a positive integer. The importance of the relationship between linear equations of the second order and Riccati equations lies in the fact that it makes all the methods developed for one type of equation available to the other type. Thus, the afore-mentioned result on the integrability by quadratures of the special Riccati equation (7.4) applies equally well to the corresponding linear equation of second order

(7.5) $$\frac{d^2 y}{dx^2} + ax^m y = 0$$

On the other hand, we derive an important result for Riccati equations from a result derived earlier for linear equations. By the theorem of Sec. 2, a homogeneous linear differential equation of the second order can be solved

by quadratures if any particular integral of the equation is known.   Because
of the theorem in this section the same must hold for Riccati equations.   Thus,
assume that u_0 is any particular integral of Eq. (7.1); that is,

$$(7.6) \qquad \frac{du_0}{dx} + b_0 u_0{}^2 + b_1 u_0 + b_2 = 0$$

Introduce a new function v by the relation

$$u = u_0 + \frac{1}{v}$$

Then

$$u' = u_0' - \frac{v'}{v^2}$$

and substitution in (7.6) gives

$$u_0' - \frac{v'}{v^2} + b_0 \left(u_0{}^2 + 2\,\frac{u_0}{v} + \frac{1}{v^2} \right) + b_1 u_0 + \frac{b_1}{v} + b_2 = 0$$

Multiplication by $-v^2$ and cancellation of those terms that add up to zero,
by (7.6), results in

$$v' - (2 b_0 u_0 + b_1) v - b_0 = 0$$

This is a *linear* equation of the first order which can be solved by quadratures.

Example 1.   For illustration, let it be required to find the general solution
of the Riccati equation

$$(7.7) \qquad \frac{dy}{dx} + y^2 + (2x + 1)y + (1 + x + x^2) = 0$$

By trial one finds the particular integral $y_0(x) = -x$.   Hence, in order to
find the general solution, one puts

$$y = -x + \frac{1}{v}$$

Then

$$y' = -1 - \frac{v'}{v^2}$$

and Eq. (7.7) becomes

$$-1 - \frac{v'}{v^2} + x^2 - \frac{2x}{v} + \frac{1}{v^2} - 2x^2 - x + \frac{2x + 1}{v} + 1 + x + x^2 = 0$$

or

$$v' - v - 1 = 0$$

The general solution of this simple equation is $v = -1 + Ce^x$. Hence, the general solution of (7.7) is

$$y(x) = -x + \frac{1}{Ce^x - 1}$$

PROBLEMS

1. Check that $u(x) = \cot x$ is a solution of the Riccati equation

$$\frac{du}{dx} + u^2 + u \sin 2x = \cos 2x$$

and find its general solution.

2. Find the general solution of the Riccati equation

$$\frac{du}{dx} + u^2 = A^2$$

where A is a constant. What is the corresponding linear equation of the second order?

3. Show that the Riccati equation (7.1) can be solved by elementary methods if

$$b_1 - \frac{b_0'}{b_0} = Ax^{-1} \qquad b_0 b_2 = Bx^{-2}$$

where A, B are constants.

★4. Let u_1, u_2, u_3, u_4 be any four different integrals of a Riccati equation. Show that their *cross ratio*

$$\frac{u_3 - u_1}{u_4 - u_1} \div \frac{u_3 - u_2}{u_4 - u_2}$$

is constant and independent of x. HINT: Let y_1, y_2, y_3, y_4 denote the corresponding integrals of the corresponding linear differential equation of second order. Then y_3 and y_4 must be linear combinations of y_1, y_2. From this fact the statement follows by straightforward calculation.

5. The space factor of the quantum-mechanical wave equation for a particle of mass m vibrating along the x axis under the influence of forces derivable from a potential-energy function $V(x)$ is

$$\frac{h^2}{8\pi^2 m} \frac{d^2y}{dx^2} + [E - V(x)]y = 0$$

where the constant E is the total energy of the particle, and h is Planck's constant. Show that by putting

$$y(x) = A \exp\left[\frac{2\pi i}{h} \int^x u(x')\, dx'\right]$$

one transforms the above equation into a Riccati equation for the function u. This leads to an important approximation method for the solution of the above equation.

8. Periodic Coefficients; Periodic Solutions

Linear differential equations with coefficients that are functions with the same period are, next to equations with constant coefficients, probably the most important linear equations as far as applications are concerned.

The equations to be considered are of the form

$$(8.1) \qquad \frac{d^n x}{dt^n} + a_1(t) \frac{d^{n-1}x}{dt^{n-1}} + a_2(t) \frac{d^{n-2}x}{dt^{n-2}} + \cdots + a_n(t)x = f(t)$$

where the coefficients are continuous, the forcing functions are piecewise continuous, and all are periodic with period τ. Coefficients that are constant also may be considered to be periodic with arbitrary period τ, since if $a(t)$ is constant it satisfies the identity $a(t + \tau) = a(t)$ for arbitrary τ.

First, we remark that if $x(t) = \varphi(t)$ is a solution of (8.1) whose coefficients have period τ, then $x(t) = \varphi(t + \tau)$ is a solution, for, since $\varphi(t)$ is a solution, we have

$$D^m \varphi(t + \tau) + a_1(t + \tau)D^{m-1}\varphi(t + \tau) + \cdots + a_m(t + \tau)\varphi(t + \tau) = f(t + \tau)$$

where $D = d/dt$. Because the a_i and f are periodic with period τ, we have

$$D^m \varphi(t + \tau) + a_1(t)D^{m-1}\varphi(t + \tau) + \cdots + a_m(t)\varphi(t + \tau) = f(t)$$

which shows that $x(t) = \varphi(t + \tau)$ is a solution of (8.1). In the same way one shows that all the functions $\varphi(t + k\tau)$, $k = \pm 1, \pm 2, \pm 3, \ldots$ are solutions. If the solution $\varphi(t + \tau)$ happens to be identically the same function as the above solution $\varphi(t)$, then this solution is itself periodic with the same period as the coefficients. This, however, cannot be expected in general. For example, the coefficients of the equation

$$D^2 x + 2x = \sin t$$

have the period $\tau = 2\pi$. It is easily checked that $x = \sin \sqrt{2}\, t + \sin t$ is a solution of this equation. But this solution is not periodic at all.

Example 1. Suppose $x(t) = \sin \omega t$ is a solution of a linear homogeneous D.E. with constant coefficients. Since the coefficients have the arbitrary period τ, $A \sin \omega(t + \tau)$ is also a solution of the D.E. Thus, a two-dimensional vector space of solutions has been obtained from a single integral.

However, it is true that, with mild restrictions, every linear differential equation whose coefficients have a period τ has exactly one solution possessing the same period τ. This important result will now be stated as a theorem, and its proof will indicate how the one solution of period τ can be determined.

Theorem. *If all the coefficients and the forcing function of a nonhomogeneous linear differential equation are periodic with period τ, then it has exactly one solution that is periodic with period τ provided the reduced equation has no solution of period τ other than the identically vanishing solution.*

Proof. That there can be no more than one solution of period τ is obvious. If there were two different solutions of period τ, their difference would be a nonidentically vanishing function of period τ that satisfies the reduced equation. This is impossible by hypothesis.

Now assume, for the moment, that there exists a solution of Eq. (8.1), say $x(t) = \varphi(t)$, which satisfies the boundary conditions

$$(8.2) \quad x(0) = x(\tau) \qquad Dx(0) = Dx(\tau) \qquad \cdots \qquad D^{n-1}x(0) = D^{n-1}x(\tau)$$

By a previous remark, $x(t) = \varphi(t + \tau)$ is also a solution, for which we write $\psi(t)$. Then, because of (8.2),

$$\psi(0) = \varphi(0 + \tau) = \varphi(0)$$
$$D\psi(0) = D\varphi(0) \qquad \cdots \qquad D^{n-1}\psi(0) = D^{n-1}\varphi(0)$$

Hence, the values of the two solutions $\varphi(t)$, $\psi(t) = \varphi(t + \tau)$ and their first $n - 1$ derivatives are equal for $t = 0$. By the fundamental theorem of Sec. 2, Chap. VI, the two solutions $\varphi(t)$, $\psi(t)$ must, therefore, be identical; that is, $\varphi(t) = \varphi(t + \tau)$ for all values of t. Hence, in order to find a periodic solution of Eq. (8.1) we need only find a solution that satisfies the special boundary conditions (8.2).

We know that the general solution of Eq. (8.1) is of the form

$$x = x_p + c_1 x_1 + c_2 x_2 + \cdots + c_n x_n$$

where x_p is a particular solution of the complete equation, and $x_1, x_2, \ldots, x_n$ are n linearly independent solutions of the reduced equation. The constants $c_1, c_2, \ldots, c_n$ are arbitrary numbers. We try to determine them so that boundary conditions (8.2) are satisfied. This leads to the equations

$$c_1[x_1(\tau) - x_1(0)] + \cdots + c_n[x_n(\tau) - x_n(0)] = -[x_p(\tau) - x_p(0)]$$
$$c_1[x_1'(\tau) - x_1'(0)] + \cdots + c_n[x_n'(\tau) - x_n'(0)] = -[x_p'(\tau) - x_p'(0)]$$
$$\cdots \cdots \cdots \cdots \cdots \cdots \cdots \cdots \cdots \cdots \cdots \cdots$$
$$c_1[x_1^{(n-1)}(\tau) - x_1^{(n-1)}(0)] + \cdots + c_n[x_n^{(n-1)}(\tau) - x_n^{(n-1)}(0)] = [x_p^{(n-1)}(\tau) - x_p^{(n-1)}(0)]$$

These are n linear equations for the n unknowns $c_1, c_2, \ldots, c_n$. It is a well-known result of algebra that such a system has exactly one solution provided the reduced system (that is, where the right-hand terms are zero) has no solution different from $c_1 = c_2 = \cdots = c_n = 0$. In our case this last condition is satisfied; otherwise the reduced equation belonging to (8.1) would have the nonidentically vanishing solution

$$c_1 x_1 + c_2 x_2 + \cdots + c_n x_n$$

of period τ, against our hypothesis. Therefore, a solution of Eq. (8.1) satisfying boundary conditions (8.2) can be found, and this is a solution of period τ.

In the special case in which the coefficients of the nonhomogeneous equation are constant, the hypotheses of the above theorem are easily checked. All the solutions of the reduced equation are then of the form

$$c_1 e^{r_1 t} + c_2 e^{r_2 t} + \cdots + c_n e^{r_n t}$$

where $r_1, r_2, \ldots, r_n$ are the roots of the auxiliary equation. There are nontrivial solutions of period τ among these if and only if at least one of the roots is equal to $2k\pi i/\tau$ $(k = 0, \pm 1, \pm 2, \ldots)$. Thus we derive from the above theorem the following special result.

Corollary. *If the forcing function of a nonhomogeneous linear differential equation with constant coefficients has period τ, then it has exactly one solution of period τ, provided that none of the roots of its auxiliary equation is equal to $2k\pi i/\tau$ $(k = 0, \pm 1, \pm 2, \ldots)$.*

Example 2. Find the periodic solutions of

(8.3) $$(D^2 + 4)x = A \sin 3t$$

The forcing function has period $2\pi/3$ and hence also has periods $4\pi/3$, 2π, $8\pi/3$, etc. The homogeneous D.E. $(D^2 + 4)x = 0$ has the general solution

$$c_1 \cos 2t + c_2 \sin 2t$$

These functions have period π and periods 2π, 3π, etc.

Therefore, by the theorem, the D.E. has a unique periodic solution of period $2\pi/3$. It also has a unique solution of period $4\pi/3$ which must coincide with that of period $2\pi/3$. But there are many solutions of period 2π. To find them we need a particular solution x_p of (8.3). We solve

$$(D^2 + 4)z = A e^{3it}$$

so that $x_p = \operatorname{Im} z$. We find easily that $z_p(t) = -A e^{3it}/5$, whence

$$x_p(t) = -\tfrac{1}{5} A \sin 3t$$

and the general solution of (8.3) is

$$x(t) = c_1 \cos 2t + c_2 \sin 2t - \tfrac{1}{5} A \sin 3t$$

From the general solution we see that, unless $c_1 = c_2 = 0$, x does not have period $2\pi/3$, but x does have period 2π for all c_1, c_2.

It should be observed that in the case of a D.E. with constant coefficients of the form

(8.4) $$P(D)x = A e^{i\omega t}$$

a solution of period ω may immediately be written. The desired solution has the form $x(t) = C e^{i\omega t}$, and one obtains

$$P(D)C e^{i\omega t} = CP(i\omega)e^{i\omega t} = A e^{i\omega t}$$

Hence $C = A/P(i\omega)$, and

$$x(t) = \frac{A}{P(i\omega)} e^{i\omega t}$$

The exceptional case of no periodic solution occurs here if and only if $P(i\omega) = 0$.

PROBLEMS

1. Assuming that the two functions f and g have the same period τ, investigate the periodicity of the following functions: (a) $af + bg$; (b) fg; (c) f/g; (d) $F(f, g)$, where $F(x, y)$ is an arbitrary function; (e) $f(t + a)$; (f) $f(at)$; (g) $f(t^2)$; (h) df/dt.

2. Establish the condition under which $F(t) = \int_a^t f(t')\, dt'$ has the same period as f.

The following differential equations have periodic coefficients. Find their general integrals, and look for periodic solutions among them. Explain the results by the use of the theorem of this section.

3. $(2 + \sin t)\dfrac{d^2x}{dt^2} + 2\cos t\,\dfrac{dx}{dt} - (\sin t)x = A,\ A \neq 0$

4. $(2 + \sin t)\dfrac{d^2x}{dt^2} + 2\cos t\,\dfrac{dx}{dt} - (\sin t)x = A\cos t$

5. $\dfrac{d^2x}{dt^2} - 2\dfrac{dx}{dt} + 10x = 37\sin 3t$

6. $\dfrac{d^4x}{dt^4} + 6\dfrac{d^2x}{dt^2} + 8x = 12\sin 4t$

7. $\dfrac{d^4x}{dt^4} + 6\dfrac{d^2x}{dt^2} + 8x = A\sin 2t,\ A \neq 0$

★8. $\dfrac{d^2x}{dt^2} + 2(1 + \sin t)\dfrac{dx}{dt} + (1 + \cos t + 2\sin t + \sin^2 t)x = 1 + \sin t.$

HINT: $e^{t-\cos t}$ is an integrating factor.

Determine the periodic solutions of the following equations:

9. $\dfrac{d^2x}{dt^2} + 8x = \sin^2 t\cos^2 t$

10. $\dfrac{d^4x}{dt^4} + \dfrac{d^2x}{dt^2} + 3x = \cos^4 \tfrac{1}{2}t$

11. $\dfrac{d^4x}{dt^4} + 16\dfrac{d^2x}{dt^2} + x = \sin \tfrac{3}{8}t\cos \tfrac{5}{8}t$

12. Show that the equation $d^2x/dt^2 + a^2x = A\cos \tfrac{1}{2}t\cos \tfrac{3}{2}t\cos \tfrac{5}{2}t\cos \tfrac{7}{2}t$ has a unique periodic solution for all positive values of a that are irrational, and determine this solution.

chapter X

Solution in Power Series; Some Classical Equations

All the methods described in the preceding chapter are designed to reduce a given differential equation to a form from which some integrals can be found by quadratures. The scope of such methods is necessarily narrow, since even among linear differential equations of second order those which can be solved by quadratures form a very special type.

The method of solution in series to be described in this chapter applies to a wide class of linear differential equations that cannot be solved by quadratures. This method is of great practical and theoretical value and has, in the case of linear equations with variable coefficients, wider use than any other method.

A complete treatment of solution in series must make use of the fundamentals of the theory of functions of a complex variable. Since knowledge of that theory is not assumed in this book, a few theorems will be presented without proof. However, all definitions and explanations necessary for an understanding of the methods will be given.

1. Analytic Functions

We shall be concerned with functions that can be represented by power series. Our purpose in this section is to state, without proofs, the essential results which will permit the reader to use power series effectively for the solution of differential equations.

Definition 1. A function f of the real variable x is *analytic* at x_0 if there are numbers $A_0, A_1, A_2, \ldots, A_n, \ldots$ and a positive number r such that, for $|x - x_0| < r$,

$$(1.1) \quad f(x) = A_0 + A_1(x - x_0) + \cdots + A_n(x - x_0)^n + \cdots$$
$$= \sum_{k=0}^{\infty} A_k(x - x_0)^k$$

The precise meaning of (1.1) is

$$f(x) = \lim_{n \to \infty} \sum_{k=0}^{n} A_k(x - x_0)^k \qquad \text{for} \qquad |x - x_0| < r$$

From (1.1) it may be shown that f has derivatives of all orders. These derivatives are also analytic at x_0 and are represented by the power series which are obtained by differentiating the series (1.1) term by term. Thus,

$$f'(x) = A_1 + 2A_2(x - x_0) + \cdots + nA_n(x - x_0)^{n-1} + \cdots$$
$$f''(x) = 2A_2 + 3 \cdot 2A_3(x - x_0) + \cdots$$
$$+ n(n - 1)A_n(x - x_0)^{n-2} + \cdots$$

(1.2)

$$\cdots \cdots \cdots \cdots \cdots \cdots \cdots \cdots \cdots \cdots \cdots \cdots$$

$$f^{(n)}(x) = n!A_n + \frac{(n + 1)!}{1!} A_{n+1}(x - x_0) + \cdots$$

$$+ \frac{(n + k)!}{k!} A_{n+k}(x - x_0)^k + \cdots$$

and these expansions are valid for $|x - x_0| < r$. Evaluating the series (1.2) at x_0, we obtain

$$(1.3) \quad f(x_0) = A_0 \qquad f^{(1)}(x_0) = A_1 \qquad \cdots \qquad f^{(n)}(x_0) = n!A_n \qquad \cdots$$

Therefore, the series (1.1) can be expressed in terms of f and the derivatives of f at x_0:

$$(1.4) \quad f(x) = f(x_0) + f^{(1)}(x_0)(x - x_0) + \cdots$$
$$+ \frac{f^{(n)}(x_0)}{n!} (x - x_0)^n + \cdots$$

This is just the familiar *Taylor's series* for f.

The question that we shall meet is the following: Given a function f defined in a neighborhood of x_0 (that is, in some interval of the real line containing x_0 in its interior), how can one tell whether or not f is analytic at x_0? Naturally, because of (1.2), f must be infinitely differentiable at x_0, but this alone does not suffice, as can be shown by examples. One answer to this question is provided by the *remainder theorem*.

If f is infinitely differentiable at x_0, then

$$f(x) = f(x_0) + f^{(1)}(x_0)(x - x_0) + \cdots + \frac{f^{(n)}(x_0)}{n!}(x - x_0)^n + R_n(x)$$

where

$$R_n(x) = \frac{f^{(n+1)}(\xi)}{(n + 1)!}(x - x_0)^{n+1}$$

and ξ is between x_0 and x. Therefore a necessary and sufficient condition for the series (1.4) to converge to $f(x)$ is that

$$(1.5) \qquad\qquad \lim_{n \to \infty} R_n(x) = 0$$

Thus f is analytic at x_0 if and only if there is a positive number r such that (1.5) is valid for $|x - x_0| < r$.

The following simple propositions permit us to circumvent the question of the analyticity of f for most of the elementary functions.

1. Polynomials and the exponential, sine, and cosine functions are analytic at all x_0.

2. If f and g are analytic at x_0, so also are $f + g$, fg, and f/g if $g(x_0) \neq 0$. It may happen that f/g is analytic at x_0 even when $g(x_0) = 0$. This will be the case if and only if $\lim_{x \to x_0} f(x)/g(x)$ exists.

3. If f is analytic at x_0, and g is a continuous branch of the inverse of f, then g is analytic at $f(x_0)$ provided that $f'(x_0) \neq 0$.

4. If f is analytic at $g(x_0)$, and g is analytic at x_0, then the composite function $f(g)$ is analytic at x_0.

Example 1. The rational function

$$f(x) = \frac{a_0 x^n + a_1 x^{n-1} + \cdots + a_n}{b_0 x^m + b_1 x^{m-1} + \cdots + b_m}$$

where the two polynomials have no common polynomial divisor of degree at least 1, is analytic everywhere except at the zeros of the denominator. This follows from (2) above.

Example 2. If $f(x) = x^{1/n}$ (n a positive integer), then f is analytic for all $x > 0$, for $x^{1/n}$ is the inverse function of the function $F(x) = x^n$ which is analytic for all x, and $F'(x) \neq 0$ if $x \neq 0$. This follows from (3) above.

Example 3. The function $\log x$ is analytic for $x > 0$ since it is the inverse of the exponential function.

Also analytic for $x > 0$ is the function $x^a = e^{a \log x}$ for any real number a.

Example 4. The function arcsin x (the principal branch of the inverse sine) is analytic for $-1 < x < 1$.

Example 5. $e^{ax} \sin (bx + c)$, where a, b, c are constants, is analytic everywhere by (4) above.

Example 6. The function $f(x) = e^{-1/x^2}$ for $x \neq 0$, with $f(0) = 0$, is analytic at all $x \neq 0$. This follows from (4), since $f(x) = e^{g(x)}$, where $g(x) = -1/x^2$. Propositions 1 to 4 say nothing about the analyticity of f at zero. However, it can be shown by direct calculation that $f(0) = f'(0) = f''(0) = \cdots = 0$. Therefore the expansion (1.4) with $x_0 = 0$ cannot be valid, and so we conclude that f is not analytic at 0 even though it is infinitely differentiable there.

Now suppose that one has determined that f is analytic at x_0 by use of propositions 1 to 4. Then there is some positive r such that Eq. (1.4) is valid for $|x - x_0| < r$, but how large r can be is not determined. For example, from proposition 2 it follows that the function f given by $f(x) = (1 + x^2)^{-1}$ is analytic at every real number x_0 and can be expanded in a power series at $x_0 = 0$. This expansion is

$$(1.6) \qquad \frac{1}{1 + x^2} = 1 - x^2 + x^4 \cdots + (-1)^n x^{2n} \cdots$$

which is known to be valid for $|x| < 1$, and the series diverges for $|x| \geq 1$. From the analyticity of the function for all real x we cannot deduce where the series (1.4) will converge to the function.

If the series (1.1) converges for $x = x_1$, then it can be shown that it converges for all x such that $|x - x_0| < |x_1 - x_0|$. It follows that either there must be an $r > 0$ such that the series (1.1) converges for $|x - x_0| < r$ and diverges for $|x - x_0| > r$, or else the series converges for all x. This maximum interval, $|x - x_0| < r$, is called the *interval of convergence*, and its half length r is called the *radius of convergence* (which may be ∞).

The name "radius" of convergence is used because if x is allowed to be a *complex* number then it is easily shown that the series (1.1) converges for $|x - x_0| < r$ and diverges for $|x - x_0| > r$. In the complex x plane the set of points x for which $|x - x_0| < r$ is the interior of a circle of radius r with center at x_0. With complex values for x in (1.1) one obtains an extension of the function f to the interior of the *circle of convergence*. The extended function is said to be a function of the complex variable x, analytic in $|x - x_0| < r$.

Although the radius of convergence of (1.1) can be found by various convergence tests, e.g., the ratio test, this is rarely a practical procedure. The theory of complex analytic functions provides, for the elementary functions, a means by which the radius of convergence can be seen at a glance. In function theory it is shown that the circle of convergence of (1.1) must contain on its periphery at least one *singularity*, that is, a point x_1 such that no extension of f is analytic at x_1. Since singularities are easily recognized, the circle of convergence is also. For example, the function $f(x) = (1 + x^2)^{-1}$ has the series expansion in (1.6). By proposition 2 it is analytic everywhere except at $x = \pm i$. These are the only singularities. Therefore the radius of convergence of (1.1) is $r = 1$.

PROBLEMS

1. Show that if r is a positive number and

$$0 = A_0 + A_1(x - x_0) + \cdots + A_n(x - x_0)^n + \cdots \qquad \text{for} \qquad |x - x_0| < r$$

then $A_0 = A_1 = A_2 = \cdots = 0$.

2. Assume that r and s are positive and

$$f(x) = \begin{cases} A_0 + A_1(x - x_0) + A_2(x - x_0)^2 + \cdots & \text{for } |x - x_0| < r \\ B_0 + B_1(x - x_0) + B_2(x - x_0)^2 + \cdots & \text{for } |x - x_0| < s \end{cases}$$

Show that $A_k = B_k$ for $k = 0, 1, 2, \ldots$.

3. The function $f(x) = (1 + x^2)^{-1}$ is expanded in powers of $(x - 1)$. What is the radius of convergence of the series?

4. If $f(x) = (\sin x)/x$ for $x \neq 0$, and $f(0) = 1$, show that f is analytic at $x = 0$.

5. If $f(x) = (1 - \cos x)/x^2$ for $x \neq 0$, and $f(0) = \frac{1}{2}$, show that f is analytic at $x = 0$.

2. Ordinary Points

We shall be concerned with linear D.E. whose coefficient functions are analytic functions. As will be seen in Theorems 1 and 2, the solutions of the D.E. will then also be analytic functions.

Definition. The point $x = x_0$ is an *ordinary* point of the linear differential equation

$$(2.1) \qquad \frac{d^n y}{dx^n} + a_1(x) \frac{d^{n-1}y}{dx^{n-1}} + a_2(x) \frac{d^{n-2}y}{dx^{n-2}} + \cdots + a_n(x)y = f(x)$$

if the coefficients $a_1(x)$, $a_2(x)$, $\ldots$, $a_n(x)$ and the right-hand member $f(x)$ are analytic at $x = x_0$.

It should be noticed that the coefficient of the highest derivative in Eq. (2.1) is unity. If there is a coefficient $a_0(x)$ of $y^{(n)}$, then the definition should be applied only to the equation that is obtained after one has divided through by $a_0(x)$. In this connection it should be recalled that if $a_0(x)$ is analytic and does not vanish at x_0, then $1/a_0(x)$ is analytic at x_0.

Theorem 1. *At an ordinary point every solution of the equation is analytic.*

For a proof of this theorem the reader is referred to more advanced texts (see, for example, Ref. 4, chap. 3).

Example 1. The D.E.

$$x \frac{d^2y}{dx^2} + x^2 \frac{dy}{dx} - 2y = 0$$

is equivalent to

$$y'' + xy' - \frac{2}{x} y = 0$$

The coefficients are $a_1 = x$ and $a_2 = -2/x$ and are analytic at every point $x_0 \neq 0$. Thus every point is an ordinary point except 0; if $x_0 \neq 0$, then every solution may be expanded in powers of $x - x_0$.

Theorem 1 asserts that the Taylor series for the solution converges in some interval about the initial point x_0, but it does not say how large this interval of convergence is. Actually, the radius of convergence can be determined by inspection of the coefficients of the equation, but this requires knowledge of the singularities of the coefficients considered as functions of a complex variable (see Sec. 1). If the resulting power series is simple enough, the convergence can be tested by one of the familiar convergence tests. However, the following general result, whose proof is closely related to the proof of Theorem 1, is found useful in the determination of the interval of convergence.

Theorem 2. *If the expansions of all the coefficient functions $a_1(x)$, $a_2(x)$, . . . , $a_n(x)$, $f(x)$ are valid for $|x - x_0| < R$, then the expansion of every solution of Eq. (2.1) is valid for $|x - x_0| < R$.*

In particular, it follows from Theorem 2 that if the functions $a_1(x)$, . . . , $a_n(x)$, $f(x)$ are polynomials, then every power-series expansion of every solution of Eq. (2.1) is valid for all values of x.

PROBLEMS

1. Determine the points on the x axis that are ordinary points of the following differential equations:

(a) $y'' + xy' - 2y = 0$
(b) $y'' + xy' - 2y = \log |x|$

(c) $\dfrac{d^3y}{dx^3} - 4x^2 \dfrac{dy}{dx} + 12xy = 0$

(d) $\dfrac{d^4y}{dx^4} + (1 + \cos x) \dfrac{d^2y}{dx^2} + (1 + \sin^2 x)y = \arctan x$

(e) $\dfrac{d^3y}{dx^3} + \dfrac{x-1}{x+2} \dfrac{d^2y}{dx^2} + \dfrac{x}{x^2-1} \dfrac{dy}{dx} + \dfrac{x}{x^2+1} y = 0$

(f) $(x^2 + x) \dfrac{d^2y}{dx^2} + (2x + 1) \dfrac{dy}{dx} + \dfrac{x}{x-2} y = 0$

(g) $\sin x \dfrac{d^2y}{dx^2} - e^x \dfrac{dy}{dx} + (\sec x)y = 0$

(h) $x \dfrac{d^2y}{dx^2} - \sin x \dfrac{dy}{dx} + (e^x - 1)y = 0$

(i) $\dfrac{d^2y}{dx^2} + x^{\frac{1}{3}} \dfrac{dy}{dx} + (\arctan x)y = 0$

2. If the solutions of Prob. 1 were to be expanded in powers of $(x - \tfrac{1}{2})$, for what values of x could the validity of the expansions be predicted?

3. A linear homogeneous differential equation of the third order has among its solutions the function $y = x(1 - \cos x)$. Show, by the use of general principles, that $x = 0$ cannot be an ordinary point of the equation. HINT: Notice that $y = 0$, $dy/dx = 0$, $d^2y/dx^2 = 0$ for $x = 0$.

3. The Method of Undetermined Coefficients; Ordinary Points

With Theorems 1 and 2 of Sec. 2 one can predict where solutions are analytic. To determine the solutions, one must calculate the coefficients of the power series. The method of *undetermined coefficients* is employed.

If x_0 is an ordinary point of the differential equation (2.1), the solution can be expanded in a series of the form

$$(3.1) \quad y(x) = c_0 + c_1(x - x_0) + c_2(x - x_0)^2 + c_3(x - x_0)^3 + \cdots$$
$$= \sum_{k=0}^{\infty} c_k(x - x_0)^k$$

where $c_0, c_1, c_2, \ldots$ are coefficients yet to be determined. Then the derivatives of $y(x)$ are found by differentiating (3.1). Now all the coefficient functions in the equation are expanded, and then the products of these coefficients and the corresponding derivatives of $y(x)$ are expanded. Finally, all the terms containing the same power of $x - x_0$ are combined, and thus an equation of the form

$$(3.2) \qquad\qquad \sum_{k=0}^{\infty} d_k(x - x_0)^k = 0$$

is obtained. Equation (3.2) can hold for all values of x in some neighborhood of x_0 only if

$$d_0 = d_1 = d_2 = \cdots = 0$$

The equation $d_k = 0$ is (for details see Example 1)

$$(3.3) \qquad \frac{(n+k)!}{k!} c_{n+k} + \cdots = 0$$

where the dots denote a linear function of $c_0, \ldots, c_{n+k-2}, c_{n+k-1}$. Clearly, once $c_0, \ldots, c_{n-1}$ are known, then $c_n, c_{n+1}, \ldots$ are uniquely determined from (3.3). The first coefficients $c_0, \ldots, c_{n-1}$ are found from the given I.C.

$$(3.4) \qquad y^{(k)}(x_0) = \eta_k \qquad k = 0, 1, \ldots, n-1$$

as follows:

$$(3.5) \qquad c_k = \frac{y^{(k)}(x_0)}{k!} = \frac{\eta_k}{k!} \qquad k = 0, 1, \ldots, n-1$$

Example 1. Let this method be applied to find the two solutions $y_1(x)$, $y_2(x)$ of the equation

$$(3.6) \qquad (1+x^2)\frac{d^2y}{dx^2} + 2x\frac{dy}{dx} - 2y = 0$$

for which

$$(3.7) \qquad y_1(0) = 0 \qquad y_1'(0) = 1$$
$$(3.8) \qquad y_2(0) = 1 \qquad y_2'(0) = 0$$

At the initial point $x_0 = 0$ the coefficients of Eq. (3.6) are analytic; the coefficient of y'' is not zero there. Hence, $x_0 = 0$ is an ordinary point of the differential equation, and each solution can be expanded in a series valid in a neighborhood of $x_0 = 0$:

$$y(x) = c_0 + c_1x + c_2x^2 + c_3x^3 + c_4x^4 + c_5x^5 + c_6x^6 + \cdots$$

Then

$$y'(x) = c_1 + 2c_2x + 3c_3x^2 + 4c_4x^3 + 5c_5x^4 + 6c_6x^5 + \cdots$$
$$y''(x) = 2x_2 + 6c_3x + 12c_4x^2 + 20c_5x^3 + 30c_6x^4 + \cdots$$

Substitution in Eq. (3.6) gives

$$(1+x^2)(2c_2 + 6c_3x + 12c_4x^2 + 20c_5x^3 + 30c_6x^4 + \cdots)$$
$$+ 2x(c_1 + 2c_2x + 3c_3x^2 + 4c_4x^3 + 5c_5x^4 + 6c_6x^5 + \cdots)$$
$$- 2(c_0 + c_1x + c_2x^2 + c_3x^3 + c_4x^4 + c_5x^5 + c_6x^6 + \cdots) = 0$$

or, after collection of like terms,

$$(2c_2 - 2c_0) + 6c_3 x + (12c_4 + 4c_2)x^2 + (20c_5 + 10c_3)x^3$$
$$+ (30c_6 + 18c_4)x^4 + \cdots = 0$$

Hence,

$$c_2 = c_0$$
$$c_3 = 0$$
$$c_4 = -\tfrac{1}{3}c_2 = -\tfrac{1}{3}c_0$$
$$c_5 = -\tfrac{1}{2}c_3 = 0$$
$$c_6 = -\tfrac{3}{5}c_4 = \tfrac{1}{5}c_0$$

For the solution y_1, by (3.7), $c_0 = 0$, $c_1 = 1$. One can conclude that

$$c_2 = c_4 = c_6 = \cdots = 0 \qquad c_3 = c_5 = c_7 = \cdots = 0$$

and

$$y_1(x) = x$$

For the solution y_2, by (3.8), $c_0 = 1$, $c_1 = 0$. Hence,

$$c_2 = 1 \qquad c_3 = 0 \qquad c_4 = -\tfrac{1}{3} \qquad c_5 = 0 \qquad c_6 = \tfrac{1}{5} \qquad \cdots$$

and

$$y_2(x) = 1 + x^2 - \tfrac{1}{3}x^4 + \tfrac{1}{5}x^6 + \cdots$$

A more efficient procedure which in many cases yields the general term in the expansion is as follows:

Put

$$y(x) = \sum_{k=0}^{\infty} c_k x^k$$

Then

$$y'(x) = \sum_{k=0}^{\infty} k c_k x^{k-1} \qquad y''(x) = \sum_{k=0}^{\infty} k(k-1)c_k x^{k-2}$$

and substitution in Eq. (3.7) results in

$$\sum_{k=0}^{\infty} k(k-1)c_k x^{k-2} + \sum_{k=0}^{\infty} k(k-1)c_k x^k + 2 \sum_{k=0}^{\infty} k c_k x^k - 2 \sum_{k=0}^{\infty} c_k x^k = 0$$

The coefficient of x^n, for $n \geqq 0$, is

$$(n+2)(n+1)c_{n+2} \qquad \text{in the first sum}$$
$$n(n-1)c_n \qquad \text{in the second sum}$$
$$2nc_n \qquad \text{in the third sum}$$
$$-2c_n \qquad \text{in the fourth sum}$$

Since the total coefficient of x^n must be zero, we have

$$(n+2)(n+1)c_{n+2} + [n(n-1) + 2n - 2]c_n = 0$$

or

$$(3.9) \qquad c_{n+2} = -\frac{n-1}{n+1}c_n \qquad \text{for} \qquad n \geqq 0$$

From this formula the successive coefficients can be found. A formula such as (3.9) is called a *recursion formula*. This example is particularly simple. Because but two coefficients are involved, it is a two-term recursion formula, and from it one can easily find a formula for the general term of the power series. With more complicated recursion formulas, possibly involving three or more coefficients, one may have to be content with finding but a few terms of the series. Recursion formulas present a problem in *difference equations*.

For the solution y_1 satisfying the I.C. (3.7) we have $c_0 = 0$ and $c_1 = 1$. Because of (3.9) we see that all the even coefficients are zero since $c_0 = 0$. For the odd coefficients we have first that

$$c_3 = -\frac{1-1}{1+1} c_1 = 0$$

Then all the other odd coefficients vanish by (3.9), and so $y_1(x) = x$.

For the solution y_2 satisfying the I.C. (3.8) we have $c_0 = 1$ and $c_1 = 0$. By (3.9) all the odd coefficients vanish.

$$c_2 = -\frac{-1}{1} c_0 = c_0 = 1$$

$$c_4 = -\frac{2-1}{2+1} c_2 = -\tfrac{1}{3}$$

$$c_6 = -\frac{4-1}{4+1} c_4 = -\tfrac{3}{5}(-\tfrac{1}{3}) = \tfrac{1}{5}$$

In general, we see that

$$c_{2k} = (-1)^{k+1} \frac{1}{2k-1}$$

Therefore,

$$y_2(x) = 1 + x^2 - \frac{x^4}{3} + \frac{x^6}{5} \cdots + (-1)^{k+1} \frac{x^{2k}}{2k-1} + \cdots$$

This power series can easily be related to the well-known expansion of an elementary function, for

$$y_2(x) = 1 + x\left[x - \frac{x^3}{3} + \frac{x^5}{5} - \frac{x^7}{7} + \cdots + (-1)^{k+1}\frac{x^{2k-1}}{2k-1} + \cdots \right]$$

$$= 1 + x \arctan x$$

Since y_1, y_2 are two linearly independent solutions of Eq. (3.3), its general solution is

$$y(x) = Ax + B(1 + x \arctan x)$$

Only in exceptional cases will it be possible to identify an obtained series as the expansion of a known function. There are many instances in the history of mathematics in which the solution of a differential equation led to a series of simple construction that could not be identified as the expansion of any of the then known functions and so was accepted as the expression of a new function. Most of the "higher" functions found their way into mathematics and science via their series expansions, derived from differential equations. A few examples of such functions will be discussed in succeeding sections.

When one wishes to find the general solution of D.E. (3.1) then no I.C. are assigned and so no equations are available for the determination of $c_0, \ldots, c_{n-1}$. These first n coefficients represent the arbitrary constants in the general solution. The remaining coefficients $c_n, c_{n+1}, \ldots$ are expressed in terms of the first n coefficients by means of (3.3). A more efficient procedure is to find n solutions $y_1, y_2, \ldots, y_n$ which satisfy the I.C.

$$(3.10) \qquad y_k^{(i-1)}(x_0) = \begin{cases} 0 & \text{if } i \neq k \\ 1 & \text{if } i = k \end{cases} \qquad i, k = 1, \ldots, n$$

Then the general solution is $C_1 y_1 + C_2 y_2 + \cdots + C_n y_n$.

PROBLEMS

1. Show that zero is an ordinary point, and expand in powers of x the general solutions of the following equations. In each case try to identify the obtained series as an expansion of a known function.

(a) $(1 + x^2) \dfrac{d^2y}{dx^2} + 2x \dfrac{dy}{dx} = 0$

(b) $(1 + x^2)y'' + 2xy = x^2$

(c) $(x^2 - 1) \dfrac{d^2y}{dx^2} - x \dfrac{dy}{dx} + y = 0$

(d) $(x^2 - 1) \dfrac{d^2y}{dx^2} - x \dfrac{dy}{dx} + y = x$

(e) $\dfrac{d^3y}{dx^3} - x^2 \dfrac{d^2y}{dx^2} - 4x \dfrac{dy}{dx} - 2y = 0$

(f) $\dfrac{d^3y}{dx^3} - x^2 \dfrac{d^2y}{dx^2} - 4x \dfrac{dy}{dx} - 2y = 1$

(g) $(1 - x^2)y'' + 2y = 0$

(h) $y'' - \dfrac{4x}{1 - x^2} y' - \dfrac{2}{1 - x^2} y = 0$

2. In each of the equations of Prob. 1 determine the circle of convergence of the power series for the solution from an examination of the coefficient functions.

3. Show in each of the following cases that x_0 is an ordinary point, and find several terms of the general solution in powers of $x - x_0$ and the circle of convergence of the series solution:

(a) $y'' - (x - 1)y = 0$, $x_0 = 1$

(b) $(1 + x^2)y'' - 2y = 0$, $x_0 = 0$

(c) $(2 - 2t + t^2)\dfrac{d^2y}{dt^2} - 2y = \cos(t - 1)$, $t_0 = 1$

(d) $y'' + y' + (x + 1)y = 0$, $x_0 = -1$

(e) $xy'' - y' + xy = 0$, $x_0 = 1$

(f) $y''' + (x + 1)y'' + y' + (x + 1)y = x + 2$, $x_0 = -1$

4. Find the series solutions of the following initial-value problems:

(a) $\dfrac{d^2y}{dx^2} + x\dfrac{dy}{dx} - 2y = 0$; $y = 1, \dfrac{dy}{dx} = 0$ for $x = 0$

(b) $\dfrac{d^2y}{dx^2} + x\dfrac{dy}{dx} - 2y = 0$; $y = 0, \dfrac{dy}{dx} = 1$ for $x = 0$

(c) $\dfrac{d^3x}{dt^3} - 4t^2\dfrac{dx}{dt} + 12tx = 0$; $x = 0, \dfrac{dx}{dt} = 0, \dfrac{d^2x}{dt^2} = 2$ for $t = 0$

(d) $\dfrac{d^3x}{dt^3} - 4t^2\dfrac{dx}{dt} + 12tx = 0$; $x = 1, \dfrac{dx}{dt} = 0, \dfrac{d^2x}{dt^2} = 0$ for $t = 0$

(e) $y'' - x^2y = \sin x$; $y(0) = y'(0) = 0$

(f) $y'' + 2xy' + y = e^x$; $y(0) = y'(0) = 0$

4. Regular Singular Points

Ordinary points are not the only ones about which solutions can be expanded in series. This can also be done for various singular points, i.e., points about which not all the coefficient functions of the differential equation can be expanded in Taylor series or at which the coefficient of the highest derivative vanishes. A specially important subclass of these points is that of so-called *regular-singular points*.

Definition. The point x_0 is a *regular-singular* point of a linear homogeneous nth-order equation if the equation can be written in the form

$$(4.1) \quad (x - x_0)^n\frac{d^ny}{dx^n} + (x - x_0)^{n-1}b_1(x)\frac{d^{n-1}y}{dx^{n-1}} + (x - x_0)^{n-2}b_2(x)\frac{d^{n-2}y}{dx^{n-2}}$$

$$+ \cdots + (x - x_0)b_{n-1}(x)\frac{dy}{dx} + b_n(x)y = 0$$

where† $b_1(x), b_2(x), \ldots, b_n(x)$ are analytic at $x = x_0$.

† If all the functions $b_1(x), b_2(x), \ldots, b_n(x)$ are constants, then this is an Euler-Cauchy equation (see Sec. 1, Chap. IX). Hence, the point $x = x_0$ in Euler-Cauchy equations is a regular-singular point.

In the neighborhoods of regular-singular points there are series solutions that are not necessarily Taylor series, but simple modifications of such series. To derive the actual form of these solutions, it would be necessary to use arguments from the theory of functions of a complex variable. To avoid this, the following theorem is offered without proof:

Theorem. *If x_0 is a regular-singular point of a linear differential equation, then there exists at least one solution of the form*

$$(4.2) \qquad y(x) = (x - x_0)^r \sum_{k=0}^{\infty} c_k(x - x_0)^k$$

where the expansion is valid in some neighborhood of x_0. More specifically, the series expansion in formula (4.2) is valid for $0 < |x - x_0| < R$ if the series expansions for the coefficient functions $b_1(x)$, . . . , $b_n(x)$ in Eq. (4.1) are valid for $|x - x_0| < R$.

For a proof of this theorem the reader is referred to more advanced texts (see, for example, Ref. 4, Chap. 3).

If in the above sum the coefficient c_0 vanishes, then some power of $(x - x_0)$ [at least $(x - x_0)^1$] can be factored out and combined with the factor $(x - x_0)^r$. In the following it will always be assumed that the highest possible power of $(x - x_0)$ is factored out of the sum and is combined with the factor $(x - x_0)^r$. With this understanding it will always be true that $c_0 \neq 0$ in expression (4.2), and the exponent r is then uniquely determined. It is called the *exponent of the solution* $y(x)$ at the point x_0. If $r = 0, 1, 2, . . .$, y is analytic at x_0; but in general r is not a nonnegative integer and y is singular at x_0. Also r may be complex, but we avoid such cases.

To determine the coefficients in expansion (4.2), one proceeds very much as in the case of ordinary points, the one important difference being that now the exponent r has to be determined too. First, one expands the coefficient functions $b_1(x)$, $b_2(x)$, . . . , $b_n(x)$ of Eq. (4.1) in powers of $(x - x_0)$. Then this equation takes the form

$$(4.3) \quad (x - x_0)^n \frac{d^n y}{dx^n} + [b_{10}(x - x_0)^{n-1} + \cdots] \frac{d^{n-1}y}{dx^{n-1}}$$

$$+ [b_{20}(x - x_0)^{n-2} + \cdots] \frac{d^{n-2}y}{dx^{n-2}} + \cdots + (b_{n0} + \cdots)y = 0$$

where $b_{10}, b_{20}, . . . , b_{n0}$ are the values of $b_1(x)$, $b_2(x)$, . . . , $b_n(x)$ at $x = x_0$.

Then $y(x)$ and its derivatives

$$y(x) = \sum_{k=0}^{\infty} c_k(x - x_0)^{k+r}$$

$$y'(x) = \sum_{k=0}^{\infty} (k + r)c_k(x - x_0)^{k+r-1}$$

$$y''(x) = \sum_{k=0}^{\infty} (k + r)(k + r - 1)c_k(x - x_0)^{k+r-2}$$

. . . .

are found and substituted in Eq. (4.3).   Like terms are collected, and the coefficients of $(x - x_0)^r$, $(x - x_0)^{r+1}$, . . . are equated to zero. The equation resulting from equating the coefficient of $(x - x_0)^r$ to zero is

$$[r(r - 1) \cdots (r - n + 1) + b_{10}r(r - 1) \cdots (r - n + 2)$$
$$+ b_{20}r(r - 1) \cdots (r - n + 3) + \cdots + rb_{n-1,0} + b_{n,0}]c_0 = 0$$

Since, according to the chosen procedure, c_0 cannot be zero, the expression in the brackets must vanish.   This expression is a polynomial of degree n in the unknown r which will be designated by $g(r)$. Hence,

$$(4.4) \quad g(r) = r(r - 1) \cdots (r - n + 1)$$
$$+ b_{10}r(r - 1) \cdots (r - n + 2)$$
$$+ b_{20}r(r - 1) \cdots (r - n + 3)$$
$$+ \cdots + rb_{n-1,0} + b_{n,0} = 0$$

This equation is called the *indicial equation*.   Each of its n roots can be used as the exponent in expression (4.2) (for exceptions, see below). Once an exponent has been decided upon, one proceeds to determine the coefficients c_k.   The coefficient c_0 remains undetermined; it will appear as a factor of the solution $y(x)$.   Of course, its value is entirely arbitrary, since any constant multiple of a solution is itself a solution of Eq. (4.1).

The coefficients of $(x - x_0)^{r+1}$, $(x - x_0)^{r+2}$, . . . are now equated to zero, and thus equations are obtained from which the coefficients c_1, c_2, . . . can be obtained successively.   It is easily checked that the equation resulting from equating the coefficient of $(x - x_0)^{r+k}$ to zero starts as follows:

$$(4.5) \quad [(k + r)(k + r - 1) \cdots (k + r - n + 1)$$
$$+ b_{10}(k + r)(k + r - 1) \cdots (k + r - n + 2) + \cdots$$
$$+ (k + r)b_{n-1,0} + b_{n,0}]c_k + \cdots = 0$$

where the terms that are not written out contain c_{k-1}, c_{k-2}, . . . , c_0. Comparing Eq. (4.5) with Eq. (4.4), one sees that (4.5) may also be written as

$$(4.6) \qquad g(r + k)c_k + \cdot \cdot \cdot = 0$$

Having determined c_1, c_2, . . . , c_{k-1} from the previous equations, one can determine c_k from Eq. (4.6) unless $g(r + k) = 0$. This *exceptional case* will be discussed below (see Sec. 7).

The outlined program can, in general, be carried out for each of the n roots of the indicial equation, and thus n linearly independent solutions expanded about the regular-singular point can be obtained.

Example 1. To illustrate the method, let it be required to find the general solution of the equation

$$(4.7) \qquad x^2 \frac{d^2y}{dx^2} + \left(x^2 + \frac{x}{2}\right)\frac{dy}{dx} + xy = 0$$

expanded about the point $x = 0$.

If the D.E. is written with leading coefficient 1, we have

$$y'' + \frac{2x + 1}{2x} y' + \frac{1}{x} y = 0$$

and we see that every point is an ordinary point except 0. Therefore we cannot expect to have solutions analytic at 0, as Theorem 1 of Sec. 2 does not apply. It is immediately checked that the point $x = 0$ is a regular-singular point of this equation, the functions $b_1(x)$, $b_2(x)$ of the general equation (4.1) being $(x + \frac{1}{2})$ and x, respectively, in this case. Hence, the theorem of this section applies. Putting

$$y(x) = \sum_{k=0}^{\infty} c_k x^{k+r}$$

we obtain

$$y'(x) = \sum_{k=0}^{\infty} (k + r)c_k x^{k+r-1}$$

$$y''(x) = \sum_{k=0}^{\infty} (k + r)(k + r - 1)c_k x^{k+r-2}$$

and Eq. (4.7) becomes

$$(4.8) \quad \sum_{k=0}^{\infty} (r + k)(r + k - 1)c_k x^{r+k} + \sum_{k=0}^{\infty} (r + k)c_k x^{r+k+1}$$

$$+ \frac{1}{2} \sum_{k=0}^{\infty} (r + k)c_k x^{r+k} + \sum_{k=0}^{\infty} c_k x^{r+k+1} = 0$$

Each power of x must have the coefficient zero in this last equation. The power with smallest exponent is x^r, so we have

$$r(r-1)c_0 + \tfrac{1}{2}rc_0 = 0$$

and, since $c_0 \neq 0$, there results the *indicial equation*

$$r(r - \tfrac{1}{2}) = 0$$

Hence,

$$r_1 = \tfrac{1}{2} \qquad r_2 = 0$$

are the exponents of the solutions.

Now, returning to Eq. (4.8), we equate the coefficient of x^{r+k} to zero, for $k \geq 1$. We get

$$(r+k)(r+k-1)c_k + (r+k-1)c_{k-1} + \tfrac{1}{2}(r+k)c_k + c_{k-1} = 0$$

or

(4.9) $$(r+k)(r+k-\tfrac{1}{2})c_k + (r+k)c_{k-1} = 0$$

Note that, for $k = 0$, Eq. (4.9) gives the indicial equation.

Equation (4.9) is a simple recurrence relation, and its use with $r = \tfrac{1}{2}$ and $r = 0$ will give us the solution. For the root $r_1 = \tfrac{1}{2}$, Eq. (4.9) becomes, after dropping the factor $(\tfrac{1}{2} + k)$, which never vanishes,

$$kc_k + c_{k-1} = 0 \qquad k \geq 1$$

or

$$c_k = -\frac{1}{k}\,c_{k-1}$$

Use of this recursion formula for $k - 1, k - 2, \ldots, 1$ gives

$$c_k = \frac{-1}{k}\frac{-1}{k-1}\cdots\frac{-1}{1}\,c_0$$

$$= \frac{(-1)^k}{k!}\,c_0$$

Hence, the solution belonging to the exponent $r_1 = \tfrac{1}{2}$ is, with $c_0 = A$,

$$y_1(x) = A \sum_{k=0}^{\infty} \frac{(-1)^k}{k!}\,x^{k+\frac{1}{2}}$$

$$= Ax^{\frac{1}{2}} \sum_{k=0}^{\infty} \frac{(-x)^k}{k!}$$

$$= A\sqrt{x}\,e^{-x}$$

We turn next to the exponent $r_2 = 0$. Equation (4.9) becomes, after dropping the factor k,

$$(k - \tfrac{1}{2})c_k + c_{k-1} = 0$$

or

$$c_k = -\frac{1}{k - \tfrac{1}{2}} c_{k-1}$$

Use of this recursion formula for $k - 1, k - 2, \ldots, 1$, with $c_0 = B$, gives

$$c_k = \frac{(-1)^k B}{(k - \tfrac{1}{2})(k - \tfrac{3}{2}) \cdots \tfrac{3}{2} \tfrac{1}{2}}$$

Hence, the solution belonging to the exponent $r_2 = 0$ is

$$y_2(x) = B \sum_{k=0}^{\infty} \frac{(-1)^k}{(k - \tfrac{1}{2})(k - \tfrac{3}{2}) \cdots \tfrac{3}{2} \tfrac{1}{2}} x^k$$

This series is not the expansion of an elementary function.

The general solution of differential equation (4.7), expanded about the point $x_0 = 0$, is

$$y(x) = A x^{\frac{1}{2}} \sum_{k=0}^{\infty} \frac{(-1)^k}{k!} x^k + B \sum_{k=0}^{\infty} \frac{(-1)^k}{(k - \tfrac{1}{2})(k - \tfrac{3}{2}) \cdots \tfrac{1}{2}} x^k$$

Since the coefficient functions in Eq. (4.7) are polynomials, the expansions in the above expression must be valid for all values of x.

Example 2. Even when the roots of the indicial equation differ by an integer, one can *sometimes* obtain two linearly independent solutions. For example, suppose we wish to solve

$$(4.10) \qquad (x^2 - x)y'' - 3y' - 2y = 0$$

in a neighborhood of $x = 0$. Writing the D.E. in the form

$$x^2 y'' + x \frac{3}{1 - x} y' + \frac{2x}{1 - x} y = 0$$

we see that 0 is a regular-singular point. We set

$$y(x) = \sum_{k=0}^{\infty} c_k x^{r+k}$$

and, using this in the D.E. (4.10), obtain

$$(4.11) \quad \sum_{k=0}^{\infty} (r + k)(r + k - 1)c_k x^{r+k} - \sum_{k=0}^{\infty} (r + k)(r + k - 1)c_k x^{r+k-1}$$

$$- 3 \sum_{k=0}^{\infty} (r + k)c_k x^{r+k-1} - 2 \sum_{k=0}^{\infty} c_k x^{r+k} = 0$$

The indicial equation is

$$-r(r-1)c_0 - 3rc_0 = 0$$

or $r^2 + 2r = 0$, which has the roots $-2, 0$. For the larger root, $r = 0$, one obtains, without trouble, the solution

$$y_1(x) = A(1 - \tfrac{2}{3}x + \tfrac{1}{6}x^2)$$

For the smaller root, $r = -2$, Eq. (4.11) gives the recurrence relation

$$[(-2+k)(-3+k)-2]c_k = [(-2+k+1)(-2+k)$$
$$+ 3(-2+k+1)]c_{k+1}$$

or

(4.12) $(k-1)(k+1)c_{k+1} = (k-1)(k-4)c_k \qquad k \geq 0$

From (4.12) we obtain for $k = 0$ and 1

$$-c_1 = 4c_0 \qquad \text{and} \qquad 0c_2 = 0c_1$$

From this last equation c_2 could be arbitrary. Let us choose $c_2 = 0$. Then, continuing,

$$1(3)c_3 = 1(-2)c_2 = 0$$

and all further coefficients also vanish. We thus obtain the second solution, using $c_0 - B$:

$$y_2(x) = Bx^{-2}(1 - 4x) = B(x^{-2} - 4x^{-1})$$

Clearly, y_2 is linearly independent of y_1, and the general solution is the sum of y_1 and y_2. For an additional remark on this example, see Prob. 14.

PROBLEMS

Expand in powers of x the general solutions of the following equations. In each case try to identify the obtained series as an expansion of a known function.

1. $4x\dfrac{d^2y}{dx^2} + 2\dfrac{dy}{dx} + y = 0$ **2.** $(2x^2 + x)\dfrac{d^2y}{dx^2} + 3\dfrac{dy}{dx} - 4y = 0$

3. $\left(x^2 + \dfrac{x}{2}\right)\dfrac{d^2y}{dx^2} + 2\dfrac{dy}{dx} - 2y = 0$ **4.** $4x^2\dfrac{d^2y}{dx^2} + 4x\dfrac{dy}{dx} + (x^2 - 1)y = 0$

5. $(2x^2 + 2x)y'' + (5x + 1)y' + y = 0$
6. $(2x^2 + 2x)y'' + (7x + 1)y' + 2y = 0$
7. $x^2y'' + xy' + (x^2 - 1)y = 0$

Find, for each of the following equations, at least one solution in powers of x:

8. $(2x^2 + 2x)y'' + (2 - 3x)y' + 2y = 0$
9. $x^2y'' + xy' + (x^2 - 1)y = 0$
10. $(x^2 + x)y'' + (x + 1)y' + y = 0$

11. Which points are not ordinary points of the following equations? Of these, which are regular-singular points? At the regular-singular points what are the radii of convergence of series solutions?

(a) $x^2 y'' + y' + xy = 0$

(b) $y'' + 2xy' + (x^2 - 2)y = 0$

(c) $(x + 1)^2 y'' + \left(1 + \dfrac{1}{x}\right) y' + xy = 0$

(d) $(x^2 - x - 2)y'' + (x - 2)y' + xy = 0$

(e) $(x^2 - 1)(x + 2)y''' + (x - 1)(x + 2)y'' + xy' + y = 0$

12. Find the solution of the equation

$$(x^2 - 1)\frac{d^2y}{dx^2} + 3x\frac{dy}{dx} - 8y = 0$$

subject to the condition $y = 3$ for $x = 1$. Why is this one condition sufficient to specify a unique solution?

★**13.** If the solution y of Eq. (4.1) has the form

$$y(x) = (x - x_0)^r \sum_{k=0}^{\infty} c_k(x - x_0)^k \qquad \text{where} \qquad c_0 \neq 0$$

show that r must be one of the numbers $0, 1, 2, \ldots, n - 1$ if x_0 is an ordinary point of the equation.   HINT: Use the uniqueness theorem of Sec. 2, Chap. VI.

14. In Example 2 let $c_0 = A$, $c_2 = B$ (A, B arbitrary), where $r = -2$. Show that the solution so obtained is the general solution.

5. Bessel's Differential Equation

Bessel's equation (Friedrich Wilhelm Bessel, 1784–1846) arises in innumerable problems of applied science, particularly in boundary-value problems for right circular cylinders.   It has the form

(5.1) $x^2 \dfrac{d^2y}{dx^2} + x\dfrac{dy}{dx} + (x^2 - n^2)y = 0$

where n^2 is a given nonnegative constant.

It is immediately recognized that $x = 0$ is a regular-singular point, whereas all other values of x are ordinary points.   In the following, the solution will be expanded about $x = 0$.

If $y(x) = \Sigma c_k x^{r+k}$ is substituted in (5.1), one gets

$$\sum_{k=0}^{\infty} (r + k)(r + k - 1)c_k x^{r+k} + \sum_{k=0}^{\infty} (r + k)c_k x^{r+k}$$

$$+ \sum_{k=0}^{\infty} c_k x^{r+k+2} - n^2 \sum_{k=0}^{\infty} c_k x^{r+k} = 0$$

Equating the coefficient of x^{r+k} to zero yields

$$[(r + k)(r + k - 1) + (r + k) - n^2]c_k + c_{k-2} = 0$$

or

(5.2) $$[(r + k)^2 - n^2]c_k + c_{k-2} = 0$$

For $k = 0$, one obtains the indicial equation

$$r^2 - n^2 = 0$$

whose roots are

$$r_1 = n \geq 0 \qquad r_2 = -n$$

For $k = 1$, Eq. (5.2) becomes

(5.3) $$[(r + 1)^2 - n^2]c_1 = 0$$

and since for neither of the roots does the bracketed expression in (5.3) vanish, we must have

$$c_1 = 0$$

for both $r_1 = n$ and $r_2 = -n$.

Let us first find the solution belonging to the exponent $r_1 = n$. Then (5.2) becomes

(5.4) $$c_k = -\frac{c_{k-2}}{(n + k)^2 - n^2} = -\frac{c_{k-2}}{k(2n + k)}$$

Since $c_1 = 0$, it follows from (5.4) that all coefficients whose subscripts are odd numbers vanish. It remains to calculate the coefficients with even subscripts. Writing $2k$ for k in formula (5.4), we have

$$c_{2k} = -\frac{c_{2k-2}}{2^2 k(n + k)}$$

Applying this recursion formula for $2k - 2$, $2k - 4$, . . . , 2, and putting $c_0 = 1$, one obtains the general coefficient with even subscript:

$$c_{2k} = \frac{(-1)^k}{2^{2k}k!(n + 1)(n + 2) \cdots (n + k)}$$

Therefore, the solution belonging to the exponent n (≥ 0) is

$$y_1(x) = x^n \sum_{k=0}^{\infty} \frac{(-1)^k}{2^{2k}k!(n + 1)(n + 2) \cdots (n + k)} x^{2k}$$

Except for special values of n (see Prob. 9 below), this is not the expansion of an elementary function. Multiplied by the constant factor

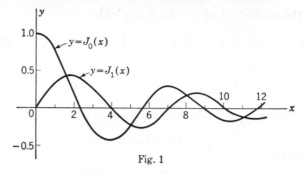

Fig. 1

$1/2^n n!$, this† is the expansion of what is known as *Bessel's function*‡ of order n, commonly designated as $J_n(x)$:

(5.5) $\quad J_n(x)$

$$= \frac{x^n}{2^n n!} \sum_{k=0}^{\infty} \frac{(-1)^k}{2^{2k} k! (n+1)(n+2) \cdots (n+k)} x^{2k}$$

$$= \left(\frac{x}{2}\right)^n \left[\frac{1}{n!} - \frac{(x/2)^2}{1!(n+1)!} + \frac{(x/2)^4}{2!(n+2)!} - \frac{(x/2)^6}{3!(n+3)!} + \cdots\right]$$

This is one solution of Bessel's equation.   Most frequently used are the Bessel functions of order 0 and 1.   They are

(5.6)
$$J_0(x) = 1 - \frac{(x/2)^2}{1!^2} + \frac{(x/2)^4}{2!^2} - \frac{(x/2)^6}{3!^2} + \cdots$$
$$J_1(x) = \frac{x}{2} - \frac{(x/2)^3}{1!2!} + \frac{(x/2)^5}{2!3!} - \frac{(x/2)^7}{3!4!} + \cdots$$

Graphs of these functions are shown in Fig. 1.   For other graphs and tables, see Ref. 6, sec. VIII.

We turn next to the exponent $r_2 = -n$.   Equation (5.2) becomes

(5.7) $$c_k = - \frac{c_{k-2}}{(-n+k)^2 - n^2} = - \frac{c_{k-2}}{k(-2n+k)}$$

This is the same recursion formula as (5.4) except that n is replaced by $-n$ and that (5.7) cannot hold for all k if n is a positive integer. Hence, except for this latter case, a solution belonging to the exponent

† For definition and tables of the factorial function $n!$ for values other than 0, 1, 2, . . . see Ref. 6, sec. II.   In this case $n!$ is often denoted as $\Gamma(n+1)$.

‡ More precisely, J_n is a Bessel function of the "first kind."   For other Bessel functions, see Sec. 7.

$-n$ is obtained by replacing n with $-n$ in (5.5):

$$(5.8) \quad J_{-n}(x) = \left(\frac{x}{2}\right)^{-n} \left[\frac{1}{(-n)!} - \frac{(x/2)^2}{1!(-n+1)!} \right.$$
$$\left. + \frac{(x/2)^4}{2!(-n+2)!} - \frac{(x/2)^6}{3!(-n+3)!} + \cdots \right]$$

If $n = 0$, then this solution is identical with the previously found solution (5.6). In all other cases J_{-n} is linearly independent of J_n. [To check this, simply substitute $x = 0$ in an assumed relation of the form $c_1 J_n(x) + c_2 J_{-n}(x) = 0$.] Therefore,

$$y = AJ_n + BJ_{-n}$$

is the general solution of Bessel's equation, except when n is an integer.

If n is one of the integers 1, 2, 3, . . . , then J_n exists, but J_{-n} as defined in (5.8) cannot be formed. If $n = 0$, then J_{-n} and J_n exist but are linearly dependent. Hence, in all cases, at least one integral is obtained; that integral is expanded in a series about the regular-singular point $x_0 = 0$, in accordance with the theorem of Sec. 4.

If n is an integer, then the present procedure does not lead to the general solution. This case is discussed in Sec. 7.

PROBLEMS

Solve, in terms of Bessel functions (of the first kind), the following equations. In cases in which the Bessel functions of the first kind do not supply the general solution, state the fact and the reasons.

1. $x \dfrac{d^2y}{dx^2} + \dfrac{dy}{dx} + xy = 0$

2. $x^2 \dfrac{d^2y}{dx^2} + x \dfrac{dy}{dx} + (a^2x^2 - n^2)y = 0, \ a \neq 0$

3. $\dfrac{d^2y}{dx^2} + \dfrac{1}{x-s} \dfrac{dy}{dx} + \left[a^2 - \dfrac{n^2}{(x-s)^2} \right] y = 0, a \neq 0$

4. $x \dfrac{d^2y}{dx^2} + (1+2n) \dfrac{dy}{dx} + xy = 0.$ HINT: Make the substitution $y = x^{-n}Y$.

5. $x \dfrac{d^2y}{dx^2} + 2 \dfrac{dy}{dx} + xy = 0.$ HINT: Make the substitution $y = x^{-\frac{1}{2}}Y$ as suggested in Prob. 4; solve also by the use of the substitution $y = x^{-1}Y$.

6. $\dfrac{d^2y}{dx^2} + a^2xy = 0, \ a \neq 0.$ HINT: Make the substitutions $x = \left(\dfrac{3}{2a} X\right)^{\frac{2}{3}}$, $y = x^{\frac{1}{2}}Y$.

7. $\dfrac{d^2y}{dx^2} + a^2x^2y = 0,\ a \neq 0$. HINT: Make the substitutions $x = \left(\dfrac{2}{a}X\right)^{\frac{1}{2}}$, $y = x^{\frac{1}{2}}Y$.

8. $\dfrac{d^2y}{dx^2} + (e^{2x} - n^2)y = 0$. HINT: Make the substitution $x = \log X$.

★**9.** Comparing the results obtained by the two different substitutions suggested in Prob. 5, show that

$$J_{\frac{1}{2}}(x) = \sqrt{\frac{2}{\pi x}}\sin x \qquad J_{-\frac{1}{2}}(x) = \sqrt{\frac{2}{\pi x}}\cos x$$

HINT: Compare first terms in power-series expansions. Use the values

$$(\tfrac{1}{2})! = \tfrac{1}{2}\sqrt{\pi} \qquad (-\tfrac{1}{2})! = \sqrt{\pi}$$

6. Gauss's Hypergeometric Equation

Gauss's equation (Karl Friedrich Gauss, 1777–1855) has the form

(6.1) $$x(1 - x)\frac{d^2y}{dx^2} + [\gamma - (\alpha + \beta + 1)x]\frac{dy}{dx} - \alpha\beta y = 0$$

where α, β, γ are given constants. Its characteristic feature is that the coefficients of y'', y', y are polynomials of degree 2, 1, 0, respectively. The seemingly more general equation

$$(x^2 + ax + b)\frac{d^2y}{dx^2} + (cx + d)\frac{dy}{dx} + ey = 0$$

can be reduced to the form (6.1) by a linear transformation of the independent variable (see Prob. 4 below). Many equations in applied science are special cases of the hypergeometric equation or can be transformed into it by suitable substitutions.

It is immediately recognized that $x = 0$ and $x = 1$ are regular-singular points, whereas all other values of x are ordinary points of the hypergeometric equation. In the following the solutions will be expanded about the point $x = 0$.

To conform with the general procedure, Eq. (6.1) is first multiplied by x:

$$x^2(1 - x)y'' + [\gamma x - (\alpha + \beta + 1)x^2]y' - \alpha\beta xy = 0$$

If $y(x) = \Sigma c_k x^{r+k}$ is substituted in (6.1), one gets

$$\sum_{k=0}^{\infty}(r + k)(r + k - 1)c_k x^{r+k} - \sum_{k=0}^{\infty}(r + k)(r + k - 1)c_k x^{r+k+1}$$

$$+ \gamma\sum_{k=0}^{\infty}(r + k)c_k x^{r+k} - (\alpha + \beta + 1)\sum_{k=0}^{\infty}(r + k)c_k x^{r+k+1}$$

$$- \alpha\beta\sum_{k=0}^{\infty}c_k x^{r+k+1} = 0$$

Equating the coefficient of x^{r+k} to zero, we have

$$(r + k)(r + k - 1)c_k - (r + k - 1)(r + k - 2)c_{k-1} + \gamma(r + k)c_k$$
$$- (\alpha + \beta + 1)(r + k - 1)c_{k-1} - \alpha\beta c_{k-1} = 0$$

or

$$(6.2) \quad (r + k)(r + k + \gamma - 1)c_k$$
$$- [(r + k - 1)(r + k + \alpha + \beta - 1) + \alpha\beta]c_{k-1} = 0$$

For $k = 0$, one obtains the indicial equation

$$r(r + \gamma - 1) = 0$$

whose roots are

$$r_1 = 0 \qquad r_2 = 1 - \gamma$$

For the root $r_1 = 0$, Eq. (6.2) becomes

$$k(\gamma + k - 1)c_k = (\alpha + k - 1)(\beta + k - 1)c_{k-1}$$

Applying this recursion formula for $k - 1, k - 2, \ldots, 1$, and putting $c_0 = 1$, one obtains the general coefficient

$$c_k = \frac{(\alpha + k - 1)(\alpha + k - 2) \cdots \alpha(\beta + k - 1)(\beta + k - 2) \cdots \beta}{k(k - 1) \cdots 1(\gamma - k - 1)(\gamma + k - 2) \cdots \gamma}$$

This result is valid except when γ is one of the numbers $0, -1, -2, \ldots$. Hence, except for one of these cases, the solution belonging to the exponent $r_1 = 0$ is

$$(6.3) \quad y_1(x) = 1 + \frac{\alpha\beta}{1 \cdot \gamma} x + \frac{\alpha(\alpha + 1)\beta(\beta + 1)}{1 \cdot 2 \cdot \gamma(\gamma + 1)} x^2$$
$$+ \frac{\alpha(\alpha + 1)(\alpha + 2)\beta(\beta + 1)(\beta + 2)}{1 \cdot 2 \cdot 3 \cdot \gamma(\gamma + 1)(\gamma + 2)} x^3 + \cdots$$

This series is known as the *hypergeometric series*, and the function defined by it is the *hypergeometric function*, commonly designated as $F(\alpha, \beta, \gamma; x)$. Only for special values of the parameters α, β, γ is this an elementary function (see Prob. 6 below). Series (6.3) converges for $|x| < 1$. This follows from the theorem of Sec. 4.

To find the solution belonging to the other exponent, let $r_2 = 1 - \gamma$ be substituted in (6.2):

$$k(1 - \gamma + k)c_k = (\alpha - \gamma + k)(\beta - \gamma + k)c_{k-1}$$

Applying this recursion formula for $k - 1$, $k - 2$, . . . , 1, and putting $c_0 = 1$, one obtains the general coefficient

$$c_k = \frac{(\alpha - \gamma + k) \cdots (\alpha - \gamma + 1)(\beta - \gamma + k) \cdots (\beta - \gamma + 1)}{k(k - 1) \cdots 1(1 - \gamma + k) \cdots (1 - \gamma + 1)}$$

This result is valid except when γ is one of the numbers 2, 3, 4, ... Hence, except for one of these cases, the solution belonging to the exponent $r_2 = 1 - \gamma$ is

$$(6.4) \quad y_2(x) = x^{1-\gamma} \left[1 + \frac{(\alpha - \gamma + 1)(\beta - \gamma + 1)}{1 \cdot (-\gamma + 2)} x \right.$$
$$\left. + \frac{(\alpha - \gamma + 1)(\alpha - \gamma + 2)(\beta - \gamma + 1)(\beta - \gamma + 2)}{1 \cdot 2 \cdot (-\gamma + 2)(-\gamma + 3)} x^2 + \cdots \right]$$

Comparing series (6.4) with series (6.3), one sees that the series in (6.4) can be obtained from the hypergeometric series by replacing α with $\alpha - \gamma + 1$, β with $\beta - \gamma + 1$, and γ with $-\gamma + 2$. Hence, (6.4) may also be written as

$$y_2(x) = x^{1-\gamma} F(\alpha - \gamma + 1, \beta - \gamma + 1, 2 - \gamma; x)$$

If $\gamma = 1$, then $y_2(x)$ is identical with $y_1(x)$. Otherwise, y_2 is linearly independent of y_1. [To check this, simply substitute $x = 0$ in an assumed relation of the form $c_1 y_1(x) + c_2 y_2(x) = 0$.] Therefore,

$$y(x) = AF(\alpha, \beta, \gamma; x) + Bx^{1-\gamma} F(\alpha - \gamma + 1, \beta - \gamma + 1, 2 - \gamma; x)$$

is the general solution of the hypergeometric equation, except when γ is an integer.

If γ is one of the integers 0, -1, -2, . . . , then y_1 does not exist, but y_2 does. If γ is one of the integers 2, 3, 4, . . . , then y_2 does not exist, but y_1 does. If, finally, $\gamma = 1$, then y_1 and y_2 both exist but are not linearly independent. Hence, in all cases, at least one integral is obtained; this integral is expanded in a series about the regular-singular point $x_0 = 0$, in accordance with the theorem of Sec. 4.

If γ is an integer, then the present procedure does not lead to the general solution. This case is discussed in Sec. 7.

PROBLEMS

Solve, in terms of the hypergeometric function, the following equations:

1. $4x(1 - x) \dfrac{d^2y}{dx^2} + 2(1 - 4x) \dfrac{dy}{dx} - y = 0$

2. $x(1 - x) \dfrac{d^2y}{dx^2} + (cx + d) \dfrac{dy}{dx} + ey = 0$

3. $x(a + x) \dfrac{d^2y}{dx^2} + (cx + d) \dfrac{dy}{dx} + ey = 0, \ a \neq 0$

4. $(x^2 + ax + b) \dfrac{d^2y}{dx^2} + (cx + d) \dfrac{dy}{dx} + ey = 0, \ a^2 > 4b.$ HINT: Let $x^2 +$

$ax + b = (x - s_1)(x - s_2).$ Make the substitution

$$X = \frac{x - s_1}{s_2 - s_1}$$

and the above equation takes the form of the hypergeometric equation.

5. $(x^2 - 5x + 4) \dfrac{d^2y}{dx^2} - \dfrac{3}{5} x \dfrac{dy}{dx} + \dfrac{16}{25} y = 0.$ HINT: Proceed as in Prob. 4.

6. Name the functions to which the hypergeometric function reduces in the following special cases:

(a) $\alpha = 1, \beta = \gamma$
(b) $\alpha = -n, \beta = \gamma$
(c) $\alpha = \beta = 1, \gamma = 2$
(d) α or β a negative integer
★(e) $\alpha = \beta = \frac{1}{2}, \gamma = \frac{3}{2}$
★(f) $\alpha = \frac{1}{2}, \beta = 1, \gamma = \frac{3}{2}$

★**7.** When $a^2 = 4b$ in the equation of Prob. 4, show that $x = -a/2$ is a regular-singular point if and only if $d/c = a/2$.

8. Find the solution of the equation

$$2x(1 - x) \frac{d^2y}{dx^2} + (3 - 5x) \frac{dy}{dx} - y = 0$$

for which $dy/dx = 1$ when $x = 0$. Why is this one condition sufficient for the determination of a unique solution?

7. Roots of Indicial Equation Differing by an Integer

As was pointed out in Sec. 4, the coefficients of expansion (4.2) can be successively determined from recursion formulas of the form (4.6), except if $g(r + k) = 0$ for some positive integer k. This cannot happen if r is the algebraically largest root of the indicial equation (in the case of complex roots, if r is the root with the algebraically largest real part). Therefore, the procedure for finding the coefficients, described in Sec. 4, can always be carried out for at least one root of the indicial equation, and thus at least one solution can be obtained in form (4.2), as asserted in the theorem of that section. But if there are roots of the indicial equation which differ by an integer, then for the smaller root it will happen that $g(r + k) = 0$ for some positive integer k. For such a root the general procedure cannot be carried out. In this case there will usually be fewer than n solutions found in the form (4.2). [But, as was seen in Example 2 of Sec. 4, there are, even then, exceptional cases in which two solutions of the form (4.2) are obtained.] This will also happen if the indicial equation has repeated roots (which can be considered as roots differing by the integer 0).

Thus, for the hypergeometric equation of Sec. 6, the indicial equation was

$$r(r + \gamma - 1) = 0$$

and only one solution of form (4.2), the one belonging to the algebraically larger of the two roots $0, 1 - \gamma$, is obtained if γ is an integer. Again, for Bessel's equation of Sec. 5, the indicial equation was

$$r^2 - n^2 = 0$$

and only one solution of form (4.2), the one belonging to the nonnegative exponent n, is obtained if n is an integer.

The general solution in these exceptional cases is somewhat more complicated. It will be discussed here only for differential equations of the second order. If $x = 0$ is a regular-singular point of such an equation, then it has the form

$$(7.1) \qquad x^2 \frac{d^2y}{dx^2} + x(b_{10} + \cdots) \frac{dy}{dx} + (b_{20} + \cdots)y = 0$$

where the dots indicate terms of at least the first degree in x. The indicial equation is

$$g(r) = r(r - 1) + b_{10}r + b_{20} = 0$$

or

$$(7.2) \qquad r^2 + (b_{10} - 1)r + b_{20} = 0$$

In the exceptional case, the two roots of the indicial equation are r and $r - m$, where m is one of the numbers $0, 1, 2, \ldots$. Since by (7.2) the sum of the two roots must be equal to $-(b_{10} - 1)$, we have

$$(7.3) \qquad 2r - m = 1 - b_{10}$$

The solution y_1 belonging to the exponent r, which is the algebraically larger of the two roots $r, r - m$, is of the form

$$(7.4) \qquad y_1(x) = x^r(1 + c_1x + c_2x^2 + \cdots)$$

where the coefficients can be determined by the method described in Sec. 4 (for convenience, the value 1 is chosen for c_0). In the preceding chapter (see Sec. 2) it is shown that if one solution of a homogeneous linear equation is known, then the order of the equation can be reduced by 1. The appropriate substitution is

$$y = y_1u$$

Then

$$y' = y_1u' + y_1'u$$
$$y'' = y_1u'' + 2y_1'u' + y_1''u$$

and Eq. (7.1) becomes, if account is taken of y_1 being a solution,

$$x^2 y_1 u'' + 2x^2 y_1' u' + x(b_{10} + \cdots) y_1 u' = 0$$

or

(7.5) $$u'' + \left(2\frac{y_1'}{y_1} + \frac{b_{10}}{x} + \cdots \right) u' = 0$$

Now, by (7.4),

$$\frac{y_1'}{y_1} = \frac{r}{x} + \cdots$$

where the dots stand for terms that do not contain negative powers of x. Hence, (7.5) can be written as

$$u'' + \left(\frac{2r + b_{10}}{x} + \cdots \right) u' = 0$$

When use is made of (7.3), this equation may also be written as

$$\frac{u''}{u'} = -\left(\frac{m+1}{x} + \cdots \right)$$

and integration gives

$$\log u' = -(m+1) \log x + \cdots$$

Hence

(7.6) $$u' = x^{-(m+1)} \exp(\cdots)$$

where the dots stand for some series of positive powers of x. When the expression $(\cdots)$ is itself expanded as a power series of the form

$$1 + a_1 x + a_2 x^2 + \cdots$$

Eq. (7.6) becomes

(7.7) $$u' = x^{-(m+1)} + a_1 x^{-m} + \cdots + a_m x^{-1} + a_{m+1} + a_{m+2} x + \cdots$$

If $m = 0$ (case of *repeated* roots of the indicial equation), then (7.7) reads

(7.8) $$u' = x^{-1} + a_1 + a_2 x + \cdots$$

Integration of (7.7) and (7.8) gives

(7.9) $$u(x) = \begin{cases} \log x + a_1 x + \dfrac{a_2}{2} x^2 + \cdots & \text{if } m = 0 \\[2ex] \dfrac{x^{-m}}{-m} + \dfrac{a_1 x^{-m+1}}{-m+1} + \cdots + a_m \log x + a_{m+1} x + \cdots \\[1ex] \hspace{5cm} \text{if } m = 1, 2, \ldots \end{cases}$$

Therefore, the desired solution $y(x) = y_1(x)u(x)$ is of the form

$$(7.10) \quad y_2(x) = \begin{cases} y_1(x) \log x + x^r(C_1 x + C_2 x^2 + \cdots) & \text{if } m = 0 \\ C_0 y_1(x) \log x + x^{r-m}\left(-\dfrac{1}{m} + C_1 x + C_2 x^2 + \cdots\right) \\ \qquad\qquad\qquad\qquad\qquad\qquad\qquad\text{if } m = 1, 2, \ldots \end{cases}$$

where $C_0 = a_m$ and $C_1, C_2, \ldots$ are coefficients to be determined.

The result, thus derived, is that if the indicial equation has repeated roots or roots that differ by an integer, then one integral (belonging to the algebraically larger exponent) has form (7.4) and a second integral has form (7.10). The coefficients $c_1, c_2, \ldots$ and $C_0, C_1, \ldots$ are found by the method of undetermined coefficients. That the resulting series are valid expansions in the neighborhood of the regular-singular point is proved in more advanced texts. See Ref. 4, chap. 9.

To illustrate the use of formula (7.10), let it be required to find the general solution of Bessel's equation of order zero, expanded about $x = 0$. The equation is

$$(7.11) \qquad\qquad x^2 y'' + xy' + x^2 y = 0$$

In Sec. 5 one integral was found:

$$y_1(x) = J_0(x) = \sum_{k=0}^{\infty} \frac{(-1)^k}{(k!)^2}\left(\frac{x}{2}\right)^{2k}$$

The indicial equation is $r^2 = 0$. Hence, $r = 0$ is a repeated root, and to find another integral one uses (7.10):

$$y(x) = y_1(x) \log x + C_1 x + C_2 x^2 + \cdots$$
$$= J_0(x) \log x + \sum_{m=1}^{\infty} C_m x^m$$

Then

$$y'(x) = J_0'(x) \log x + \frac{J_0(x)}{x} + \sum_{m=1}^{\infty} mC_m x^{m-1}$$

$$y''(x) = J_0''(x) \log x + \frac{2J_0'(x)}{x} - \frac{J_0(x)}{x^2} + \sum_{m=1}^{\infty} m(m-1)C_m x^{m-2}$$

When we substitute these expansions in (7.11) and remember that J_0 satisfies this equation, we find

$$2xJ_0'(x) - J_0(x) + \sum_{m=1}^{\infty} m(m-1)C_m x^m + J_0(x) + \sum_{m=1}^{\infty} mC_m x^m$$
$$+ \sum_{m=1}^{\infty} C_m x^{m+2} = 0$$

or, since

$$J_0'(x) = \sum_{k=1}^{\infty} \frac{(-1)^k}{(k-1)!k!} \left(\frac{x}{2}\right)^{2k-1}$$

we have

(7.12) $$\sum_{m=1}^{\infty} m^2 C_m x^m + \sum_{m=1}^{\infty} C_m x^{m+2} = \sum_{k=1}^{\infty} \frac{(-1)^{k-1}}{(k-1)!k!2^{2k-2}} x^{2k}$$

Since on the right-hand side of this equation there are only even powers of x, it is clear that it can be satisfied only if the coefficients C with odd subscripts are zero. Hence, it remains to find the coefficients C with even subscripts. Putting $m = 2k$ and equating the coefficients of x^{2k} in Eq. (7.12), we find

$$4k^2 C_{2k} + C_{2k-2} = \frac{(-1)^{k-1}}{(k-1)!k!2^{2k-2}}$$

From this recursion formula the general coefficient C_{2k} can be determined:

$$C_{2k} = \frac{(-1)^{k-1}}{(k!)^2 2^{2k}} \left(1 + \frac{1}{2} + \frac{1}{3} + \cdots + \frac{1}{k}\right)$$

For the first three coefficients, one obtains $C_2 = \frac{1}{4}$, $C_4 = -\frac{3}{128}$, $C_6 = \frac{11}{13,824}$. Therefore,

$$y_2(x) = J_0(x) \log x + \left(\tfrac{1}{4}x^2 - \tfrac{3}{128} x^4 + \frac{11}{13,824} x^6 \cdots\right)$$

is the desired solution of Eq. (7.11). [This function is called *Neumann's Bessel function of the second kind* (Karl Neumann, 1832–1925) and is commonly designated by $K_0(x)$.] Hence, the general solution of Eq. (7.11) may be written as

$$y = AJ_0 + BK_0$$

Various other Bessel functions of the second kind are in use. They are all solutions of Bessel's differential equation and form, together with the Bessel functions of the first kind, a fundamental system of linearly independent solutions.

8. The Point at Infinity

For many purposes of theoretical and applied science, the solution of a differential equation is required for large values of the independent variable. In particular, if the independent variable is time, one may want to know the solution at a distant time when the disturbances due to temporary causes are sufficiently weakened. For such applications the series expansions of the preceding sections would be unsuited, since, even if those series converge for all values of the independent variable, they become impractical for numerical calculation when the values of the variable involved are large.

In this section expansions "about the point at infinity" are discussed. These are expansions that are valid for all sufficiently large values of the variable. No new theory is necessary for such expansions, for the substitution

$$(8.1) \qquad x = \frac{1}{z} \qquad z = \frac{1}{x}$$

transforms every neighborhood of the point $x = \infty$ into a neighborhood of the point $z = 0$. Hence, all that is necessary is to transform the differential equation by this substitution and then to expand the solution in the neighborhood of $z = 0$ by the methods described in the preceding sections. On replacing z with $1/x$ in the expansions thus found, the desired expansions about the point at infinity are obtained.

In accordance with this explanation the point at infinity will be said to be an ordinary point or a regular-singular point with the exponents r_1, r_2, if, for the transformed equation, the point $z = 0$ is an ordinary point or a regular-singular point with the exponents r_1, r_2, respectively.

Example 1. Let it be required to expand the general solution of the equation

$$4x^3 \frac{d^2y}{dx^2} + 6x^2 \frac{dy}{dx} + y = 0$$

in the neighborhood of $x = \infty$ (that is, for large values of x).

We make the substitution (8.1), putting $y(x) = y(1/z) = Y(z)$, and obtain

$$\frac{dy}{dx} = \frac{dY}{dz}\frac{dz}{dx} = -\frac{1}{x^2}\frac{dY}{dz} = -z^2\frac{dY}{dz}$$

$$\frac{d^2y}{dx^2} = \frac{1}{x^4}\frac{d^2Y}{dz^2} + \frac{2}{x^3}\frac{dY}{dz} = z^4\frac{d^2Y}{dz^2} + 2z^3\frac{dY}{dz}$$

Then the equation becomes

$$4z\frac{d^2Y}{dz^2} + 2\frac{dY}{dz} + Y = 0$$

It is seen that $z = 0$ is a regular-singular point. Hence, we put

$$Y(z) = \sum_{k=0}^{\infty} c_k z^{k+r}$$

$$\frac{dY}{dz} = \sum_{k=0}^{\infty} (k+r)c_k z^{k+r-1}$$

$$\frac{d^2Y}{dz^2} = \sum_{k=0}^{\infty} (k+r)(k+r-1)c_k z^{k+r-2}$$

With these expansions the above equation becomes

$$4 \sum_{k=0}^{\infty} (k + r)(k + r - 1)c_k z^{k+r-1} + 2 \sum_{k=0}^{\infty} (k + r)c_k z^{k+r-1} + \sum_{k=0}^{\infty} c_k z^{k+r} = 0$$

Equating the coefficient of z^{k+r-1} to zero,

$$2(k + r)(2k + 2r - 1)c_k + c_{k-1} = 0$$

For $k = 0$ the indicial equation

$$r(2r - 1) = 0$$

is obtained, with roots $r_1 = 0$, $r_2 = \frac{1}{2}$.

For $r_1 = 0$ we have the recursion formula

$$c_k = - \frac{c_{k-1}}{2k(2k - 1)}$$

Applying this formula for $k - 1$, $k - 2$, . . . , 1, and setting $c_0 = 1$, we find

$$c_k = \frac{(-1)^k}{(2k)!}$$

and the solution is

$$Y_1(z) = \sum_{k=0}^{\infty} \frac{(-1)^k}{(2k)!} z^k$$

Replacing z with $1/x$, we obtain

$$y_1(x) = \sum_{k=0}^{\infty} \frac{(-1)^k}{(2k)!} x^{-k}$$

which is readily identified as the expansion of

$$y_1(x) = \cos x^{-\frac{1}{2}}$$

For $r_2 = \frac{1}{2}$ we obtain the recursion formula

$$c_k = - \frac{1}{2k(2k + 1)} c_{k-1}$$

If we proceed as above, we find

$$c_k = \frac{(-1)^k}{(2k + 1)!}$$

and

$$Y_2(z) = \sum_{k=0}^{\infty} \frac{(-1)^k}{(2k + 1)!} z^k$$

or

$$y_2(x) = \sum_{k=0}^{\infty} \frac{(-1)^k}{(2k+1)!} x^{-k}$$

$$= x^{\frac{1}{2}} \sum_{k=0}^{\infty} \frac{(-1)^k}{(2k+1)!} x^{-\frac{2k+1}{2}}$$

which is readily identified as the expansion of

$$y_2(x) = x^{\frac{1}{2}} \sin x^{-\frac{1}{2}}$$

PROBLEMS

Expand in series that are valid in the neighborhood of $x = \infty$ the solutions of the following equations.   Try to identify the obtained series as expansions of known functions.

1. $x^2(x^2 - 1) \dfrac{d^2y}{dx^2} + x(2x^2 - 3) \dfrac{dy}{dx} - y = 0$

2. $x^6 \dfrac{d^3y}{dx^3} + x^2(6x^3 + 1) \dfrac{d^2y}{dx^2} + 2x(3x^3 - 1) \dfrac{dy}{dx} + 2y = 0$

3. $x^2(x + 2) \dfrac{d^2y}{dx^2} - x(x - 4) \dfrac{dy}{dx} - 4y = 0$

4. $4x^4 \dfrac{d^2y}{dx^2} + 4x^3 \dfrac{dy}{dx} - (x^2 - 1)y = 0$

5. $x^4 \dfrac{d^2y}{dx^2} + x^3 \dfrac{dy}{dx} + (1 - n^2x^2)y = 0$

6. $x^2(x - 1) \dfrac{d^2y}{dx^2} + x[\alpha + \beta - 1 + (1 - \delta)x] \dfrac{dy}{dx} - \alpha\beta y = 0$

Find the solutions of the following "terminal-value" problems.   Name the interval of convergence, and try to identify the solutions.

7. $t^4 \dfrac{d^2x}{dt^2} + t(2t^2 - 1) \dfrac{dx}{dt} - 2x = 0; x \to 1, \dfrac{dx}{dt} \to 0$ as $t \to \infty$

8. $t^4 \dfrac{d^2x}{dt^2} + t(2t^2 - 1) \dfrac{dx}{dt} - 2x = 0; x \to 0, t^2 \dfrac{dx}{dt} \to 1$ as $t \to \infty$

9. $t^7 \dfrac{d^3x}{dt^3} + 6t^6 \dfrac{d^2x}{dt^2} + 2t(3t^4 - 2) \dfrac{dx}{dt} - 12x = 0; x \to 1, \dfrac{dx}{dt} \to 0, \dfrac{d^2x}{dt^2} \to 0$

as $t \to \infty$

★10. Show that $x = \infty$ is an ordinary point of the equation

$$\frac{d^2y}{dx^2} + a_1(x) \frac{dy}{dx} + a_2(x)y = f(x)$$

if the functions $x^2a_1(x) - 2x$, $x^4a_2(x)$, $x^4f(x)$ are analytic in the neighborhood of $x = \infty$.

★11. Show that $x = \infty$ is a regular-singular point of the differential equation

$$\frac{d^2y}{dx^2} + a_1(x)\frac{dy}{dx} + a_2(x)\,y = 0$$

if $xa_1(x)$ and $x^2a_2(x)$ are analytic in the neighborhood of $x = \infty$.

12. What kind of point (ordinary, regular-singular, nonregular-singular) is $x = \infty$ (a) in Gauss' equation? (b) In Bessel's equation?

9. Legendre's Differential Equation

Legendre's equation (Adrien-Marie Legendre, 1752–1833) arises in numerous problems of applied science, particularly in boundary-value problems for spheres. It has the form

$$(9.1) \qquad (1 - x^2)\frac{d^2y}{dx^2} - 2x\frac{dy}{dx} + n(n + 1)y = 0$$

where n is a given constant, usually a positive integer (the only case that will be considered here). We propose to expand its solution in the neighborhood of the point at infinity. Making the transformation $x = 1/z$, $y(x) - Y(z)$, we have, as in the preceding section,

$$\frac{dy}{dx} = -\frac{1}{x^2}\frac{dY}{dz}$$

$$\frac{d^2y}{dx^2} = z^4\frac{d^2Y}{dz^2} + 2z^3\frac{dY}{dz}$$

With these substitutions Eq. (9.1) becomes

$$(9.2) \qquad (z^4 - z^2)\frac{d^2Y}{dz^2} + 2z^3\frac{dY}{dz} + n(n + 1)Y = 0$$

It is immediately recognized that $z = 0$ is a regular-singular point of this equation. Hence, the point at infinity is a regular-singular point of Legendre's equation. Then,

$$Y(z) = \sum_{k=0}^{\infty} c_k z^{k+r}$$

$$\frac{dY}{dz} = \sum_{k=0}^{\infty} (k + r)c_k z^{k+r-1}$$

$$\frac{d^2Y}{dz^2} = \sum_{k=0}^{\infty} (k + r)(k + r - 1)c_k z^{k+r-2}$$

With these expansions Eq. (9.2) becomes

$$\sum_{k=0}^{\infty} (k + r)(k + r - 1)c_k z^{k+r+2} - \sum_{k=0}^{\infty} (k + r)(k + r - 1)c_k z^{k+r}$$

$$+ 2 \sum_{k=0}^{\infty} (k + r)c_k z^{k+r+2} + n(n + 1) \sum_{k=0}^{\infty} c_k z^{k+r} = 0$$

Equating the coefficient of z^{k+r} to zero, we obtain

$$[(k + r - 2)(k + r - 3) + 2(k + r - 2)]c_{k-2}$$
$$- [(k + r)(k + r - 1) - n(n + 1)]c_k = 0$$

or

(9.3) $[(k + r)(k + r - 1) - n(n + 1)]c_k - (k + r - 2)(k + r - 1)c_{k-2} = 0$

For $k = 0$ the indicial equation

$$r(r - 1) - n(n + 1) = 0$$

is obtained, with roots

$$r_1 = -n \qquad r_2 = n + 1$$

For $k = 1$, formula (9.3) becomes

$$[r(r + 1) - n(n + 1)]c_1 = 0$$

and since for neither of the roots r_1, r_2 does the bracketed factor vanish, c_1 must be zero in both cases. Then, because of recursion formula (9.3), $c_3 = 0 = c_5 = c_7 = \cdots$. It remains to calculate the coefficients c with even subscripts. Replacing k with $2k$ in (9.3), we have

(9.4) $$c_{2k} = \frac{(2k + r - 2)(2k + r - 1)}{(2k + r)(2k + r - 1) - n(n + 1)} c_{2k-2}$$

Let us consider, at first, the solution belonging to the exponent $r_1 = -n$. Then (9.4) becomes

$$c_{2k} = \frac{-(n + 2 - 2k)(n + 1 - 2k)}{2k(2n + 1 - 2k)} c_{2k-2}$$

Applying this formula for $2k - 2$, $2k - 4$, ... , 2, and setting $c_0 = 1$, we find

$$c_{2k} = (-1)^k \frac{n(n - 1)(n - 2) \cdots (n - 2k + 1)}{2 \cdot 4 \cdot 6 \cdots 2k(2n - 1)(2n - 3) \cdots (2n - 2k + 1)}$$

It follows from this formula that $c_{n+1} = c_{n+2} = c_{n+3} = \cdots = 0$. Hence, the only coefficients different from zero in this solution are c_0, c_2, c_4, ... , c_n

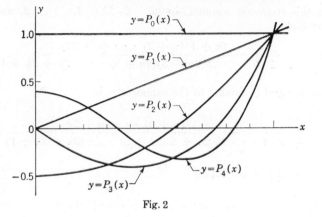

Fig. 2

(or c_{n-1} if n is odd), and the solution is

$$Y_1(z) = \sum_{k=0}^{\frac{n}{2} \text{ or } \frac{n-1}{2}} (-1)^k \frac{n(n-1) \cdots (n-2k+1)}{2 \cdot 4 \cdots 2k(2n-1)(2n-3) \cdots (2n-2k+1)} z^{2k-n}$$

Replacing z with $1/x$, we obtain

$$y_1(x) = \sum_{k=0}^{\frac{n}{2} \text{ or } \frac{n-1}{2}} (-1)^k \frac{n(n-1) \cdots (n-2k+1)}{2 \cdot 4 \cdots 2k(2n-1)(2n-3) \cdots (2n-2k+1)} x^{n-2k}$$

$$= x^n - \frac{n(n-1)}{2(2n-1)} x^{n-2} + \frac{n(n-1)(n-2)(n-3)}{2 \cdot 4 \cdot (2n-1)(2n-3)} x^{n-4} \cdots$$

This is a polynomial of degree n, and when multiplied† by the constant factor $(2n)!/2^n(n!)^2$ it is known as a *Legendre polynomial* of degree n, commonly designated as $P_n(x)$:

$$P_n(x) = \frac{(2n)!}{2^n(n!)^2} y_1(x)$$

The first five Legendre polynomials are

$$P_0(x) = 1 \qquad P_1(x) = x \qquad P_2(x) = \tfrac{1}{2}(3x^2 - 1)$$
$$P_3(x) = \tfrac{1}{2}(5x^3 - 3x) \qquad P_4(x) = \tfrac{1}{8}(35x^4 - 30x^2 + 3)$$

Graphs of these functions are shown in Fig. 2. For further graphs and tables, see, for example, Ref. 6, sec. VII.

For the exponent $r_2 = n + 1$, formula (9.4) becomes

$$c_{2k} = \frac{(n+2k)(n+2k-1)}{2k(2n+2k+1)} c_{2k-2}$$

† This factor is chosen so as to make $P_n(1) = 1$ for all n.

Applying this recursion formula for $2k - 2$, $2k - 4$, $\ldots$, 2, and setting $c_0 = 1$, we find

$$c_{2k} = \frac{(n + 1)(n + 2) \cdots (n + 2k)}{2 \cdot 4 \cdot 6 \cdots 2k(2n + 3)(2n + 5) \cdots (2n + 2k + 1)}$$

Hence, the integral belonging to the exponent r_2 is

$$Y_2(z) = \sum_{k=0}^{\infty} \frac{(n + 1)(n + 2) \cdots (n + 2k)}{2 \cdot 4 \cdots 2k(2n + 3)(2n + 5) \cdots (2n + 2k + 1)} z^{2k+n+1}$$

Replacing z with $1/x$, we obtain

$$y_2(x) = \sum_{k=0}^{\infty} \frac{(n + 1)(n + 2) \cdots (n + 2k)}{2 \cdot 4 \cdot 6 \cdots 2k(2n + 3)(2n + 5) \cdots (2n + 2k + 1)} x^{-2k-n-1}$$

$$= x^{-(n+1)} \left[1 + \frac{(n + 1)(n + 2)}{2(2n + 3)} x^{-2} \right.$$
$$\left. + \frac{(n + 1)(n + 2)(n + 3)(n + 4)}{2 \cdot 4(2n + 3)(2n + 5)} x^{-4} + \cdots \right]$$

From the theorem in Sec. 4 it follows that this expansion is valid for $|x| > 1$. This can also be readily verified by the ratio test. The function thus obtained, when multiplied by the constant factor $2^n(n!)^2/(2n + 1)!$, is known as a *Legendre function* of the *second kind* and is commonly denoted as $Q_n(x)$:

$$Q_n(x) = \frac{2^n(n!)^2}{(2n + 1)!} y_2(x)$$

The general solution of Legendre's equation can now be written as

$$y = AP_n + BQ_n$$

PROBLEMS

Solve, in terms of Legendre polynomials and functions, the following equations:

1. $(1 - x^2) \dfrac{d^2y}{dx^2} - 2x \dfrac{dy}{dx} + 12y = 0$

2. $(a^2 - x^2) \dfrac{d^2y}{dx^2} - 2x \dfrac{dy}{dx} + n(n + 1)y = 0$, $a \neq 0$

3. $\dfrac{d}{dx} \left[(x^2 + ax + b) \dfrac{dy}{dx} \right] - n(n + 1)y = 0$, $a^2 - 4b > 0$. HINT: Make the substitution $x = \sqrt{\frac{1}{4}a^2 - b} \, X - \frac{1}{2}a$.

4. Prove that

$$P_{2m+1}(0) = 0 \qquad P_{2m}(0) = (-1)^m \frac{1 \cdot 3 \cdot 5 \cdots (2m-1)}{2^m m!}$$

5. Show that $x = 1$ and $x = -1$ are regular-singular points of the Legendre equation and that the indicial equation for either point is $r^2 = 0$.

6. Prove that the only solution of Legendre's equation that stays bounded at $x = 1$ (or $x = -1$) is $cP_n(x)$, where c is an arbitrary constant.

7. Expand in the neighborhood of $x = 1$ the solution of Legendre's equation for which $y = 1$ when $x = 1$ [this solution is, by the result of Prob. 6 and by the footnote on page 375, $P_n(x)$ itself].

★8. Show that

$$P_n(x) = x^n F\left(\frac{-n}{2}, \frac{1-n}{2}, \frac{1-2n}{2}; x^{-2}\right)$$

$$Q_n(x) = x^{-n-1} F\left(\frac{n+1}{2}, \frac{n+2}{2}, \frac{2n+3}{2}; x^{-2}\right)$$

where $F(\alpha, \beta, \gamma; x)$ is the hypergeometric function.

★9. Prove that

$$y(x) = \frac{d^n}{dx^n}(x^2 - 1)^n$$

is a solution of Legendre's equation. Then, from the result of Prob. 6 and from the footnote on page 375, it follows that

$$P_n(x) = \frac{1}{2^n n!} \frac{d^n}{dx^n}(x^2 - 1)^n \qquad Rodrigues'\ formula$$

★10. Show that the equation

$$\frac{d}{d\theta}\left(\sin\theta \frac{dY}{d\theta}\right) + n(n+1)\sin\theta\, Y = 0$$

is satisfied by $Y(\theta) = P_n(\cos\theta)$ and by $Y(\theta) = Q_n(\cos\theta)$.

References

1. Milne, W. E.: "Numerical Solution of Differential Equations," John Wiley & Sons, Inc., New York, 1953.
2. Murphy, G. M.: "Ordinary Differential Equations and Their Solutions," D. Van Nostrand Company, Inc., Princeton, N.J., 1960.
3. Kaplan, W.: "Advanced Calculus," Addison-Wesley Publishing Company, Inc., Reading, Mass., 1952.
4. Birkhoff, G., and G. C. Rota: "Ordinary Differential Equations," Ginn and Company, Boston, 1962.
5. Hoffman, K., and R. Kunze: "Linear Algebra," Prentice-Hall, Inc., Englewood Cliffs, N.J., 1961.
6. Jahnke, E., and F. Emde: "Tables of Functions," Dover Publications, Inc., New York, 1943.
7. Kaplan, W.: "Operational Methods for Linear Systems," Addison-Wesley Publishing Company, Inc., Reading, Mass., 1962.
8. Knopp, K.: "Elements of the Theory of Functions," Dover Publications, Inc., New York, 1952.
9. Whittaker, E. T., and G. N. Watson: "Modern Analysis," Cambridge University Press, London, 1950.

Answers

1. (a) $y = x - \ln|x + 1| + c$.   (b) $y = \frac{1}{2} \ln(1 + x^2) + c$ or $1 + x^2 = ke^{2v}$.
(c) $y = \frac{1}{6} \log[(x^2 - x + 1)/(1 + x)^2] + (1/\sqrt{3}) \arctan[(2x - 1)/\sqrt{3}] + c$.
(d) $x = h - \frac{1}{2}g(t - t_0)^2$.   (e) $x = \sqrt{E/k} \sin \sqrt{k/m}\,(t - t_0)$.
(f) $y = \frac{1}{2}(\arctan x)^2 + c$.   (g) $y = (1/x)(e^x + ce^{-x})$.
(h) $w = \int (dz/\sqrt{4z^3 - g_2 z - g_3}) + c$ (standard form of elliptic integral of
first kind).   (i) $\sqrt{x^2 + y^2} - \sqrt{x^2 + a^2} = c$.   (j) $\sqrt{1 + u^2} = 1/(c - x)$.

(k) $y = x(1 + |x|) + c$.   (l) $y = \begin{cases} c - 1 & x \le 0 \\ c - \cos x & 0 < x < \pi \\ c + 1 & x \ge \pi \end{cases}$

(m) $y = \begin{cases} c - 4 - \cos x & -2\pi \le x < -\pi \\ c - 2 + \cos x & -\pi \le x < 0 \\ c - \cos x & 0 \le x < \pi \\ c + 2 + \cos x & \pi \le x < 2\pi \\ c + 4 - \cos x & 2\pi \le x < 3\pi \end{cases}$

2. (a) $y = \pi/4 + \arctan x$.   (b) $y = -\pi/2 + \arctan 2x$.   (c) $y = -x$.
(d) $y = \frac{3}{2}e^{x^2} - \frac{1}{2}$.   (e) $y = x$.   (f) $y = 5 - 4x + 4x \log x$, $x > 0$ (solution
cannot be extended to $x < 0$ since $x \log|x|$ is not differentiable at $x = 0$).

3. $\sqrt{v_0^2 + \pi}$.   **4.** $\frac{1}{2}\sqrt{\pi} - 1$.   ★**5.** $\pi/2 = \int_0^\infty [(\sin x)/x]\,dx$.
★**6.** $\Gamma(r) [= (r - 1)!,$ if r is an integer].
7. (a) $1 + \int_0^{0.2} [(\sin x)/(1 + x^2)]\,dx = 1.01913$.
(b) $\int_0^{0.4} (d\phi/\sqrt{1 - 0.75 \sin^2 \phi}) = 0.41$.   **11.** $f(x) = \sin(x + c)$.

Chap. I, Sec. 4, page 13

1. (a) $x = c(y - 1)e^y$. (b) $x^{-2} + y^{-2} = c$. (c) $|x|^a|y + b|^b = ce^{y-x}$.
(d) $|x + A|^{a-A}|y + B|^{b-B} = ce^{y-x}$. (e) $y = [x - 1 + c(1 + x)]/$
$[1 - x + c(1 + x)]$. (f) $\sin y = cxe^{-x^2}$. (g) $x^2y^2(y - 1) = c(y + 1)$.
(h) $i = i_0 e^{-Rt/L}$. (i) $e^{-2x} + 2 \arctan \sqrt{y} = c$.
(j) $(1 + x) \sin^2 y = c(1 - x)$. (k) $x + y = c(a^2 - xy)$. (l) $e^x + e^{-y} = c$.
(m) $1 + y = c(1 - y)e^{2x}$.
(n) $y[x^2 - 2x + c(x - 1)] = x^2 - 6x + 4 + c(x^2 - x - 1)$.
2. (a) $y = 2x^2/(1 + 2x - 2x^2)$. (b) $\tan y = 1 + \sec x$. (c) $\rho = e^{\theta/k}$.
(d) $(1 + e^x) \sin y = \sqrt{2}$. (e) $xy^2 = 2x^2 + x - 2$.
(f) $\log y^2 = e^{2x} - 2e^x + \log (1 + e^x)^2$. (g) $x = 2ye^{(-1+1/y)}$.
(h) $x + y + \log (x - 1)^2(y - 1)^2 = 5 + e$. (i) $\tan y = 2 \sin x$.
(j) $e^{x^2} + e^{-y^2} = 3$. (k) $\log (1 + y^2) = (x + \frac{1}{2})e^{-2x} - \frac{1}{2}$.
5. Either $f(x) \equiv 0$ or $f(x) = e^{kx}$.

Chap. I, Sec. 6, page 30

1. (a) $y(0) = -0.004375$. (b) $y(2.5) = 9.418$. (c) $y(2) = 2.230$.
(d) $y(1) = y(-1) = 0.1867$. (e) $y(1.5) = 1.070, y(-1.5) = 17.04$.
(f) $y(1) = -2.575, y(-2) = -0.8973$. (g) $y(1) = 2.705$.
(h) $y(1) = 2.714$. (i) $y(-1) = 0.04941$. (j) $y(5) = 5.436$.
(k) $y(0) = 0.06872$. (l) $y(1.5) = 1.060, y(-1.5) = -1.060$.
(m) $y(1) = 2.714$. (n) $y(110) = -44.53$. (o) $y(0) = 0.06872$.
(p) $y(1) = 2.714$. (q) $y(-1) = 0.1434$. (r) $y(2) = 0.0303$.
(s) $y(2) = -y(-2) = 0.7757$. **6.** $y(2) = 6.679$.
16. $(1 + 1/n)^n$, $\lim_{n \to \infty} (1 + 1/n)^n = e$. **17.** $(1 + 1/n + 1/2n^2)^n$, error < 0.005.
18. Same as Prob. 17. **19.** $(1 + 1/n + 1/2n^2 + 1/6n^3 + 1/24n^4)^n$,
error $< 10^{-4}$. **20.** (a) $y_n = y_0(1 - \alpha h)^n$; (b) $y_n = y_0(1 - \alpha h + \frac{1}{2}\alpha^2h^2)^n$.

Chap. I, Sec. 8, page 37

1. $y_n(x) = \sum_{k=2}^{n} x^k/k!, \; y(x) = e^x - x - 1$. **2.** $y_n(x) = \sum_{k=0}^{n-1} x^{2k}/(2k)!$,

$y(x) = e^{x^2}$. **3.** $y_n(x) = \sum_{k=0}^{n-1} x^{3k+1}/[1 \cdot 4 \cdot 7 \cdots (3k + 1)]$.

4. $y_3(x) = \frac{17}{48} + x/4 + e^{2x}/4 + e^{3x}/3 + e^{4x}/16$.
5. $y_4(x) = 4x - 3 \log (x + 1) - \log^2 (x + 1) - \frac{1}{6} \log^3 (x + 1)$.

6. $y(x) \equiv x$. **8.** $y_n(x) = \sum_{k=0}^{n-1} x^k/k! + 10^{-n} \left[e^{10x} - \sum_{k=0}^{n-1} (10x)^k/k! \right]$.

Chap. II, Sec. 1, page 43

1. (a) $y = x + c/x$. (b) $y = x^2 + cx$. (c) $xy - \log |\sin x| = c$.
(d) $y = -x + c \sqrt{1 + x^2}$. (e) $\rho = -2 \cos \theta + 2 + ce^{-\cos \theta}$.
(f) $(x^2 + x + 1)^2y = x^4/4 + x^3/3 + x^2/2 + c$.
(g) $(1 + x^2)^2y - 2 \log |x| - y^2 = c$.

(h) $(\sec 2x + \tan 2x)y = 2\tan x - 2x - 4\log|\cos x| - 2\sin^2 x + c$.
(i) $y(\sin x + c) = \tan x + \sec x$.　(j) $v\sin u - u\sin u - \cos u = c$.
(k) $3\rho\cos^2\theta - 2\cos^3\theta = c$.　(l) $y = (x + c)e^{-ax}$.　(m) $y = (x^2/2 + c)e^{-ax}$.
(n) $y = [x^{m+1}/(m + 1) + c]e^{-ax}$.　(o) $x^5 + x^2(x^2 - 1)y = c$.
2. (a) $y = -x(1 + e^{1-1/x})$.　(b) $y = 2(\sin x - 1 + e^{-\sin x})$.
(c) $2y = (x^2 - 2x - 8)e^x + 2x^3$.　(d) $2y\arctan x = \pi/2 - \log[(1 + x^2)/2]$.
(e) $6\rho\sin\theta = 6\sin\theta - 4\sin^3\theta - 1$.
(f) $2y = (a/3)[1 - x^2 + (1 - x^2)^{-\frac{1}{2}}]$.　(g) $(1 + y^2)x + \log|\cos y| = 0$.
(h) $i = E(R\sin\omega t - \omega L\cos\omega t)/(R^2 + \omega^2L^2) + [\omega LE/(R^2 + \omega^2L^2)]e^{-Rt/L}$.
(i) $v = F(r\cos\omega t + \omega m\sin\omega t)/(r^2 + \omega^2m^2) - [rF/(r^2 + \omega^2m^2)]e^{-rt/m}$.

Chap. II, Sec. 2, page 50

1. (b), (d), (g), (h), (l) not exact.　2. (a) $x^2y = c$.　(b) $y^2 - 2y/x = c$.
(c) $(1 + e^x)(1 + e^y) = c$.　(d) $y = cx$.　(e) $y = cx$.　3. (a) $x^3 - 3xy^2 = c$.
(b) $3xy - x^2 + 2y^2 = c$.　(c) $xy = c(x + 1)(y - 1)$.
(d) $x^3/3 + x/y + \log|y| = c$.　(e) $(x + \frac{1}{2})^2 = (c - x)(y - 1)$.
(f) Not exact.　(g) $y\cos x - x + x\sin y = c$.
(h) $x^2 + \log|(1 + xy)/(1 - xy)| = c$.　(i) $xy[\log(x^2 + y^2) + 1] = c$.
(j) $\cos x\sin^2 y = c$.　(k) $\cos^2 x\sin 2y = c$.　(l) $xy = c$.
(m) $1 - 3y = c(2x - 3y + 1)$.　(n) $\arctan(x + y) - (x + y) = c$.
4. (a) $xy^2 - yx^2 = 2$.　(b) $x + e^x\sin y = 1$.
(c) $\sin(x + y) + \sin(x - y) = 1$.
(d) $\log(x^2 + y^2) + 2\arctan(x/y) = \log 2 + \pi/2$.

Chap. II, Sec. 3, page 55

1. (a) $y^2 + cy + x = 1$.　(b) $x(y^4 + cy) = 3$.　(c) $y = 3x\tan(3x + c)$.
(d) $xy = \cos x + x\sin x + c$.　(e) $y = x/(\log|x| + c)$.
(f) $3x + x^3y^4 + cy = 0$.　(g) $\arctan(y/x) = \log(x^2 + y^2) + c$.
(h) I.F. $= 1/y(x + y)(x^2 + 1)$, $(x^2 + 1)y^2(x + y)^2 = c$.　(i) I.F. $= \cos y$,
$-\cos(x + y) + \sin^2 y = c$.　(j) I.F. $= 1/(\csc x + \sin y)$;
$\log(\csc x + \sin y) - \cos x = c$.　(k) I.F. $= y^3$; $y^4(y^4 - 2x^4) = c$.
(l) I.F. $= 1/x\sqrt{x^2 - y^2}$, $y = x\sin(\log|x| + c)$.　2. I.F. $= x^{-7}$.
3. I.F. $= e^{x^2/2}$, $(y^3 + x^2 - 2)e^{x^2/2} = c$.
4. $(1/\mu)(d\mu/dy) = (1/M)(\partial N/\partial x - \partial M/\partial y)$.
5. $(1/\mu)\mu'(ax + by) = (\partial M/\partial y - \partial N/\partial x)/(aN - bM)$.
6. $(1/\mu)\mu'(x/y) = y^2(\partial M/\partial y - \partial N/\partial x)/(yN + xM)$.
7. $y^2 = 1/(x + \frac{1}{2} + ce^{2x})$.

Chap. II, Sec. 4, page 61

1. (a) $y = -x + (1/a)\tan a(x - c)$.　(b) $(x - 2y - 2)e^x = c(x - 2y - 1)$.
(c) $3(1 + 2x + 3y) = 2\tan 3(x - c)$.　(d) $7 + 2x - 2y = ce^{4x}(5 + 2x - 2y)$.
(e) $x - y = c(2x + y)^2$.　(f) $x^2 + y^2 = cy$.
(g) $\log(x^2 + y^2) - 2\arctan(y/x) = c$.　(h) $x^3 + y^3 + 2x^2y = c$.
(i) $y = 2x\operatorname{arccot} cx$.　(j) $x^2\log|y| = 6xy + cx^2$.　(k) $y = cx^2/(c^2 - x^2)$.
(l) $y = cx - x\log|x|$.　(m) $(x - y + 1)^2(x + y + 3)^3 = c$.
(n) $\log(x - 2y + 2)^2 = x - y + c$.

(*o*) $\log (5y - 30x + 4)^4 = 5y - 5x + c.$

(*p*) $\log |x - 3y + 8|^5 = x - 2y + c.$ (*q*) $y - 4x - 1 = cx^3(y - x - 1).$

(*r*) $\log |y + a| + 2 \arctan [(y + a)/x] = c.$

(*s*) $(x - 4y + 6)^5(4x - y - 9)^5 = c(5x - 5y - 3).$

(*t*) $x^2y - 3x - 6xy^2 + 12y^3 = c.$

2. (*a*) $2xy(c - \log |x|) = 1.$

(*b*) $y(\cos 2x - 2 \sin 2x + ce^x) = 5.$

(*c*) $Ay(a \sin \omega x + \omega \cos \omega x + ce^{ax}) = a^2 + \omega^2.$ (*d*) $2y^{-2} = x + 1 + ce^x.$

(*e*) $y^{-1} = (x + 2 + ce^x)^2.$ (*f*) $y^{-2} = -2 \sec x \tan x + c \sec^2 x.$

(*g*) $y^3(\tan x + \sec x) = c - \sin x.$ (*h*) $y^{1-l}e^{(1-l)ax} = A(1 - l)x^{m+1}/(m + 1) + c.$

(*i*) $y = (m - a)/(bx^m + cx^a)$ if $m \neq a$; $y = 1/(bx^a \log |x| + cx^a)$ if $m = a.$

(*j*) $(1 + a^2)y^2 = A(a \sin x - \cos x) + ce^{-ax}.$ (*k*) $x^4 + y^4 = cx^2.$

(*l*) $y^m = [mA/(ma + n)]x^n + cx^{-ma}$ if $ma + n \neq 0$;

$y^m = mAx^n \log |x| + cx^{-ma}$ if $ma + n = 0.$ **3.** I.F. $= e^{(1-m)\int P(x)\,dx}y^{-m}.$

4. (*a*) $bx^2 + ay = c(bx^2 - ay)e^{abx^2}.$ (*b*) $2 \tan y = 1 + x^2 + ce^{x^2}.$

(*c*) $xy = e^{cx}.$ (*d*) $2 \sqrt{x^2 + y^2} = c - x^2.$ (*e*) $x^2 + y^2 = ce^{2 \arctan (y/x)}.$

(*f*) $x^2 + y^2 - 1 = c(x^2 + y^2)e^{2 \arctan (y/x)}.$ **5.** (*a*) $\cos y = -A + ce^{-x^2/2}.$

(*b*) $\log |y| = \tan x + c \sec x.$ (*c*) $e^y = 10 \cos x - 5 \sin x + ce^{2x}.$

(*d*) $(x + \sqrt{1 + x^2}) \tan y = x^2 + x \sqrt{1 + x^2} - \log |x + \sqrt{1 + x^2}| + c.$

6. The transformed equations are: (*a*) $dY/dX + aY^2 = A,$

(*b*) $dY/dX + aY^2 = 9AX^{-4}.$

Chap. III, Sec. 2, page 70

1. $y_n(1) \to 1.$ **2.** If $f(x) = \sum\limits_{k=0}^{\infty} a_k x^k,$ then $y(x) = \eta + \sum\limits_{k=0}^{\infty} a_k y_k(x).$

Chap. III, Sec. 3, page 79

1. (*a*) Existence and uniqueness: all points (x, y) with $y \neq (2k + 1)\pi/2,$ $k = 0, \pm 1, \ldots$ (*b*) Existence and uniqueness: whole plane.   (*c*) Existence and uniqueness: all (x, y) with $y \neq \pm x.$ (*d*) Existence and uniqueness: whole plane.   (*e*) Existence and uniqueness: all (x, y) with $-1 < y < 1.$ (*f*) Existence and uniqueness: all (x, y) with $y \neq \pm 1.$ (*g*), (*h*) Existence and uniqueness: whole plane.   (*i*) Existence: all (x, y) with $36 - 4x^2 - 9y^2 \geq 0$; uniqueness: all (x, y) with $36 - 4x^2 - 9y^2 > 0.$ (*j*) Existence and uniqueness: whole plane.   **3.** Existence: all (x, y) with $x \geq 0$ and $y \geq 0,$ or with $x \leq 0$ and $y \leq 0$; uniqueness: all (x, y) with $x \geq 0$ and $y > 0,$ or with $x \leq 0$ and $y < 0.$ **4.** Existence: whole plane; uniqueness: all (x, y) with $y \neq 0.$ **5.** Existence: whole plane; uniqueness: all (x, y) with $y \neq 0.$ **6.** Uniqueness: all (x, y) with $x \neq 0$; through $(0, 0)$; parabolas $y = c_1x^2, c_1 > 0$ for $x \geq 0$ and $y = c_2x^2, c_2 < 0$ for $x \leq 0.$ **8.** Yes.   **9.** I_y: all $(0, y)$ with $2 \leq y \leq 4$; I_x: all $(x, 3)$ with $-0.008 \leq x \leq 0.008.$

Chap. IV, Sec. 1, page 86

1. $x^2 - y^2 = c.$ **2.** $y = \mu e^{a\theta},$ where $a = \cot \alpha.$

3. $y = -x \pm \log |1 \pm 2x| + \mu.$ **4.** $y = -x + \sqrt{2} \arctan (y/\sqrt{2}) + \mu.$

5. $y = (c/x)e^{kx}$. **6.** $x = l \log [(l + \sqrt{l^2 - y^2})/y]$, where x is the distance walked along the shore, and y is the distance of the boat from shore. **7.** If $a\theta$ is the distance walked along the shore and ρ is the distance of the boat from the center of the pond, then the D.E. of the path is $d\theta/d\rho = \sqrt{X}/\rho(\rho^2 - b^2)$, and the solution is

$$\theta = (b/l) \log \{ [l(b^2 + \rho^2) + b\sqrt{X}]/a(b^2 - \rho^2) \} - \tfrac{1}{2} \arcsin [(b^2 + \rho^2)\sqrt{X}/2a^2\rho^2],$$

where $b = \sqrt{a^2 - l^2}$, and $X = (\rho + a + l)(\rho + a - l)(\rho - a + l)(\rho - a - l)$.
8. $\rho(1 + \cos \theta) = c$. **9.** $x + y = c$ and $xy = c$. **10.** $\rho = \lambda e^{a\theta}$.
11. $y = c \pm \cosh x$. **12.** $(x - c)^{\frac{2}{3}} + y^{\frac{2}{3}} = 1$. **13.** $\rho = \rho_0 e^{\theta/\sqrt{3}}$ if $\theta = 0$ is
the ray $\overline{OP_0}$ and $\overline{OP_0} = \rho_0$. **14.** $\theta = 0$ $(5 \geq \rho \geq 1)$ and $\rho = e^{\theta/\sqrt{15}}$; also
other answers.

Chap. IV, Sec. 2, page 92

1. (a) $x^2 + (y - \mu)^2 = \mu^2$. (b) $x^2 - y^2 = \mu$. (c) $y = \mu x^a$.
(d) $x^{2-a} - y^{2-a} = \mu$. (e) $x = \mu e^{y^2}$. (f) $y^3 = 3a \log |x| + \mu$.
(g) $x^2 + y^2 - 2a^2 \log |x| = \mu$. (h) $a(2 - a)y^2 + 2x^{2-a} = \mu$ if $a \neq 2$;
$x = \mu e^{-y^2}$ if $a = 2$. **2.** (a) $\rho = \mu \sin \theta$. (b) $\rho^2 = \mu \sin 2\theta$.
(c) $\rho^{b^2} = \mu \sin^a b\theta$. (d) $\rho(1 + 2 \cos \theta) = \mu$. (e) $\rho^a \sin^{1+a} \theta = \mu(1 + \cos \theta)$.
(f) $\rho^2 = \mu e^{\theta^2}$. (g) $\rho(\csc \theta - \cot \theta) = \mu$. (h) $\rho(a \sin \theta - b \cos \theta) = \mu$.
3. $(M - N \tan \alpha) dx + (N + M \tan \alpha) dy = 0$.
4. If $M(\rho, \theta) d\rho + \rho N(\rho, \theta) d\theta = 0$ is the D.E. of $\mathfrak{D}_\mathrm{I}$, then
$(M - N \tan \alpha) d\rho + \rho(N + M \tan \alpha) d\theta = 0$ is the D.E. of $\mathfrak{D}_\mathrm{II}$.

Chap. IV, Sec. 3, page 97

1. (a) $y = \lambda x \pm a \sqrt{1 + \lambda^2}$.
(b) $y = \lambda x + a[1 + (-\lambda)^{p/(p-1)}]^{(p-1)/p}$ $(\lambda < 0)$.
(c) $y = \lambda(x - a) \pm 2/(3\sqrt{3\lambda})$.
(d) $y = \lambda x + \tfrac{1}{2} \pm \tfrac{1}{2} \sqrt{1 - \lambda^2} - (\lambda/2) \arcsin \lambda$.
(e) $y = \lambda x + 2a(1 \pm \lambda^2)/(1 + \lambda^2) \mp a\lambda \arcsin [2\lambda/(1 + \lambda^2)]$. **2.** (a) $y = x^{\frac{1}{3}}$.
(b) $16y^3 + 27x^4 = 0$. (c) $y^4 - x^4 = a^4$.
(d) $\sqrt{x} + \sqrt{y} = \sqrt{xy}$ $(x > 0, y > 0)$.
3. (a) $y = \lambda x \pm (a^2 - b^2)\lambda/\sqrt{a^2 + b^2\lambda^2}$. (b) $(ax)^{\frac{2}{3}} + (by)^{\frac{2}{3}} = (a^2 - b^2)^{\frac{2}{3}}$.
4. (a) $y = \lambda x \pm a(\lambda/\sqrt{1 + \lambda^2})$. (b) $x^{\frac{2}{3}} + y^{\frac{2}{3}} = a^{\frac{2}{3}}$.
5. (a) $y = cx \pm 2\sqrt{1 + c^2}, x^2 + y^2 = 4$. (b) $y = cx + c^3, 4x^3 + 27y^2 = 0$.
(c) $y = cx + c^p, (x/p)^p + [y/(p - 1)]^{p-1} = 0$. (d) $y = cx \pm (1 - c^{\frac{2}{3}})^{\frac{3}{2}}$,
$y^{\frac{2}{3}} - x^{\frac{2}{3}} = 1$.
6. $y = \begin{cases} x + 1 & x < -2 \\ -x^2/4 & -2 \leq x \leq 2; \text{ also } y = \\ -x + 1 & x > 2 \end{cases} \begin{cases} 4x + 16 & x < -8 \\ -x^2/4 & -8 \leq x \leq 8 \\ -4x + 16 & x > 8 \end{cases}$

Chap. IV, Sec. 4, page 100

2. (a) $(x, y = x, p = 0)$. (b) $(x, y = \pm 2\sqrt{x + 1}, p = x + 2)$.
(c) $(x, y = -x^2/4, p = -x/2)$. (d) $(x, y = \pm x/2, p = x/2)$.
(e) $(x = 0, y = 0, p = 0); (x, y = 0, p = 0); (x, y = x, p = 0);$

$(x, y = -x, p = 0)$; $[x, y = (1 \pm \sqrt{2})x, p^2 = 2(-1 + \sqrt{2})x^2]$. **3.** Locus of singular points is $y = 0$; arcs of the solutions $y = \pm (x - c)^2$ can be pieced together at $y = 0$. **4.** $y = (x - c)^2 \, (-\infty < x < \infty)$.

Chap. IV, Sec. 5, page 104

1. 5,315 years. **2.** \$149.18. **3.** \$7,869.40. **4.** 31,300. **5.** 1 hr 9 min.
6. 281.25 lb; 1.406 lb/gal. **7.** 1,000 ft³/min, 11 min.
8. (a) $dT/dt = k(T - T_0)$. (b) 22.6 min. **9.** (a) $p(h) = p_0 e^{-gh/k}$.
(b) $[p(h)]^{\frac{2}{3}} = p_0^{\frac{2}{3}} - \frac{2}{7}ghk^{-\frac{2}{7}}$, where p_0 is the pressure at sea level, h the height above sea level. **10.** $x = S(3G - S)e^{k(3G-S)t/G}/(3G - Se^{k(3G-S)t/G})$.
11. $P = P_0 e^{(b-d)t/1,000}$, where b and d are births and deaths per 1,000 per day, and t is in days. **12.** $dA/dt = \alpha A - \gamma A^2$; $A(t) = (\gamma/\alpha + ce^{-\alpha t})^{-1}$; $\lim_{t \to \infty} A(t) = 0$ if $\alpha < 0$, $= \alpha/\gamma$ if $\alpha > 0$; if $\alpha = 0$, then $A(t) = (\gamma t + c)^{-1}$.
13. $dA/dt = \alpha A - \gamma e^{-\beta t}A^2$; $A(t) = (\alpha - \beta)(\gamma e^{-\beta t} + ce^{-\alpha t})^{-1}$ if $\alpha \neq \beta$, $A(t) = (\gamma t + c)^{-1}e^{\alpha t}$ if $\alpha = \beta$. **14.** $dy/dx = (\gamma_2 xy - \alpha_2 y)(\alpha_1 x - \gamma_1 xy)$; $(y/y_0)^{\alpha_1}(x/x_0)^{\alpha_2} = e^{\gamma_1(y-y_0)+\gamma_2(x-x_0)}$, where x_0, y_0 are the values of x, y at some initial time. **15.** $(A - u)^a(B - u)^b(C - u)^c = A^a B^b C^c e^{-Kt}$, where $K = \alpha\beta\gamma k/(\alpha + \beta + \gamma)^3$, $A = (\alpha + \beta + \gamma)/\alpha$, $B = (\alpha + \beta + \gamma)/\beta$, $C = (\alpha + \beta + \gamma)/\gamma$; A, B, C distinct, and $a = 1/(B - A)(C - A)$, $b = 1/(C - B)(A - B)$, $c = 1/(A - C)(B - C)$.

Chap. IV, Secs. 6, 7, 8, page 111

1. 4 min 21 sec. **2.** 5 min 48 sec. **3.** 2.16 in. **4.** $x = 4/(1 + 0.00356t)^2$.
5. 4 min 16 sec. **6.** 2 min 58 sec.
7. $317 + 120 \int_{1.75}^{3.5} \sqrt{(7 - x)/(41x - x^2 - 59.5)} \, dx$ sec.
8. $T = \pi/(kA \sqrt{2g}) \int_0^{\theta_1} f^{\frac{3}{2}}(\theta) \cos^2 \theta \sin^{-\frac{1}{2}} \theta[f(\theta) \cos \theta + f'(\theta) \sin \theta] \, d\theta$, where θ_1 is the solution of $f(\theta) \sin \theta = h$. **9.** Heat loss: $21,600\pi$ Btu/hr; $T = 600/r - 200$. **10.** Heat loss: 3740 Btu; $T = 112 - 57.7 \log (2 + x)$.
11. Heat gain: 9480 Btu; $T = -30 + 87.3 \log 6r$. **12.** $Q = ck(T_1 - T_2)/(cw + k)$.
13. $Q = c[k_0 + (\beta/2)(T_i + T_0)]/cw + 2[k_0 + (\alpha/2)(T_i + T_0)](T_i - T_0)$.
14. In all cases $S = \log (p_i/p_0)^{c_v} \log (v_i/v_0)^{c_v}$; Q equals the following:
(a) $c_p p_0(v_1 - v_0) + c_v v_1(p_1 - p_0)$. (b) $c_p p_1(v_1 - v_0) + c_v v_0(p_1 - p_0)$.
(c) $c_p p_0(v_1 - v_0) - (c_p - c_v)p_0 v_0 \log (p_1/p_0)$.
(d) $c_p p_1(v_1 - v_0) - (c_p - c_v)p_0 v_0 \log (p_1/p_0)$.
(e) $c_v v_0(p_1 - p_0) + (c_p - c_v)p_0 v_0 \log (v_1/v_0)$.
(f) $c_v v_1(p_1 - p_0) + (c_p - c_v)p_0 v_0 \log (v_1/v_0)$. (g) $c_p p_0(v_1 - v_0)$.
(h) $c_p p_1(v_1 - v_0)$. (i) $c_v v_0(p_1 - p_0)$. (j) $c_v v_1(p_1 - p_0)$.
(k) $-(c_p - c_v)p_0 v_0 \log (p_0 v_0^\gamma/p_1 v_1^\gamma)^{1/(\gamma-1)}$.
(l) $-(c_p - c_v)p_1 v_1 \log (p_0 v_0^\gamma/p_1 v_1^\gamma)^{1/(\gamma-1)}$.
15. $v = (p_0/p_1)^{1/\gamma}(v_0 + \alpha\gamma p_0) + \alpha p_1 - \alpha(1 + \gamma)p_0$, where $\gamma = c_p/c_v$, $\alpha = 2/k^2(c_p + c_v)$. **16.** $S_1 = c_v(pv^\gamma - p_0 v_0^\gamma)$, $S_2 = c_p(vp^{\frac{1}{\gamma}} - v_0 p_0^{1/\gamma})$.
18. $V = c_v(T_1 - T_0)$.

Chap. IV, Sec. 9, page 117

1. 19 ft/sec, 20 ft/sec. **2.** 7.2° from the horizontal, $v = 8(1 - e^{-t/2})$.
3. $mv^2 = -kx^2 + 2mgx + mv_0^2$. **4.** 26,000 ft/sec. **5.** 36,750 ft/sec.
6. $v = \sin 2t - 2 \cos 2t + 2e^{-t}$. **7.** $v = 180(1 - e^{-8t/45})$, 106 ft/sec.
9. $v^2 = 2g(x - 25)(x - 20)/55$, where x is the distance of the weight below the pulley. **10.** $v^2 = 16(x^2 - 25)/25$. **11.** HINT: The tangential acceleration is d^2s/dt^2, where s is the arc length. Then $m \, d^2s/dt^2 = -mg \sin \theta = -mg \, dy/ds$ and multiplication by ds/dt renders the equation integrable.
12. $v^2 + 6xv + 13x^2 = ce^{3 \arctan [(v+3x)/2x]}$, motion is damped oscillation.
13. (a) $\frac{1}{2}mv^2 + k(x^2 - x_0^2) = 2k(\sqrt{x^2 + l^2} - \sqrt{x_0^2 + l^2})$.
(b) $T = 4(m/2k)^{\frac{1}{2}} \int_0^{x_0} (-x^2 + 2 \sqrt{x^2 + l^2} + x_0^2 - 2l \sqrt{x_0^2 + l^2})^{-\frac{1}{2}} \, dx$.
14. (a) $\frac{1}{2}mv^2 + w \sqrt{x^2 + a^2} = w \sqrt{x_0^2 + a^2}$.
(b) $T = 4(m/2w)^{\frac{1}{2}} \int_0^{x_0} (\sqrt{x_0^2 + a^2} - \sqrt{x^2 + a^2})^{-\frac{1}{2}} \, dx$.

Chap. IV, Sec. 10, page 122

1. $\int_0^{\pi^2} d\theta / \sqrt{1 - \frac{1}{2} \sin^2 \theta} = 1.125\pi/2$ as compared with $\pi/2$.
2. $\sec \frac{1}{2}\varphi + \tan \frac{1}{2}\varphi = e^{\sqrt{g/l}(t - t_0)}$.
3. (a) $\frac{1}{2}mv^2 - a/x + b/2x^2 = -a/x_0 + b/2x_0^2 = h$.
(b) $T = \sqrt{2m} \int_{x_1}^{x_2} (a/x - b/2x^2 + h)^{-\frac{1}{2}} \, dx$, where
$x_{1, 2} = (1/2h)(-a \pm \sqrt{a^2 + 2bh})$. (c) If $x_0 = b/a$, motion is not periodic.
5. If $(x_i, 0)$ is the end point of the ith arc and $x_i \gtrless 0$, then $mu^2 + k(x^2 - x_i^2) \mp 2q(x - x_i) = 0$ is the equation of the $(i + 1)$st arc and $x_{i+1} = -x_i \pm 2q/k$.

Chap. IV, Sec. 11, page 125

1. $v^2 \geq \frac{15}{8}gR$, that is, $v \geq$ approximately 7 miles/sec. **3.** Uniform circular motion, $T = 2\pi \sqrt{r_0^3/k}$. **4.** $r = r_0 \sec^2 \frac{1}{2}\theta$, parabolic orbit,
$t = (\sqrt{2} \, r_0/3 \sqrt{K}) \tan (\theta/2)[2 + \sec^2 (\theta/2)]$.
6. $(r_0/r)(1 - \sqrt{1 - r^2/r_0^2}) = e^{-c\theta/v}$, where $c = \sqrt{v_0^2 + k/r_0^2}$;
$r = \sqrt{r_0^2 - c^2t^2}$; $\theta = (v_0/2c) \log [(r_0 + ct)/(r_0 - ct)]$; $T = r_0/c$.

Chap. IV, Sec. 12, page 130

1. $i(t) = (\omega E_0/R)[1/(1/R^2C^2 + \omega^2)][(1/RC) \cos \omega t + \omega \sin \omega t] - [\omega E_0/R^2C(1/R^2C^2 + \omega^2)]e^{-t/RC}$; $i_s(t) = (\omega E_0/R \sqrt{1/R^2C^2 + \omega^2}) \sin (\omega t + \delta)$, where $\tan \delta = 1/RC\omega$. **2.** $i(t) = 2.10 \sin (120\pi t - 1.44) + 2.08e^{-50t}$.
3. $q(t) = E_0C(1 - e^{-(t-t_0)/RC})$. **4.** $q(t) = q_0 e^{-t/RC}$. **7.** $i(t) = (E/R)e^{-Rt/L}$.
8. $q(t) = C_0E_0(1 - e^{-(1/2R_0C_0)(t + \sin 2\omega t/2\omega)})$, $\lim_{t \to \infty} q(t) = C_0E_0$.
9. $q_{max} = (q_0 + \frac{1}{2}RCi_0)e^{-\frac{1}{2}RCi_0}/(q_0 + \frac{1}{2}RCi_0)$.

Chap. IV, Sec. 13, page 133

1. $(1/LC)(q - CE)^2 + i^2 = A^2$; $i(t) = A \sin (t/\sqrt{LC} + \phi)$.
2. $V(t) = V_0 e^{-t/RC}/[1 + (RV_0/S)(1 - e^{-t/RC})]$. **3.** If $V_0 \neq 0$ then

$[(V/V_0)^{\frac{1}{2}} - 1]^{\frac{1}{2}} + 3[(V/V_0)^{\frac{1}{2}} - 1]^{\frac{1}{2}} = \frac{3}{2}(j/\epsilon_0 v_0 V_0)^{\frac{1}{2}}x$, where $v_0 = (2eV_0/m)^{\frac{1}{2}}$; if $V_0 = 0$, then $j = (4\epsilon_0/9x)(2e/m)^{\frac{1}{2}}V^{\frac{3}{2}}$.

4. (a) $C_0 L_0 i^2 + q^2 + \frac{2}{3}Aq^3 + \frac{1}{2}Bq^4 = c$.

(b) $T = (2/\sqrt{C_0 L_0}) \int_{q_1}^{q_2} (dq/\sqrt{c - q^2 - \frac{2}{3}Aq^3 - \frac{1}{2}Bq^4})$, where q_1, q_2 are the real roots of $c - q^2 - \frac{2}{3}Aq^3 - \frac{1}{2}Bq^4 = 0$. **5.** If $(q_n, 0)$ is the end point of the nth arc and $q_n \gtrless 0$, then $i^2 = \pm q/CS + L/2CS^2 - (\pm q_n/CS + L/2CS^2)e^{\pm 2S(q-q_n)/L}$ is the equation of the $(n + 1)$st arc, and q_{n+1} is determined from $[1 \pm (2S/L)q_{n+1}]/[1 \pm (2S/L)q_n] = e^{\pm(2S/L)(q_{n+1}-q_n)}$.

Chap. V, Sec. 1, page 138

1. (b) $\frac{1}{4}e^{-x} \sin 2x$. **2.** (b) $1 + 2x + x^2$.
(c) $1 - x + x^2$. **3.** $\frac{1}{4}xe^{2x} - \frac{1}{4}e^{2x} + c_1 x + c_2$.
4. $\log |\sec x|$.
5. $2 - \frac{1}{2}x^2 + \frac{1}{2} \log (x + \sqrt{1 + x^2})$.
6. $c_1 x - c_1(1 + c_1) \log |x + c_1| + c_2$. **7.** $\int_0^x (ds/\sqrt[3]{1 - s^3})$.
8. $\log \cosh (x + \pi/2)$. **9.** $\arcsin (1 + x)$.
10. $y = -1$. **11.** $y^2 = 2 + e^x$. **★13.** Place the origin at the position of the rabbit when sighted, with the x axis east and the y axis north. The D.E. for the path is $3xy'' + 2(1 + y^2)^{\frac{1}{2}} = 0$, and its solution is $y(x) = 240 + 60[(x/200)^{\frac{5}{3}} - 5(x/200)^{\frac{1}{3}}]$. The distance after $6\frac{5}{16}$ sec is 52.7 ft.

Chap. V, Sec. 2, page 141

1. (a) $c_1 e^{2x} + c_2 e^{-x}$. (b) $c_1 e^{-2x} + c_2 e^{-x}$.
(c) $c_1 e^{(-2+\sqrt{2})x} + c_2 e^{(-2-\sqrt{2})x}$. (d) $c_1 + c_2 e^{-2x}$.
(e) $c_1 e^{-3x} + c_2 x e^{-3x}$. (f) $c_1 e^{3x} + c_2 e^{-3x}$. (g) $c_1 e^{\sqrt{5}x} + c_2 x e^{\sqrt{5}x}$.
(h) $c_1 e^{(k+\sqrt{k^2+12})x/2} + c_2 e^{(k-\sqrt{k^2+12})x/2}$. (i) $c_1 e^{3x/2} + c_2 e^{-x}$.
(j) $c_1 e^{mx/k} + c_2 e^{-mx/l}$. (k) $c_1 e^{mx} + c_2 x e^{mx}$. (l) $c_1 e^{-5x} + c_2 e^{3x}$.
(m) $c_1 e^{2x/3} + c_2 x e^{2x/3}$.

(n) $c_1 \exp\left(\dfrac{-R + \sqrt{R^2 - 4L/C}}{2L} t\right) + c_2 \exp\left(\dfrac{-R - \sqrt{R^2 - 4L/C}}{2L} t\right)$.

(o) $c_1 e^{-Rt/2L} + c_2 t e^{-Rt/2L}$. **2.** (a) $2e^{-x} + e^{2x}$. (b) $\frac{5}{8}e^{2x} + \frac{3}{8}e^{-2x}$.
(c) $3e^{2x} - 2xe^{2x}$. (d) $9e^{x/2} - 4e^{-x}$. (e) e^{3x-1}.
(f) $2.02e^{3x} - 51e^{-x}$. (g) $2.95e^{-x} + 3.1xe^{-x}$.
(h) $e^{(-2+\sqrt{2})x} - 2e^{(-2-\sqrt{2})x}$. (i) $0.9e^x + 1.3e^{-x}$.
(j) $\frac{4}{5}e^{5x} - 2e^{-3x}$. (k) $10^{-9}(11.70e^{(-0.383\times10^7)t} - 1.70e^{(-2.618\times10^7)t})$.
(l) $0.5e^{2x} + 4.5e^{-x}$. **7.** (a) $c_1 x^2 + c_2 x^{-3}$.
(b) $c_1 x^4 + c_2 x^{-4}$. (c) $c_1 x^{\frac{3}{2}} + c_2 x^{-\frac{1}{2}}$.
(d) $c_1 x^{\sqrt{2}} + c_2 x^{-\sqrt{2}}$. (e) $c_1 x^{2+\sqrt{3}} + c_2 x^{2-\sqrt{3}}$.
(f) $c_1(x + 1)^3 + c_2(x + 1)^{-2}$.

Chap. V, Sec. 3, page 145

1. (a) $e^{-3x/2}[c_1 \sin (\sqrt{3} x/2) + c_2 \cos (\sqrt{3} x/2)]$.
(b) $e^x(c_1 \sin x + c_2 \cos x)$. (c) $c_1 e^{2x} + c_2 e^x$.

(d) $e^{x/2}[c_1 \sin (\sqrt{11}\ x/2) + c_2 \cos (\sqrt{11}\ x/2)]$. (e) $c_1 e^x + c_2 e^{3x/2}$.

(f) $c_1 e^{4t} + c_2 e^{-t}$. (g) $e^{kx}(c_1 \sin x + c_2 \cos x)$.

(h) $e^{3x/4}[c_1 \sin (\sqrt{7}\ x/4) + c_2 \cos (\sqrt{7}\ x/4)]$.

(i) $e^{2x}(c_1 \sin kx + c_2 \cos kx)$. (j) $e^{3x}[c_1 \sin (x/2) + c_2 \cos (x/2)]$.

(k) $e^{-3x}(c_1 \sin 2x + c_2 \cos 2x)$. (l) $e^{2x}[c_1 \sin (x/k) + c_2 \cos (x/k)]$.

(m) $e^{-x/k}(c_1 \sin x + c_2 \cos x)$.

(n) $e^{-Rt/2L}\left(c_1 \sin \dfrac{\sqrt{4L/C - R^2}}{2L}\ t + c_2 \cos \dfrac{\sqrt{4L/C - R^2}}{2L}\ t\right)$.

(o) $e^{-x/a}\left(c_1 \sin \dfrac{\sqrt{ab - 1}}{a}\ x + c_2 \cos \dfrac{\sqrt{ab - 1}}{a}\ x\right)$.

(p) $c_1 e^{-x/a} + c_2 x e^{-x/a}$.

(q) $e^{-bgt/2w}\left(c_1 \sin \dfrac{\sqrt{4kwg - g^2 b^2}}{2w}\ t + c_2 \cos \dfrac{\sqrt{4kwg - g^2 b^2}}{2w}\ t\right)$.

(r) $e^{-bgt/2w}(c_1 + c_2 t)$.

(s) $e^{-kz/6}[c_1 \cos (\sqrt{60 - k^2}\ z/6) + c_2 \sin (\sqrt{60 - k^2}\ z/6)]$.

2. (a) $e^{x/2}[\cos (\sqrt{3}\ x/2) + 2\sqrt{3} \sin (\sqrt{3}\ x/2)]$.

(b) $e^{-2x}(4 \cos 3x + 3 \sin 3x)$. (c) $e^{-x}(\sqrt{3} \sin \sqrt{3}\ x + 3 \cos \sqrt{3}\ x)$.

(d) $e^{-2t}(3 + 2.017t)$. (e) $1.51 \times 10^{-9} e^{(-0.75 \times 10^7)t} \sin (0.661 \times 10^7)t$.

(f) $e^{-0.08t}(0.04 \sin 4t + 2 \cos 4t)$. (g) $-e^{-x/2} \cos (x + \pi/3)$.

(h) $e^{-x} \cos (3x - \pi/2)$. (i) $2e^t \cos (t + \pi/6)$. (j) $e^{-2x} + e^{-x-1}$.

(k) $e^{-x-2} \cos x$. **4.** $c + Ae^{-2x} \sin 3(x + \delta)$.

5. $c_1 + c_2 x + Ae^{2x} \sin 5(x + \delta)$. **6.** $c_1 e^{2x} + c_2 \cos x + c_3 \sin x$.

Chap. V, Sec. 4, page 147

3. $c_1 e^x + c_2 - x^2/2 - x - \sin x$. **4.** $c_1 e^{-x} + c_2$.

Chap. V, Sec. 5, page 151

1. (a) $c_1 e^{2x} + c_2 e^{-2x} - \frac{1}{8} \sin 2x$. (b) $c_1 e^{3x} + c_2 e^x + \frac{1}{4} e^{-x} - \frac{2}{3}$.

(c) $c_1 e^{-4x} + c_2 e^{2x} - 2x - \frac{1}{2}$. (d) $e^x[c_1 \sin x + c_2 \cos x - (x/2) \cos x]$.

(e) $c_1 \sin 2x + c_2 \cos 2x + x/4 - (x/4) \cos 2x$.

(f) $e^x(c_1 + c_2 x + x^3/2)$.

(g) $e^{-x}(c_1 + c_2 x) + a - 3 \sin 2x - 4 \cos 2x$.

(h) $a_0 x^{n+2}/(n + 2)(n + 1) + a_1 x^{n+1}/(n + 1)n + \cdots + a_n x^2/2.1 + c_1 x + c_2$.

(i) $c_1 \sin 4x + c_2 \cos 4x + A/32 + (Ax/16) \sin 4x$.

(j) $c_1 e^x + c_2 e^{2x} + x^2 + 4x + 5$. (k) $c_1 + c_2 e^{-2x} + x^2 - x$.

(l) $e^{-2x}(c_1 \cos x + c_2 \sin x) + (A/65) \sin 2x - (8A/65) \cos 2x$.

(m) $e^{2x}(c_1 + c_2 x + x^2 + x^3/6)$.

(n) $c_1 + c_2 e^{-x} - \frac{1}{5} \sin 2x - \frac{1}{10} \cos 2x$.

(o) $c_1 + e^{2x}(c_2 + x - x^2 + 2x^3/3)$.

(p) $-\frac{1}{2} - \frac{3}{2} e^{-x} + (c_1 - x)e^{-2x} + \frac{1}{4} e^{-2x} + \frac{1}{4} e^{-3x} + c_2 e^x$.

(q) $\frac{1}{6} e^{2x} + \frac{1}{14} e^{-2x} + e^{\frac{1}{2}x}[c_1 \cos (\frac{1}{2}\sqrt{3}x) + c_2 \sin (\frac{1}{2}\sqrt{3}\ x)]$.

(r) $(x/6 + c_1) \sinh 3x + c_2 \cosh 3x$.

(s) $\frac{1}{10}(x^2 - x + c_1)e^x + \frac{1}{8}(2x - 1)e^{-x} + c_2 e^{-2x}$.

(t) $-x^{2n} - 2n(2n-1)x^{2n-2} - 2n(2n-1)(2n-2)(2n-3)x^{2n-4}$
$- \cdots - (2n)! \, x^0 + c_1 e^x + c_2 e^{-x}$.

(u) $1 + \frac{1}{2}e^x + \frac{1}{5}e^{2x} + \cdots + [1/(k^2+1)]e^{kx} + \cdots$
$+ e^{(n-1)x}/[(n-1)^2 + 1] + c_1 \cos x + c_2 \sin x$.

(v) $\frac{1}{2}\sinh x + \cdots + [1/(k^2+1)] \sinh kx + \cdots$
$+ [1/(n^2+1)] \sinh nx + c_1 \cos x + c_2 \sin x$.

2. (a) $-\frac{5}{2} + 7e^{2x} - 3e^x + 2e^{-x}$.

(b) $\frac{1}{2}e^{2x} - \frac{1}{2} - x$. ($c$) $\frac{1}{3}e^{2x} + \frac{1}{6}e^{-x} - \frac{3}{2}\sin x + \frac{1}{2}\cos x$.

(d) $[A/\lambda(\lambda^2 - \omega^2)](\lambda \sin \omega x - \omega \sin \lambda x)$.

(e) $-\frac{3}{52}e^{3x} - \frac{1}{20}e^{-x} + \frac{4}{65}\sin 2x + \frac{7}{65}\cos 2x - \frac{1}{3}$.

(f) $\frac{1}{3}e^{3x} - e^{-x} - x + \frac{2}{3}$.

Chap. V, Sec. 6, page 155

1. (a) $c_1 e^{2x} + c_2 e^{-x} + xe^{2x}/3$. ($b$) $e^{-x}(c_1 + c_2 x + x \log |x|)$.

(c) $c_1 \sin x + c_2 \cos x - (x/2) \cos x$.

(d) $c_1 \sin 2x + c_2 \cos 2x - \frac{1}{4}\cos 2x \log |\sec 2x + \tan 2x|$.

(e) $c_1 e^x + c_2 e^{-x} + \frac{1}{2} + (e^x/2) \log (1 - e^{-x}) + (e^{-x}/2) \log (e^x - 1)$.

(f) $c_1 e^{2x} + c_2 e^{-x} - \cos e^{-x} + 2e^x \sin e^{-x} + 2e^{2x} \cos e^{-x}$.

(g) $c_1 \sin 2x + c_2 \cos 2x + \frac{1}{4}\sin 2x \log |\sin 2x| - (x/2) \cos 2x$.

(h) $c_1 \sin 2x + c_2 \cos 2x + \frac{1}{8} - \frac{1}{8}x \sin 2x$.

(i) $c_1 + c_2 e^{-2x} - e^{-x} + 5x/2$.

(j) $c_1 \sin 2x + c_2 \cos 2x + \frac{1}{4}\sin 2x \log |\sec 2x + \tan 2x| - \frac{1}{2}$.

(k) $\sqrt{2} \log |x| - x^{-1} + A e^{-\frac{1}{2}\sqrt{2}x} \sin \sqrt{\frac{3}{2}} (x + \delta)$.

2. (a) $\sin x \log |\csc x - \cot x| - \cos x \log |\sec x + \tan x|$.

(b) $\frac{1}{2}\sin x \log |\csc x - \cot x| + \frac{1}{2}\cos x \log |\sec x + \tan x|$.

(c) $-\frac{1}{2}xe^{-x} \cos x$. ($d$) $-e^{-x}(\frac{1}{128} + x/32 + x^2/16 + x^3/12)$.

(e) $|x|$. **3.** (a) $\frac{1}{5}x^3 + c_1 x^2 + c_2 x^{-2}$.

(b) $\frac{1}{3}x^2 \log |x| + c_1 x^2 + c_2 x^{-1}$. ($c$) $e^{-x}(1 + x^{-1}) + c_1 x + c_2 x^{-1}$.

(d) $-\frac{1}{2}(\log |x|)^2 - \frac{1}{2}\log |x| - \frac{3}{4} + x \log |x| + c_1 x + c_2 x^{-1}$.

(e) $2x \sin (1/x) + 2x^2 \cos (1/x) - \cos (1/x) + c_1 x^2 + c_2 x^{-1}$.

4. x^{-1}.

Chap. V, Sec. 9, page 160

1. $a = 12, b = 142{,}000$. **2.** $(2\pi\nu)A$, $(2\pi\nu)^2 A$. **3.** 1.59 cycles/sec.

4. 1.54 cycles/sec; logarithmic decrement is 1.62. **5.** $k = 40$. **6.** 0.0722 sec.

7. 35.5 cycles/sec; 44.7 ohms. **8.** $2\pi \sqrt{l/g}$. **9.** 0.77 sec. **10.** 637 lb.

11. 0.636. **12.** $x(t) = \frac{1}{2} + \frac{1}{4}\cos 8t$ ft.

13. $x(t) = 0.5 - 0.155 \sin 8t + 0.394 \sin \pi t$. **14.** 85 min; maximum speed is $0.074L$ miles/min.

Chap. V, Sec. 10, page 163

2. $e^{-50t}(-5.53 \sin 218t + 1.212 \cos 218t) + 1.168 \sin 400t$
$- 3.212 \cos 400t + 4 \sin 200t + 2 \cos 200t$.

3. $-0.305 \sin 4.90t + 1.333 \cos 4.90t + 0.696 \sin t + 0.4 \sin 2t$.

5. $\dfrac{A e^{\gamma t}[(\gamma^2 - \omega^2 + a\gamma + b) \cos \omega t + (2\gamma\omega + a\omega) \sin \omega t]}{(\gamma^2 - \omega^2 + a\gamma + b)^2 + (2\gamma\omega + a\omega)^2}$

Chap. V, Sec. 11, page 166

1. $-\frac{1}{2}\cos t + \frac{1}{2}\sin t - \frac{1}{8}\cos 2t - \frac{1}{8}\sin 2t - \frac{1}{58}\cos 3t - \frac{7}{174}\sin 3t.$

2. $2\cos(t/2) + 2\sin(t/2) - \cos t - \sin t.$ **3.** $-\frac{2}{5}\cos 2t - \frac{1}{5}\sin 2t.$

4. $c_1\sin\sqrt{\frac{5}{3}}\,t + c_2\cos\sqrt{\frac{5}{3}}\,t - \sin t - \frac{4}{7}\sin 2t - \frac{1}{35}\sin 5t.$

5. $\frac{1}{2}a_0 C + \sum_{k=1}^{n}\frac{1}{k\omega}\left[\frac{-a_k(Lk\omega - 1/Ck\omega) - b_k R}{(Lk\omega - 1/Ck\omega)^2 + R^2}\cos k\omega t\right.$

$\left. + \frac{a_k R - b_k(Lk\omega - 1/Ck\omega)}{(Lk\omega - 1/Ck\omega)^2 + R^2}\sin k\omega t\right].$

6. $\frac{1}{2}\sum_{k=1}^{n}(a_k{}^2 + b_k{}^2)/[(Lk\omega - 1/Ck\omega)^2 + R^2].$

Chap. V, Sec. 12, page 169

1. (a) $y(x) = 2x^{-1} + c_1 e^x + c_2 e^{-x}$, $z(x) = c_1 e^x - c_2 e^{-x}.$

(b) $y(x) = (c_1\sin\frac{1}{2}x + c\cos\frac{1}{2}x)e^{3x}$, $z(x) = (3c_1 - \frac{1}{2}c_2)\sin\frac{1}{2}x$
$+ (3c_2 + \frac{1}{2}c_1)\cos\frac{1}{2}x.$

(c) $y(x) = -\cos x\log|\sec x + \tan x| + c_1\cos x + c_2\sin x$,
$z(x) = \cos x(-1 + \sin x\log|\sec x + \tan x| + c_2\cos x - c_1\sin x).$

(d) $y(x) = -2x - \frac{1}{2} + c_1 e^{-4x} + c_2 e^{2x}$, $z(x) = -x^2 - 2 - 4c_1 e^{-4x} + 2c_2 e^{2x}.$

(e) $y(x) = \sqrt{c_1 + c_2 e^x}$, $z(x) = \frac{1}{2}c_2 x e^x/\sqrt{c_1 + c_2 e^x}.$

2. (a) $y(x) = e^{-x}(\sqrt{3}\sin\sqrt{3}\,x + 3\cos\sqrt{3}\,x)$, $z(x) = 4\sqrt{3}\sin\sqrt{3}\,x.$

(b) $y(x) = e^{2x}$, $z(x) = 2e^x.$ (c) $y(x) = \log\cosh(x + 2)$,
$z(x) = \sinh(x + 2)\cosh(x + 2).$ (d) $y(x) = -\frac{1}{2}x\cos x$,
$z(x) = \frac{1}{2}\sin x - (1/2x)\cos x.$ **3.** (a) $1(a), (b), (c), (d); 2(a), (d).$

(b) $1(b); 2(a);$ (c) $1(a).$ **4.** (a) No. (b) Yes. **5.** L.C. in Theorem 1:
$|f(x_1, y_1, z_1) - f(x_2, y_2, z_2)| \leq M_1|y_1 - y_2| + M_2|z_1 - z_2|,$
$|g(x_1, y_1, z_1) - g(x_2, y_2, z_2)| \leq M_3|y_1 - y_2| + M_4|z_1 - z_2|;$ L.C. in Theorem 2:
$|g(x_1, y_1, p_1) - g(x_2, y_2, p_2)| \leq M_1|y_1 - y_2| + M_2|p_1 - p_2|.$

Chap. V, Sec. 13, page 173

1. (a) $y(1) = 1.146, h = 0.1; y(1) = 1.108, h = 0.05.$ (b) $y(-1) = -1.598,$
$h = 0.1; \; y(-1) = -1.572, \; h = 0.2.$ (c) $y(2) = 2.754.$ (d) $y(2) = 2.819.$
(e) $y(1) = 0.1186.$ **3.** $g_{k-1} = g(x_{k-1}, y_{k-1}, p_{k-1});$
$g_k = g(x_k, y_{k-1} + hp_{k-1}, p_{k-1} + hg_{k-1}); \; p_k = p_{k-1} + \frac{1}{2}h(g_{k-1} + g_k);$
$y_k = y_{k-1} + hp_{k-1} + \frac{1}{2}h^2 g_{k-1} + 0(h^3).$ **4.** $y(2) = 2.709.$

5. $y_k = y_{k-1} + hf_{k-1} + \frac{1}{2}h^2(f_{x,k-1} + f_{y,k-1}f_{k-1} + f_{z,k-1}g_{k-1}) + 0(h^3);$
$z_k = z_{k-1} + hg_{k-1} + \frac{1}{2}h^2(g_{x,k-1} + g_{y,k-1}f_{k-1} + g_{z,k-1}g_{k-1}) + 0(h^3) \; (f_x = \partial f/\partial x,$
etc.). **6.** $p_k = p_{k-1} + hg_{k-1} + \frac{1}{2}h^2(g_{x,k-1} + g_{y,k-1}p_{k-1} + g_{p,k-1}g_{k-1});$
$y_k = y_{k-1} + hp_{k-1} + \frac{1}{2}h^2 g_{k-1} + 0(h^3) \; (g_x = \partial g/\partial x,$ etc.).

7. $y_{2n} = (1 + 1/n)^{2n}; \lim y_{2n} = e^2.$ **8.** $y(h) = \frac{1}{6}h^2[g(0) + 2g(\frac{1}{2}h)],$ which coincides with the result obtained by Simpson's rule.

Chap. V, Sec. 14, page 178

1. (a) $\sin x - \cos x + e^{-2x}(2\cos x + e^\pi \sin x).$

(b) $e^x\sin\sqrt{3}\,x.$ (c) $e^{-\frac{1}{2}x}(2\cos\frac{1}{2}\sqrt{3}\,x - \sin\frac{1}{2}\sqrt{3}\,x) + x\sin x.$

(d) $\frac{1}{3} \cos x - \frac{1}{4}(x + \pi) \cos 2x + \frac{1}{3} \sqrt{2} \sin 2x$.   (e) 0.

(f) $\sin \omega t - \frac{1}{2} \sin 2\omega t$.   (g) $0.4 - 0.2 \sin 2t - 0.1 \cos 2t$.

(h) $-0.4 \cos 2t - 0.2 \sin 2t$.

(i) $|\sin x - x \cos x| \cos x + |\cos x + x \sin x - 1| \sin x$ $+ (1 - \pi/2) \sin x$.   (j) $\sqrt{2e^x - 1}$.

(k) $-\frac{1}{2}x^2 + \log 3(x + \sqrt{x^2 + \frac{16}{9}})$.   **2.** (a) $A \sin kx$.

(b) $A \cos kx$.   (c) 0.   (d) $A \sin kx$.

(e) $y(x) = 0$ unless $k = 1, 2, \ldots$, in which case $y(x) = A \sin kx + B \cos kx$.

3. $b = k\pi/3$ $(k = 1, 2, \ldots)$; $Ae^{-2x} \sin 3x$.   **4.** $\alpha = 0$,

$e^{-2x}(\sin^2 x + A \sin 2x)$.   **5.** (a) $\lambda_k = k^2\pi^2/L^2$,

$y_k(x) = A \sin (k\pi x/L)$ $(k = 1, 2, \ldots)$.   (b) $\lambda_k = (k - \frac{1}{2})^2\pi^2/L^2$,

$y_k(x) = A \cos [(k - \frac{1}{2})\pi x/L]$ $(k = 1, 2, \ldots)$.   (c) $\lambda_k = k^2\pi^2/L^2$,

$y_k(x) = A \cos [k\pi x/L] + B \sin [k\pi x/L]$ $(k = 0, 1, 2, \ldots)$.

(d) $\lambda_k = \frac{1}{4}a^2 + k^2\pi^2/L^2$, $y_k(x) = Ae^{-\frac{1}{2}ax} \sin [k\pi x/L]$ $(k = 1, 2, \ldots)$.

6. $y(x) = (1/k)(\cosh kx - \cosh kL)$.   **7.** The curve joining $(0, 0)$ with $(1, \eta)$ is given by $x = y^3 + [(1 - \eta^3)/\eta]y$; there is no inverse $y = y(x)$ on $0 \leq x \leq 1$ if $\eta > 1$, and no differentiable one if $\eta = 1$.

Chap. V, Sec. 15, page 185

1. $y(x) = (k/2X)x^2 + c_1x + c_2$.   **2.** $\frac{3}{4}\delta$.   **3.** $y(x) = (1/k) \log (\cos ka/\cos kx)$, where $k = w/X$.   **4.** Choose the x axis in the top of the sand and the y axis downward. If the top of the circle is at $x = 0$, then $y = A \cosh \sqrt{w} \, x$, where w is the weight of the sand per unit volume.   **5.** $\frac{11}{48}wl^3/EI$.

6. $\frac{19}{192}\rho l^4/EI$.   **7.** $\frac{1}{8}\rho l^4/EI$.   **8.** Theoretically it may bulge at the characteristic speeds $\omega_k = (k\pi/l) \sqrt{X/\rho}$ $(k = 1, 2, \ldots)$.

Chap. V, Sec. 16, page 190

1. $y_k(x, t) = A \sin [(2k - 1)\pi x/l] \sin [(2k - 1)\pi ct/l + \delta]$ $(k = 1, 2, \ldots)$.

3. $\theta_k(x, t) = A \cos (k\pi x/l) \, e^{-k^2\pi^2a^2t/l^2}$ $(k = 1, 2, \ldots)$.

4. $w_k(x, y) = A \sin [(2k - 1)\pi x/2l] \sinh [(2k - 1)\pi y/2l + \delta]$ $(k = 1, 2, \ldots)$.

5. $w_k(x, y) = A \sin [2k\pi(x + \delta_1)/l] \sinh [2k\pi(y + \delta_2)/l]$ $(k = 1, 2, \ldots)$.

6. $y_k(x, t) = A \sin (k\pi x/l) \, e^{-\frac{1}{2}bt} \sinh \sqrt{b^2/4 - (k\pi c/l)^2} \, t$ $(k = 1, 2, \ldots)$ for $k < lb/2\pi c$; $y_k(x, t) = A \sin (k\pi x/l) \, e^{-\frac{1}{2}bt} \sin \sqrt{(k\pi c/l)^2 - b^2/4}$ $(k = 1, 2, \ldots)$ for $k > lb/2\pi c$.   **7.** $\theta_k(x, t) = A \sin \lambda_k x \, e^{-\lambda_k^2 a^2 t}$, where λ_1, λ_2 are the positive roots of the transcendental equation $\kappa \tan \lambda l = \lambda$.

8. $y_k(x, t) = A \sin \lambda_k x \sin (\lambda_k ct + \delta)$, where λ_1, λ_2 are the positive roots of the transcendental equation $\lambda \tan \lambda l = \kappa/c^2$.

Chap. VI, Sec. 1, page 193

1. (a) $L[y] \equiv y'' + 3y' - 4y$.   (b) $L[y] \equiv y'' + k^2y$.

(c) $L[u] \equiv u'' + au' + bu$, $L[e^{\alpha x}] = e^{\alpha x}(\alpha^2 + 3\alpha - 4)$, $L[e^{\alpha x}] = e^{\alpha x}(\alpha^2 + k^2)$, $L[e^{\alpha x}] = e^{\alpha x}(\alpha^2 + a\alpha + b)$.   **2.** (d) $d^2y/dx^2 - dy/dx + 2y/(1 - x^2)$.

(e) $2 \cot x + (\log \sin x)/(1 + x) - 1$.

(f) $\log \sin x L_1[y] + 2 \cos x \sin x \, dy/dx + (2 \cot x - 1)y$.

Chap. VI, Sec. 3, page 200

1. (a) $\cos^2 x - \sin^2 x$. (b) $2\cos^2 x - 1$. (c) $-\frac{1}{3}(-3) + (-2)\sin^2 x$.
2. (b) $2(x-1)^2 + 12(x-1) + 13$. (c) $2(x+2)^2 + (-1)5$.
(d) Impossible. **4.** (a), (d), (h), (j), (l) are all dependent.
6. $A \sinh (ax + b) = (Ae^b/2)e^{ax} - (Ae^{-b}/2)e^{-ax}$,
$A \cosh (ax + b) = (Ae^b/2)e^{ax} + (Ae^{-b}/2)e^{-ax}$. **7.** $e^{ax} = \cosh ax + \sinh ax$,
$e^{-ax} = \cosh ax - \sinh ax$.

8. $\cos^n x = 2^{1-n}\left[\dfrac{1}{2}\dfrac{n!}{\left(\dfrac{n}{2}\right)!\left(\dfrac{n}{2}\right)!} + \dfrac{n!}{\left(\dfrac{n-2}{2}\right)!\left(\dfrac{n+2}{2}\right)!}\cos 2x\right.$

$\left. + \dfrac{n!}{\left(\dfrac{n-4}{2}\right)!\left(\dfrac{n+4}{2}\right)!}\cos 4x + \cdots + \dfrac{n!}{0!n!}\cos nx\right]$ (if n is even)

$= 2^{1-n}\left[\dfrac{n!}{\left(\dfrac{n-1}{2}\right)!\left(\dfrac{n+1}{2}\right)!}\cos x + \dfrac{n!}{\left(\dfrac{n-3}{2}\right)!\left(\dfrac{n+3}{2}\right)!}\cos 3x\right.$

$\left. + \dfrac{n!}{\left(\dfrac{n-5}{2}\right)!\left(\dfrac{n+5}{2}\right)!}\cos 5x + \cdots + \dfrac{n!}{0!n!}\cos nx\right]$ (if n is odd)

9. Not for n even. HINT: $\sin^n(-x) = \sin^n x$ if n is even.

Chap. VI, Sec. 4, page 204

3. For example: (a) 3, $x - 1$, $(x+1)^2$. (b) $3x$, $x + e^x$. (c) 1, x, x^3.
(d) e^x, $e^x + e^{2x}$, $e^{2x} + e^{3x}$. (e) $e^{2x}\cos 3x$, $e^{2x}\sin 3x$. **4.** 1, x, x^2;
dimension $= 3$.

Chap. VI, Sec. 5, page 208

1. (a) $c_1e^x + c_2e^{2x} + c_3e^{-4x}$. (b) $c_1e^{-x} + c_2e^{(-1+\sqrt{2})x} + c_3e^{(-1-\sqrt{2})x}$.
(c) $c_1 + c_2e^{-x} + c_3e^{\sqrt{2}x} + c_4e^{-\sqrt{2}x}$. (d) $c_1e^{i\sqrt{2}x} + c_2e^{-i\sqrt{2}x}$.
(e) $e^{-\frac{1}{2}x}(c_1e^{i\sqrt{3}x} + c_2e^{-i\sqrt{3}x})$. (f) $c_1e^{2x} + c_2e^{-2x} + c_3e^{i\sqrt{3}x} + c_4e^{-i\sqrt{3}x}$.
2. $c_1x + c_2x^2 + c_3x^{-1}$. **3.** $(c_0 + c_1t + c_2t^2 + c_3t^3)e^{-at}$.

Chap. VI, Sec. 6, page 212

3. (a) $e^{-2x}(3\sin x - 4\cos x)$. (b) $e^x(-11\sin 2x - 2\cos 2x)$.
(c) $e^{2x}(11x^2 + 41x + 40)$. (d) 0. (e) $e^{ax}D^nf$. (f) 0.

Chap. VI, Sec. 7, page 217

1. $c_0 + c_1x + c_2e^{3x}$, $y = 1 + 6x - e^{3x}$. **2.** $c_0 + c_1e^{-x} + c_2e^{-4x}$.
3. $c_0 + c_1x + (c_2 + c_3x)e^{-x}$, $x + xe^{-x}$.
4. $c_1e^x + c_2e^{-x} + c_3\sin x + c_4\cos x$, $e^{-x} + \frac{1}{2}\sin x$.
5. $[c_1\sin (\frac{1}{2}\sqrt{2}\,x) + c_2\cos (\frac{1}{2}\sqrt{2}\,x)]e^{\frac{1}{2}\sqrt{2}x} + [c_3\sin (\frac{1}{2}\sqrt{2}\,x)$
$+ c_4\cos (\frac{1}{2}\sqrt{2}\,x)]e^{-\frac{1}{2}\sqrt{2}x}$. **6.** $(c_0 + c_1x)e^{-x} + (c_3 + c_4x)e^{2x}$,
$xe^{-x} - xe^x$. **7.** $(c_0 + c_1x + c_2x^2)e^x + c_3e^{-2x}$.

8. $(c_0 + c_1 x) \sin x + (c_2 + c_3 x) \cos x.$

9. $c_1 e^{-x} + c_2 \sin x + c_3 \cos x + [c_4 \sin (\frac{1}{2} \sqrt{3} \, x) + c_5 \cos (\frac{1}{2} \sqrt{3} \, x)] e^{x/2}.$

10. $(c_0 + c_1 x + c_2 x^2) \sin x + (c_3 + c_4 x + c_5 x^2) \cos x.$

11. $c_0 + c_1 x + c_2 x^2 + \cdots + c_{n-2} x^{n-2} + c_{n-1} e^{-ax}.$

12. $[(c_0 + c_1 x + c_2 x^2 + \cdots + c_{n-1} x^{n-1}) \sin ax$
$+ (c_n + c_{n+1} x + \cdots + c_{2n-1} x^{n-1}) \cos ax] e^{-ax}.$

13. $c_1 e^{-x} + c_2 e^{-2x} + e^{-\frac{1}{2}x}(c_3 \cos \frac{1}{2} \sqrt{7} \, x + c_4 \sin \frac{1}{2} \sqrt{7} \, x).$

14. $(c_1 + c_2 x) e^{-\frac{1}{2}x} + e^{\frac{1}{2}x}(c_3 \cos \frac{1}{2} \sqrt{3} \, x + c_4 \sin \frac{1}{2} \sqrt{3} \, x).$

15. $(c_0 + c_1 x) e^{2x} + c_2 e^{-3x} + c_3 \cos x + c_4 \sin x.$

16. $c_1 e^x + (c_2 + c_3 x) e^{(-\frac{3}{2}+\frac{1}{2}\sqrt{5})x} + (c_4 + c_5 x) e^{(-\frac{3}{2}-\frac{1}{2}\sqrt{5})x}.$

17. $(c_0 + c_1 x) \cos \pi x + (c_2 + c_3 x) \sin \pi x + c_4 e^{-\pi x}.$

Chap. VI, Sec. 8, page 221

1. $(A/a^3) e^{ax} + c_0 + c_1 x + c_2 x^2, \; a \neq 0;$
$(A/6) x^3 + c_0 + c_1 x + c_2 x^2, \; a = 0.$

2. $(A/\omega^3)(2 \sin \omega t - \omega t \cos \omega t) + c_0 + c_1 t, \; \omega \neq 0;$
$(A/6) t^3 + c_0 + c_1 t, \; \omega = 0.$

3. $(A x^4/288)(-25 + 12 \log x) + c_0 + c_1 x + c_2 x^2 + c_3 x^3.$

4. $- \sqrt{a^2 - x^2}/a^2 + c_0 + c_1 x.$ **5.** $c_1 e^{4x} + c_2 e^{9x} + \frac{1}{26} \cos 6x.$

6. $c_1 e^x + c_2 \cos 2x + c_3 \sin 2x + \frac{1}{2} e^{2x}.$

7. $c_1 e^x + c_2 \cos 2x + c_3 \sin 2x - \frac{1}{3} \sin x - \frac{1}{3} \cos x.$

8. $(c_0 + c_1 x) e^{-2x} + (c_2 + c_3 x) e^{2x} + \frac{1}{32} x^2 e^{2x}.$

9. $c_1 e^{\frac{1}{2}t} + c_2 e^{-t} + c_3 e^t + (\sin \omega t + 2\omega \cos \omega t)/(\omega^2 + 1)(4\omega^2 + 1).$

10. $(c_0 + c_1 x) \cos 2x + (c_2 + c_3 x) \sin 2x + k e^{ax}/(a^2 + 4)^2.$

11. $-x^{-2} + c_1 x^3 + c_2 x^{-3}.$ **12.** $\frac{1}{2} x^3 + c_1 x + c_2 (1 - x^2).$

13. $- k/9x + c_0 + (c_1 + c_2 \log x) x^2.$

Chap. VI, Sec. 9, page 223

1. $c_1 \cos \sqrt{5} x + c_2 \sin \sqrt{5} \, x + \frac{2}{5} + \sin x.$ **2.** $\frac{1}{2} x^2 - \frac{1}{12} x^3.$

4. (a) $\frac{1}{2} + [1/2(1 + 16\beta^4)] \cos 2\beta t.$

(b) $\frac{1}{8} - [1/8(1 + 256\beta^4)] \cos 4\beta t.$

(c) $a_0/2c + \sum_{k=1}^{n} [a_k/(c + k^4\beta^4)] \cos k\beta t + [b_k/(c + k^4\beta^4)] \sin k\beta t.$

(d) $\frac{1}{24} \sin 2t + \frac{1}{264} \sin 4t - (1/1,304) \sin 6t.$

5. $1 + x/1^2 + x^2/3^2 + x^3/5^2 + \cdots + x^{n-1}/(2n - 3)^2.$

Chap. VI, Sec. 11, page 226

1. (a) $\int^x e^{2(x-x_1)}(x_1 + e^{x_1}) \, dx_1.$

(b) $\int^x dx_3 \int^{x_3} dx_2 \int^{x_2} e^{2(x-x_1)}(x_1 + e^{x_1}) \, dx_1.$

(c) $\int^x dx_2 \int^{x_2} e^{-3(x-x_1)} \sin \omega x_1 \, dx_1.$

(d) $\int^x e^{-2(x-x_2)}\,dx_2 \int^{x_2} e^{-(x_2-x_1)} \sin x_1\,dx_1.$

(e) $\int^x e^{-i(x-x_2)}\,dx_2 \int^{x_2} e^{i(x_2-x_1)} \cos \omega x_1\,dx_1.$

Chap. VI, Sec. 12, page 229

1. (a) A. (b) $5/\omega^2$. (c) $-2x^3$. (d) $-x$.

(e) $-6x/\pi$. **2.** (a) $\frac{1}{2}, -e^x + \frac{1}{2}e^{2x} + \frac{1}{2}$. (b) $\frac{1}{2}x + \frac{1}{4}$.

(c) $-x^2, \cosh x - \cos x - x^2$. (d) $-x^2 - 2x$.

(e) $-x^4/12, -x^4/12$. (f) $-x^4 - 12x^2 - 24$.

(g) $-x^5/5 - 2x^4 - 12x^3 - 60x^2 - 192x$.

(h) $x^2 + 6x + 14, x^2 + 6x + 14$. (i) $x^6 - 15x^3$.

Chap. VI, Sec. 13, page 231

1. (a) $(e^{-x}/13)(3 \sin x - 2 \cos x)$.

(b) $(e^{-x}/12)(x^4 + 4x^3 + 8x^2 + 8x)$.

(c) $(\omega^3 \cos \omega x + \sin \omega x)/(1 + \omega^6)$. (d) $e^x(x^2 - 3x)/8$.

(e) $-e^x \cos (x/5)$. (f) $Ae^{sx}/(r + s)^n$. (g) $e^{2x}/8$.

(h) $-x(\cos 2x + \sin 2x)/16$. (i) $-2x(\sin x + \cos x)$.

(j) $-3 \sin (3x/4)$. (k) $-(x^2/8) \cos x - (x^3/24) \sin x$.

(l) $Axe^{ax}/(a - b)(a - c)$. (m) $Ax^2e^{ax}/2(a - b)$.

(n) $Ax^2e^{ax}/2(a - b)^2$.

(o) $-A\left[\dfrac{1}{(r_1 - r_2)(r_1 - r_3)\,\cdots\,(r_1 - r_n)(r_1 - s)}\right.$

$\qquad + \dfrac{1}{(r_2 - r_1)\,\cdots\,(r_2 - r_n)(r_2 - s)}$

$\qquad + \cdots + \left.\dfrac{1}{(r_n - r_1)\,\cdots\,(r_n - r_{n-1})(r_n - s)}\right] e^{sx}.$

(p) $Ax \cos [ax/2a(a^2 - b^2)]$. (q) $-Ax^2 \sin [ax/8a^2]$.

2. (a) $\frac{1}{5} \sin x$. (b) $\frac{1}{32} \sin 2x$. (c) $-(\sin \omega x)/\omega(\omega^2 + 2)$.

3. (a) $x^6e^{-x}/120$. (b) $(\frac{1}{2} \log x + \frac{3}{4} - x + \frac{1}{4}x^2)e^x$.

(c) $\frac{1}{40}(x^2 - \frac{1}{2}x + \frac{61}{200})e^{2x} - \frac{1}{64}e^{-2x} + \frac{1}{125}e^{-3x}$. (d) $[k!/(n + k)!]x^{n+k}e^{-rx}$.

(e) $\int_0^x dx_n \cdots \int_0^{x_3} dx_2 \int_0^{x_2} e^{-r(x-x_1)} f(x_1)\,dx_1$

$\qquad\qquad = [1/(n - 1)!] \int_0^x (x - x_1)^{n-1} e^{-r(x-x_1)} f(x_1)\,dx_1.$

(f) $[1/(r - s)^2] \int_0^x \{[x - x_1 + 2/(r - s)]e^{-r(x-x_1)}$

$\qquad\qquad\qquad + [x - x_1 + 2/(s - r)]e^{-s(x-x_1)}\} f(x_1)\,dx_1.$

(g) $e^x + \int_0^x [-1 + \cosh (x - x_1)]f(x_1)\,dx_1.$

(h) $\sin x + \int_0^x [1 - \cos (x - x_1)]f(x_1)\,dx_1.$

(i) $1 + \int_0^x dx_n \cdots \int_0^{x_3} dx_2 \int_0^{x_2} e^{a(x_2-x_1)} f(x_1)\,dx_1 =$

$1 - \int_0^x [(x - x_1)^{n-2}/a(n - 2)! + (x - x_1)^{n-3}/a^2(n - 3)! + \cdots + 1/a^{n-1}$

$\qquad\qquad\qquad\qquad\qquad - e^{a(x-x_1)}/a^{n-1}] f(x_1)\,dx_1.$

Chap. VI, Sec. 14, page 242

1. (a) $2h[\frac{1}{2}\mathbf{1}(t) - \mathbf{1}(t - \tau) + \mathbf{1}(t - 3\tau) - \mathbf{1}(t - 5\tau) + \cdots]$.

(b) $h[\mathbf{1}(t) - \mathbf{1}(t - \tau) - \mathbf{1}(t - 2\tau) + \mathbf{1}(t - 3\tau) + \mathbf{1}(t - 4\tau) - \cdots]$.

(c) $(h/\tau)[t\mathbf{1}(t) - (t - \tau)\mathbf{1}(t - \tau)]$.

(d) $(2h/\tau)[(t/2)\mathbf{1}(t) - (t - \tau)\mathbf{1}(t - \tau) + (t - 2\tau)\mathbf{1}(t - 2\tau) - (t - 3\tau)\mathbf{1}(t - 3\tau) + \cdots]$.

(e) $(2h/\tau)[(t/2)\mathbf{1}(t) - (t - \tau)\mathbf{1}(t - \tau) + (t - 3\tau)\mathbf{1}(t - 3\tau) - (t - 5\tau)\mathbf{1}(t - 5\tau) + \cdots]$.

2. (a) $K(t, \tau) = (1/k^2)[1 - \cos k(t - \tau)]$, $G(t, \tau) = (1/k) \sin k(t - \tau)$; for $t \geq \tau$. (b) $K(t,\tau) = (1/k^2)[\cosh k(t - \tau) - 1]$, $G(t,\tau) = (1/k) \sinh k(t - \tau)$; for $t \geq \tau$. (c) $K(t, \tau) = (t - \tau)/a + (1/a^2)(e^{-a(t-\tau)} - 1)$, $G(t, \tau) = (1/a)(1 - e^{-a(t-\tau)})$; for $t \geq \tau$.

(d) $K(t, \tau) = (1/b)[1 - (r_2 e^{r_1(t-\tau)} - r_1 e^{r_2(t-\tau)})/(r_2 - r_1)]$, $G(t, \tau) = (e^{r_1(t-\tau)} - e^{r_2(t-\tau)})/(r_1 - r_2)$; for $t \geq \tau$, where $r_{1,2} = \frac{1}{2}(-a \pm \sqrt{a^2 - 4b})$.

(e) $K(t, \tau) = [1/(a - 1)] \log (t/\tau) + [1/(a - 1)^2][(t/\tau)^{1-a} - 1]$, $G(t, \tau) = [1/(a - 1)\tau][1 - (t/\tau)^{1-a}]$; for $t \geq \tau$.

(f) $K(t, \tau) = \dfrac{1}{b}\left[1 - \dfrac{r_2(t/\tau)^{r_1} - r_1(t/\tau)^{r_2}}{r_2 - r_1}\right]$, $G(t, \tau) = \dfrac{(t/\tau)^{r_1} - (t/\tau)^{r_2}}{(r_1 - r_2)\tau}$; for $t \geq \tau$, where $r_{1,2} = \frac{1}{2}[1 - a \pm \sqrt{(1 - a)^2 - 4b}]$.

(g) $K(t, \tau) = (1/a)(1 - e^{-\frac{1}{2}a(t^2-\tau^2)}) - \tau \int_\tau^t e^{\frac{1}{2}a(t'^2-t^2)} dt'$,

$G(t, \tau) = \int_\tau^t e^{\frac{1}{2}a(t'^2-t^2)} dt'$; for $t \geq \tau$.

4. $(V_0/\sqrt{R^2 + L^2\omega^2}) [\sin (\omega t - \phi) + e^{-(R/L)t} \sin \phi]$, where $\tan \phi = L\omega/R$.

5. $(V_0/R)[e^{-\nu t}\mathbf{1}(t) - 2e^{-\nu(t-\tau)}\mathbf{1}(t - \tau) + 2e^{-\nu(t-3\tau)}\mathbf{1}(t - 3\tau) - \cdots]$, where $\nu = 1/RC$. **6.** $F_{\max} = [F_0/(1 + m/M)][1 + |\sin (\nu\tau/2)|/(\nu\tau/2)]$; $F_{\max} = 2F_0/(1 + m/M)$, where $\nu^2 = k(1/M + 1/m)$.

Chap. VII, Sec. 2, page 253

1. (a) $f(t) = 3 - e^{-t} + 2 \sin t$. (b) $f(t) = \frac{1}{2}e^{at} - \frac{1}{2}e^{\frac{1}{2}-at} = \sinh at$.

(c) $f(t) = A - 2 \cosh 2t$. (d) $f(t) = A \sin \omega t + B \cos \omega t$.

(e) $f(t) = \sin 4t - 2e^{2t} \sin 4t$. (f) $f(t) = (\omega/2i)e^{i\omega t} - (\omega/2i)e^{-i\omega t} = \omega \sin \omega t$.

(g) $f(t) = \cos \omega t$. (h) $f(t) = \frac{2}{9}te^{-2t/3}$. (i) $f(t) = \frac{5}{4}(2te^t - e^t + e^{-t})$.

(j) $f(t) = 5e^{-t} \sin 4t$. (k) $f(t) = \frac{1}{2}e^{-2t} \cosh 3t$.

(l) $f(t) = (2/\sqrt{7})e^{\frac{1}{2}t} \sin (\sqrt{7}/2)t$.

(m) $f(t) = \frac{1}{3}\{e^t - e^{-\frac{1}{2}t}[\cos (\sqrt{3}/2)t + \sqrt{3} \sin (\sqrt{3}/2)t]\}$

$= \frac{1}{3}\left[e^t - e^{-\frac{1}{2}t}\left(\dfrac{1 - i\sqrt{3}}{2}e^{-i\sqrt{3}/2t} + \dfrac{1 + i\sqrt{3}}{2}e^{-i\sqrt{3}/2t}\right)\right]$.

(n) $f(t) = 1 - \frac{1}{4}e^{\frac{1}{4}t}[\cos (\sqrt{7}/4)t - (1/\sqrt{7}) \sin (\sqrt{7}/4)t]$.

(o) $f(t) = 2te^t - \frac{5}{3}e^t + 3e^{-t} - \frac{4}{3}e^{-2t}$. **6.** (a) any $c > 0$. (b) any $c > a$.

(c) any $c > 0$. (d) any $c > 0$. (e) any $c > 0$. (f) any $c > 0$.

(g) any $c > a/2$. (h) any $c > 0$.

Chap. VII, Sec. 3, page 257

1. (a) 0.   (b) $\frac{3}{7}e^{-4t} + \frac{4}{7}e^{3t}$.   (c) $-\frac{1}{7}e^{-4t} + \frac{1}{7}e^{3t}$.

(d) $\frac{1}{35}e^{-4t} + \frac{1}{14}e^{3t} + \frac{1}{10}e^{-t}$.   (e) $-\frac{1}{7}te^{-4t} - \frac{1}{49}e^{-4t} + \frac{1}{49}e^{3t}$.

(f) $\frac{1}{28}e^{-4t} + \frac{1}{21}e^{3t} - \frac{1}{12}$.   (g) $1 + 6t - e^{3t}$.   (h) $t + te^{-t}$.

(i) $\frac{4}{9}(e^{-t} + 3te^{-t} - e^{2t})$.   (j) $-e^{t} + \frac{1}{2}e^{2t} + \frac{1}{2}$.

(k) $\cosh t - \cos t - t^2$.   (l) $\frac{1}{8}(2 + t^2 - \frac{1}{3}t^4 - 2\cosh \sqrt{2}\,t)$.

(m) $t^6 e^{-t}/120$.   (n) $t^2 e^{2t} - \frac{1}{10}(e^{2t} - 5e^{-2t} + 4e^{-3t})$.

(o) $-[\omega/2(\omega^2 - 1)]\cos t + [\omega/2(\omega^2 - 1)]\sin t + [\omega/2(1 + \omega^2)]e^{-t}$
$+ [\omega/(\omega^4 - 1)]\cos \omega t + [1/(\omega^4 - 1)]\sin \omega t$.

(p) $\frac{1}{2}(\cos t + 3\sin t + e^{-t}) + y$ of part o.

3. $\frac{1}{28}e^{-4(t-t_0)} + \frac{1}{21}e^{3(t-t_0)} - \frac{1}{12}$.   **4.** $(\sin \omega t - \omega t \cos \omega t)/2\omega^2$, $t > 0$;
$-[\cos \omega t + (\omega t - \pi/2)\sin \omega]/2\omega^2$, $t > \pi/2\omega$.

5. $0 = y_0 = \cdots = y_{n-k-2} = y_{n-k} = \cdots = y_{n-1}$, $y_{n-k-1} = 1/\alpha_0$.

Chap. VII, Sec. 4, page 260

1. (a) $(\sin \omega t)/\omega$.   (b) $t^3/6$.   (c) $(\omega e^{t} - \sin \omega t - \omega \cos \omega t)(1 + \omega^2)$.

(d) $(e^{3t} - e^{t})/2$.   (e) t.

(f) $(1/4\omega)[2\cos \omega t(1 - \cos 2\omega t) + \sin \omega t(2\omega t - \sin 2\omega t)]$.

(g) $(t - t_1 - t_2)\mathbf{1}(t - t_1 - t_2)$.   (h) $\mathbf{1}(t - t_0)\int_0^{t-t_0} f(\tau)\,d\tau$.

(i) $t^{2k-1}/(2k - 1)!$ **2.** (a) $\mathcal{L}\{(e^{at} - e^{bt})/(a - b)\}(s) = 1/(s - a)(s - b)$.

(b) $\mathcal{L}\{te^{at}\}(s) - 1/(s - a)^2$.   (c) $\mathcal{L}\{(t - t_0)\mathbf{1}(t - t_0)\}(s) - e^{-st_0}/s^2$.

(d) $s/(s - 1)(s^2 + 1)$.   **3.** (a) te^{-t}.   (b) $(\sin \omega t - \omega t \cos \omega t)/2\omega^3$.

(c) $(t - t_0)\mathbf{1}(t - t_0)$.   **4.** (a) $k!l!t^{k+l+1}/(k + l + 1)!$.

(b) $e^{at}/(a - b)(a - c) + e^{bt}/(b - a)(b - c) + e^{ct}/(c - a)(c - b)$.

(c) $(\omega e^{at} - \omega \cos \omega t - a \sin \omega t)/(a^2 + \omega^2)$.

Chap. VII, Sec. 5, page 263

1. $T = 1/(s^2 - 3s + 2)$, $\mathcal{L}^{-1}T = e^{2t} - e^{t}$, $g(t - \tau) = e^{2(t-\tau)} - e^{t-\tau}$,
$\int_0^t f(\tau)(e^{2(t-\tau)} - e^{t-\tau})\,d\tau$.   **2.** $g(t - \tau) = (1/\omega)\sin \omega(t - \tau)$,

$(\sin \omega t - \omega t \cos \omega t)/2\omega^2$.   **3.** $(1/\omega)\int_0^t f(\tau)\sin \omega(t - \tau)\,d\tau$.

4. $g(t - \tau) = (e^{r_1(t-\tau)} - e^{r_2(t-\tau)})/(r_1 - r_2)$, $u_1 = [1/(r_1 - r_2)]\int_0^t e^{-r_1\tau}f(\tau)\,d\tau$,

$u_2 = [1/(r_2 - r_1)]\int_0^t e^{-r_2\tau}f(\tau)\,d\tau$.

5. $K(t, t_0) = [1/r_1(r_1 - r_2)]e^{r_1(t-t_0)} + [1/r_2(r_2 - r_1)]e^{r_2(t-t_0)} + \frac{1}{b}$.

6. $g(t - t_0) = [\sinh a(t - t_0) - \sin a(t - t_0)]/2a^3$.

Chap. VII, Sec. 6, page 267

1. (a) Unstable.   (b) Unstable.   (c) Unstable.   (d) Stable.

2. (a) $\dfrac{A}{(c - a\omega^2)^2 + b^2\omega^2}[(c - a\omega^2)\sin \omega t - b\omega \cos \omega t]$.

(b) $-(2A/ab)\cos \sqrt{b}\,t$.   (c) $-A \sin t - B \cos t$.

Chap. VII, Sec. 7, page 274

2. $6 + x - \frac{9}{4}e^{-x} + (-\frac{15}{4} + \frac{5}{2}x - x^2)e^x$.

3. $-1 - x + \frac{1}{2}e^{-x} + \frac{1}{5}e^{-2x} + \frac{9}{10}\sin x + \frac{3}{10}\cos x$.

4. $-\frac{1}{4}\cos x + \frac{1}{4}x \sinh x + \frac{3}{4}\cosh x$. **5.** $-\frac{1}{3}\sin x - \frac{8}{3}\sin 2x$.

Chap. VIII, Sec. 1, page 281

1. $x = e^t + ce^{-t}$, $y = -ce^{-t}$. **2.** $x = c_1 e^{2t} + c_2 e^{-t}$, $y = -t^2 + c_1 e^{2t} - c_2 e^{-t}$.

3. $x = t^{-1} - e^{-t}$, $y = t^{-2}$. **4.** $x = (c + t/2)e^{-t}$, $y = t^{-1} - \frac{1}{2}e^{-t}$.

5. $x = \sin t + c_1 \sin 2t + c_2 \cos 2t$,

$y = \frac{1}{2}\cos t - (2c_1/5)\cos 2t + (2c_2/5)\sin 2t + c_3 e^t + c_4 e^{-t}$.

6. $x = -\frac{1}{2}f(t) + c_1 e^t$, $y = \frac{1}{2}f(t)$. **7.** $x = c_1 e^t$, $y = -(3c_1/4)e^t + c_2 e^{-t}$,

$z = -(3c_1/2)e^t + (2c_2/5)e^{-t} + c_2 e^{\frac{3}{2}t}$. **8.** $x = 1 - 2e^{2t}$, $y = -1 + 3e^{2t}$.

9. $x = t^2 + t - 1$, $y = -t$, $z = -t^2 - 3t + 1$.

Chap. VIII, Sec. 2, page 287

1. $x = (1 - D^2)h$, $y = D^3 h$. **2.** $x = c_1 \sin t + c_2 \cos t + c_3 e^t$,

$y = (c_1 + c_2)\sin t - (c_1 - c_2)\cos t + 2c_3 e^t - 2e^{\frac{1}{2}t}$.

3. $x = A - (B/2)\sin \sqrt{3}\,(t + \delta) - (\sqrt{3}/2)\,B \cos \sqrt{3}\,(t + \delta)$,

$y = A + B \sin \sqrt{3}\,(t + \delta)$,

$z = A - (B/2)\sin \sqrt{3}\,(t + \delta) + (\sqrt{3}/2)\,B \cos \sqrt{3}\,(t + \delta)$.

4. $x = A_1 + A_2 t e^{-t} + A_3 e^t + A_4 e^{-t}$, $y = (2A_2 t + 3A_2 + 2A_4)e^{-t}$.

$z = A_1 - 2A_2 e^{-t}$. **5.** $x = f$ arbitrary, $y = -D^2 f$,

$z = h + (D^2 - 1)f$, where the system is consistent if and only if $D^2 h = 0$.

6. $x = f$ arbitrary, $y = c_1 e^{-t} + (D + 1)f$,

$z = c_1 e^{-t} - c_2 e^{-2t} - \int^t e^{2(t_1 - t)} D^2 f(t_1)\, dt_1$.

$u = -c_1 e^{-t} - 2c_2 e^{-2t} + Df(t) + 2 \int^t e^{2(t_1 - t)} D^2 f(t_1)\, dt_1$.

7. $x = (c_0 + c_1 t)e^{2t} + c_2 e^{-3t}$, $y = \frac{1}{2}e^t - \frac{1}{4}(2c_0 + c_1 + 2c_1 t)e^{2t} + \frac{3}{4}c_2 e^{-3t}$.

8. $x = c_1 e^{-t} + c_2 e^{3t}$, $y = (2c_1 - 1)e^{-t} - 2c_2 e^{3t}$.

9. $x = \cos 2t + c_1 e^{-t}$, $y = 4 \cos 2t$. **10.** $x = c_1 \sin 2t + c_2 \cos 2t$,

$y = 2c_2 \sin 2t - 2c_1 \cos 2t$, $z = c_0 - c_2 \sin 2t + c_1 \cos 2t$.

11. (a) $x = \frac{2}{5}e^{4t} + \frac{3}{5}e^{-t}$, $y = -\frac{3}{5}e^{4t} + \frac{3}{5}e^{-t}$. (b) $x = -\frac{2}{5}e^{4t} + \frac{2}{5}e^{-t}$,

$y = \frac{3}{5}e^{4t} + \frac{2}{5}e^{-t}$. **12.** $x = -\frac{1}{2} + 3e^t - \frac{3}{2}e^{4t}$, $y = -2e^t + 2e^{4t}$.

13. $x = A \sinh t + (aA - bB)(1 - \cosh t)$,

$y = B \sinh t + (bA - aB)(1 - \cosh t)$. **14.** $x = 3e^t - 2e^{3t}$,

$y = -6e^t + 6e^{3t}$, $z = 6e^t - 6e^{3t}$. **15.** $x = e^t$, $y = e^t$.

16. $x = -\frac{1}{10}\cos 3t + \frac{1}{10}\cosh t$, $y = \frac{1}{10}\cos 3t - \frac{1}{10}\cosh t$.

17. $x = (A/2a)t \sin at$, $y = (A/2a^2)(\sin at - at \cos at)$. **18.** $x = y = t \sin t$,

$z = z_1 t - 2t \sin t + 2(1 - \cos t) + z_0$. **19.** $a = 0$, $x = f$ arbitrary,

$y = e^t + (1 - D^2)f$.

Chap. VIII, Sec. 3, page 292

1. (a) $x = \frac{2}{5}e^{4t} + \frac{3}{5}e^{-t}$, $y = -\frac{3}{5}e^{4t} + \frac{3}{5}e^{-t}$. (b) $x = -\frac{2}{5}e^{4t} + \frac{2}{5}e^{-t}$,

$y = \frac{3}{5}e^{4t} + \frac{2}{5}e^{-t}$. **2.** $x = -\frac{1}{2} + 3e^t - \frac{3}{2}e^{4t}$, $y = -2e^t + 2e^{4t}$.

3. $x = A \sinh t + (aA - bB)(1 - \cosh t)$,
$y = B \sinh t + (bA + aB)(1 - \cosh t)$.
4. $x = 3e^t - 2e^{3t}$, $y = -6e^t + 6e^{3t}$, $z = 6e^t - 6e^{3t}$. **5.** $x = e^t$, $y = e^t$.
6. $x = -\frac{1}{10} \cos 3t + \frac{1}{10} \cosh t$, $y = \frac{1}{10} \cos 3t - \frac{1}{10} \cosh t$.
7. $x = (A/2a)t \sin at$, $y = (A/2a^2)(\sin at - at \cos at)$.
8. $x = y = t \sin t$, $z = z_1 t - 2t \sin t + 2(1 - \cos t) + z_0$.
9. $x = \cos 2t + ce^{-t}$, where $c = x_0 - 1$; $y = 4 \cos 2t$.
10. $x = c_1 e^{-t} + c_2 e^{3t}$, $y = (2c_1 - 1)e^{-t} - 2c_2 e^{3t}$,
$c_1 = \frac{1}{4}(1 + 2x_0 + y_0)$, $c_2 = x_0 - c_1$.
11. $x = x_0 \cos 2t + \frac{1}{2}x_1 \sin 2t$, $y = 2x_0 \sin 2t - x_1 \cos 2t$,
$z = -x_0 \sin 2t + \frac{1}{2}x_1 \cos 2t + z_0 - \frac{1}{2}x_1$.
12. $x = (c_0 + c_1 t)e^{2t} + c_2 e^{-3t}$, $y = \frac{1}{2}e^t - \frac{1}{4}(2c_0 + c_1 + 2c_1 t)e^{2t} + \frac{3}{4}c_2 e^{-3t}$,
where $c_0 = \frac{1}{25}(-18 + 21x_0 - 16y_0 + 4y_1)$, $c_1 = -\frac{1}{5}(2 + 6x_0 + 4y_0 + 4y_1)$,
$c_2 = \frac{1}{25}(18 + 4x_0 + 16y_0 - 4y_1)$.
13. $x = cK + (x_0 - cK) \cos t + (bz_0 - ay_0) \sin t$,
$y = bK + (y_0 - bK) \cos t + (ax_0 - cz_0) \sin t$,
$z = aK + (z_0 - aK) \cos t + (cy_0 - bx_0) \sin t$; $K = az_0 + by_0 + cx_0$.
14. $x = \frac{1}{8}(e^t - e^{-t}) - \frac{1}{4}te^{-t} + \frac{1}{2}(3x_0 + y_0 + 2z_0)e^{-t} - \frac{1}{2}(x_0 + y_0 + 2z_0)e^t$,
$y = -\frac{1}{8}(e^t - e^{-t}) + \frac{1}{4}te^{-t} - \frac{1}{2}(x_0 - y_0 + 2z_0)e^{-t} + \frac{1}{2}(x_0 + y_0 + 2z_0)e^t$,
$z = z_0 e^t + \frac{1}{2}(x_0 + y_0)(e^t - e^{-t})$.

Chap. VIII, Sec. 4, page 302

1. (a) $x_1(t) = 2e^{4t}$, $y_1 = -3e^{4t}$, $x_2 = e^{-t}$, $y_2 = e^{-t}$.
(b) $x(t) = (aA - bB) + c_1 be^t + c_2 be^{-t}$,
$y(t) = (bA - aB) + c_1(1 + a)e^t + c_2(a - 1)e^{-t}$.
(c) $x(t) = c_1 e^t + c_2 e^{3t} + 5c_3 e^{2t}$, $y(t) = -2c_1 e^t - 3c_2 e^{3t} - 12c_3 e^{2t}$,
$z(t) = 2c_1 e^t + 3c_2 e^{3t} + 12c_3 e^{2t}$. (d) $x(t) = c_1 e^t + e^t \int^t f(\tau)e^{-\tau}\, d\tau$,
$y(t) = c_2 e^t + c_3 e^{2t} + e^t \int^t g(\tau)e^{-\tau}\, d\tau$, $z(t) = c_3 e^{2t}$. (e) $x(t) = c_1 e^t - 2c_3 e^{-t}$,
$y(t) = c_2 e^t - 5c_3 e^{-t}$, $z(t) = -c_2 e^t + 4c_3 e^{-t}$.
(f) $x(t) = c_1 c + c_2(c^2 - 1)e^{it} + c_3(c^2 - 1)e^{-it}$,
$y(t) = c_1 b + c_2(ai + bc)e^{it} + c_3(bc - ai)e^{-it}$,
$z(t) = c_1 a + c_2(ac - bi)e^{it} + c_3(ac + bi)e^{-it}$. **2.** $x(t) = 1 - e^{-t} + e^{-2t}$,
$y(t) = -1 + e^{-t}$, $z(t) = -\frac{1}{2} + 2e^{-t} - \frac{3}{2}e^{-2t}$.
4. $x_k = \Delta_k(D)/\Delta(D)$, where

$$\Delta(D) = \begin{vmatrix} a_{11} - D & a_{12} & \cdots & a_{1n} \\ a_{21} & a_{22} - D & \cdots & a_{2n} \\ \cdots\cdots\cdots\cdots\cdots\cdots\cdots\cdots\cdots\cdots \\ a_{n1} & a_{n2} & \cdots & a_{nn} - D \end{vmatrix}$$

and $\Delta_k(D)$ is formed from $\Delta(D)$ by replacing the kth column with $-\Sigma a_{1j}\xi_j$,
$\ldots$, $-\Sigma a_{nj}\xi_j$. **5.** $Dx_k = x_{k+1}$ $(k = 1, \ldots, n - 1)$, $Dx_n = f - a_1 x_n - \cdots$
$-a_n x_1$. **8.** Replace x, y, z, f_1, f_2, f_3, and D with $X(s), Y(s), Z(s), F_1(s), F_2(s)$,
$F_3(s)$, and s, respectively, in the solution of Theorem 3.

Chap. VIII, Sec. 5, page 307

1. $X_1(s) = (m_2s^2 + bs + k)F(s)/\Delta(s)$, $X_2(s) = (bs + k)F(s)/\Delta(s)$, where
$\Delta(s) = s^2[m_1m_2s^2 + (m_1 + m_2)(bs + k)]$;
$x_1 = [(m_2D^2 + bD + k)/\Delta(D)]f$, $x_2 = [(bD + k)/\Delta(D)]f$.
2. $X_1(s) = v_0/s^2 - m_2v_0(bs + k)/\Delta(s)$, $\Delta(s)$ as in Prob. 1,
$X_2(s) = v_0m_1(bs + k)/\Delta(s)$; $b_{\min} = 2\sqrt{m_1m_2k/(m_1 + m_2)}$.
3. $X_1(s) = v_0/s^2 - \dfrac{(ms^2 + 2bs + 2k)(bs + k)}{s^2(ms^2 + bs + k)[ms^2 + 3(bs + k)]}$,

$X_2(s) = \dfrac{v_0(bs + k)}{s^2[ms^2 + 3(bs + k)]}$,

$X_3(s) = \dfrac{v_0(bs + k)^2}{s^2(ms^2 + bs + k)[ms^2 + 3(bs + k)]}$, $b_{\min} = 2\sqrt{mk}$.

4. $\theta = \dfrac{T_0}{4I}\left[\dfrac{t}{\omega} + \dfrac{\omega_0^3 \sin \omega t - \omega^3 \sin \omega_0 t}{\omega_0\omega^2(\omega^2 - \omega_0^2)}\right]$, where $\omega_0 = \sqrt{2k/I}$.

5. $\sqrt{2k/I}, \sqrt{19k/I}, \sqrt{44k/I}$. **6.** The Laplace transform of x_1 is
$$\dfrac{[s^3 + b(1/I_2 + 1/I_3)s^2 + ks/I_2 + bk/I_1I_2]\mathcal{L}T}{s^2[I_1s^3 + b(I_1/I_2 + I_1/I_3)s^2 + k(1 + I_1/I_2)s + bk(1/I_2 + I_1/I_2I_3 + 1/I_3)]};$$
the frequency is $1/\pi$. **7.** $(1/2\pi)\sqrt{g/l}$, $(1/2\pi)\sqrt{g/l + 2kh^2/ml^2}$.

Chap. VIII, Sec. 6, page 310

1. $q = 10^{-3}[1 - e^{-500t}(\cos 1{,}000t + \frac{1}{2}\sin 1{,}000t)]$ coulomb.
2. The Laplace transforms of the currents are
$I_1(s) = (L_2s^3 + R_2s^2 + C_2^{-1}s)\mathcal{L}E/\Delta(s)$, $I_2(s) = (L_1s^3 + C_1^{-1}s)\mathcal{L}E/\Delta(s)$, where
$\Delta(s) = (L_1s^2 + R_1s + C_1^{-1})(L_2s^2 + R_2s + C_2^{-1}) + (L_1s^2 + C_1^{-1})R_1s$.
4. $V = 10^4\int_0^t \{\frac{1}{2}e^{10^4(t_1-t)} + (1/\sqrt{3})e^{\frac{1}{2}10^4(t_1-t)}\sin[(\sqrt{3}/2)10^4(t - t_1)] - \pi/3]\}E(t_1)\,dt_1$.

Chap. IX, Sec. 1, page 315

1. $c_1x^{-3} + c_2x^2$. **2.** $(A/6)x + B + c_1x^{-\frac{1}{2}} + c_2x^{-1}$.
3. $(A/9)x^2 + (B/4)x + C + (c_0 + c_1 \log x)x^{-1}$.
4. $(x/4)(\log x - 1) + (c_0 + c_1 \log x)x^{-1}$.
5. $1 + (\log x)^2 + (c_0 + c_1 \log x)x + c_2x^{-1}$.
6. $\frac{1}{4}\sin(2\log x) + \frac{1}{4}\cos(2\log x) + (c_0 + c_1 \log x + c_2 \log^2 x)x + c_3x^{-2}$.
7. $(c_0 + c_1 \log x + c_2 \log^2 x)x^m$.
8. $-\frac{1}{2}(\frac{3}{2} - x + x^2) + c_1(2x - 1)^{-1} + c_2(2x - 1)^3$.
9. $x^3y''' - 3x^2y'' + 6xy' - 6y = 0$. **10.** $x^3y''' + xy' - y = 0$.

Chap. IX, Sec. 2, page 319

1. $c_0(1 + x) + c_1e^x$.
2. $x^{-\frac{1}{2}}[c_0 + c_1 \log(x - \frac{1}{2} + \sqrt{x^2 - x})]$. **3.** $\frac{2}{3}x^2 + c_1x + c_2x^{-1}$.
4. $x^{-\frac{1}{2}}(c_1 \sin x + c_2 \cos x)$.
5. $c_1(3x^2 - 1) + c_2\{[(3x^2 - 1)/2]\log[(1 + x)/(1 - x)] - 3x\}$.

6. $-1/8x + x(c_0 + c_1 \log x + c_2 \log^2 x)$.

7. $-x \int^x (x_1^{-3} \cos x_1 - 2x_1^{-4} \sin x_1 + 2x_1^{-5} \cos x_1)\, dx_1$.

Chap. IX, Sec. 3, page 322

1. $A \arctan x + (c_0 + c_1 x)(1 + x^2)^{-\frac{1}{2}}$.

2. $-1/8x + x(c_0 + c_1 \log x + c_2 \log^2 x)$.

3. $x^2/8 + (c_0 + c_1 x^2)e^{x^2} + c_2 e^{-x^2}$.

4. $\left[A - \int^x (x - x_1)f(x_1)\, dx_1 \right] \cos x +$
$\left[C + \int^x \cot x_2\, dx_2 \int^{x_2} f(x_1)\, dx_1 \right] \sin x +$
$B(x \cos x - \sin x \log \sin x)$.

Chap. IX, Sec. 4, page 325

1. $c_1 \sin (x^2/2) + c_2 \cos (x^2/2)$.

2. $[(1 + x^2)/3] \log (1 + x^2) + c_1(1 + x^2) + c_2(1 + x^2)^{-2}$.

3. $\arctan (c_1 x + c_2/x)$.

4. $-x^{-1}[\log (x + 1) + c_1(x + 1) + c_2(x + 1)^{-1}]$.

5. $\log (c_1 e^{\sqrt{x}} + c_2 e^{-\sqrt{x}})$. **6.** $c_1 x^{-1} + c_2 x^{-1} \int^x e^{-4 \arctan x'}\, dx'$.

7. $c_1 x^{-2} + c_2 x^{-3} + c_3 x^3$. **10.** $x^{-1} - A x^{-2} \tanh (A x^{-1} + c)$.

11. $u e^{x^2/4}$.

Chap. IX, Sec. 5, page 328

1. $x(c_1 \sin x + c_2 \cos x)$. **2.** $c_1 x^{-1}(x + 1)^2 + c_2 x^{-1}(x + 1)^{-1}$.

3. $x^{-2}\{e^x + e^{-x/\sqrt{2}}[c_1 \cos (x/\sqrt{2}) + c_2 \sin (x/\sqrt{2})]$
$+ e^{x/\sqrt{2}}[c_3 \cos (x/\sqrt{2}) + c_4 \sin (x/\sqrt{2})]\}$.

4. $\frac{7}{10} - \frac{1}{10} \cot x + [(c_0 + c_1 x)e^x + c_2 e^{-x}] \csc x$.

Chap. IX, Sec. 6, page 331

1. $(c_1 - 1)x + c_1(1 + x^2) \arctan x + c_2(1 + x^2)$.

2. $(1 + x^2)^{-2}[c_0 + c_1(x^2/2 + \log x)]$.

3. $y^2 - xy + x^4 + c_1 x + c_2 = 0$.

4. $(x - c_1)^2 + y^2 = c_2$. **5.** $c_1 x + c_2 x e^{-x^2/2} + c_3 x \int^x e^{(x'^2 - x^2)/2}\, dx'$.

9. $c_1 x + c_2 x e^{-4/x^4}$.

Chap. IX, Sec. 7, page 335

1. $y = \cot x + 1 \Big/ \int^x (\sin^2 x/\sin^2 x')e^{\frac{1}{2}(\cos 2x' - \cos 2x)}\, dx'$.

2. $u = A \tanh (Ax + c)$; $y'' - A^2 y = 0$.

3. $u = (1/b_0 x)(r_1 + r_2 c x^{r_2 - r_1})/(1 + c x^{r_2 - r_1})$ and $u = r_2/b_0 x$,
where $r_{1,2} = \frac{1}{2}[1 - A \pm \sqrt{(1 - A)^2 - 4B}]$.

5. $u' + (2\pi i/h)u^2 - (4\pi m i/h)(E - V) = 0$.

Chap. IX, Sec. 8, page 339

2. $\int_a^{a+\tau} f(t') \, dt' = 0$.   **3.** $(\frac{1}{2}At^2 + c_1 t + c_0)/(2 + \sin t)$;
no periodic solution.   **4.** $(-A \cos t + c_1 t + c_0)/(2 + \sin t)$;
all solutions for which $c_1 = 0$ are periodic.
5. $6 \cos 3t + \sin 3t + e^t(c_1 \sin 3t + c_2 \cos 3t)$; unique periodic solution is
$6 \cos 3t + \sin 3t$.
6. $\frac{1}{14} \sin 4t + c_1 \sin \sqrt{2}\, t + c_2 \cos \sqrt{2}\, t + c_3 \sin 2t + c_4 \cos 2t$; unique
solution of period $\pi/2$ is $\frac{1}{14} \sin 4t$.
7. $(A/8)t \cos 2t + c_1 \sin \sqrt{2}\, t + c_2 \cos \sqrt{2}\, t + c_3 \sin 2t + c_4 \cos 2t$; no
periodic solution.   **8.** $e^{-(t-\cos t)} \int^t e^{t_1 - \cos t_1} \, dt_1 + (c_0 + c_1 t)e^{-(t-\cos t)}$;
unique periodic solution is $e^{-(t-\cos t)} \left(\int_0^t e^{t_1 - \cos t_1} \, dt_1 + c_0 \right)$, where $c_0 =$
$[e^{2\pi}/(e^{2\pi} - 1)] \int_{-2\pi}^0 e^{t_1 - \cos t_1} \, dt_1$.   **9.** $\frac{1}{64} + \frac{1}{64} \cos 4t$.
10. $\frac{1}{8} + \frac{1}{6} \cos t + \frac{1}{120} \cos 2t$.   **11.** $x = -128 \sin \frac{1}{4}t - \frac{1}{28} \sin t$.
12. $\{1/a^2 + [1/(a^2 - 1)] \cos t + [1/(a^2 - 4)] \cos 2t + [1/(a^2 - 9)] \cos 3t$
$+ [1/(a^2 - 16)] \cos 4t + [1/(a^2 - 25)] \cos 5t + [1/(a^2 - 49)] \cos 7t$
$+ [1/(a^2 - 64)] \cos 8t\}(A/8)$.

Chap. X, Sec. 1, page 344

3. $\sqrt{2}$.

Chap. X, Sec. 2, page 345

1. (a), (c), (d), (h) All points are ordinary points. (b), (i) All points are
ordinary except 0. (e) All points ordinary except $-2, 1, -1$. (f) All points
ordinary except $-1, 0, 2$. (g) All points are ordinary except 0, $\pm \frac{1}{2}\pi$, $\pm \pi$,
$\pm \frac{3}{2}\pi$, ... **2.** (a), (c), (h) for all x. (b), (e), (f), (g), (i) for $0 < x < 1$.
(d) for $|x - \frac{1}{2}| < \sqrt{5}/4$ because the series for arctan x converges to the func-
tion in the same circle as the series for $1/(1 + x^2)$. There is a singularity at
$x = i$.

Chap. X, Sec. 3, page 350

1. (a) $A + B \sum_{n=0}^{\infty} [(-1)^n/(2n + 1)]x^{2n+1} = A + B$ arctan x.
(b) $y_c + (x^4/6)[\frac{1}{2} - x^2/3 + x^4/4 - x^6/5 + \cdots + (-1)^n x^{2n}/(n + 2)$
$+ \cdots] = y_c + \frac{1}{6}[x^2 - \log (1 + x^2)]$, where y_c is the solution of part a.
(c) $Ax + B \sum_{n=0}^{\infty} [(2n - 3)^2(2n - 5)^2 \cdots (-1)^2/(2n)!]x^{2n}$.
(d) $y_c - x^3/3! - 2^2 x^5/5! - 2^2 \cdot 4^2 x^7/7!$
$- \cdots - 2^{2k-2}[(k - 1)!]^2 x^{2k+1}/(2k + 1)! - \cdots$, where y_c is the solution
of part c.
(e) $Ae^{x^3/3} + Bx(1 + x^3/4 + x^6/4 \cdot 7 + x^9/4 \cdot 7 \cdot 10 + \cdots)$
$+ Cx^2(1 + x^3/5 + x^6/5 \cdot 8 + x^9/5 \cdot 8 \cdot 11 + \cdots)$,
where $e^{x^3/3} = 1 + x^3/3 \cdot 1 + x^6/3^2 \cdot 2! + \cdots$.
(f) $y_c - \frac{1}{2}$, where y_c is the solution of part e.

(g) $A + B[x - x^3/3 \cdot 1 - x^5/5 \cdot 3 - \cdots - x^{2n+1}/(2n+1)(2n-1)$
$- \cdots]$. (h) $A/(1+x) + B/(1-x)$.

2. (a) to (d) and (g) to (i) $|x| < 1$. (e), (f) $|x| < \infty$.

3. (a) $A[1 + (x-1)^3/2 \cdot 3 + (x-1)^6/2 \cdot 3 \cdot 5 \cdot 6$
$+ (x-1)^9/2 \cdot 3 \cdot 5 \cdot 6 \cdot 8 \cdot 9 + \cdots] + B(x-1)[1 + (x-1)^3/3 \cdot 4$
$+ (x-1)^6/3 \cdot 4 \cdot 6 \cdot 7 + (x-1)^9/3 \cdot 4 \cdot 6 \cdot 7 \cdot 9 \cdot 10 + \cdots], |x-1| < \infty$.

(b) $A(1 + x^2) + B[x + x^3/3 \cdot 1 - x^5/5 \cdot 3 + \cdots$
$+ (-1)^{n+1}x^{2n+1}/(2n+1)(2n-1) + \cdots], |x| < 1$.

(c) $C_0[1 + (t-1)^2] + C_1[t - 1 + (t-1)^3/3 \cdot 1 - (t-1)^5/5 \cdot 3 \cdots]$
$+ (t-1)^2/2 - (t-1)^4/24 + \frac{11}{720}(t-1)^6 \cdots, |t-1| < 1$.

(d) $A[x + 1 - (x+1)^2/2 + (x+1)^3/6 - (x+1)^4/8$
$+ (x+1)^5/20 \cdots] + B[1 - (x+1)^3/6 + (x+1)^4/24$
$- (x+1)^5/120 \cdots], |x+1| < \infty$.

(e) $A[1 - (x-1)^2/2 - (x-1)^3/6 + (x-1)^4/12 + (x-1)^6/360$
$+ \cdots] + B[x - 1 - (x-1)^2/2 - (x-1)^3/6 - (x-1)^4/12$
$+ (x-1)^6/60 + \cdots]$.

(f) $A[1 + \frac{1}{6}(x+1)^3 - \frac{1}{40}(x+1)^5 + \cdots]$
$+ B[(x+1) + \frac{1}{24}(x+1)^4 - \frac{1}{60}(x+1)^5 + \cdots]$
$+ C[(x+1)^2 + \frac{1}{6}(x+1)^3 - \frac{1}{8}(x+1)^4 - \frac{1}{40}(x+1)^5 + \cdots], |x+1| < \infty$.

4. (a) $1 + x^2$.

(b) $x + (1/3!)x^3 - (1/5!)x^5 + (3/7!)x^7 - (3 \cdot 5/9!)x^9$
$+ (3 \cdot 5 \cdot 7/11!)x^{11} \cdots$.

(c) $t^2 + 2^2(-1/4 \cdot 5 \cdot 6)t^6 + 2^4(-1 \cdot 3/4 \cdot 5 \cdot 6 \cdot 8 \cdot 9 \cdot 10)t^{10}$
$+ 2^6(-1 \cdot 3 \cdot 7/4 \cdot 5 \cdot 6 \cdot 8 \cdot 9 \cdot 10 \cdot 12 \cdot 13 \cdot 14)t^{14} \cdots$.

(d) $1 + 2^2(-3/2 \cdot 3 \cdot 4)t^4 + 2^4(-3 \cdot 1/2 \cdot 3 \cdot 4 \cdot 6 \cdot 7 \cdot 8)t^8$
$+ 2^6(-3 \cdot 1 \cdot 5/2 \cdot 3 \cdot 4 \cdot 6 \cdot 7 \cdot 8 \cdot 10 \cdot 11 \cdot 12)t^{12} \cdots$.

(e) $x^3/6 - x^5/120 + x^7/240 \cdots$.

(f) $x^2/2 + x^3/6 - x^4/6 - x^5/20 + 37x^6/720 \cdots$.

Chap. X, Sec. 4, page 357

1. $A \sum_{n=0}^{\infty} [(-1)^n/(2n)!]x^n + B \sum_{n=0}^{\infty} [(-1)^n/(2n+1)!]x^{n+\frac{1}{2}} = A \cos \sqrt{x}$
$+ B \sin \sqrt{x}$.

2. $A(1 + \frac{4}{3}x + \frac{2}{3}x^2) + Bx^{-2}(1 + 8x)$.

3. $A(1 + x + \frac{2}{5}x^2) + Bx^{-3}(1 + 10x + 40x^2)$.

4. $Ax^{\frac{1}{2}} \sum_{n=0}^{\infty} [(-1)^n/2^{2n+1}(2n+1)!]x^{2n} + Bx^{-\frac{1}{2}} \sum_{n=0}^{\infty} [(-1)^n/2^{2n}(2n)!]x^{2n}$
$= Ax^{-\frac{1}{2}} \sin (x/2) + Bx^{-\frac{1}{2}} \cos (x/2)$.

5. $A/(1+x) + B\sqrt{x}/(1+x) = (A + Bx^{\frac{1}{2}}) \sum_{n=0}^{\infty} (-x)^n$.

6. $A[1 - 2x + 3x^2 - 4x^3 \cdots + (-1)^n(n+1)x^n + \cdots]$
$+ Bx^{\frac{1}{2}}[3 - 5x + 7x^2 \cdots + (-1)^n(2n+3)x^n + \cdots] = A(1+x)^{-2}$
$+ Bx^{\frac{1}{2}}(3+x)(1+x)^{-2}$.

7. $A[1 - x^3/5 \cdot 3 + x^6/8 \cdot 6 \cdot 5 \cdot 3 \cdots$
$+ (-1)^n/(3n + 2)(3n)(3n - 1)(3n - 3) \cdots 5 \cdot 3 + \cdots]$
$+ Bx^{-1}[1 - x^3/3 \cdot 1 + x^6/6 \cdot 4 \cdot 3 \cdot 1 - \cdots$
$+ (-1)^n x^{3n}/3n(3n - 2)(3n - 3)(3n - 5) \cdots 3 \cdot 1 + \cdots].$

8. $c_0(1 - x - \frac{1}{8}x^2).$

9. $c_0 x[1 - x^2/4 \cdot 2 + x^4/6 \cdot 4^2 \cdot 2 \cdots$
$+ (-1)^n x^{2n}/(2n + 2)(2n)^2(2n - 2)^2 \cdots 2^2 \cdot 2 + \cdots].$

10. $c_0\{1 - x + 2x^2/4 - 5 \cdot 2x^3/9 \cdot 4 + \cdots$
$+ (-1)^n[(n - 1)^2 + 1][(n - 2)^2 + 1] \cdots (2)/n^2(n - 1)^2 \cdots 2^2\}.$

11. (a) All ordinary except 0, which is not regular-singular. (b) All points are ordinary. (c) All ordinary except -1, 0; both are regular-singular; $|x + 1| < 1$ and $|x| < 1$. (d) -1 and 2 are regular-singular; $|x + 1| < 3$ and $|x - 2| < 3$. (e) -2, -1, 1 are regular-singular; $|x + 2| < 1$, $|x + 1| < 1$, $|x - 1| < 2$. **12.** $y = 4x^2 - 1.$

Chap. X, Sec. 5, page 361

1. $AJ_0(x).$ **2.** $AJ_n(ax) + BJ_{-n}(ax).$

3. $AJ_n[a(x - s)] + BJ_{-n}[a(x - s)].$ **4.** $Ax^{-n}J_n(x) + Bx^{-n}J_{-n}(x).$

5. $Ax^{-\frac{1}{2}}J_{\frac{1}{2}}(x) + Bx^{-\frac{1}{2}}J_{-\frac{1}{2}}(x) = Cx^{-1}\sin x + Dx^{-1}\cos x.$

6. $Ax^{\frac{1}{2}}J_{\frac{1}{3}}(2ax^{\frac{3}{2}}/3) + Bx^{\frac{1}{2}}J_{-\frac{1}{3}}(2ax^{\frac{3}{2}}/3).$

7. $Ax^{\frac{1}{2}}J_{\frac{1}{4}}(ax^2/2) + Bx^{\frac{1}{2}}J_{-\frac{1}{4}}(ax^2/2).$ **8.** $AJ_n(e^x) + BJ_{-n}(e^x).$

Chap. X, Sec. 6, page 364

1. $AF(\frac{1}{2}, \frac{1}{2}, \frac{1}{2}; x) + Bx^{\frac{1}{2}}F(1, 1, \frac{3}{2}; x).$

2. $AF(\alpha, \beta, d; x) + Bx^{1-d}(\alpha - d + 1, \beta - d + 1, 2 - d; x)$, where
$\alpha = -\frac{1}{2}(c + 1) + \frac{1}{2}\sqrt{(c + 1)^2 + 4e}$, $\beta = -\frac{1}{2}(c + 1) - \frac{1}{2}\sqrt{(c + 1)^2 + 4e}.$

3. $AF(\alpha, \beta, d/a; -x/a) + Bx^{1-d/a}F(\alpha - d/a + 1, \beta - d/a + 1, 2 - d/a; -x/a)$,
$\alpha = -\frac{1}{2}(1 - c) + \frac{1}{2}\sqrt{(1 - c)^2 - 4e},$
$\beta = -\frac{1}{2}(1 - c) - \frac{1}{2}\sqrt{(1 - c)^2 - 4e}.$

4. $AF[\alpha, \beta, \gamma; (x - s_1)/(s_2 - s_1)] + B[(x - s_1)/(s_2 - s_1)]^{1-\gamma}$
$\times F[\alpha - \gamma + 1, \beta - \gamma + 1, 2 - \gamma; (x - s_1)/(s_2 - s_1)]$, where
$\alpha = -\frac{1}{2}(1 - c) + \frac{1}{2}\sqrt{(1 - c)^2 - 4e}$, $\beta = -\frac{1}{2}(1 - c) - \frac{1}{2}\sqrt{(1 - c)^2 - 4e}$,
$\gamma = (cs_1 + d)/(s_1 - s_2).$

5. $AF[-\frac{4}{5}, -\frac{4}{5}, -\frac{4}{5}; (4 - x)/3] + B[(4 - x)/3]^{\frac{9}{5}}F[1, 1, \frac{14}{5}; (4 - x)/3]$
$= A_1(x - 1)^{\frac{3}{5}} + B[(4 - x)/3]^{\frac{9}{5}}F[1, 1, \frac{14}{5}; (4 - x)/3].$

6. (a) $(1 - x)^{-1}$; (b) $(1 - x)^n$; (c) $-x^{-1}\log(1 - x)$; (d) a polynomial;
(e) $\frac{1}{2}x^{-\frac{1}{2}}\arccos(1 - 2x)$; (f) $\frac{1}{2}x^{-\frac{1}{2}}\log[(1 + x^{\frac{1}{2}})/(1 - x^{\frac{1}{2}})].$

8. $3F(\frac{1}{2}, 1, \frac{3}{2}; x) = \frac{3}{2}x^{-\frac{1}{2}}\log[(1 + x^{\frac{1}{2}})/(1 - x^{\frac{1}{2}})].$

Chap. X, Sec. 8, page 372

1. $Ax^{-1} + B\sum_{n=0}^{\infty}[(2n - 3)^2(2n - 5)^2 \cdots (-1)^2/(2n)!]x^{-2n}.$

2. $Ae^{\frac{1}{2}x^{-2}} + Bx^{-1}(1 + x^{-3}/4 + x^{-6}/4 \cdot 7 + x^{-9}/4 \cdot 7 \cdot 10 + \cdots)$
$+ Cx^{-2}(1 + x^{-3}/5 + x^{-6}/5 \cdot 8 + x^{-9}/5 \cdot 8 \cdot 11 + \cdots).$

3. $A(1 + \frac{4}{3}x^{-1} + \frac{2}{3}x^{-2}) + Bx^2(1 + 8x^{-1}).$

4. $Ax^{-\frac{1}{2}} \sum\limits_{n=0}^{\infty} [(-1)^n/2^{2n+1}(2n+1)!]x^{-2n} +$

$Bx^{\frac{1}{2}} \sum\limits_{n=0}^{\infty} [(-1)^n/2^{2n}(2n)!]x^{-2n} = Ax^{\frac{1}{2}} \sin (1/2x) + Bx^{\frac{1}{2}} \cos (1/2x)$.

5. $AJ_n(1/x) + BJ_{-n}(1/x)$.

6. $AF(\alpha, \beta, 1 + \delta; 1/x) + Bx^{\delta}F(\alpha - \delta, \beta - \delta, 1 - \delta; 1/x)$.

7. $1 + t^{-2}$.

8. $-t^{-1} - (1/3!)t^{-3} + (1/5!)t^{-5} - (3/7!)t^{-7} + (3 \cdot 5/9!)t^{-9}$
$- (3 \cdot 5 \cdot 7/11!)t^{-11} \cdots$.

9. $1 + 2^2(-3/2 \cdot 3 \cdot 4)t^{-4} + 2^4(-3 \cdot 1/2 \cdot 3 \cdot 4 \cdot 6 \cdot 7 \cdot 8)t^{-8}$
$+ 2^6(-3 \cdot 1 \cdot 5/2 \cdot 3 \cdot 4 \cdot 6 \cdot 7 \cdot 8 \cdot 10 \cdot 11 \cdot 12)t^{-12} \cdots$.

12. (*a*) Regular-singular. (*b*) Nonregular-singular.

Chap. X, Sec. 9, page 376

1. $AP_3(x) + BQ_3(x)$. **2.** $AP_n(x/a) + BQ_n(x/a)$.

3. $AP_n[(x + a/2)/\sqrt{a^2/4 - b}] + BQ_n[(x + a/2)/\sqrt{a^2/4 - b}]$.

7. $P_n(x) = 1 + [n(n + 1)/2 \cdot 1^2](x - 1)$
$+ [(n - 1)n(n + 1)(n + 2)/2^2 \cdot 1^2 \cdot 2^2](x - 1)^2$
$+ [(n - 2)n(n + 1)(n + 2)(n + 3)/2^3 \cdot 1^2 \cdot 2^2 \cdot 3^2](x - 1)^3 + \cdots$
$+ [(2n)!/2^n \cdot 1^2 \cdot 2^2 \cdots n^2](x - 1)^n$.

Index